Mathematics for Economists
An Elementary Survey

Second Edition

Mathematics
for Economists

An Elementary Survey

Taro Yamane
Department of Economics
New York University

PRENTICE-HALL, INC., *Englewood Cliffs, New Jersey*

Library of Congress Catalog Card No.: 68–25583

Printed in the United States of America

Current printing (last digit):
10 9 8 7 6 5 4 3 2 1

Prentice-Hall International, Inc., *London*
Prentice-Hall of Australia, Pty. Ltd., *Sydney*
Prentice-Hall of Canada, Ltd., *Toronto*
Prentice-Hall of India Private, Ltd., *New Delhi*
Prentice-Hall of Japan, Inc., *Tokyo*

To My Parents

PREFACE TO SECOND EDITION

The main change in this second edition is the addition of a discussion of differentials in Chapters 3 through 5. Other minor changes (mainly additions) are in Chapters 1 and 2, concerning set theory and limits and in Chapters 10 and 11, concerning determinants and matrices. New problems have been added to Chapters 1 through 5, 10, and 11.

I would like to take this occasion to thank the many persons who have been kind enough to send in various helpful comments. I would also like to thank the Department of Economics, Graduate School of Arts and Science, New York University for providing me the opportunity and facilities to revise this book.

Taro Yamane

PREFACE TO FIRST EDITION

The increasing application of mathematics to various branches of economics in the past decade has made it necessary for economists to have an elementary knowledge of mathematics. A large number of articles covering many fields such as economic theory, public finance, etc. in, for example, the *American Economic Review* and the *Review of Economics and Statistics* use mathematics to varying degrees. Also, the use of elementary mathematics in teaching graduate economic courses and courses such as mathematical economics and econometrics is becoming common.

In teaching mathematical economics and econometrics, I found that students who have had a year of calculus were not quite familiar with the various mathematical techniques economists use. For example, the Lagrange multiplier technique used to explain maximum and minimum problems is usually not covered in an elementary calculus course. Furthermore, to ask the student to have a background in such topics as set theory, differential and difference equations, vectors and matrices, and certain basic concepts of mathematical statistics would require him to take a considerable amount of mathematics at the expense of his main line of interest, economics. And yet when discussing, for example, demand theory in a mathematical economics course most of the above-mentioned topics are necessary, although at an elementary level.

To fill in this gap I experienced in teaching these courses, I selected certain topics from various branches of mathematics that are frequently used and taught a separate course, mathematics for economists. I had found it very difficult to teach mathematical economics and the necessary mathematical techniques at the same time without disrupting the continuity of an economic discussion.

These courses in mathematical economics and econometrics were introductory courses for graduate students, some of whom were planning to major in mathematical economics or econometrics, but many of whom were majoring in other branches such as labor, finance, etc. The mathematics for economists course therefore had to be less than three or four credits; it should not become too professional and yet should give enough coverage to serve as a preliminary for the mathematical economics and econometrics courses. With this in mind I have written a general survey of four topics; calculus, differential and difference equations, matrix algebra, and statistics at an elementary level for economists with only a high school algebra background and have adopted the following points:

(1) The topics are discussed in a heuristic manner. References are provided for those interested in proofs and derivations. Furthermore, the various algebraic steps which are usually omitted in mathematics texts have been included. For an experienced mathematician this is a trivial matter, but for an unexperienced economist the omission of these steps sometimes creates unusual difficulties.

(2) The selection of topics has been based on the need of economists and is quite different from standard mathematics courses.

(3) Emphasis is on surveying the mathematics and not on applications. It is assumed that students will take a course in mathematical economics that is solely devoted to applications.

(4) Problems have been kept simple to avoid complicated algebraic manipulations and yet give exercise of the material covered.

It is difficult to decide how much mathematics an economist should know. It will probably depend on his field of interest. The mathematical economics major will have to take advanced professional mathematics courses, but for the other economists it is hoped that this book will enable them to read the mathematically orientated articles in such journals as the *American Economic Review* and the *Review of Economics and Statistics*.

I am indebted to the economists and mathematicians whose works have formed the basis of this book; they are listed throughout the book. I would also like to acknowledge my thanks to an unknown reviewer who provided many helpful suggestions. Thanks are also due to the Graduate School of Arts and Science of New York University and Professor Emanuel Stein for providing the conducive environment for study and the necessary secretarial work for typing the manuscript. Finally I wish to express my special appreciation to Miss Cecilia Liang for her excellent job of typing the entire manuscript.

Taro Yamane

Suggested Outline

At New York University the course is given once a week for two hours and is for two semesters. The first ten chapters are covered during the first semester. Chapters 1 and 2 are mainly for background purposes. Chapters 3 through 7 give basic calculus techniques. Either Chapter 8 (differential equations) or Chapter 9 (difference equations) is covered, the one not covered being assigned for winter vacation homework.

During the second semester the Chapters 11 through 18 are covered. Chapter 18 may be assigned as homework for spring vacation.

If the course is given twice a week for two hours each, the book may be covered in one semester.

I require students to submit 3×5 cards at the beginning of the lectures on which they indicate what homework problems they have been able to do. Based on this students are called upon to do problems with which the majority of the class seems to have had difficulty. Then the problems are discussed and questions answered. After all questions concerning homework and material covered during the last session are answered, the new topics are lectured on very briefly. Since the students are graduate students, only important key points are discussed and the rest are assigned as homework. A simple problem is usually assigned to do in class. Short (15 minute) quizzes are given now and then.

Thus, theoretically, the student covers the same material six times. (1) He reads material before coming to class. (2) He listens to lectures, and does a problem in class. (3) He does homework. (4) Homework is put on the blackboard and discussed; questions are answered. (5) He prepares for a quiz. (6) He takes the quiz. When the quiz is difficult, the troublesome problems are put on the blackboard at the next session and discussed.

CONTENTS

xiii

Mathematics for Economists
An Elementary Survey

CHAPTER 1

Sets

Set theory plays a basic role in modern mathematics and is finding increasing use in economics. In this chapter we shall introduce some elementary principles of set theory and follow this with a discussion of the Cartesian product, relations, and the concept of functions.

1.1 Sets

A group of three students, a deck of 52 cards, or a collection of telephones in a city are each an example of a *set*. A set is a collection of definite and well-distinguished objects.

Let a set be S, and call the objects *elements*. An element a is related to the set as

$$a \text{ is an element of } S \qquad a \in S$$
$$a \text{ is not an element of } S \qquad a \notin S$$

We use the symbol $\in$, which is a variation of ϵ (*epsilon*), to indicate that a "is an element of" the set S. The expressions, a "belongs to" S, or a "is contained in" S are also used. For example, the set S may be three numbers, 1, 2, and 3, which are its elements. We use braces $\{1, 2, 3\}$ to indicate a set. Then, for the element 2, we write,

$$2 \in \{1, 2, 3\}$$

In establishing a set, the elements must be distinct, repeated elements being deleted: 1, 2, 3, 3, is a set $\{1, 2, 3\}$. For the present the order of the elements does not matter. Also note that $\{2\}$ is a set of one element, 2.

A set with no elements is called a *null set* or an *empty set*, and is denoted by 0. Consider a set S of students who smoke. If three students smoke, we have a set of three elements. If only one smokes, we have a set of one element. If no one smokes, we have a set of no elements; i.e., we have a null set. Another example is a set of circles going through three points on a straight

1

line. Note that 0 is a null set with no elements, but $\{0\}$ is a set with one element.

The elements of a set may be sets themselves. For instance, if we let S be a set of five Y.M.C.A.'s, we may also say that each element (Y.M.C.A.) is a set in which its elements are its members. Another example:

$$S = \{\{1\}, \{2, 3\}, \{4, 5, 6\}\}$$

Two sets S_1 and S_2 are *equal* if and only if they have the same elements. This is shown by

$$S_1 = S_2$$

For example, let S_1 be the set of numbers

$$S_1 = \{2, 3, 5, 7\}$$

Let S_2 be a set of one-digit prime numbers. Then $S_1 = S_2$. If S_1 and S_2 are not equal, we write

$$S_1 \neq S_2$$

If every element in S_i is an element of S, we say S_i is a *subset* of S. Let $S = \{1, 2, 3\}$. Then the subsets will be

$$S_0 = 0, \qquad S_1 = \{1\}, \qquad S_2 = \{2\}, \qquad S_3 = \{3\}$$
$$S_4 = \{1, 2\}, \qquad S_5 = \{1, 3\}, \qquad S_6 = \{2, 3\}, \qquad S_7 = \{1, 2, 3\}$$

We write

$$S_i \subseteq S$$

and read: S_i is a subset of S. The symbol $\subseteq$ is called the *inclusion sign*. We can also say S "includes" S_i and write

$$S \supseteq S_i$$

When $S_i \subset S$, that is, when S contains at least one element not in S_i, S_i is called a *proper subset* of S. In our present example, $S_i (i = 0, 1, \ldots, 6)$ are proper subsets.

With this concept of set inclusion, we can redefine the equality of two sets S_1 and S_2 by the axiom: S_1 and S_2 are equal (i.e., $S_1 = S_2$) if and only if $S_1 \subseteq S_2$ and $S_2 \subseteq S_1$.

Let S be any set. Then

$$0 \subseteq S$$

This is so because, if $0 \subseteq S$ were not true, then 0 must have an element that is not in S. But 0 has no elements. Thus, $0 \subseteq S$ must hold.

Furthermore, 0 is unique, for if it were not unique, then there must be a null set Δ such that $0 \neq \Delta$. This means Δ must contain an element not in 0. But it is a contradiction for Δ to contain an element. Therefore, $\Delta = 0$, and the null set is unique.

An alternative way to show this uniqueness is to let 0 and Δ be two null sets. Then, by definition, $0 \subseteq \Delta$ and $\Delta \subseteq 0$. But this implies by definition that $0 = \Delta$. Thus, 0 is unique.

There are $2^3 = 8$ subsets from the set of three elements. There will be 2^n subsets from a set of n elements (see Chapter 13 for proof).

Let A be a set of freshmen, B be a set of freshmen and juniors, and C be the entire student body. The concept of set inclusion tells us that $A \subseteq A$. That is, each set A is a subset of itself. We say set inclusion is *reflexive*.

Next, we see that $A \subset B$, which implies that $A \neq B$; i.e., the set of freshmen is not equal to the set of freshmen and juniors. Or to state it differently, $A \subset B$ implies that we cannot have $B \subset A$. We say that set inclusion is *anti-symmetric*. We know that if $A \subseteq B$ and $B \subseteq A$, then $A = B$.

Also, if

$$A \text{ (freshmen)} \subset B \text{ (freshmen and juniors)}$$

$$B \text{ (freshmen and juniors)} \subset C \text{ (student body)}$$

then

$$A \text{ (freshmen)} \subset C \text{ (student body)}$$

We say that set inclusion is *transitive*.

To summarize:

$A \subseteq A$; i.e., set inclusion is *reflexive*.

$A \subset B$ and $B \subset A$ cannot hold simultaneously ($A \subseteq B$ and $B \subseteq A$ implies $A = B$); i.e., set inclusion is *anti-symmetric*.

$A \subset B$, $B \subset C$, then, $A \subset C$; i.e., set inclusion is *transitive*.

Compare these properties of set inclusion with set equivalence.

$A = A$; i.e., set equivalence is reflexive.

$A = B$, then, $B = A$; i.e., set equivalence is symmetric.

$A = B$, $B = C$, then, $A = C$; i.e., set equivalence is transitive.

Problems

1. Explain which pair of sets are equal.

(a) $S_1 = \{1, 5, 7, 3\}$ $S_2 = \{3, 5, 7, 1\}$
(b) $S_1 = \{1, 5, 7, 3, 3\}$ $S_2 = \{3, 5, 7, 1\}$
(c) $S_1 = \{1, 5, 7, 3, 3\}$ $S_2 = \{3, 5, 7, 7, 1\}$
(d) $S_1 = \{1, 5, 7, 3\}$ $S_2 = \{3, 5, 1, 6\}$

2. Let $A = \{5\}$, $b = 5$. Is $A = b$?

3. Prove that a null set is unique. Give at least two examples of null sets.

4. Given a set $S = \{a, b, c\}$, generate all possible subsets and indicate which are proper subsets of S.

5. Let $S = \{a, \{b, c\}, d\}$. Which of the following statements are incorrect and why?

    (a) $\{b, c\} \subset S$ (b) $\{b, c\} \in S$ (c) $b \in S$

6. Given

$$S = \{a, \{b, \{c, d\}\}, e\}$$
$$S_1 = \{b, \{c, d\}\}$$
$$S_2 = \{c, d\}$$

which of the following statements are incorrect and why?

    (a) $S_1 \subset S$ (b) $S_2 \subset S$
    (c) $\{S_1\} \subset S$ (d) $S_2 \subset S_1$

7. Let $A = \{a, b, c\}$, $B = \{a, b, c, d\}$, and $C = \{a, b, c, d, e\}$. Then we can see that $A \subset B$ and $B \subset C$. By developing the argument that any element in A is also an element in C, prove that $A \subset B$, $B \subset C$ implies $A \subset C$.

8. Consider the following situations, and explain whether or not the three properties, (*i*) reflexive, (*ii*) symmetric, and (*iii*) transitive, hold.

    (a) (*i*) $A \subset A$, (*ii*) $A \subset B$, then $B \subset A$. (*iii*) $A \subset B$, $B \subset C$, then $A \subset C$.
    (b) (*i*) $A \subseteq A$, (*ii*) $A \subseteq B$, then $B \subseteq A$. (*iii*) $A \subseteq B$, $B \subseteq C$, then $A \subseteq C$.
    (c) (*i*) $a > a$, (*ii*) $a > b$, then $b > a$. (*iii*) $a > b$, $b > c$, then $a > c$.
    (d) (*i*) $a \geq a$, (*ii*) $a \geq b$, then $b \geq a$. (*iii*) $a \geq b$, $b \geq c$, then $a \geq c$.
    (e) (*i*) $a = a$, (*ii*) $a = b$, then $b = a$. (*iii*) $a = b$, $b = c$, then $a = c$.
    (f) (*i*) $A = A$, (*ii*) $A = B$, then $B = A$. (*iii*) $A = B$, $B = C$, then $A = C$.

9. Consider the following statements and explain whether the three properties hold: (*i*) reflexive (*ii*) symmetric (*iii*) transitive.

    (a)   (*i*) a is the father of a.
          (*ii*) a is the father of b, then b is the father of a.
          (*iii*) a is the father of b, b is the father of c, then a is the father of c.
    (b)   (*i*) a is the brother of a.
          (*ii*) a is the brother of b, then b is the brother of a.
          (*iii*) a is the brother of b, b is the brother of c, then a is the brother of c.
    (c)   (*i*) a is as tall as a.
          (*ii*) a is as tall as b, then b is as tall as a.
          (*iii*) a is as tall as b, b is as tall as c, then a is as tall as c.
    (d)   (*i*) a is stronger than a.
          (*ii*) a is stronger than b, then b is stronger than a.
          (*iii*) a is stronger than b, b is stronger than c, then a is stronger than c.

1.2 Set operations

Let $S_1 = \{a, b, c, 2\}$ and $S_2 = \{1, 2, 3\}$. Then the *union* (or *sum*) of S_1 and S_2 will be the set S

$$S = S_1 \cup S_2 = \{a, b, c, 1, 2, 3\}$$

$S_1 \cup S_2$ is the set that consists of all the elements that belong to either S_1 or S_2 or both (Figure 1–1).

The *intersection* (or product) of S_1 and S_2 is the set S

$$S = S_1 \cap S_2 = \{2\}$$

$S_1 \cap S_2$ is the set of elements that belong to both S_1 and S_2 (Figure 1–2). If the set S_1 were $\{a, b, c\}$, then, since S_1 and S_2 have no element in common,

$$S_1 \cap S_2 = 0$$

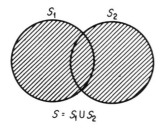

$S = S_1 \cup S_2$

Fig. 1–1

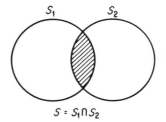

$S = S_1 \cap S_2$

Fig. 1–2

The sets S_1 and S_2 are called *disjoint* (or *non-overlapping* or *mutually exclusive*). In this case instead of using the symbol $\cup$, we sometimes use the symbol $+$ for the union of disjoint sets.

Let

$$S = S_1 \cup S_2 = \{a, b, c, 1, 2, 3\}$$

The set of all points S is called the *universal set* for a given discussion, or simply the *universe*. Frequently the universe is not explicitly specified.

Let $S_3 = \{a, b, 1, 2\}$ be a subset of S. The *complement* of S_3 with respect to the universe S is the set

$$\bar{S}_3 = \{c, 3\}$$

That is, it will be those elements of the universe $\{a, b, c, 1, 2, 3\}$ that are not elements of $S_3 = \{a, b, 1, 2\}$ (Figure 1–3).

Fig. 1–3

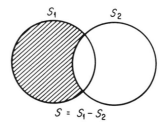

$S = S_1 - S_2$

Fig. 1–4

Next, the *difference* of sets S_1 and S_2 is the set S.

$$S = S_1 - S_2 = \{a, b, c, 2\} - \{1, 2, 3\} = \{a, b, c\}$$

where a, b, c, are elements of S_1, but are not elements of S_2, and 2 is an element of S_2 (Figure 1–4).

We may reverse the S_1 and S_2 and find the difference of S_2 and S_1, as

$$S = S_2 - S_1 = \{1, 2, 3\} - \{a, b, c, 2\} = \{1, 3\}$$

and the difference is the set of elements $\{1, 3\}$ which belong to S_2 but which do not belong to S_1. To avoid confusion we may say, "S_2 minus S_1" for the first case and "S_1 minus S_2" for the second case.

Problems

1. Find the union of the following sets.
   (a) $S_1 = \{a, b, c\}$;
        $S_2 = \{1, 2, 3\}$.
   (b) $S_1 = \{a, b, c\}$;
        $S_2 = \{a, 1, 2\}$.
   (c) $S_1 = \{a, b, c\}$;
        $S_2 = \{a, b, 3\}$.

2. Find the intersection of the sets given in Problem 1 above.

3. Given the following universal set

$$S = \{a, b, c, 1, 2, 3\}$$

Find the complement of S_2 in Problem 1 above.

4. Using the sets S_1 and S_2 of Problem 1, find $S_1 - S_2$ and $S_2 - S_1$.

5. Using the S_1 and S_2 of Problem 1, show that $(S_1 - S_2) \subset S_1$ and $(S_2 - S_1) \subset S_2$.

6. Using the S_1 and S_2 of Problem 1, find
   (a) $(S_1 - S_2) \cap (S_2 - S_1)$.
   (b) $(S_1 - S_2) \cap (S_1 \cap S_2)$.

1.3 Finite and infinite sets

Assume a set of three chairs $S_1 = \{A, B, C\}$, a set of three students $S_2 = \{K, L, M\}$, and a set of natural numbers $S_3 = \{1, 2, 3\}$. There are two ways we can compare S_1 (chairs) and S_2 (students): by counting the elements in both sets (in this case there are 3 elements in each set), or by matching each element of S_1 with one and only one element of S_2. For example,

$$A \rightarrow K, \quad B \rightarrow L, \quad C \rightarrow M$$

There are altogether $3! = 6$ different ways the elements may be matched. We have what is known as a *one-to-one correspondence* between the

(1)	(2)	(3)
$A \rightarrow K$	$A \rightarrow K$	$A \rightarrow L$
$B \rightarrow L$	$B \rightarrow M$	$B \rightarrow K$
$C \rightarrow M$	$C \rightarrow L$	$C \rightarrow M$

(4)	(5)	(6)
$A \rightarrow L$	$A \rightarrow M$	$A \rightarrow M$
$B \rightarrow M$	$B \rightarrow K$	$B \rightarrow L$
$C \rightarrow K$	$C \rightarrow L$	$C \rightarrow K$

elements of S_1 and S_2. As is seen, the elements of S_1 (chairs) may be matched with S_2 (students) or, conversely, the elements of S_2 (students) may be matched with the elements of S_1 (chairs). When such a one-to-one correspondence holds for two sets S_1 and S_2, we say the two sets are *equivalent* to each other.

It is apparent that S_1 and S_3 are equivalent and, likewise, S_2 and S_3, and this shows that two sets will be equivalent if they have the same number of elements. If there are 3 chairs and 4 students in the sets S_1 and S_2, they are not equivalent.

If we abstract the physical properties such as student or chair from the sets, the remaining common characteristic of the sets will be the number of elements in the set. This may be expressed by a set of natural numbers equivalent to the sets, and it will suffice if we consider only sets of natural numbers in our subsequent discussion.

So far only *finite* sets have been discussed. Let us now consider the following set

$$\{1, 2, 3, ..., n, ...\}$$

What is the number of elements in this set? Obviously, we cannot associate a "number" with this set. Let us call such a set an *infinite set*. We consider it to exist. For example, we usually say there are an infinite number of stars. This set of all stars is considered an infinite set.

Let us now compare the infinite set of numbers and the infinite set of stars. There were two ways of comparing sets. The first was by counting the elements. This we cannot do any more. However, the second method of matching elements and establishing a one-to-one correspondence can be done. Using this method, we can say that the infinite set of stars is equivalent to the infinite set of natural numbers.

Several other examples of infinite sets that are equivalent to an infinite set of natural numbers are

$$\{2, 4, 6, 8, ...\}$$
$$\{3, 5, 7, 9, ...\}$$

and so forth.

A set is said to be *denumerable* if it can be put into a one-to-one correspondence with a set $\{1, 2, 3, \ldots, n, \ldots\}$ of natural numbers. Finite and denumerable sets are called *countable* sets. Sets other than countable sets are called *non-denumerable* sets.

1.4 Non-denumerable sets

A technical explanation of non-denumerable sets is beyond the level of this book. Only a heuristic explanation will be presented.

The numbers we have been considering so far were integers and fractions which are called rational numbers. Let us draw a line segment from 0 to 2 and then impose a square that has sides of length one as shown in Figure 1–5

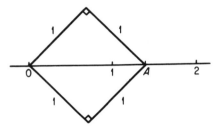

Fig. 1–5

We can plot points such as $\frac{1}{2}, \frac{1}{3}, 1\frac{1}{2}, 1\frac{1}{3}$, and so forth. But what is the point A? From Pythagoras' theorem we know that

$$\overline{0A}^2 = 1^2 + 1^2 = 2$$

The point A will correspond to a number that, when squared, will be 2 and we know that $0^2 = 0$ and $1^2 = 1$. Thus, the number is neither 0 nor 1. Any other integer will give us a number larger than 2 when squared. Therefore, let us assume A to be a fraction p/q that has been reduced to its lowest term (i.e., there is no common divisor other than 1) and set it

$$\frac{p^2}{q^2} = 2$$

Then $p^2 = 2q^2$. We see that p is an even number, and, since p/q has been reduced to its lowest term, q must be an odd number. Now, since p is an even number, we can set $p = 2k$; then

$$4k^2 = 2q^2$$

Therefore, $2k^2 = q^2$ and q must be an even number. But this contradicts our first assertion that q is an odd number, so we conclude that there is no fraction p/q that will satisfy the point A. This indicates that there is a gap in this straight line at the point A which is not represented by an integer or a fraction.

To fill in this gap, a number $\sqrt{2}$ is defined. To the left of this are the fractions smaller than $\sqrt{2}$, and to the right are the fractions greater than $\sqrt{2}$. This number $\sqrt{2}$, as we know, is called an irrational number. For any two points on the line that represent rational numbers, we can find points that correspond to irrational numbers between them.

Let us call the points that correspond to rational numbers rational points, and the points that correspond to irrational numbers irrational points. The rational numbers and irrational numbers together are called real numbers. Thus, when we take a line segment, the points on that line segment will be a set that corresponds to a set of real numbers.

Without proof, the following statement is made: The set of all real numbers in an interval is non-denumerable. The common sense of this is, if we have two successive points on a line segment, we can always find other real points between them. Because of this, they cannot be put into a one-to-one correspondence with a set of natural numbers. (But note that we have a one-to-one correspondence between a set of real numbers and points on a line segment.)

Examples of non-denumerable sets are sets that include irrational numbers (or points). The set of points in a square or circle or cube are examples.

So far we have given a heuristic explanation of sets, denumerable sets, and non-denumerable sets. No immediate use will be made of these ideas, but they will serve as a background to subsequent discussions.

1.5 Cartesian product

(i) Sentences

In mathematical logic (symbolic logic) we learn about the calculus of *sentences* (or *sentential calculus*). By sentence we mean a statement that is (1) either true or false or (2) neither. For example,

All men are married.   (false)

All men will eventually die.   (true)

are sentences that are either true or false. Let us call such sentences *closed sentences*.

On the other hand, consider the following.

The number x is larger than 5.

This is neither true nor false. Let us call such a sentence an *open sentence*. When x is given a specific number (value), the open sentence becomes a closed sentence. For example,

> The number $x = 1$ is larger than 5.   (false)
>
> The number $x = 6$ is larger than 5.   (true)
>
> The number $x = 5$ is larger than 5.   (false)

This open sentence can be expressed mathematically as

$$x > 5$$

which is an inequality. In this case, x is called a *variable*.

Take as another example the sentence

$$x + 5 \text{ is equal to } 8$$

This is an open sentence. When $x = 5$ or $x = 4$, this sentence becomes a closed sentence and is false. When $x = 3$, it is a closed sentence and is true. We may write this sentence mathematically as

$$x + 5 = 8$$

which is an *equation*. The statement, $x = 3$, which makes it true, is a *solution*.

Now let us consider a set S

$$S = \{0, 1, 2, \ldots, 10\}$$

Let $x \in S$. Furthermore, find the x such that the sentence (inequality) $x > 5$ is *true*. Then the set of x will be

$$\{x \in S: \quad x > 5\} = \{6, 7, 8, 9, 10\}$$

The left hand side is read: the set of all x belonging to (or contained in) the set S such that (the sentence) $x > 5$ (is true).

For the other example we have

$$\{x \in S: \quad x + 5 = 8\} = \{3\}$$

The left hand side is read: the set of all $x \in S$ such that $x + 5 = 8$ is true.

What have we accomplished? We have manufactured new sets (subsets) by use of a sentence. That is, we have generated a subset from the universal set whose elements make the sentence true.

We shall further state as an axiom that: When given a set A, we can find a set B whose elements will make true (satisfy) the sentence (condition) $S(x)$. Here $S(x)$ denotes a sentence.

Thus, if $A = \{4, 5, 6\}$, and $S(x)$ is the condition $x > 4$:

$$\{x \in A: \quad x > 4\} = \{5, 6\} = B$$

Likewise,

$$\{x \in A: \quad x > 5\} = \{6\} = B$$
$$\{x \in A: \quad x > 6\} = \{\ \} = B = 0 \text{ (the null set)}$$

Let us show set operations using our newly acquired concepts.

$$S = S_1 \cup S_2 = \{x: \quad x \in S_1 \quad \text{or} \quad x \in S_2\}$$
$$S = S_1 \cap S_2 = \{x: \quad x \in S_1 \quad \text{and} \quad x \in S_2\}$$
$$S = S_1 - S_2 = \{x: \quad x \in S_1 \quad \text{and} \quad x \notin S_2\}$$
$$\bar{S}_1 = S - S_1 = \{x: \quad x \in S \quad \text{and} \quad x \notin S_1\}$$

Recall that, when $S = \{1, 2, 3\}$, we had $2^3 = 8$ subsets. Let them be S_i ($i = 0, 1, 2, ..., 7$). Then the collection of these 8 subsets also forms a set in which each S_i is an element. Let this set be R. Then

$$R = \{S_i: \quad S_i \subseteq S\}$$

This R will be called the *power of the set* S and will be denoted by $R(S)$.

(ii) Ordered pairs and Cartesian product

We now introduce the concept of ordered pairs. With the concept of sentences and ordered pairs we shall be able to define the concept of relation which in turn will lead to the concept of a function. We say $\{a, b\}$ is a set of two elements. Furthermore, we know that

$$\{a, b\} = \{b, a\}$$

That is, the two sets are equivalent, and the order of the elements is not considered. Let us now group together two elements in a definite order and denote it by

$$(a, b)$$

This is called an *ordered pair* of elements. The two elements do not need to be distinct. That is, (a, a) is an ordered pair, whereas the set $\{a, a\}$ becomes the set $\{a\}$; and, as can be seen, $(a, b) \neq (b, a)$ if $a \neq b$.

This can best be described by using a graph. Figure 1–6 shows three points

Fig. 1–6

a, b, c on the horizontal and vertical axes. The ordered pair (a, b) is given by the point M, whereas the ordered pair (b, a) is given by N. As we shall see, ordered pairs of numbers (x, y) are shown as points on a plane. In connection with this form of presentation, the first number x is called the *x-coordinate*, and the second number y is called the *y-coordinate*.

Given a set

$$S = \{1, 2, 3\}$$

how many ordered pairs can we manufacture from S? This can be approached as follows: There are two places in an ordered pair. Since we have three elements, we have three choices in the first place. Similarly, we have three choices in the second place. Thus there are a total of

$$3 \times 3 = 3^2 = 9$$

ordered pairs. This can be shown diagrammatically as

1st place	2nd place	Ordered pair
	1	(1, 1)
1	2	(1, 2)
	3	(1, 3)
	1	(2, 1)
2	2	(2, 2)
	3	(2, 3)
	1	(3, 1)
3	2	(3, 2)
	3	(3, 3)

If we have $S_1 = \{1, 2, 3\}$, $S_2 = \{4, 5\}$, how many ordered pairs (x, y) exist where x belongs to S_1 and y belongs to S_2? Since there are three choices for the first place and two choices for the second place, there are $3 \times 2 = 6$ ordered pairs. This is shown as

1st place	2nd place	Ordered pair
	4	(1, 4)
1	5	(1, 5)
	4	(2, 4)
2	5	(2, 5)
	4	(3, 4)
3	5	(3, 5)

In general, if S_1 has n elements and S_2 has m elements, we may form $m \times n$ ordered pairs.

The six ordered pairs we obtained above will form a set in which each ordered pair is an element. This set of ordered pairs will be denoted by

$$S_1 \times S_2 = \{(x, y): \quad x \in S_1 \quad \text{and} \quad y \in S_2\}$$

That is, $S_1 \times S_2$ is the set of ordered pairs (x, y) such that the first coordinate x belongs to S_1 and the second coordinate y belongs to S_2.

In general, if we have two sets A and B, the *set* of all ordered pairs (x, y) that can be obtained from A and B such that $x \in A$, $y \in B$, is shown by

$$A \times B = \{(x, y): \quad x \in A \quad \text{and} \quad y \in B\}$$

This *set* is called the *Cartesian product* of A and B, or the *Cartesian set of A and B* and is denoted by $A \times B$. $A \times B$ is read *A cross B*.

As we saw earlier, ordered pairs were represented as points on a graph. The Cartesian product may also be shown graphically. For example, let

$$A = \{1, 2, 3, 4, 5, 6\}$$

We may think of A as the set of possible outcomes when a die is tossed. Then the Cartesian product $A \times A$ is shown in Figure 1–7. There are

$$6 \times 6 = 6^2 = 36$$

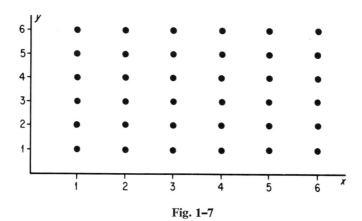

Fig. 1–7

ordered pairs. The expression $A \times A$ is the set of these 36 ordered pairs. This is interpreted as the 36 possible outcomes when a die is tossed twice.

If A is the set of all points on a line, then $A \times A$ is the set of all ordered pairs on the plane, i.e., the whole plane.

It is possible to extend this to more than two elements. We then have ordered triples, ordered quadruples, and so forth. In the case of ordered triples the relationship may be shown in a three-dimensional Cartesian diagram. Each appropriate point will consist of an ordered triple. Thus if

$$S_1 = \{a, b, c\}, \qquad S_2 = \{1, 2, 3\}, \qquad S_3 = \{4\}$$

then the Cartesian product P will be

$$P = S_1 \times S_2 \times S_3 = \{(a, 1, 4), (a, 2, 4), (a, 3, 4), (b, 1, 4), (b, 2, 4)$$
$$(b, 3, 4), (c, 1, 4), (c, 2, 4), (c, 3, 4)\}$$

The first element of the ordered triple belongs to S_1, the second to S_2, and the third to S_3. Thus there are $3 \times 3 \times 1 = 9$ ordered triples. Note that $(3, 3, 3)$ is an ordered triple that indicates a point on a three-dimensional Cartesian diagram, whereas $\{3, 3, 3\}$ is not a set of three elements but rather the set $\{3\}$.

Problems

1. Given the following sets, find the Cartesian product (which is also called the product set), and graph your results.

(a) $S_1 = S_2 = \{a, b, c\}$.
(b) $S_1 = \{a, b\}$, $S_2 = \{c, d, e\}$.
(c) $S_1 = \{x: \ x = 1, 2, 3\}$,
   $S_2 = \{y: \ y = x + 2\}$.
(d) $S_1 = \{x: \ x = 1, 2, 3\}$,
   $S_2 = \{y: \ y = x^2\}$.

1.6 Relations

Let us now use sentences and ordered pairs to define *relations*. Consider Figure 1–8, which shows the 36 possible outcomes when a die is tossed twice.

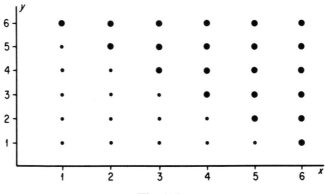

Fig. 1–8

Let A and B be the sets of possible outcomes for the first and second throw respectively. Then

$$A = B = \{1, 2, 3, 4, 5, 6\}$$

and $A \times B$ is the Cartesian set. Let the ordered pair be denoted by (x, y). Then $x \in A$, $y \in B$.

Now consider the sentence (condition): The sum of the first and second throw is greater than 6. This is shown by

$$x + y > 6$$

This is an open sentence, and we have two variables x and y instead of one variable. The values of x and y that satisfy this sentence, i.e., make it *true*, are

$$(1, 6), \quad (2, 5), \quad (2, 6), \quad (3, 4), \quad (3, 5), \quad (3, 6)$$
$$(4, 3), \quad (4, 4), \quad (4, 5), \quad (4, 6), \quad (5, 2)$$
$$(5, 3), \quad (5, 4), \quad (5, 5), \quad (5, 6), \quad (6, 1)$$
$$(6, 2), \quad (6, 3), \quad (6, 4), \quad (6, 5), \quad (6, 6)$$

These "solutions" are ordered pairs and are shown by the heavy dots of Figure 1–8. They form a subset of $P = A \times B$. Let this subset be denoted by R. Then we show this subset R by

$$R = \{(x, y): \ x + y > 6, \ (x, y) \in P\}$$

As another example, let

$$x + y = 6$$

Then

$$R = \{(x, y): \ x + y = 6, \ (x, y) \in P\}$$

will be the set of ordered pairs

$$\{(1, 5), \quad (2, 4), \quad (3, 3), \quad (4, 2), \quad (5, 1)\}$$

These ordered pairs are easily identified in Figure 1–8. Thus, the sentence in two variables selects ordered pairs from the Cartesian product so that the selected subset of ordered pairs makes the sentence true.

The subset R of a Cartesian product is called a *relation*.

Let us give several more examples. Let

$$x = y$$

That is, the number on the first throw of the die is equal to that of the second throw. The relation R is

$$R = \{(x, y): \ x = y, \ (x, y) \in P\}$$

This is shown in Figure 1–9.

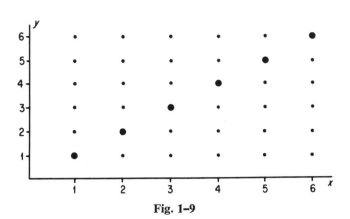

Fig. 1–9

Next, consider the following case

$$x = \tfrac{1}{2}y$$

That is, the number of the second throw is to be twice that of the first throw. The relation R is

$$R = \{(x, y): \quad x = \tfrac{1}{2}y, \quad (x, y) \in P\}$$

This is shown in Figure 1–10.

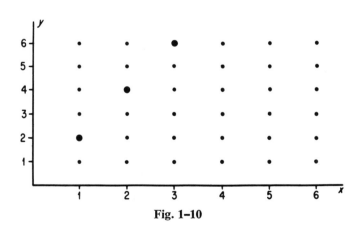

Fig. 1–10

Let A be a set of real numbers. Then the relation obtained from $x = y$ will be

$$R = \{(x, y): \quad x = y, \quad (x, y) \in P\}$$

where $P = A \times A$. Graphically, this is the straight line in Figure 1–11.

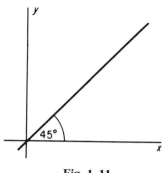

Fig. 1–11   Fig. 1–12

The relation obtained from $x > y > 0$ will be

$$R = \{(x, y): \quad x > y > 0, \quad (x, y) \in P\}$$

Graphically, it is the shaded part in Figure 1–12.

A relation is formally defined as follows: Given a set A and a set B, a relation R is a subset of the Cartesian product $A \times B$. The elements of the subset R which are ordered pairs (x, y) are such that $x \in A$, $y \in B$.

Let us next reverse our process and assume we have a relation R,

$$R = \{(x, y): \quad x = \tfrac{1}{2}y, \quad (x, y) \in P\}$$

where P is a Cartesian product $A \times B$. Let A and B be the outcomes of a toss of a die as in our previous illustration. Then

$$A = B = \{1, 2, ..., 6\}$$

The x and y of the ordered pairs (x, y) that are elements of R need not necessarily range over all of the elements of A and B. In fact, usually x and y only range over some of the elements of A and B. How shall we show which elements of A and B the x and y vary over? We may show this as

$$\text{Set of } x = \{x: \quad \text{for some } y, \quad (x, y) \in R\}$$

This shows the x's that are paired with the y in (x, y) which belong to R. This set of x is called the *domain* of the relation R and is denoted by dom R.

Similarly, the subset of y in B over which y varies will be shown by

$$\{y: \quad \text{for some } x, \quad (x, y) \in R\}$$

This subset is called the *range* of R and is denoted by ran R.

In our present example, we know that

$$\text{dom } R = \{1, 2, 3\}$$
$$\text{ran } R = \{2, 4, 6\}$$

For the example where $x < y$, we have

$$\text{dom } R = \{1, 2, 3, 4, 5\}$$
$$\text{ran } R = \{2, 3, 4, 5, 6\}$$

1.7 Functions

(i) Mappings of sets

Reconsider two of our previous examples of relations. They are reproduced in Figure 1–13(a) and (b) for convenience. In (a) for each x there is

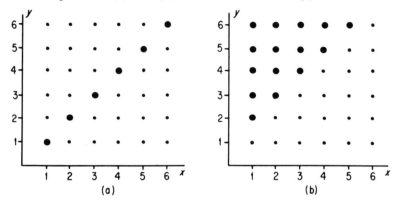

Fig. 1–13

only one corresponding y, whereas in (b) for each x there are several corresponding y's (except for $x = 5$). A *function* is a special case of a relation where
for each x (or several x's), there is only one corresponding y. Thus, the relation in (a) is also a function, while the relation in (b) is not a function. We
may now investigate this idea of a function in more detail.

Consider a suburb that has 3 families and 6 telephones. Each family
has a telephone, and 3 are kept in reserve. Assume that after a certain period
of time the number of families have increased to 6 and so each family has
a telephone and there are no extra telephones. Finally, let us assume the
number of families have increased to 12 and as a result 2 families share one
telephone.

We shall denote the set of families by X and the set of telephones by Y.
The first case of 3 families (set X) and 6 telephones (set Y) may be shown as in
Figure 1–14. With every element x (family) of the set X there corresponds an
element y (telephone) of set Y. As Figure 1–14(a) shows, only 3 of the
elements of Y (telephones) are paired with the elements of X (families).
In such a case where all of the elements of Y are not paired with the elements
of X, we shall say the set X has been *mapped into* the set Y.

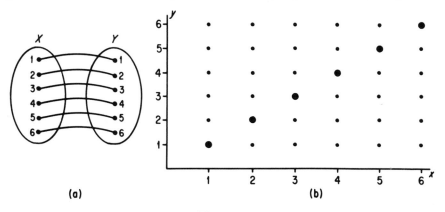

Fig. 1–14

Let us look at this in terms of ordered pairs. The Cartesian product P is

$$P = X \times Y$$

and the ordered pairs (x, y) are shown in Figure 1–14(b). As can be seen, there are $3 \times 6 = 18$ such ordered pairs. The ordered pairs we are interested in are

$$(1, 1), \quad (2, 2), \quad (3, 3)$$

This set of three ordered pairs is a subset of P and thus is a relation R which is shown as

$$R = \{(x, y): \ x = y, \ (x, y) \in P\}$$

The dom $R = \{1, 2, 3\} = X$, ran $R = \{1, 2, 3\} \subset Y$.

We now consider the second case where we have 6 families and 6 telephones. This is shown in Figure 1–15, where every element x (family) of X

Fig. 1–15

is paired with an element y (telephone) of Y and all the elements of Y are paired. In this case, we shall say the set X has been mapped *onto* the set Y.

In terms of relations, we have the Cartesian product $P = X \times Y$ which has 36 ordered pairs (x, y) as shown in Figure 1–15(b). We are concerned with the relation (subset) R such that

$$R = \{(x, y): \quad x = y, \quad (x, y) \in P\}$$

This will be the subset of the six ordered pairs

$$(1, 1), (2, 2), ..., (6, 6)$$

The dom $R = X$, ran $R = Y$.

Finally, we have the case where there are 12 families and 6 telephones. This is shown in Figure 1–16 where with every element x (family) of X there is

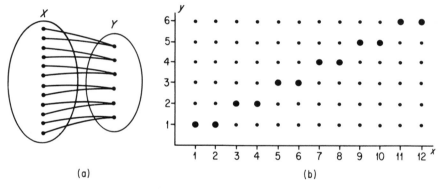

(a)   (b)

Fig. 1–16

associated (related) an element y (telephone) of Y, and conversely, with every element y (telephone) there is associated at least one (in our present case two) element(s) x (family). In this case, we also say that the set X has been mapped *onto* the set Y.

The Cartesian product $P = X \times Y$ has $6 \times 12 = 72$ ordered pairs. The relation R we are interested in is the subset of 12 ordered pairs shown in Figure 1–16(b).

The characteristic of all three cases is that with every element x (family) there is associated only one element y (telephone), whereas to every element y (telephone) there may correspond more than one element x (family). Furthermore, the mapping of X onto Y can be obtained from the mapping of X into Y as follows: Consider the first case where we had 3 families and 6 telephones. The 3 telephones (y) that correspond with the 3 families (x) can be considered as a subset of Y for which there exists at least one x in X. Let this subset of y's be A. Then X maps onto A, where $A \subset Y$.

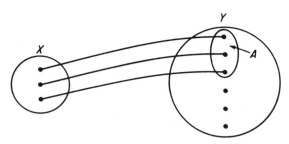

Fig. 1–17

(ii) Functions defined

A *function* is a relation *f* (i.e., a subset of ordered pairs) such that for each element $x \in X$ there is a unique element $y \in Y$.

Thus, a function is a subset of ordered pairs characterized by certain given conditions. The term *mapping* is used synonymously with function. Mapping conveys the impression of an activity of relating the element of X to Y. Sacrificing rigor, we shall occasionally use the word *rule* and say a function is a rule of mapping which emphasizes the conditions under which the mapping takes place.

These ideas are expressed symbolically as

$$f \colon \; X \to Y$$

which we shall read as f is a function that maps X onto Y. Let us now formally redefine a function as follows: A function is a relation f (i.e., a subset of ordered pairs) that has the following characteristics:

(1) The domain of f [i.e., the set of x which consists of the x's that are paired with y in (x, y)] is equal to X.

(2) To each x there corresponds a unique $y \in Y$.

To show the association between the element x and the corresponding unique element y of the ordered pair (x, y) that is an element of the function (subset) f, we write

$$f(x) = y$$

The set of the elements y that corresponds to x such that $f(x) = y$ is the *range* of the function f. For example, in our first case where we had 3 families and 6 telephones, the set of 3 families (X) is the domain of the function f. The set of 6 telephones is Y, but the range of the function is the subset of 3 telephones for which there exist families such that $f(x) = y$. In the second and third case the 6 telephones become the range. That is, Y itself becomes the range, and, as we saw, this was the case where we said X maps onto Y.

If x (family) is any element of X, the element $y = f(x)$ (telephone) of Y which corresponds to x is called the *image* of x under (the mapping) f. Conversely, the set of x (family or families) in X whose image is $y \in Y$ is called the inverse image of y in the mapping f and is denoted by $f^{-1}(y)$. Note that we said the *set* of x. This is because there may be 2 or more x (families) that correspond to a definite y (telephone). The image is unique, but the pre-image or *inverse image* may be more than one element.

We can state what was just said about images and inverse images in terms of *sets*. If A is a subset of X, the set of all elements $\{f(x): \ x \in A \subset X\}$ of Y is called the image of the subset A and is denoted by $f(A)$. Conversely, if B is a subset of Y, the inverse image of B is the set of elements

$$\{f^{-1}(y): \ y \in B \subset Y\}$$

in X. This is denoted by $f^{-1}(B)$.

When we use the term function and the symbol $y = f(x)$, we say x is the *argument* and y is the *value* of the function f. Functions such as $y = f(x)$ are sometimes called *point functions* because x can be considered a point on a line. Also, $f(A)$ is sometimes called a *set function* because A is a set.

Problems

1. Given the following sets

$$S_1 = \{a, b, c, d\}$$
$$S_2 = \{1, 2, 3, 4\}$$

carry out the following steps.

(a) Find the Cartesian product P.
(b) Graph the Cartesian product.
(c) Construct a function f that maps S_1 into S_2.
(d) Show this function on your graph by connecting the points by straight lines.
(e) Check and see that f is a subset of P.
(f) Let

$$y = f(x)$$

Find the values of y when x takes on the values a, b, c, d according to the function you have constructed.
(g) Construct another function and repeat what you have done in (c), (d), (e), and (f) above.

2. Graph the following functions f.

(a) $S_1 = \{a, b, c, d\}$,
   $S_2 = \{1, 2, 3\}$;
   $f = \{(a, 2), (b, 1), (c, 2), (d, 3)\}$.

(b) $S_1 = \{a, b, c, d\}$,
$S_2 = \{1, 2, 3\}$;
$f = \{(a, 1), (3, 1), (c, 3), (d, 2)\}$.
(c) $S_1 = \{a, b, c, d\}$,
$S_2 = \{1, 2\}$;
$f = \{(a, 1), (b, 2), (c, 2), (d, 2)\}$.

3. Using the S_1 and S_2 of Problem 2, construct the Cartesian product $S_1 \times S_2$ and check that the functions f in Problem 2 are subsets of $P = S_1 \times S_2$.

4. Graph the following relations and check whether they are functions of S_1 into S_2.

(a) $S_1 = \{a, b, c, d\}$,
$S_2 = \{1, 2, 3\}$;
$f = \{(a, 2), (b, 1), (b, 3), (c, 3), (d, 2)\}$.
(b) $S_1 = \{a, b, c, d\}$,
$S_2 = \{1, 2, 3\}$;
$f = \{(a, 1), (b, 3), (c, 2), (c, 3), (d, 2)\}$.
(c) $S_1 = \{a, b, c, d\}$,
$S_2 = \{1, 2, 3\}$;
$f = \{(a, 1), (b, 3), (c, 2)\}$.
(d) $S_1 = \{a, b, c, d\}$,
$S_2 = \{1, 2, 3\}$;
$f = \{(b, 1), (c, 3), (a, 2), (b, 1), (d, 2)\}$.
(e) $S_1 = \{a, b, c, d\}$,
$S_2 = \{1, 2, 3\}$;
$f = \{(c, 1), (a, 2), (b, 4), (d, 3)\}$.

1.8 Ordered sets

We have discussed Cartesian products, relations, and functions using the basic ideas of sets. A characteristic of these discussions was that the emphasis was mainly on the relations between sets, and between elements of a set and the set. We have not as yet systematically considered relations between the elements of a set. Let us now approach set theory from this standpoint and explain the idea of an ordered set.

It will turn out that all of our subsequent discussions will be in terms of real numbers. And we know from high-school mathematics that real numbers may be represented by points on a straight line and that they may be ordered according to their magnitude. That is, the real numbers constitute an ordered set.

Our understanding of real numbers as an ordered set in high-school mathematics is, however, not sufficient to analyze various concepts we shall be using in our subsequent discussions. So let us first explain what is meant by an ordered set and then with this background explain the characteristics of linear point sets.

Consider the following sets.

$$S_1 = \{1, 2, 3, 4\}$$
$$S_2 = \{4, 3, 2, 1\}$$
$$S_3 = \{1, 2, 3, 4, \ldots\}$$
$$S_4 = \{\ldots, 4, 3, 2, 1\}$$

We shall say a set S_i is an *ordered set* if any two elements of the set are such that

$$x \text{ precedes } y \qquad x < y$$

or

$$y \text{ precedes } x \qquad y < x$$

Note that in the present context $<$ or $>$ is used to indicate *before* or *after* and not "greater than" or "less than." We are for the moment not considering the magnitude of the elements.

Hence, there are two things: The first is the set S_i, and the second is a relation that defines an order for two elements. For example, in S_2 the rule is that the natural numbers will be ordered in descending magnitude. If the elements of a set are boys, we may assign a rule that they be ordered from the highest to the lowest in height or according to alphabetical order or according to age, and so forth. As is seen, the rule is something we determine and does not necessarily rely on the magnitude of the elements. However, in most of our subsequent discussion, the rule will be according to the magnitude of the elements. For the present though, the $<$ considers only the order of the elements according to the rule we define.

When we consider the set $S_2 = \{4, 3, 2, 1\}$ and attach an order to S_2, we usually assume the element written to the left of an element to be the element that precedes, and the one to the right, the element that follows. Thus, in S_2, 3 precedes 2, and 2 follows 3.

The characteristics of an ordered set are:

(1) $x < x$ does not hold; i.e., the ordering relation is *non-reflexive*.

(2) $x < y$ and $y < x$ do not hold simultaneously; i.e., the ordering relation is *anti-symmetric*.

(3) If $x < y$, $y < z$, then $x < z$; i.e., the ordering relation is *transitive*.

Therefore, S_1 has a first element 1 and a last element 4. Similarly, the first and last elements of S_2 are 4 and 1, and S_3 has a first element 1 but no last element, while S_4 has a last element but no first element. Moreover, S_1 and S_2 have the same elements. Thus, as sets they are equal. But as ordered sets they are different sets.

On the other hand, we may establish a one-to-one correspondence between the two ordered sets S_1 and S_2.

$$S_1 = \{1, 2, 3, 4\}$$
$$\downarrow \downarrow \downarrow \downarrow$$
$$S_2 = \{4, 3, 2, 1\}$$

When $1 < 2$ for S_1, the relation holds for the corresponding elements in S_2; i.e., $4 < 3$. When this relation holds between the elements of two sets like S_1 and S_2, we say the sets are *similar*.

More generally, we say S_1 and S_2 are similar when the elements of S_1 and S_2 can be put in a one-to-one correspondence and when the ordering relation of S_1 holds also for the corresponding elements of S_2. As is seen, the relationship of similarity is stronger than equivalence. That is, if S_1 and S_2 are similar, they are also equivalent.

However, two equivalent sets may not be similar. For example, S_3 is equivalent to S_4 but is not similar to S_4 because S_4 does not have an element that corresponds to 1 of S_3.

Note also that similarity is reflexive, symmetric, and transitive. For example, suppose we have

$$S_1 = \{1, 2, 3, 4\}$$
$$S_2 = \{4, 3, 2, 1\}$$
$$S_5 = \{a, b, c, d\}$$

Then letting $\simeq$ indicate the relation similarity, we have

$S_1 \simeq S_2$ reflexive

$S_1 \simeq S_2$, then $S_2 \simeq S_1$ symmetric

$S_1 \simeq S_2$ and $S_2 \simeq S_5$ implies $S_1 \simeq S_5$ transitive

The characteristic of

$$S_3 = \{1, 2, 3, ...\}$$

is that it has a first element. In contrast,

$$S_4 = \{..., 4, 3, 2, 1\}$$

does not have a first element. An ordered set is said to be well ordered if it and every one of its non-empty subsets have a first element.

Let us next consider the relation $\leq$. For example, let $x \in S$ and $y \in S$. Then, when $x \leq y$, we say x precedes y or is equal to y. If we write $x \geq y$, we say x is a successor of y or is equal to y.

The characteristics of the relation $\leq$ are:

(1) $x \leq x$, i.e., reflexive.

(2) $x \leq y$, $y \leq x$ implies $x = y$, i.e., anti-symmetric.

(3) $x \leq y, y \leq z$ implies $x \leq z$, i.e., transitive.

As an example, consider a set S with the relation $\leq$ for every $x_i \in S$, $x_j \in S$.

$$S = \{x_1, x_2, x_3, \ldots, x_{20}\}$$

Let E be the subset

$$E = \{x_3, x_4, \ldots, x_{18}\}$$

which is also an ordered set. The element x_1 is $x_1 \leq x_i$ for all $x \in S$ and is called the *first* or *smallest* element of S. The x_{20} is $x_i \leq x_{20}$ for all $x \in S$ and is called the *last* or *largest* element of S.

The elements x_1, x_2, and x_3 have the ordering relation $\leq$ with every element in E. That is, these 3 elements precede or are equal to all the elements in E. We shall also use the term *less than or equal to* instead of precede or are equal to. For example, the ordering relation of x_3 and the elements of E is $x_3 \leq x_3 \leq x_4 \leq \ldots \leq x_{18}$. The 3 elements are called the *lower bounds* of the subset E. That is, an element $a \in S$ is a lower bound of the subset E if and only if $a \leq x_i$ for all $x_i \in E$.

Similarly, the 3 elements x_{18}, x_{19}, x_{20} have the ordering relation $\geq$ with every element in E, and they are greater than (follow or succeed) or equal to all elements in E. They are called the *upper bounds* of the subset E. That is, an element $a \in S$ is an upper bound of the subset E if and only if $a \geq x_i$ for all $x_i \in E$.

Let $E_1 = \{x_1, x_2, x_3\}$; i.e., the set of all lower bounds. Then

$$E_1 \cap E = \{x_3\}$$

This x_3, which is the *last* (or *greatest*) element of E_1, is called the *greatest lower bound* of E or the *infimum* of E. We write g.l.b. or inf of E.

Similarly, let $E_2 = \{x_{18}, x_{19}, x_{20}\}$. Then,

$$E_2 \cap E = \{x_{18}\}$$

This x_{18}, which is the *first* (or *least*) element of E_2, is called the *least upper bound* (l.u.b.) or *supremum* (sup) of E.

As a concrete example, consider the set S and its subset E.

$$S = \{1, 2, 3, \ldots, 19, 20\}$$
$$E = \{3, 4, 5, \ldots, 17, 18\}$$

The rule of ordering is according to the magnitude of the numbers where the element with the smaller magnitude precedes the element with the greater magnitude. $E_1 = \{1, 2, 3\}$ and $E_2 = \{18, 19, 20\}$. Then $E_1 \cap E = \{3\}$ and $E_2 \cap E = \{18\}$.

Note that when we have

$$S = \{1, 2, 3, 4, \ldots\}$$
$$E = \{3, 4, \ldots\}$$

the subset E has no upper bounds but has two lower bounds 1 and 2. For

$$S = \{\ldots, 4, 3, 2, 1\}$$
$$E = \{\ldots, 4, 3\}$$

the E has no lower bounds but has two upper bounds 2 and 1.

In our subsequent discussion, we shall be concerned with real numbers, and the relation $a \leq b$ of two elements of a set S will be determined by the magnitudes of a and b. For example, let $a = 3$ and $b = 4$. Then $3 \leq 4$ showed the relation that 3 precedes or is equal to 4. But now instead of precedes we may say 3 is less than or equal to 4, and the term, less than, is in accordance with our daily usage of the term. In our present case we know that 3 is less than 4 and we write $3 < 4$, $3 \neq 4$.

1.9 Linear point sets

Let us now, with the help of set theory, investigate the properties of numbers. We have three objectives in this section. One is to investigate the characteristics of real numbers, the second is to investigate the idea of continuity, and the third is to establish the relation between points on a line and real numbers.

(i) Natural numbers

The basic system of numbers is the natural numbers which we denote by N

$$N: \quad 1, 2, 3, 4, \ldots$$

In high-school mathematics we learn four basic rules of arithmetic: addition, subtraction, multiplication, and division. We can easily see that when we add or multiply any two natural numbers, we shall obtain a natural number. For example, $3 + 5 = 8$, $4 \times 3 = 12$, and 8 and 12 are both natural numbers.

However, for subtraction we may have

$$3 - 5 = -2$$

and -2 is not a member of N. Similarly,

$$\tfrac{4}{3} = 1.33 \ldots$$

is not a member of N.

We say that N is a closed system in addition and multiplication.

If we wish to perform the operation of subtraction, we need to expand our number system. This leads us to integers.

(ii) Integers

By integers, which we denote by I, we mean

1, 2, 3, ...	positive integers
−1, −2, −3, ...	negative integers
0	neither positive nor negative

The relation $\leq$ applied to I gives us

$$..., -3, -2, -1, 0, 1, 2, 3, ...$$

That is, we define that a is less than b (i.e., $a < b$) if $b - a$ is a positive integer. Hence, when $b = -3$ and $a = 1$,

$$b - a = -3 - 1 = -4$$

and is a negative integer. Hence, $a = 1$ is greater than $b = -3$. We know that this relation $<$ is defined with respect to the magnitude of the integers.

We can easily see that I is closed in addition, subtraction, and multiplication. That is, when we perform these 3 operations on any two integers, we end up with an integer.

But, as with natural numbers, when we perform division, we end up with a number not in the system I.

So let us now extend the number system to include fractions.

(iii) Rational numbers

By rational numbers, which we denote by Q, we mean the ratio of two integers reduced to their lowest common denominator. For example,

$$\tfrac{1}{1}, \tfrac{1}{2}, \tfrac{1}{3}, \tfrac{1}{4}, \tfrac{2}{1}, \tfrac{2}{2}, \tfrac{3}{2}, ...$$

are rational numbers. As is seen, $\tfrac{1}{1} = 1$, $\tfrac{2}{1} = 2$, which are integers, are also part of the rational number system.

When we perform addition, subtraction, multiplication, and division with rational numbers, we obtain rational numbers. Hence the system Q is closed in these 4 operations.

We shall call a system such as Q that is closed in the 4 operations a *field*.

There is one very important difference between integers and rational numbers. Consider the integers

$$1, 2, 3, 4$$

We note that there is no integer between 1 and 2, say. There is a break or a hole between integers. But when we consider 1 and 2 as rational numbers, there is a rational number between 1 and 2. For example,

$$\frac{1 + 2}{2} = 1.5$$

is between 1 and 2. We may continue this process and find

$$\frac{1.5 + 2}{2} = 1.75$$

between 1 and 2, and, as seen, we may continue this process indefinitely. That is, there are an infinite number of rationals between 1 and 2. We express this by saying the rational domain is *everywhere dense*.

We may express this idea of *dense* more precisely as follows: A set of points S is called everywhere dense if between any two different points x and y of S there is another point $z \in S$. Applying the process we used above, we may find z between x and y as $z = (x + y)/2$. Then repeat this process, and find w between z and y; and then a point between w and y; and, as is seen, we can find an infinite number of points between x and y.

Let us investigate this property that the rational domain is everywhere dense a little further. Suppose we have the interval from 0 to 1. Let us select a rational number 1.2. What is the next number? Suppose we pick 1.3 as the next number. But then we can find

$$\frac{1.2 + 1.3}{2} = 1.25$$

between 1.2 and 1.3. Hence 1.3 is not the next number. Applying this same process, we note that 1.25 also is not the next rational number to 1.2. And, as can be seen, we can repeat this indefinitely and conclude we cannot find the rational number next to 1.2.

This raises the following question. For natural numbers and integers, we were able to enumerate the numbers. Can we enumerate rational numbers?

We may restate the question as follows: Are rational numbers a denumerable set? Since the set is dense and we cannot find the next number, it would seem at first glance that the answer is no. However, the answer is: Yes, the set of rational numbers is denumerable. For this we construct the following schema called the *diagonal process*.

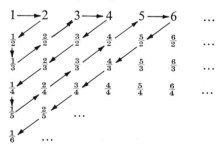

Hence we get

$$1, 2, \tfrac{1}{2}, \tfrac{1}{3}, \tfrac{2}{2}, 3, 4, \tfrac{3}{2}, \ldots$$

Canceling out all duplicate terms, we get every positive rational number. By adding the corresponding negative rational numbers and starting from zero, we get

$$Q = \{0, 1, -1, 2, -2, \tfrac{1}{2}, -\tfrac{1}{2}, \ldots\}$$

We may put this Q into a one-to-one correspondence with

$$N = \{1, 2, 3, \ldots\}$$

and hence Q is denumerable.

Note that the order of the elements in Q is not according to their magnitude. However, it is clear that, for every pair of elements (rational numbers) in Q, we have the relation $<$ according to magnitude, and hence Q is an ordered set.

(iv) Rational numbers and points on a line

We are familiar with the device of letting the points on a line represent rational numbers. Let us, however, present this correspondence between rational numbers and points on a line in terms of the concepts of sets we have been studying.

We note that the set Q of rational numbers extends in the positive and negative direction to infinity and that any two rational numbers are ordered according to their magnitude.

Let us draw a line, as in Figure 1–18, and let A be a point to denote zero

Fig. 1–18

and call it the *origin*. Let point B denote 1 and point C be -1, where $AB = AC$. Then, we can mark off on this line to the right the rational numbers $2, 3, \ldots$ by letting the intervals be equal to $AB = 1$. Furthermore, we may mark off any fraction by dividing these unit intervals. We may do this very simply by geometry. Figure 1–19 shows how the point corresponding to $\frac{1}{3}$

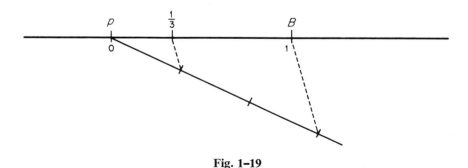

Fig. 1–19

may be found.

Hence, we may conclude that any rational number may be represented by a point on the line. But the question arises: Does the converse hold, i.e., does any point on the line have a corresponding rational number? The answer is: No! Let us explain this next.

(v) Irrational numbers

We have seen in Section 1.4 how a number $\sqrt{2}$ was found on a line. Figure 1–5 is reproduced here as Figure 1–20 for convenience. We also saw that $\sqrt{2}$ was not a rational number and called it an irrational number. We also note that $\sqrt{2}$ is between 1 and 2. That is, $1 < \sqrt{2} < 2$.

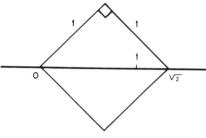

We can also see that $\sqrt[3]{2}$ is between $1 < \sqrt[3]{2} < \sqrt{2}$. Furthermore, we may use the process of $(1 + \sqrt{2})/2$ to obtain another irrational number. And it is not difficult to see that there are infinitely many irrational numbers such as $\sqrt{2}$, $\sqrt[3]{2}$, and $(1 + \sqrt{2})/2$ between 1 and 2. It is not hard to see in-

Fig. 1–20

tuitively that there are many more irrational numbers than rational numbers.

We have said the set of rational numbers Q was dense everywhere, but, when compared with the set of irrational numbers, the Q is relatively porous. The Q is, so to speak, full of holes.

In terms of the points on the line, the rational points are relatively porous compared with the irrational points.

Hence, the irrational points have, so to speak, filled in the holes in the line between the rational numbers. We shall call the set of all rational and irrational numbers the set of *real numbers* and denote it by *R*.

A question that arises is: Do the real numbers cover the whole line without breaks, and hence may we consider the points corresponding to these numbers continuous? We are for the moment using the term, continuous, in a commonsense manner, i.e., in the sense that there is no break in the line.

Let us consider this question in the following manner. When we were considering integers and their corresponding points (integer points) on a line, we could have cut the line and found the cut to be between two integers, say 1 and 2. The cut does not "hit" an integer point and there is a break (hole) between 1 and 2 and so the set *I* is not continuous.

For the rational points on the line, we can also cut the line, and we may cut it at a point such as $\sqrt{2}$, in which case the cut is through a hole between two rational numbers and we may think that this is a break in the continuity of the set of rational points.

This leads us to the observation that, if we cut the line and the cut always hits an irrational number when it does not hit a rational number, then the irrational numbers have filled the holes in the line and the real numbers R will form a continuous set of points.

What we wish to do now is to pursue this idea of a cut, define irrational numbers, and show how we have a correspondence between points and real numbers.

In passing, there are two properties of the real numbers that we should note. One is that the set of real numbers R is dense, and the second is that the set R is non-denumerable.

As for the second point, proof that R is non-denumerable may be found in algebra books; furthermore, it is not necessary for our subsequent discussion and hence will be omitted.

As for the first point, since the set R includes the rational numbers, it is clear that R is everywhere dense.

Let us now return to our main line of discussion and investigate this idea of a cut.

(vi) *Dedekind cut*

We have introduced irrational numbers in a non-rigorous way in the previous section. What we wish to do now is to investigate the idea of continuity and also consider irrational numbers in a more rigorous manner.

The problem of continuity will be approached from two directions. One is to consider the continuity of a line, which we may call the *linear continuum*. The other is to consider the continuity of a set, which we may call the *arithmetic continuum*. And postulating the correspondence of the two, we shall be able to state that any real number can be represented by a point on the line and vice versa.

The problem of the linear continuum will be explained by Dedekind's theory. He states:

> I find the essence of continuity in the converse, i.e., in the following principle: If all points of the straight line fall into two classes such that every point of the first class lies to the left of every point of the second class, then there exists one and only one point which produces this division of all points into two classes, this severing of the straight line into two portions ... .
>
> The assumption of this property of the line is nothing else than an axiom by which we attribute to the line its continuity, by which we find continuity in the line.*

Dedekind also states:

> I think I shall not err in assuming that every one will at once grant the truth of this statement ... . I am utterly unable to adduce any proof of its correctness, nor has any one the power.*

* Richard Dedekind, "Continuity and irrational numbers," 1872. English translation in W. W. Beman, ed., "Essays on the Theory of Numbers," The Open Court Publishing Co., Chicago, 1901, pp. 11 and 12.

We shall also accept this axiom and consider it a definition of the continuity of a straight line.

The special characteristic of this axiom is that it uses the idea of a cut, or partition, of a straight line. Let us now apply this idea of a cut to a set of numbers and define irrational numbers and the arithmetic continuum.

We already have natural numbers, integers, and rational numbers. Using the idea of a cut and rational numbers, we wish to define irrational numbers. That is, we are going to "create" irrational numbers. And we shall consider these defined irrational numbers as legitimate numbers if they obey the 4 arithmetic rules and are also closed under these operations.

Suppose we have an ordered set of points, S. Let us cut this set into two sets S_1 and S_2, where (1) the points belong to either S_1 or S_2; (2) S_1 and S_2 are non-empty sets, i.e., all the points do not belong only in one set; and (3) all the points in S_1 lie to the left of S_2. Then we have the following 4 possible ways of cutting (partitioning) the set S.

(1) Jump cut: S_1 has a last and S_2 has a first element.

(2) Continuous cut: S_1 has a last but S_2 has no first element.

(3) Continuous cut: S_1 has no last but S_2 has a first element.

(4) Gap cut: S_1 has no last and S_2 has no first element.

An example of the jump cut is as follows. Suppose we have the set

$$S = \{1, 2, 3, 4, 5\}$$

and let

$$S_1 = \{1, 2\}$$
$$S_2 = \{3, 4, 5\}$$

Then S_1 has a last element 2 and S_2 has a first element 3, and the cut that produces two such sets S_1 and S_2 is called a jump cut.

For the continuous cut, consider the set of rational numbers

$$S = \{x \mid 1 < x < 5\}$$
$$S_1 = \{x \mid 1 < x < 2\}$$
$$S_2 = \{x \mid 2 \leq x < 5\}$$

As is seen, S_1 has no last element, but S_2 has a first element 2. Let us find an element in S_1 very close to 2, say a. But we can always find an infinite number of additional elements between a and 2. A cut which divides the S into S_1 and S_2 as above is called a continuous cut (partition).

To bring this point out more clearly, let

$$S = \{x \mid 1 < x < 5\}$$
$$S_1 = \{x \mid 1 < x < 1.5\}$$
$$S_2 = \{x \mid 2 \leq x < 5\}$$

Then, S_1 has no last element, but S_2 has a first element 2. Is this a continuous cut? In this case, there is a break between 1.5 and 2. However, these two sets are not cut (partitioned) in accordance with the way we have defined a cut, i.e., that $S_1 \cup S_2 = S$. We must cut the set S according to the 3 rules stated above.

The second continuous cut may be shown by the set of rational numbers

$$S = \{x \mid 1 < x < 5\}$$
$$S_1 = \{x \mid 1 < x \leq 2\}$$
$$S_2 = \{x \mid 2 < x < 5\}$$

An example of a gap cut may be shown by letting S be a set of rational numbers

$$S = \{x \mid 1 < x < 5\}$$
$$S_1 = \{x \mid 1 < x < 2\}$$
$$S_2 = \{x \mid 2 < x < 5\}$$

As is seen, S_1 has no last element and S_2 has no first element, and we say this cut is a gap cut. Note, however, this is not a jump cut. It is also not a continuous cut.

The reader may feel a little uneasy with this situation of a gap cut for rational numbers. We have cut S, but, unlike the other cuts, there is no corresponding rational number to this cut which partitions the set.

To fill in this void, let us extend the number system by adding new numbers to rationals, just as we did by adding integers to natural numbers and rationals to integers. We cut (partition) the set S of rational numbers into S_1 and S_2. When this cut (partition) is not produced by a rational number, as in our example above in the gap cut, "we create a new, an irrational number i, which we regard as completely defined by this cut. We shall say that the number i corresponds to this cut or that it produces this cut."*

Hence i is created by this cut; and this irrational number i cuts the set of rationals into two exclusive and non-empty sets S_1 and S_2.

As an example, let us partition the set of rational numbers S so that

$$S_1 = \{x \mid x^2 \leq 2, \quad x > 0\}$$
$$S_2 = \{x \mid 2 < x^2, \quad x > 0\}$$

This may be written as

$$S_1 = \{x \mid x \leq \sqrt{2}, \quad x > 0\}$$
$$S_2 = \{x \mid \sqrt{2} < x, \quad x > 0\}$$

* R. Dedekind, op. cit., p. 15.

and S is cut by $\sqrt{2}$. Since $\sqrt{2}$ is not a rational number, we define it as an irrational number.

But note that in this case $\sqrt{2}$ does not belong to the set of rationals S_1. It clearly does not belong to S_2. Hence, when S is considered as a set of rationals, this cut is still a gap cut.

But now let S be a set of rational and irrational numbers, i.e., a set of real numbers. Then $\sqrt{2}$ belongs to S_1 and is the last element of S_1, and S_2 has no first element. Hence, when S is considered a set of real numbers, this cut by $\sqrt{2}$ is a continuous cut.

Several questions arise. One is: Just as we performed a cut between rational numbers and found an irrational number, can we repeat this process and perform a cut between irrational numbers and find a (say) super-irrational number? We state without proof that the answer is: No; when we cut real numbers, we obtain real numbers.

This result implies that, when we cut a set of real numbers, we shall get a continuous cut because the cut produces a real number which is either the last element of S_1 or the first element of S_2. That is, a cut in the set of real numbers is always a continuous cut.

We shall say that a set is continuous if every cut in the set is continuous.

The second question that arises is: Do the real numbers we have obtained by cuts obey the 4 arithmetic rules as do the rational numbers? We again state without proof that the answer is yes. Furthermore, the real numbers are closed in the 4 operations. Hence the set of real numbers is a closed system under the 4 basic arithmetic rules and, furthermore, is a continuous set. We shall say that the set of real numbers is an arithmetic continuum.

(vii) The arithmetic continuum and the linear continuum

We have explained in a non-rigorous manner Dedekind's theory of the continuity of a straight line and the continuity of a set of real numbers. The question that arises next is: Is there a correspondence between the two? The Dedekind-Cantor axiom states that there is a one-to-one correspondence between the points of a straight line and a set of real numbers. That is, to any point on a straight line, we may assign a real number; and, conversely any real number may be represented by a point on the straight line.

Compare this result with the correspondence of points on a line and a set of rational numbers. We found earlier that any rational number may be represented by a point on a straight line, but the converse did not hold.

In non-rigorous terms, we may say that, although the set of rational numbers is everywhere dense, it is not a continuous set and is very porous compared to the set of real numbers.

In Chapter 2, we shall use these results and develop some additional concepts concerning points on a straight line.

(viii) Open and closed intervals

Take the line segment from a to b, which we shall call an interval (Figure 1–21). When we write

$$[a, b] = \{x: \quad a \leq x \leq b\}$$

Fig. 1–21

this will mean the points a and b are included in the interval, and it is called a *closed interval*. The two intervals

$$[a, b) = \{x: \quad a \leq x < b\}$$
$$(a, b] = \{x: \quad a < x \leq b\}$$

are called *half-open* intervals, where in the first case b and in the second case a is not included in the interval. Finally,

$$(a, b) = \{x: \quad a < x < b\}$$

which does not include either point a or b, is called an *open* interval.

Notes and References

Two books written on an elementary level are Breuer (1959) and Trimble and Lott (1960). Intermediate references are Halmos (1960); Thielman (1953), Chapters 1–4; and Wilder (1952), Chapters 3–6. Advanced references are Hausdorff (1957), Kamke (1950), and Fraenkel (1953). Of these various references, Breuer (1959) and Halmos (1960) are recommended as a starting point. To see the relation between set theory and logic, see Kemeny (1959), Chapters 1–2, and Tarski (1946).

Applications of set theory to economics may be found in Papandreou (1958), Koopmans (1957), and Debreu (1959).

Breuer, J., *Introduction to the Theory of Sets*, trans. by H. F. Fehr. Englewood Cliffs, N.J.: Prentice-Hall, Inc., 1958.

Debreu, G., *Theory of Value*. New York: John Wiley & Sons, Inc., 1959.

Fraenkel, A. A., *Abstract Set Theory*. Amsterdam: North-Holland Publishing Co., 1953.

Halmos, P. R., *Naive Set Theory*. Princeton, N. J.: D. Van Nostrand Co., Inc., 1960.

Hausdorff, F., *Set Theory*, trans. by J. R. Aumann. New York: Chelsea Publishing Co., 1957.

Kamke, E., *Theory of Sets*, trans. by F. Bagemihl. New York: Dover Publications, Inc., 1950.

Kemeny, J. G., Mirkil, H., Snell, J. L., and Thompson, G. L., *Finite Mathematical Structures.* Englewood Cliffs, N.J.: Prentice-Hall, Inc., 1959.

Koopmans, T. C., *Three Essays on the State of Economic Science.* New York: McGraw-Hill Book Co., 1957.

Lipschutz, S., *Set Theory and Related Topics.* New York: Schaum Publishing Co., 1964.

Papandreou, A. G., *Economics as a Science.* Philadelphia: J. B. Lippincott Co., 1958.

Selby, S., and Sweet, L., *Sets, Relations, Functions, An Introduction.* New York: McGraw-Hill Book Co., 1963.

Tarski, A., *Introduction to Logic*, 2nd ed. New York: Oxford University Press, Inc., 1946.

Thielman, H. P., *Theory of Functions of Real Variables.* Englewood Cliffs, N.J.: Prentice-Hall, Inc., 1953.

Trimble, H. C., and Lott, F. W., *Elementary Analysis.* Englewood Cliffs, N.J.: Prentice-Hall, Inc., 1960.

Wilder, R. L., *The Foundations of Mathématics.* New York: John Wiley & Sons, Inc., 1952.

CHAPTER 2

Functions and Limits

The idea of a limit is basic to our subsequent discussion of calculus. We shall first discuss it in connection with a sequence, which is a special kind of a function, and then in connection with a function.

This idea of a limit is dependent on the idea of the *distance* between two points. Very roughly speaking, as two points come closer together, we eventually reach a situation which we call a *limit*. We first must determine what is meant by the *distance* between two points. This is usually discussed under the title *space*, but at the level of this book we cannot present such a rigorous discussion of this topic. Only a heuristic explanation of one of the spaces, i.e., the metric space, will be discussed. Furthermore, we shall confine our discussion here to *Euclidean space*.

2.1 Metric space

Consider the ordered set

$$S = \{x, y, z, w\}$$

We shall now ask the question: What is the *distance* between, say, x and y or x and z? To answer this, we need to define what is meant by distance. Depending on the way distance is defined, various kinds of spaces may be constructed. Here, we shall define distance so that the *metric space* is obtained.

The elements of the set S will be called points, and S will be called a point set. Let (x, y) be a pair of points, and assign a real number $\rho = \rho(x, y)$ and call it the *distance* between the two points x and y. Then, $\rho = \rho(x, y)$ must satisfy the following conditions:

(1)
$$\rho(x, x) = 0$$

i.e., the distance between two points x, x which are the same point is zero.

(2)
$$\rho(x, y) = \rho(y, x) > 0 \quad \text{for} \quad x \neq y$$

That is, when x and y are two different points, the distance from x to y equals the distance from y to x and the distance is a positive real number.

(3)
$$\rho(x,y) + \rho(y,z) \geq \rho(x,z)$$

This is known as the *triangle inequality* and can be understood with the help of Figure 2–1; it is the familiar axiom concerning a triangle we learn in high-school geometry.

When we have a set S and a *distance function* or *metric* defined as above that is associated with the points of S, we call this point set a *metric space*.

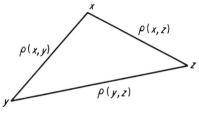

Note that we have defined the distance between two points as $\rho = \rho(x, y)$. Depending on how we specify this real-valued function, we shall obtain various kinds of metric spaces. Let

Fig. 2–1

us now define this distance function and construct a Euclidean space. The process is explained by a simple illustration. Consider an ordered set

$$S = \{1, 2, 3, 4\}$$

When this is mapped onto a line as in Figure 2–2, we have a linear point set

Fig. 2–2

that is similar to S. To each pair of points, such as $(1, 2)$, $(1, 3)$, $(2, 4)$ and so forth, we shall assign a real number $\rho(1, 2)$, $\rho(1, 3)$, $\rho(2, 4)$ and call it the distance between the two points. In our present case we shall define

$$\rho(1, 2) = |1 - 2| = 1$$
$$\rho(1, 3) = |1 - 3| = 2$$
$$\rho(2, 4) = |2 - 4| = 2$$

as the distance between the two points. That is, we have taken the absolute value of the difference between two numbers. Let us call this linear point set with such a distance function a one-dimensional Euclidean space.

Extending our discussion, consider the Cartesian product $P = S_1 \times S_2$. Here the set P will have as its elements ordered pairs which become the points of P. Let two points be x and y, which we shall denote by

$$x = (x_1, x_2)$$
$$y = (y_1, y_2)$$

Then the question is: What is the distance between the points x and y of $P = S_1 \times S_2$? That is, what is

$$\rho(x, y) = \rho[(x_1, x_2), (y_1, y_2)]$$

Illustrating by use of a simple example, we may let $S_1 = S_2 = \{1, 2, 3, 4\}$
Then $P = S_1 \times S_2$ is as shown in Figure 2–3.

Fig. 2–3

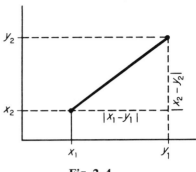

Fig. 2–4

The point $x = A$ corresponds to the ordered pair $(1, 1)$, and $y = B$, to
the ordered pair $(4, 3)$. Therefore, the distance is

$$\rho[(1, 1), (4, 3)] = \overline{AB}$$

But we know from Pythagoras' theorem that

$$\overline{AB} = \sqrt{\overline{AC^2} + \overline{BC^2}}$$
$$= \sqrt{(1 - 4)^2 + (1 - 3)^2}$$

Using this relationship, we *define* the distance between two ordered pairs
(x_1, x_2) and (y_1, y_2) as (see Figure 2–4)

$$\rho(x, y) = \rho[(x_1, x_2), (y_1, y_2)] = \sqrt{(x_1 - y_1)^2 + (x_2 - y_2)^2}$$

We may extend our discussion one more step. Consider $P = S_1 \times S_2 \times S_3$.
Then the elements of P will be ordered triples. If we let $x = (x_1, x_2, x_3)$ and
$y = (y_1, y_2, y_3)$ be two points (elements) of P, what is

$$\rho(x, y) = \rho[(x_1, x_2, x_3), (y_1, y_2, y_3)]$$

This is defined as

$$\rho(x, y) = [(x_1 - y_1)^2 + (x_2 - y_2)^2 + (x_3 - y_3)^2]^{1/2}$$

Thus we have a 3-dimensional Euclidean space with the distance between any
two points defined.

In general, if we let $P = S_1 \times \ldots \times S_n$ and two of its points x and y be

$$x = (x_1, x_2, \ldots, x_n)$$
$$y = (y_1, y_2, \ldots, y_n)$$

then the distance between the two points x and y will be

$$\rho(x, y) = [(x_1 - y_1)^2 + (x_2 - y_2)^2 + \ldots + (x_n - y_n)^2]^{1/2}$$

The set P with a distance function as just defined is called an *n-dimensional Euclidean space*.

Note that each ordered set is plotted as a point in the Euclidean space.

Problems

1. Verify that the distance functions (metrics) below satisfy the 3 conditions for a metric.

    (a) $\rho(x, y) = |x - y|$.
    (b) $\rho(x, y) = [(x_1 - y_1)^2 + (x_2 - y_2)^2]^{1/2}$.
    (c) $\rho(x, y) = [(x_1 - y_1)^2 + (x_2 - y_2)^2 + (x_3 - y_3)^2]^{1/2}$.

2. Let there be 3 points x, y, and z. Then we know that

$$\rho(x, z) \leq \rho(x, y) + \rho(y, z)$$

Let there be 4 points x, y, z, and w. Then, using the above result, prove that

$$\rho(x, w) \leq \rho(x, y) + \rho(y, z) + \rho(z, w)$$

2.2 Neighborhood and point of accumulation

Let us pause here for a moment and review the important ideas we have covered so far. We first explained the concept of a set. Then we defined a function. Next we directed our attention to the relation between the elements of a set and explained the concept of an ordered set. Next we explained the real number system and then explained how the system of real numbers has a one-to-one relation with the points on a straight line.

In Section 2.1 we added the idea of distance to a set and defined a metric space. In particular, we explained the construction of a Euclidean metric space, which is the space we shall be mainly using in our subsequent discussion.

We expressed the idea of distance between two points x and y in a space by

$$\rho(x, y)$$

and for the Euclidean space obtained

$$\rho(x, y) = [(x_1 - y_1)^2 + \ldots + (x_n - y_n)^2]^{1/2}$$

for the distance between x and y in an n-dimensional space.

Having explained the idea of distance, we are now able to start our investigation of the idea of a limit of a function, which will be the basic idea of the differential and integral calculus that we shall be discussing in the subsequent chapters. This is because the idea of a limit is based on the idea of bringing two points x and y closer and closer together, and this idea is at the basis of calculus. In symbols it is expressed by

$$\rho(x, y) \to 0$$

The steps we shall take to investigate this idea of a limit will be first to define several basic concepts to be used for analysis, and then to consider the simplest limit, i.e., the limit of a sequence of numbers. After this we shall consider the limit of a function.

The two basic ideas we shall discuss in this section are the neighborhood of a point and the point of accumulation (limit point) of a set.

But first let us remind ourselves that a set of real numbers has a one-to-one correspondence with points on a straight line. Diagrammatically, we have

$$S = \{x: \quad -\infty < x < \infty\}$$
$$= \{..., -2, ..., -1, ..., 0, ..., 1, ..., 2, ...\}$$

$$-2 \quad ... \quad -1 \quad ... \quad 0 \quad ... \quad +1 \quad ... \quad +2 \quad ...$$

The elements of the set S are real numbers. But since they have a one-to-one correspondence with points on a straight line, we may use the term *points* instead of elements. Hence we have a *set of points* S, or S is a set of points.

Note carefully, when we have an abstract set of points (elements), the arrangement of the points do not matter. That is, for example,

$$S = \{1, 2, 3\}$$
$$= \{2, 1, 3\}$$
$$= \{3, 2, 1\}$$

But the points on the straight line are in a certain order.

We shall use the term, set of points, to represent various sets of numbers. For example, let S be the set of integers. Then, in this context, the term, set of points, will mean the set of integers. Likewise, the term, set of points, may mean the set of rational numbers or the set of real numbers or a set of certain specified numbers (such as even numbers). As can be seen, in each case, the numbers can be represented by points on a straight line. It will be clear from the context of the discussion what the set of points represents.

(i) Neighborhood

Suppose we have a set of points S in a Euclidean metric space. Select a point p in S. Then the set of all of the points $x \in S$ such that the distance between p and x is

$$\rho(p, x) < \epsilon$$

where $\epsilon > 0$ is called a *neighborhood* of the point p.

Sometimes it is necessary to consider the neighborhood of p, excluding the point p. The neighborhood of p without the point p is called the *deleted neighborhood* of p.

Note that we have used $<$ and not $\leq$. Hence the points at distance ϵ from p are not included in the neighborhood. We have expressed the idea of a neighborhood in set terminology, but let us now apply it to the points on the number axis.

For this, select a point p on the straight line (Figure 2–5). Then the

Fig. 2–5

ϵ-neighborhood of point p is the open interval $(p - \epsilon, p + \epsilon)$. Note that the end points $p - \epsilon$, and $p + \epsilon$ do not belong to the neighborhood.

For a two-dimensional Euclidean space, i.e., a plane, we get a circle as shown in Figure 2–6, where ϵ becomes the radius of the circle. Note that the points on the circumference of the circle do not belong to the neighborhood.

Let us denote the ϵ-neighborhood of point p by $N(p, \epsilon)$. Then

$$N(p, \epsilon) = \{x: \quad x \in S \quad \text{and} \quad \rho(p, x) < \epsilon\}$$

The deleted neighborhood of p may be shown by

$$N(p, \epsilon) - \{p\}$$

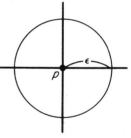

Fig. 2–6

(ii) Point of accumulation of a set

Let us now select a subset S_1 from S, i.e., $S_1 \subset S$. Let a point $p \in S$. This point p may or may not belong to S_1. Construct a neighborhood $N(p, \epsilon)$ around p (Figure 2–7). Next select a point x which belongs to both $N(p, \epsilon)$ and S_1, where $x \neq p$. Then, since S is dense, we can find an infinite number of points between x and p, and, hence, there are an infinite number of points in the neighborhood of p.

Fig. 2–7

Suppose we let $\epsilon' < \epsilon$ and construct a new neighborhood $N(p, \epsilon')$. Let x' belong to both S_1 and $N(p, \epsilon')$ and $x' \neq p$. Then we can again find an infinite number of points between x' and p. That is, there are an infinite number of points in the neighborhood.

As is seen, by changing ϵ, we can get an infinite number of different neighborhoods around p.

Suppose in general that every $N(p, \epsilon)$ of p contains at least one point of S_1 different from p. Then, as we have seen above, every $N(p, \epsilon)$ will contain an infinite number of points of S_1, and, as ϵ becomes smaller, there will be a pile-up of points around p. We shall say a point p is a *point of accumulation* (or *limit point*) of the set S_1 if every neighborhood of p contains at least one point of S_1 different from p. As we have seen, this implies that the neighborhood contains an infinite number of points of the set S_1.

Note carefully that the point p may or may not belong to S_1. Let us give several examples.

Example 1. Suppose we have a space of real numbers

$$S = \{x: \quad a \leq x \leq b\}.$$

Then every point in $[a, b]$ is a point of accumulation, including the end points a and b.

Example 2. Suppose $S_1 = \{x: \quad a < x \leq b\}$. Then every point in $(a, b]$ is a point of accumulation, but this half-open interval does not include a. However, this point a which is outside the interval is also a point of accumulation of the set S_1.

Example 3. Suppose $S = \{x: \quad a < x < b\}$. Then every point in (a, b) is a point of accumulation, and the two points a and b which are outside the open interval are also points of accumulation of S.

Example 4. Suppose $S = \{x: \quad -\infty < x < \infty\}$ is a set of real numbers. Then all points in the open interval $(-\infty, \infty)$ are points of accumulation. For convenience, we may consider $-\infty$ and $+\infty$ numbers and write $S = \{x: \quad -\infty \leq x \leq \infty\}$. Then $-\infty$ and $+\infty$ may be thought of as members of the set S.

The subset S_1 is said to be *closed* if it contains all its points of accumulation. Hence $S = \{x: \quad a \leq x \leq b\}$ is closed, but $S = \{x: \quad a < x \leq b\}$ is not closed. Also $S = \{x: \quad -\infty \leq x \leq \infty\}$ is closed, but $S = \{x: \quad -\infty < x < \infty\}$ is not.

(*iii*) *Boundary points and closed sets*

Let us investigate the idea of a closed set a little further to obtain a better

understanding of the relations between sets of points in space S.
For simplicity, consider the diagram in Figure 2–8. Let $S =$
$\{x : 1 \leq x \leq 4\}$, and we shall partition it with the point 2. Let the
two sets be

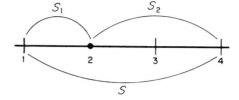

Fig. 2–8

$$S_1 = \{x : \quad 1 \leq x \leq 2\}$$

and

$$S_2 = S - S_1 = \{x : \quad 2 < x \leq 4\}$$

As is seen, we may consider the point 2 a *boundary* between S_1 and S_2. Let
us now investigate this idea of a boundary more carefully with the aid of the
neighborhood concept.

Let $N(2, \epsilon)$ be a neighborhood around the point 2 (Figure 2–9). Then,
clearly, the neighborhood $N(2, \epsilon)$
will include some points to the left
and to the right of 2. That is, it
will include some points of S_1 and
also of S_2. Let us formalize this
idea and say: A point p is called a
boundary point of S_1 if every neigh-

Fig. 2–9

borhood $N(p, \epsilon)$ contains a point of S_1 and a point of $S_2 = S - S_1$. Clearly
if p is a boundary point of S_1, it is also a boundary point of S_2.

To bring out the implication of this idea, let us select a point a little to the
right of 2 and for simplicity call it 2'. Then we can construct a neighborhood
$N(2', \epsilon)$ around 2' that will be to the right of point 2 (Figure 2–10). Then
$N(2', \epsilon)$ will not include points of S_1. Hence 2' is not a boundary point.

Fig. 2–10

To be a boundary point, the $N(p, \epsilon)$ must include points of both S_1 and
$S - S_1$.

If $N(p, \epsilon) \subset S_1$, i.e., all of the points of $N(p, \epsilon)$ belong to S_1 and none to
$S - S_1$, then p is called an *interior point* of S_1.

If $N(q, \epsilon) \subset S - S_1$, i.e., all points of $N(q, \epsilon)$ belong to $S - S_1$ and none
to S_1, q is called an interior point of $S - S_1$. It is also an *exterior point* of S_1.
Likewise, the interior point of S_1 is the exterior point of $S - S_1$.

Let us give some examples of boundary points.

Example 1.

$$S = \{x: \quad 1 \le x \le 4\}$$
$$S_1 = \{x: \quad 1 \le x \le 2\}$$
$$S_2 = S - S_1 = \{x: \quad 2 < x \le 4\}$$

Then 2 is a boundary point of S_1 and S_2. Note that it belongs to S_1.

Example 2. Let

$$S_1 = \{x: \quad 1 \le x < 2\}$$
$$S_2 = \{x: \quad 2 \le x \le 4\}$$

Then 2 is a boundary point of S_1 and S_2. In this case, the point 2 belongs to S_2.

Example 3. Let

$$S_1 = \{x: \quad 1 \le x < 2\}$$
$$S_2 = \{x: \quad 2 < x \le 4\}$$

In this case $S_2 \ne S - S_1$ because the point 2 does not belong to either S_1 or S_2. Hence the point 2 is not the boundary point of S_1.

Example 4. Let S be the set of points of the real line, and

$$S_1 = \{x: \quad 1 \le x < 2\}$$

Then the points $(1, 2)$ are the boundary points of S_1 and also of $S - S_1$.

Example 5. Let S be the set of points of a plane. Let

$$S_1 = \{(x, y): \quad x^2 + y^2 < r^2\}$$

Then the points on the circumference of the circle will be the boundary points of S_1 (Figure 2–11). That is, the points $\{(x, y): \quad x^2 + y^2 = r^2\}$ will be the boundary points. These points are not included in S_1.

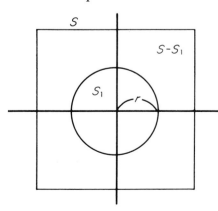

Fig. 2–11

Example 6. If, in Example 5,

$$S_1 = \{(x, y): \quad x^2 + y^2 \le r^2\}$$

then the boundary points $\{(x, y): x^2 + y^2 = r\}$ belong to S_1.

When the subset S_1 of S contains all its boundary points, as in Example 6, S_1 is called a *closed set*.

When S_1 does not contain any of its boundary points, as in Example 5, S_1 is called an *open set*. The set $S_1 = \{x: \ 1 < x < 2\}$ of Example 4 is also an open set.

If, in Example 4, the set should be

$$S_1 = \{x: \ 1 < x \leq 2\}$$

its boundary points are the two points $(1, 2)$. It includes 2 but does not include 1. The set is neither open nor closed.

Let us now see how points of accumulation, boundary points, and closed sets are related. Consider S the set of real points, and

$$S_1 = \{x: \ 1 \leq x \leq 3\}$$

Hence S_1 is a closed set. Let p be a point of accumulation of S_1. Then $N(p, \epsilon)$ contains an infinite number of points of S_1. Hence p cannot be an interior point of $S - S_1$, because, if it were, we should have $N(p, \epsilon) \subset S - S_1$ and none of the points of $N(p, \epsilon)$ would be in S_1. Hence p is either an interior point of S_1 or a boundary point of S_1. If p is an interior point of S_1, then clearly the point of accumulation $p \in S_1$. If p is a boundary point of S_1, then, since S_1 is a closed set, $p \in S_1$. Hence, all the points of accumulation belong to S_1.

It turns out that, if S_1 contains all its points of accumulation, then it is also closed.

Problems

1. Let $S = \{(x, y) \mid x^2 + y^2 < 1\}$ be a subset in a 2-dimensional space.

    (a) Draw a graph of the space and subset.
    (b) Find the boundary points of S, and show them on the diagram.
    (c) Find the interior and exterior points of S, and show them on the diagram.
    (d) Is S an open or closed set?

2. Show that the null set is both open and closed.

3. Give several examples of sets which are neither open nor closed.

2.3 Sequence

Let us now consider the idea of a sequence. Suppose we have a function

$$x_n = 3 + n$$

where $n = 1, 2, 3, \ldots$. Then the values of x_n will be

$$4, 5, 6, 7, \ldots$$

We may interpret this illustration as follows: We have a set of positive integers $n = 1, 2, 3, \ldots$, and this is mapped into a set of real numbers $\{x: \quad 4, 5, 6, 7, \ldots\}$ by the function $x_n = 3 + n$.

We shall call a function whose domain is a set of positive integers a *sequence*. The x_n is called an *entry* or a *term* of the sequence.

Note that we have defined a sequence as a function. This means that the sequence is formed according to a rule of mapping or a law. The implication is that we shall not consider an arbitrary arrangement of numbers a sequence.

We shall express a sequence as

$$f(n): \quad f(1), f(2), f(3), \ldots$$

or

$$x_n: \quad x_1, x_2, x_3, \ldots$$

If n is finite, we have a finite sequence; if n is infinite, we have an infinite sequence. We are mainly interested in infinite sequences. Let us give several examples.

Let $x_n = 3(-1)^n$. Then the sequence will be

$$2, 4, 2, 4, 2, 4, \ldots$$

and the entries are merely a repetition of 2 and 4. Or we may say the range is the set $\{2, 4\}$.

Another illustration is $x_n = 1/n$. Then the sequence is

$$1, \tfrac{1}{2}, \tfrac{1}{3}, \tfrac{1}{4}, \ldots$$

Note that we may consider $1, \tfrac{1}{2}, \tfrac{1}{3}, \tfrac{1}{4}, \ldots$ as an ordered set. However, in an ordered set, as we have studied it in Chapter 1, we may interchange the terms; for example,

$$\tfrac{1}{2}, 1, \tfrac{1}{4}, \tfrac{1}{3}, \ldots$$

and it is still the same ordered set. We may not, however, interchange terms of a sequence.

Let us now consider the idea of a sequence in terms of set theory so that we may apply the ideas of set theory we have been studying. We may show the relation between a sequence and a straight line as follows:

Domain: $n = 1, 2, 3, 4, \ldots$
Function: $x_n = 2n$
Sequence: $2, 4, 6, 8, \ldots$
Range: $\{2, 4, 6, 8, \ldots\}$
Real space: $\{x: \quad -\infty < x < \infty\}$
Line:

As is seen, the sequence has 4 elements; domain, function, sequence of entries, and range. We may consider this sequence of entries a subset of the real space E and write

$$S = \{2, 4, 6, 8, ...\}$$

The 2, 4, 6, 8, ... are the *entries* of the sequence, but, as can be seen from the above schema, they may be shown by points on the straight line. Hence, we shall use the term *sequence of points* to express this set S.

Note carefully that, when we have an abstract set

$$S = \{2, 4, 6, 8, ...\}$$

the arrangement of the elements does not matter. That is, S may also be written, for example, as

$$S = \{4, 2, 8, 6, ...\}$$

But when we use the term, sequence of points, we shall specifically refer to a situation where the elements of the set S are the entries of a sequence.

We may express this sequence of points by

$$x_n = \{x_1, x_2, ...\}$$

and say we have a set of points in the Euclidean metric space E.

Let us consider another example. Let

$$x_n = 2 + (-1)^n$$

Then,

Domain: 1, 2, 3, 4, ...
Sequence: 1, 3, 1, 3, ...
Range: $\{1, 3\}$
E: $\{x: \quad -\infty < x < \infty\}$
Straight line:

In this case the sequence of points is

$$\{x_n\} = 1, 3, 1, 3, 1, 3, ...$$

but the range is merely the set $\{1, 3\}$. As is seen, as an abstract set, the $\{1, 3, 1, 3, ...\}$ is merely the set $\{1, 3\}$.

The point to understand clearly is that a sequence is a function which maps the set of integers $\{1, 2, 3, 4, ...\}$ into a set of real numbers $\{x: \quad -\infty < x < \infty\}$ and the values of the function $f(n)$, i.e., the entries of the sequence, which may be shown by

$$f(n): \quad f(1), f(2), ...$$

or

$$x_n: \quad x_1, x_2, ...$$

may in turn be mapped into points on a straight line. And we call these points a sequence of points.

Problems

1. Write the numerical values of the first 5 terms of the following sequences.

(a) $f(n) = 2n - 1$
(b) $f(n) = 2^n - 1$
(c) $f(n) = 4 + (-1)^n$

(d) $f(n) = \dfrac{1}{2n} - 1$

(e) $f(n) = \dfrac{1}{2n - 1}$

(f) $f(n) = (-1)^{n+1} \dfrac{1}{n}$

2. Find, without proof, the limit of the following sequences.

(a) $\dfrac{1}{2n} - 1$

(b) $\dfrac{1}{2n - 1}$

3. Write out the first 5 terms of the following sequences and plot the first 5 terms on a 2-dimensional diagram.

(a) $f(n) = (n + 1, n - 1)$

(b) $f(n) = \left(\dfrac{1}{n}, 1 - \dfrac{1}{n} \right)$

2.4 Limit of a sequence

The sequence $x_n = 1/n$ was

$$1, \tfrac{1}{2}, \tfrac{1}{3}, \tfrac{1}{4}, \ldots$$

and is presented graphically as shown in Figure 2–5(a) or (b). The distance between any two entries of the sequence can be expressed as

$$x_1 - x_2 = 1 - \tfrac{1}{2}, \quad x_2 - x_3 = \tfrac{1}{2} - \tfrac{1}{3}, \ldots$$

The distance between an entry x_n and 0 is shown as $x_n - 0$. We observe intuitively and from the graph that the sequence is getting closer to 0 as n becomes larger so that the distance $x_n - 0$ becomes smaller as n becomes larger. If this distance $x_n - 0$ continues to diminish and hence approach zero as n becomes larger, we say the sequence is *convergent* and converges to (in this case) 0.

Another example is the sequence

$$x_n = \frac{1}{n} + 2$$

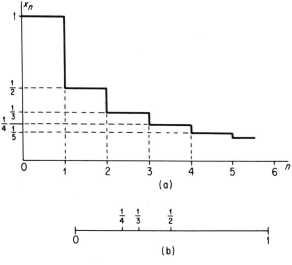

Fig. 2–12

If we take the distance between x_n and 2 we have

$$x_n - 2 = \left(\frac{1}{n} + 2\right) - 2 = \frac{1}{n}$$

We see that the distance

$$x_n - 2 = \frac{1}{n} \to 0 \qquad \text{as} \qquad n \to \infty$$

Then the sequence converges to 2 in this case.

In the above examples we determine intuitively that it converges to 0 in the first case and to 2 in the second case. We may use a general symbol x instead of 0 or 2 and state as follows: When given a sequence $(x_1, x_2, x_3, \ldots)$ and the distance between x_n and x which is denoted as $\rho(x_n, x)$ approaches 0 as $n \to \infty$, x_n is a convergent sequence and converges to x, which is called the *limit*. In symbols this is expressed as

$$\lim_{n \to \infty} x_n = x$$

If x_n should converge to x and also to y, that would mean

$$\rho(x_n, x) \to 0 \qquad \text{and} \qquad \rho(x_n, y) \to 0$$

We know from the axiom of the triangle inequality that

$$\rho(x, y) \le \rho(x_n, x) + \rho(x_n, y)$$

When

$$\rho(x_n, x) \to 0 \qquad \text{and} \qquad \rho(x_n, y) \to 0$$

as $n \to \infty$, then $\rho(x, y) \to 0$ also. But this means $x = y$. Thus there can be only one limit for a sequence $\{x_n\}$.

When a sequence does not have a limit, we say the sequence *diverges* or is a *divergent sequence*. An example of a divergent sequence is

$$x_n = n + 3; \quad 4, 5, 6, 7, \ldots$$

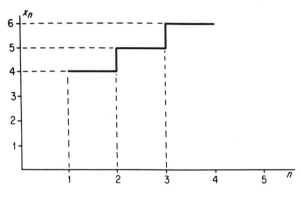

Fig. 2–13

As the reader will notice, all our examples have been in one-dimensional Euclidean space. When we wrote

$$\rho(x_n, x) \to 0 \qquad \text{as} \qquad n \to \infty$$

the x_n, x were points in this one-dimensional Euclidean space. But, since we have defined a distance function for an m-dimensional Euclidean space, we may interpret our results as follows: Let $x_1, x_2, \ldots, x_n, \ldots$ be a sequence of points in m-dimensional Euclidean space E_m. Then

$$x_n = (x_{n1}, x_{n2}, \ldots, x_{nm})$$

is a point E_m. This sequence of points will converge to a limit x if

$$\lim_{n \to \infty} \rho(x_n, x) = 0$$

In our discussion above, we wrote

$$\rho(x_n, x) \to 0 \qquad \text{as} \qquad n \to \infty$$

Note in this case that ∞ is not a number and we cannot compute it. To be able to compute the limit of a sequence and, furthermore, to be able to apply it to other mathematical operations, we must express the idea of a limit in "finite quantities." Let us now restate the ideas of a limit in terms of finite quantities and eliminate such quantitative ambiguities as ∞. As we shall see, the definition is much more complicated than the one we have presented above, but it is absolutely necessary for the purpose of proving theorems.

Let us explain with an illustration. Consider again the sequence

$$x_n = \frac{1}{n} + 2, \qquad n = 1, 2, 3, \ldots$$

dom n

ran $x_n = \frac{1}{n} + 2$

The limit was 2. Call the sequence of integers $n = 1, 2, 3, \ldots$ the domain, and call the sequence of values $x_n = 1/n + 2$ the range. As the integers $n = 1, 2, 3, \ldots$ progress to larger numbers, the range $x_n = 1/n + 2$ decreases toward 2, and the distance $|x_n - 2|$ becomes smaller. Let the distance be less than a small positive number ϵ, say $\epsilon = \frac{1}{2}$, i.e.,

(1) $$|x_n - 2| < \epsilon = \tfrac{1}{2}$$

Can we find an integer N such that, when $n \geq N$, the inequality (1) holds? The answer is yes. By letting $N = 3$, we find

$$|x_n - 2| = \left| \frac{1}{n} + 2 - 2 \right| = \left| \frac{1}{n} \right| = \frac{1}{3} < \epsilon = \frac{1}{2}$$

What if we let the distance be less than $\epsilon = 1/10$? For this take $N = 11$. Then

$$|x_n - 2| = \left| \frac{1}{n} \right| = \frac{1}{11} < \epsilon = \frac{1}{10}$$

Letting $\epsilon \to 0$ is equivalent to saying that the distance between x_n and 2 approaches zero. Then 2 is the limit of x_n. Therefore, we can summarize the process explained above and give a *definition* of convergence of a sequence to a limit as follows:

The sequence $x_1, x_2, \ldots, x_n, \ldots$ has a limit x as $n \to \infty$ if, for each given $\epsilon > 0$, no matter how small, we can find an N such that

$$|x_n - x| < \epsilon$$

for all $n \geq N$.

Example. Consider the sequence

$$x_n = \frac{1}{n^2}, \qquad n = 1, 2, \ldots$$

We observe that the limit is 0. Let us apply the definition of convergence to a limit and check that it is the limit. Given an ϵ say $\epsilon = 1/100$, construct the inequality (which shows the distance)

$$(2) \qquad\qquad |x_n - 0| < \epsilon = 1/100$$

Can we find an N such that, when $n \geq N$, this inequality (2) is true? Let $N = 11$. Then

$$|x_n - 0| = \left|\frac{1}{n^2} - 0\right| = \left|\frac{1}{11^2}\right| = \left|\frac{1}{121}\right| < \epsilon = \frac{1}{100}$$

Thus, when $n \geq N = 11$, inequality (2) is true, i.e., we have found an N that satisfies our requirements. This process may be repeated, and we can find an N that corresponds to a given arbitrarily small ϵ such that

$$|x_n - 0| < \epsilon$$

holds for $n \geq N$. Thus 0 is the limit.

Note that in this process we first choose an ϵ, then find the independent variable n. Choosing an ϵ means we have fixed $|x_n - x|$.

In contrast, the sequence is $\{x_1, x_2, x_3, ...\}$, and we feel that x_n is moving toward x. That is, $x_n \rightarrow x$. For computational purposes, we have "taken a photo" of this moving situation at a certain moment, and that moment is when $|x_n - x| < \epsilon$. We have, so to speak, stopped the process at distance ϵ and are performing our analysis under "static" conditions.

Let us now go one step further and express our results in terms of set theory. Suppose we have a sequence of points

$$x_n = \{x_1, x_2, x_3, ...\}$$

in the metric space S. Then the sequence $\{x_n\}$ is convergent if there exists an $x \in S$ such that for each given $\epsilon > 0$, no matter how small, we can find an N such that

$$|x_n - x| < \epsilon$$

for all $n \geq N$.

The main point to note here is that $x \in S$. That is, the limit belongs to the space S.

For example, consider the space

$$S = \{x: \quad 0 < x \leq 1\}$$

and the sequence $x_n = 1/n$. Then

$$x_n: \quad 1, \tfrac{1}{2}, \tfrac{1}{3}, ...$$

and $x_n \rightarrow 0$ as $n \rightarrow \infty$.

Note, however, that 0 is not an element of S. Hence, the point to which x_n wishes to converge is outside the space. In this case the $\{x_n\}$ is not a convergent sequence.

We know that this point 0 is a point of accumulation of the sequence of points.

Note carefully that, when we consider 0 a point of accumulation, we are considering $\{1, \frac{1}{2}, \frac{1}{3}, ...\}$ a set of points. That is, the point of accumulation is a concept associated with a set. In contrast, limit is a concept associated with a function.

But, by considering the sequence

$$1, \tfrac{1}{2}, \tfrac{1}{3}, ...$$

mapped into the points on a straight line, we are also thinking of the sequence as a sequence of points and are applying the ideas of set theory.

Problems

1. Given the sequence

$$f(n) = \frac{1}{n} + 1, \qquad n = 1, 2, 3, ...$$

Prove that 1 is the limit of $f(n)$.

2. Given the space

$$S = \{x \mid 1 < x \le 2\}$$

and the sequence $x_n = 1/n + 1$, is there a limit of x_n? Is there a point of accumulation?

2.5 Cauchy sequence

We have stated that a convergent sequence converges to a limit and $\rho(x_n, x)$ approaches zero as $n \to \infty$. It has been assumed here that the limit x is known. But, when x is not known, we cannot calculate $\rho(x_n, x)$ and thus cannot tell whether or not a sequence is convergent.

Cauchy's test enables us to determine whether or not a sequence is convergent without first knowing the limit x.

If we have a sequence $\{x_n\}$ and if

$$\rho(x_1, x_2), \quad \rho(x_2, x_3), \quad \rho(x_3, x_4), \quad ...$$

becomes smaller as n becomes larger, we shall finally come to a point x_m and from there on the distance

$$\rho(x_m, x_{m+1}), \quad \rho(x_m, x_{m+2}), \quad \rho(x_m, x_{m+3}), \quad ...$$

becomes smaller than an arbitrary very small quantity ϵ, i.e.,

$$\rho(x_m, x_{m+1}) < \epsilon, \quad \rho(x_m, x_{m+2}) < \epsilon, \text{ etc.}$$

This may be written

$$\rho(x_m, x_n) < \epsilon$$

where $n > m$.

Using this idea, let us define a Cauchy sequence, or fundamental sequence, as follows: A sequence $\{x_n\}$ is called a *Cauchy sequence*, or *fundamental sequence*, if for any $\epsilon > 0$, no matter how small, there exists a number N such that

$$|x_m - x_n| < \epsilon$$

for all $m, n > N$.

As an example, consider the sequence

$$\{x_n\} = \frac{1}{n}: \quad 1, \tfrac{1}{2}, \tfrac{1}{3}, \ldots$$

in the space $[0, 1]$, as in Figure 2–14. The points 0 and 1 are included in the space. It is easy to see that by making m and n large enough we can make the difference

Fig. 2–14

$$|x_m - x_n| = \left| \frac{1}{m} - \frac{1}{n} \right|$$

as small as we wish. Hence this sequence is a Cauchy sequence.

In addition, we can also see that

$$\lim_{n \to \infty} x_n = \lim_{n \to \infty} \frac{1}{n} = 0$$

and the sequence converges to 0.

Thus, when given the space $[0, 1]$, the sequence $x_n - 1/n$ is both a Cauchy sequence and convergent.

Let us consider $x_n = 1/n$ again but this time with the space $(0, 1]$, i.e., we have a half-open interval and the point 0 is not included in the space.

From our discussion above, we can easily see that the sequence is a Cauchy sequence. It is, however, not a convergent sequence because the point to which it converges, namely, zero, is not in the space.

From this example, we see that a Cauchy sequence is not necessarily a convergent sequence.

Is the converse true, i.e., that every convergent sequence is a Cauchy sequence? The answer is yes. Let us explain this as follows.

Suppose $\{x_n\}$ is a convergent sequence. Then

$$|x_n - x| < \frac{\epsilon}{2}$$

for $n > N$. Also

$$|x_m - x| < \frac{\epsilon}{2}$$

for an $m > N_0$. Let $N > N_0$. Then,

$$|x_n - x| < \frac{\epsilon}{2}$$

$$|x_m - x| < \frac{\epsilon}{2}$$

for $m, n > N$. Adding the two gives us

$$|x_n - x| + |x_m - x| < \frac{\epsilon}{2} + \frac{\epsilon}{2} = \epsilon$$

But from the triangle inequality, we have

$$|x_m - x_n| \le |x_n - x| + |x_m - x| < \epsilon$$

That is,

$$|x_m - x_n| < \epsilon$$

Hence, if $\{x_n\}$ is convergent, for every $\epsilon > 0$, no matter how small, there exists an N such that

$$|x_m - x_n| < \epsilon$$

for all $n, m > N$. That is, every convergent sequence is a Cauchy sequence.

To illustrate the above conclusions again, suppose we have a sequence $\{x_n\}$ in a space made up of rational numbers. Suppose also that this sequence is a Cauchy sequence. Is it also a convergent sequence? The answer is yes if $\{x_n\}$ converges to a rational number. The answer is no if it converges to an irrational number.

What is the factor that causes this difference between a Cauchy sequence and a convergent sequence? It is that the Cauchy sequence depends only on the terms in the sequence, whereas a convergent sequence depends on a point in the space to which it converges.

Is there a space in which a Cauchy sequence will always be a convergent sequence? The answer is: Yes; in the space of real numbers, a Cauchy sequence will always be convergent. We shall not prove this statement, but the reader can see heuristically, that, if $\{x_n\}$ is a sequence of real numbers and it is a Cauchy sequence, it will converge to a real number and, since the real number is in the space, we have a convergent sequence.

If every Cauchy sequence in a space S converges in S, this space S is called a *complete space*. Hence, the space of real numbers is a complete space.

What about $S_1 = [0, 1]$ we used above as an illustration? We can see that every Cauchy sequence in $S_1 = [0, 1]$ will converge in S_1, and hence S_1 is a complete space.

Our illustration above shows $S_1 = (0, 1]$ is not a complete space. However, by adding the point 0 to S_1, we get $S_1 = [0, 1]$ and S_1 can be made into a complete space.

Problems

1. Construct a Cauchy sequence that is not a convergent sequence.

2. Construct a Cauchy sequence that is also a convergent sequence.

3. Explain with an example the meaning of a complete space.

2.6 Limit of a function

In the sequence $\{x_n\}$ the domain was a set of positive integers. Let it now be a set S_1 of real numbers. The function f defined on this set S_1 maps the elements of S_1 into the set S_2. Let $x \in S_1$ and $y \in S_2$; then

$$y = f(x)$$

In Figure 2–15 the S_1 is the x-axis, and S_2 the y-axis.

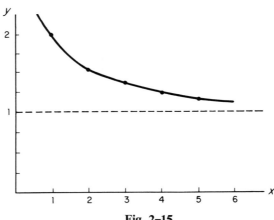

Fig. 2–15

Consider as an example a function

$$y = f(x) = \frac{1}{x} + 1$$

which is shown in Figure 2–15. Let us set $S_1 = [1, \infty]$. As $x \to \infty$, then $y \to 1$, and we may write

$$\lim_{x \to \infty} f(x) = 1$$

or

$$f(x) \to 1 \quad \text{as} \quad x \to \infty$$

That is, 1 is the limit of the function $f(x)$ as $x \to \infty$.

Let us compare this process with that of a sequence. Let the sequence be

$$x_n = \frac{1}{n} + 1$$

Then

$$x_n: \quad 2, 1\tfrac{1}{2}, 1\tfrac{1}{3}, \ldots$$

as $n \to \infty$ and the limit of the sequence is 1. In this sequence case, the limiting process involves letting the n go from 1 to the next number (point) 2, from 2 to the next point 3, and so forth. The situation here is that we know the next number.

In our present case, we let $x \to \infty$ and we can see intuitively that we are letting x move from 1 to infinity through all real numbers. But we may ask: What is the number next to 1? We know that the set of real numbers is dense and non-denumerable, and we cannot find the number next to 1. How, then, are we going to calculate this limiting process?

This is a problem that had bothered mathematicians from the time of Greek philosophers. The mathematicians of the 18th century answered the problem by taking a photo of this process, obtaining a static picture, and then they expressed this static picture of the process in terms of finite quantities. And this procedure has provided mathematicians with an adequate mathematical model which has enabled them to perform mathematical analysis, prove theorems, and obtain useful results. Let us now show how this limiting process is expressed in terms of finite quantities.

The formal definition of the limit of a function is as follows: The function $f(x)$ has a limit as x approaches x_1 if for each given $\epsilon > 0$, no matter how small, we can find a positive δ (that depends on ϵ) such that

$$|f(x) - L| < \epsilon$$

is satisfied for all values of x in the interval

$$|x - x_1| < \delta$$

except at the point $x = x_1$ itself.

Note that x is a point of accumulation. This is called the ($\epsilon - \delta$) *definition of a limit of a function* and is a basic concept in mathematical analysis. Compared with the definition

$$f(x) \to L \quad \text{as} \quad x \to x_1$$

it is quite complicated and difficult to grasp, but it is in terms of finite quantities and can be calculated.

Note in the definition that we are first given an ϵ and then we find a δ. Let us attempt to explain this in terms of our photo analogy. Suppose a rocket $f(x)$ is approaching the moon L, and we expect it, $f(x)$, to hit the moon L at 5 P.M. (x_1). Then $|x - x_1|$ may be thought of as the time still left before the rocket $f(x)$ hits the moon L.

Suppose we wish to take a picture of the rocket at $\epsilon = 10,000$ miles from the moon. Let $|f(x) - L|$ indicate the distance between the rocket and the moon. Then this is to be $|f(x) - L| = 10,000$ miles $= \epsilon$. How many minutes before 5 P.M. (x_1) should the picture be taken? Suppose it is $\delta = 5$ minutes. Then

$$|x - x_1| = \delta = 5 \text{ minutes}$$

If $\epsilon = 10$ miles, then δ may be $\delta = 2$ seconds. If $\epsilon = 1$ mile, δ may be 0.3 second, and so forth.

The time δ will be determined by the distance ϵ at which we wish to take the photo. Hence, given ϵ (distance), we determine δ (time) and take our photo. We end up with a static picture of the distance at time δ between the rocket $f(x)$ and the moon L.

Let us now give several examples of the use of the $(\epsilon - \delta)$ definition of a limit.

Example 1. Let

$$y = f(x) = x^2$$

Then, clearly

$$\lim_{x \to 0} f(x) = 0$$

Let us check that $L = 0$ is the limit of $f(x) = x^2$ when $x \to x_1 = 0$ by finding $\delta = \varphi(\epsilon)$. Assume we are given $\epsilon = \frac{1}{10}$. Then

(1) $$|f(x) - L| = |x^2 - 0| = |x^2| < \epsilon = \tfrac{1}{10}$$

Next let $\delta = \sqrt{\epsilon}$. Then

(2) $$|x - x_1| = |x - 0| = |x| < \delta = \sqrt{\epsilon}$$

which leads to

$$|x^2| < \epsilon$$

Therefore, if we let $\delta = \sqrt{\epsilon}$, inequality (2) implies that inequality (1) is true. This process may be repeated for an arbitrarily small ϵ, which means the distance between $f(x)$ and $L = 0$ may be made as small as we wish, and the set of values of x that satisfies (1) is obtained from (2). Thus $L = 0$ is the limit when $x \to x_1 = 0$.

This is written

$$\lim_{x \to 0} x^2 = 0$$

or

$$f(x) \to 0 \quad \text{as} \quad x \to 0$$

Example 2. Consider the function $f(x) = x^2$ which is shown graphically in Figure 2–16. Then, obviously,

$$\lim_{x \to 2} f(x) = 4$$

In terms of our definition, this is expressed as follows: The function $f(x) = x^2$ has a limit $L = 4$ as $x \to x_1 = 2$, if for a given $\epsilon > 0$, no matter how small, we can find a δ such that

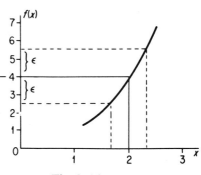

Fig. 2–16

$$|f(x) - 4| < \epsilon$$

holds true for all x that satisfies the inequality

$$|x - 2| < \delta$$

except at the point $x = 2$.

The δ is found as follows. We have

$$|f(x) - 4| = |x^2 - 4| < \epsilon \qquad 0 < x < 2$$

Let $\delta = \epsilon/(x + 2)$. Then

$$|x - 2| < \delta = \frac{\epsilon}{x + 2}$$

which leads to

$$|x^2 - 4| < \epsilon$$

That is, we have found a $\delta = \epsilon/(x + 2)$ such that, whenever $|x - x_1| < \delta$, the inequality $|f(x) - 4| < \epsilon$ holds for a given ϵ, no matter how small. Thus, 4 is the limit of $f(x) = x^2$ as $x \to x_1 = 2$.

Example 3. Consider the function $f(x) = \sqrt{x}$. Then $f(x) \to 1$ as $x \to 1$. Let us find δ as follows. We have

$$|f(x) - 1| = |\sqrt{x} - 1| < \epsilon \qquad 0 < x < 1$$

Let $\delta = \epsilon$. Then

$$|x - x_1| = |x - 1| = |(\sqrt{x} - 1)(\sqrt{x} + 1)| < \delta = \epsilon$$

From this we find, since $\sqrt{x} + 1 > 1$,

$$|\sqrt{x} - 1| < \frac{\delta}{\sqrt{x} + 1} = \frac{\epsilon}{\sqrt{x} + 1} < \epsilon$$

That is, we have found a δ ($= \epsilon$) such that, whenever $|x - x_1| < \delta$, the inequality $|f(x) - 1| < \epsilon$ holds for a given ϵ, no matter how small. Thus, 1 is the limit of $f(x) = \sqrt{x}$ as $x \to 1$.

Example 4. Consider the following function

$$y = f(x) = 4 + \frac{1}{1 + 1/(1 - x)} \qquad 0 < x < 1$$

By observation, we see that

$$\lim_{x \to 1} f(x) = 4$$

But we also note that, when $x = 1$, $1/(1 - x)$ will become meaningless, so that, when finding the limit, we must exclude the point $x = 1$. Let us find a $\delta = \varphi(\epsilon)$ as follows. The function can be shown as

$$y = f(x) = 4 + \frac{1 - x}{2 - x} \qquad 0 < x < 1$$

Then

$$|f(x) - 4| = \left| \frac{1 - x}{2 - x} \right| < \epsilon$$

Also

$$|x_1 - x| = |1 - x| < \delta$$

Let $\delta = \epsilon$. Then, since $0 < x < 1$, we have $2 - x > 1$, which leads to

$$\left| \frac{1 - x}{2 - x} \right| < |1 - x| < \delta = \epsilon$$

That is, for a given ϵ, no matter how small, we have found a $\delta \ (= \epsilon)$ such that

$$|f(x) - 4| < \epsilon$$

is satisfied for all values of x in the interval

$$|x_1 - x| < \delta$$

except at the point $x_1 = 1$ itself. Thus $f(x)$ has the limit 4 as $x \to 1$. Note how the provision "except at the point $x_1 = 1$ itself" was necessary.

In the above examples, we investigated the limits of functions by the $(\epsilon - \delta)$ definition. This was to familiarize the student with this $(\epsilon - \delta)$ definition. In many cases, however, we may find the limit by observation. For example,

$$\lim_{x \to \infty} \left(\frac{1}{x} \right) = 0, \qquad S = (1, \infty)$$

$$\lim_{x \to \infty} \frac{x + 1}{x} = \frac{3}{2}$$

and so forth.

We state without proof that

$$\lim [f(x) + g(x)] = \lim f(x) + \lim g(x)$$
$$\lim [f(x) - g(x)] = \lim f(x) - \lim g(x)$$
$$\lim [f(x)g(x)] = \lim f(x) \lim g(x)$$
$$\lim \left[\frac{f(x)}{g(x)} \right] = \frac{\lim f(x)}{\lim g(x)}$$

Check these formulas by letting

$$f(x) = \frac{1}{x} \quad \text{and} \quad g(x) = \frac{x+1}{x}$$

and letting $x \to x_1 = 2$.

Problems

1. Find the limits of the following functions by observation.

(a) $\lim_{x \to 3} \frac{x^2}{3}$

(b) $\lim_{x \to 2} \frac{x^2 + 4}{4}$

(c) $\lim_{x \to 2} \frac{(x + 2)^2}{2}$

(d) $\lim_{x \to 0} 2^x$

2. Using the (ϵ, δ) method, show that the limit of the following functions is 1.

(a) $\lim_{x \to 1} x^2 = 1$

(b) $\lim_{x \to 2} \frac{2}{x} = 1$

(c) $\lim_{x \to 2} \frac{x^2}{4} = 1$

3. Using the rules concerning the limit of the sums, products, and quotients of functions, find the limit of the following functions.

(a) $\lim_{x \to 1} (4x^2 - x)$

(b) $\lim_{x \to 1} \frac{4x^2 - 3}{2x^2 + 1}$

(c) $\lim_{x \to 1} (4x^2 - x)(2x^2 + 1)$

(d) $\lim_{x \to 1} (4x^2 - x)^2$

(e) $\lim_{x \to 1} (4x^2 - 3x + 1)^5$

2.7 Continuity

Using the ideas of functions and limit, we may now define the continuity of a function. Let us first consider the problem in a heuristic manner.

Suppose we have a function

$$y = f(x)$$

which is shown schematically in Figure 2–17. As is seen, in scheme (a) of

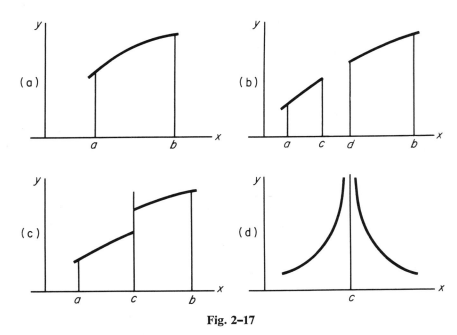

Fig. 2–17

the figure the function $f(x)$ is continuous. That is, we have a continuous curve. In parts (b), (c), and (d), we note there is a break in the curve, and the function is not continuous.

There is, however, a difference in the discontinuity of the curves. In scheme (b), we note there is also a break in the domain $[a, b]$. That is, there are no points between c and d, and hence the break in the curve cannot, so to speak, be blamed on the function (curve) itself. If there were points between c and d and there was no break in the domain $[a, b]$, we shall assume that there would be no break in the curve either.

But, in parts (c) and (d), we see that there is no break in the interval $[a, b]$ and, in spite of this, there is a break in the curve at point c. As we can see, in scheme (c) there are two values of $f(x)$ for the same point c. This type of discontinuity is called a *jump discontinuity*. In scheme (d), the value of $f(x)$ at point c becomes infinity, and we shall call this type of discontinuity, *infinite discontinuity*. Our main interest in the subsequent several chapters will be the jump discontinuity, so let us investigate this now.

For our investigation, let us consider the diagram in Figure 2–18. Let

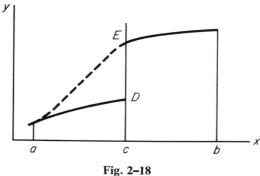

Fig. 2–18

$f(c)$ be the value of $f(x)$ at point c. It is shown by the point E in the diagram.

Suppose now that, as x goes from $a \to c$, the curve goes toward D rather than E. At point c, the curve jumps from D to E. As can be seen, to avoid this kind of a discontinuity, the curve must also tend toward E. That is, when point x is near C, the curve must be near E; and, as x gets closer to C, the curve must get closer to E if the curve is to be continuous at point E.

What we wish to do now is to express this non-rigorous idea of continuity in more precise terms. Let point A in Figure 2–19 be the value of $f(x)$ at x_1,

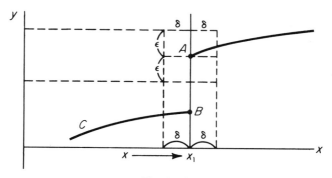

Fig. 2–19

i.e., $f(x_1) = A$. Then, for the curve to be continuous, point B must coincide with point A, and at a point just a small distance to the left of x_1, say at x', the $f(x')$ should be close to $f(x_1)$. That is, we should have

$$|f(x') - f(x_1)| < \epsilon$$

where $\epsilon > 0$ and is very small when x' is close to x_1. This may be shown by

$$|x' - x_1| < \delta$$

where $\delta > 0$ and is very small.

We may state this concept of continuity more formally as follows: A function $f(x)$ is continuous at the point x_1 if for any $\epsilon > 0$, no matter how small, there exists a $\delta > 0$ (depending on ϵ) such that

$$|f(x) - f(x_1)| < \epsilon$$

for all x satisfying

$$|x - x_1| < \delta$$

This is called the $(\epsilon - \delta)$ definition of continuity.

An alternative way of expressing this is: A function $f(x)$ is continuous at x_1 if, as $x \to x_1$, we have $f(x) \to f(x_1)$. That is,

$$\lim_{x \to x_1} f(x) = f(x_1)$$

As is seen, there are three different requirements in this definition of continuity.

(1) $f(x_1)$ exists.

(2) $\lim_{x \to x_1} f(x)$ exists.

(3) $\lim_{x \to x_1} f(x) = f(x_1)$.

When a function is continuous at each point in the domain S, then we say *the function is continuous over S* (which may be an interval).

We state without proof that the sum, difference, product, and quotient of any finite number of continuous functions are continuous.

Problems

1. Given the function

$$\begin{aligned} f(x) &= 5 - x &&\text{for } x \neq 4 \\ &= 0 &&\text{for } x = 4 \end{aligned}$$

(a) Draw a graph of this function.
(b) Identify the discontinuity of the function in the graph.
(c) Find $\lim_{x \to 4} (5 - x)$, and show that the limit is not equal to the value of the function at $x = 4$. Hence it does not satisfy the requirement that $\lim_{x \to x_1} f(x) = f(x_1)$, and there is a discontinuity.

2. Given the function

$$\begin{aligned} f(x) &= x + 1 &&\text{for } x < 2 \\ &= x + 2 &&\text{for } x > 2 \\ &= \text{undefined} &&\text{for } x = 2 \end{aligned}$$

Explain the discontinuity of this function following the procedure in Problem 1.

3. Given the function

$$f(x) = \frac{1}{x}, \qquad x \neq 0$$

(a) Draw a graph of this function, letting x range from -3 to $+3$.
(b) Show by observation that $f(x)$ has no value at $x = 0$.
(c) Show by observation that $f(x)$ has no limit at $x = 0$.
(d) Explain, non-rigorously, the infinite discontinuity of this function.

2.8 Necessary and sufficient conditions

Several terms that will appear frequently in subsequent discussion are

  i. necessary condition for a statement
 ii. sufficient condition for a statement
iii. necessary and sufficient condition for a statement

Let us explain their meaning with the following illustrations.

statement q	condition p
1. This substance is sugar.	1. the substance is sweet.
2. He will receive an A in this course.	2. His grade is 98 in this course.
3. He will receive an A in this course.	3. His grade is above 90 in this course

* Assume the grade A is 90–100.

For the first illustration, we can see that the condition p_1 (the substance is sweet) is the logical consequence of the statement q_1 (this substance is sugar). We shall express this in symbols as

(1) $$q_1 \Rightarrow p_1$$

and read this as; statement q_1 implies condition p_1.

We can see that this relation also holds for the third illustration. That is,

(2) $$q_3 \text{ (receives an A)} \Rightarrow p_3 \text{ (his grade is above 90)}$$

We can also see that it does not hold for the second illustration.

In cases 1 and 3, where (1) and (2) hold, we say p is a *necessary* condition for the statement q. That is, when a condition p is the logical consequence of the statement q, p is called the necessary condition for q.

Let us now reverse the process. We can see that for case 2, the statement q_2 (he will receive an A) logically follows from the condition p_2 (his grade is 98). We shall express this in symbols as

(3) $$q_2 \Leftarrow p_2$$

and read this as: condition p_2 implies statement q_2.

We can see this relation also holds for case 3. That is,

(4) $\quad q_3$ (he receives an A) $\Leftarrow p_3$ (his grade is above 90)

But it does not hold for case 1. That is, q_1 (this substance is sugar) does not logically follow from the condition p_1 (this substance is sweet). p_1 may imply that the substance is honey, or some other sweet substance.

In cases 2 and 3 where relations (3) and (4) hold, we say p is a *sufficient* condition for q. That is, when statement q logically follows from the condition p, this p is called the sufficient condition for q to be true.

To summarize, we have:

Necessary condition	sufficient condition
$q_1 \Rightarrow p_1$	$q_2 \Leftarrow p_2$
$q_3 \Rightarrow p_3$	$q_3 \Leftarrow p$

Hence we have:

$q_1 \Rightarrow p_1 \quad$ p_1 is a necessary condition for q_1

$q_2 \Leftarrow p_2 \quad$ p_2 is a sufficient condition for q_2

$q_3 \Leftrightarrow p_3 \quad$ p_3 is a necessary and sufficient condition for q_3

The following terms are also used:

only if ... necessary condition

if ... sufficient condition

if and only if ... necessary and sufficient condition

Using our illustration, we have:

Necessary: q_1 (the substance is sugar) only if p_1 (the substance is sweet)

Sufficient: q_2 (he will receive an A) if p_2 (his grade is 98)

Necessary and sufficient: q_3 (he will receive an A) if and only if p_3 (his grade is above 90)

Note how the following relations do not hold.

q_1 (the substance is sugar) if p_1 (the substance is sweet)

q_2 (he will receive an A) only if p_2 (his grade is 98)

Notes and References

The topics in this chapter are basic to mathematical analysis and of primary interest to professional mathematicians. Since our main object is not mathematical analysis, but merely to obtain a general idea on certain subjects which are useful in economic analysis, only a heuristic explanation of a limited number of topics has been considered to provide a background for subsequent chapters.

References for the topics covered in this chapter are numerous but usually on a mathematically advanced level. The student is advised to have on hand for reference a standard elementary calculus text, an advanced calculus text, and a book on real variable theory. An excellent advanced calculus text is Courant (1937, 1936), Vols. I and II. Along with this advanced text, the student is referred to Courant and Robbins (1941), *What is Mathematics?* which explains basic ideas of mathematics in less technical terms.

In addition, the following eight books are recommended: Taylor (1955); Brand (1955); Buck (1956); Sokolnikoff (1939); Hardy (1938); Apostol (1962); Allen (1964); and Smith and Albrecht (1966).

For real variable theory, see Rudin (1953); Thielman (1953); McShane and Botts (1959); Graves (1956); Royden (1963); and Bartle (1963). An excellent guide to the literature of mathematics is a paperback edition of Parke's (1958) book.

Allen, R. G. D., *Basic Mathematics.* New York: St. Martin's Press, 1964.

Apostol, T. M., *Calculus*, Vol. I, II. New York: Blaisdell Publishing Co., 1962.

Bartle, R. G., *The Elements of Real Analysis.* New York: John Wiley and Sons, Inc., 1963.

Brand, L., *Advanced Calculus.* New York: John Wiley and Sons, Inc., 1955.

Buck, R. C., *Advanced Calculus.* New York: McGraw-Hill Book Co., 1956.

Courant, R., *Differential and Integral Calculus*, transl. by E. J. McShane. New York: Interscience Publishers, Inc. (now John Wiley and Sons, Inc.), Vol. I, 2nd ed., 1937, Vol. II, 1936.

Courant, R., and Robbins, H., *What is Mathematics?* New York: Oxford University Press, 1941.

Graves, L. M., *The Theory of Functions of Real Variables*, 2nd ed. New York: McGraw-Hill Book Co., 1956.

Hardy, G. H., *A Course of Pure Mathematics*, 8th ed. Cambridge: Cambridge University Press, 1938.

McShane, E. J., and Botts, T. A., *Real Analysis.* Princeton, N.J.: D. Van Nostrand Co., Inc., 1959.

Parke, N. G., *Guide to the Literature of Mathematics and Physics*, 2nd ed. New York: Dover Publications, Inc., 1958.

Royden, H. L., *Real Analysis*. New York: The Macmillan Company, 1963.

Rudin, W., *Principles of Mathematical Analysis*. New York: McGraw-Hill Book Co., 1953.

Simmons, G. F., *Topology and Modern Analysis*. New York: McGraw-Hill Book Co., 1963.

Smith, A. B. H., and Albrecht, W. A., Jr., *Fundamental Concepts of Analysis*. Englewood Cliffs, N.J.: Prentice-Hall, Inc., 1966.

Smail, L. L., *Calculus*. New York: Appleton-Century-Crofts, Inc., 1949.

Sokolnikoff, I. S., *Advanced Calculus*. New York: McGraw-Hill Book Co., 1939.

Taylor, A., *Advanced Calculus*. New York; Ginn and Co., 1955.

Waismann, F., *Introduction to Mathematical Thinking*, transl. by T. J. Benac. New York: Hafner Publishing Co., Inc., 1951.

CHAPTER 3

Differentiation

In Chapters 3 through 5 we shall discuss one aspect of the classical techniques of calculus, differential calculus, which includes the concept of a derivative of functions with a single variable and several variables, the idea of differentials, and the problem of finding maximum and minimum values of functions. In Chapter 6 the other main aspect, integral calculus, will be discussed. We start with the basic idea of differential calculus, i.e., the derivative.

3.1 The derivative

Let us assume we have a product y produced by labor x and that as we increase x (labor) by one unit, the amount of y (wheat) increases by two units. This relationship is shown by

$$y = 2x \tag{1}$$

When x is increased by a small increment Δx, y increases by Δy and we have

$$y + \Delta y = 2(x + \Delta x)$$
$$= 2x + 2\,\Delta x$$

This becomes, since $y = 2x$,

$$\Delta y = -y + 2x + 2\,\Delta x = 2\,\Delta x$$

Dividing through Δx, we arrive at

$$\frac{\Delta y}{\Delta x} = 2$$

That is, for a small unit change of x (labor), y (wheat) increases by 2 bushels. The unit attached to the quotient is

$$\frac{\Delta y}{\Delta x} = 2 \text{ bushels/labor unit}$$

71

Another familiar example is the consumption function. Let

(2) $$C = a + bY$$

where C is consumption expenditures and Y is income. When Y is increased by a small increment ΔY, C increases by ΔC and we have

$$C + \Delta C = a + b(Y + \Delta Y)$$
$$= a + bY + b\,\Delta Y$$

Then

$$\Delta C = -C + a + bY + b\,\Delta Y = b\,\Delta Y$$

Dividing through by the small increment ΔY, we find

$$\frac{\Delta C}{\Delta Y} = b$$

That is, for a small unit change of Y (income), C (consumption) increases by the amount b. The unit attached to this quotient is

$$\frac{\Delta C}{\Delta Y} = b \qquad \text{consumption \$/income \$}$$

The b is called the *marginal propensity to consume.*

Let us present one more example. Consider a car that travels 3 meters every second. This can be shown as

(3) $$y = 3t$$

where y (meters) is the distance the car travels, and t (seconds) is time. Then, by a similar process, we find

$$\frac{\Delta y}{\Delta t} = 3 \text{ meters/second}$$

This shows that for a small unit change of t (seconds), y (meters) changes by three units. It is the velocity of the car.

Let us call y of equation (1) the dependent variable and x the independent variable. Then the quotient $\Delta y/\Delta x (\Delta C/\Delta Y, \Delta y/\Delta t)$ shows the rate of change of the dependent variable $y(C, y)$ with respect to the independent variable $x(Y, t)$. Or, we can say, the change of y with respect to a small unit change (or increment) of x. For example, the change in consumption expenditures C with respect to a one dollar change in income Y.

Now, let us assume the relation between x (labor) and y (wheat) is

(4) $$y = 3x^2$$

When x increases by a small increment Δx, we have

$$y + \Delta y = 3(x + \Delta x)^2$$

$$= 3x^2 + 6x\,\Delta x + 3\,\Delta x^2$$
$$\therefore \quad \Delta y = 6x\,\Delta x + 3\,\Delta x^2$$

Dividing through by Δx, we find

$$\frac{\Delta y}{\Delta x} = 6x + 3\Delta x$$

When labor is increased by a very small amount, i.e., when Δx is made very small, $3\Delta x$ is negligible compared with $6x$, and we may delete it. Then we have, as an *approximation*,

$$\frac{\Delta y}{\Delta x} = 6x$$

where Δx is very small.

The reader may be puzzled at this point and ask: When there is a very small change (increment) in x (labor), how can there be a change in y (wheat) of $6x$, which seems large compared with Δx? The point to note is that we are concerned with the rate of change. It is an average. For example, assume one unit of labor produces 6 bushels of wheat. Then (assuming a linear relation) 0.1 unit of labor will produce 0.6 bushel of wheat. Thus, the average amount of wheat that labor produces is

$$\frac{0.6}{0.1} = 6 \text{ bushels/labor unit}$$

Now let us write dy for Δy and dx for Δx. Then

$$\frac{dy}{dx} = 6x$$

The dy/dx is interpreted as the change in y due to a very small unit change (increment) in x. Or, we may say it is the rate of change of y with respect to x. This dy/dx is called the *derivative* of the function $y = 3x^2$ with respect to x, which is a very non-rigorous interpretation of the idea of a derivative.

We shall now reconsider the derivative more rigorously and show it *as a limit* and also show it *as a slope* of a curve.

Instead of using such functions as $y = 2x$ or $y = 3x^2$, we may take a more rigorous approach and write it in abstract form as $y = f(x)$. The function $y = f(x)$ is shown as a curve on a two-dimensional graph as in Figure 3–1. Using this graph to help explain the idea of a derivative, consider a point P with coordinates (x_1, y_1) on the curve expressed by $y = f(x)$, and another point Q expressed by $(x_1 + \Delta x, y_1 + \Delta y)$. We form a quotient

$$\frac{f(x_1 + \Delta x) - f(x_1)}{(x_1 + \Delta x) - x_1} = \frac{(y_1 + \Delta y) - y_1}{(x_1 + \Delta x) - x_1} = \frac{\Delta y}{\Delta x}$$

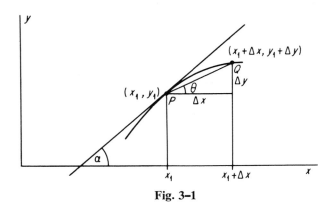

Fig. 3–1

where Δy is the difference between the two points P and Q in terms of the y-coordinates and where we make a similar interpretation for Δx in terms of the x-coordinate. This quotient is called the *difference quotient*.

As the point Q moves toward P along the curve $y = f(x)$, the $\Delta y/\Delta x$ also changes and will approach a limit, providing a limit exists. This *limit* is called the *derivative of the function $f(x)$ at the point P* and is written as follows:

$$\lim_{Q \to P} \frac{\Delta y}{\Delta x} = \text{derivative} = \frac{dy}{dx}$$

The symbol dy/dx is used to express the derivative. This process of $Q \to P$ is the same as $\Delta x \to 0$. Thus, we write

$$\text{derivative} = \lim_{\Delta x \to 0} \frac{f(x_1 + \Delta x) - f(x_1)}{(x_1 + \Delta x) - x_1} = \lim_{\Delta x \to 0} \frac{\Delta y}{\Delta x}$$

From our graph we see that

$$\frac{\Delta y}{\Delta x} = \tan \theta$$

in our present case, and we observe

$$\lim_{\Delta x \to 0} \frac{\Delta y}{\Delta x} = \tan \alpha$$

which is the *slope* of the curve $y = f(x)$ at the point (x_1, y_1).

It should be noted that $\Delta x \neq 0$, for, if $\Delta x = 0$, the difference quotient $\Delta y/\Delta x$ is meaningless.

The process of obtaining the derivative is called *differentiation* of the function $f(x)$. When a function has a derivative, it is said to be *differentiable*.

Another notation that will be used frequently is

$$f'(x) = \frac{dy}{dx}$$

Strictly speaking, the derivative is a limit and dy/dx does not express a quotient. But from a non-rigorous standpoint, it is helpful to interpret it as a quotient. A quotient in turn shows an average, or rate of change. Thus dy/dx may be interpreted as the amount of change of y per unit change (increment) of x.

Another consideration from a practical standpoint is to interpret $\Delta x \rightarrow 0$ in a relative sense. For example, consider the aggregate consumption function $C = a + bY$ again. The derivative of C with respect to Y was $b = dC/dY$, and the limiting process was carried out by letting $\Delta Y \rightarrow 0$. The Y may be \$400 billion. Then, theoretically, $\Delta Y \rightarrow 0$ means a change of Y that approaches zero so that ΔY may be $1¢, 0.1¢, 0.01¢, \ldots$. However, a change of income of $1¢$ when $Y = \$400$ billion has very little practical meaning. For most applications, it will suffice to consider the small change in Y in relative terms. That is, if $Y = \$400$ billion, then $\Delta Y = \$1$ billion will be considered a small unit change. If $Y = \$500$, then $\Delta Y = \$1$ will be considered a small unit change.

But then the question arises: When one says a small change (increment) of x (the independent variable) in a relative sense, how small should it be? From our illustration in equation (4), $y = 3x^2$, we found

$$\frac{\Delta y}{\Delta x} = 6x + 3\Delta x$$

When we say Δx is to be small in a relative sense, we shall mean it is small compared to $6x$ so that it may be omitted without having practically any effect on $\Delta y/\Delta x$. Thus when we say a small unit change in the independent variable x in our subsequent discussion, it should be interpreted in this manner. We shall use the terms small unit change of x, small change of x, or small increment of x interchangeably. This Δx indicates a small increase, not a decrease of x.

Although these practical compromises have been made, it should be remembered that theoretically the derivative dy/dx is a limit. Let us check this statement by applying the definition of a limit stated in Chapter 2 to an example.

Equation (4) was $y = 3x^2$, and the difference quotient was

(5) $$\frac{\Delta y}{\Delta x} = 6x + 3\Delta x$$

Let the difference between $\Delta y/\Delta x$ and $6x$ be smaller than a fixed positive (small) number ϵ, say, $\epsilon = \frac{1}{10}$. That is,

(6)
$$\left| \frac{\Delta y}{\Delta x} - 6x \right| < \epsilon = \frac{1}{10}$$

A certain range of values of x will satisfy the inequality (6). Given $\epsilon = \frac{1}{10}$, *can we find* an interval around x that is of width δ, where δ is dependent on ϵ, such that, for all values of x in this interval except the value x itself, equation (6) is satisfied? In other words, let $\delta = \varphi(\epsilon)$, then does

(7)
$$|(x + \Delta x) - x| < \delta$$

imply the inequality (6)? Note that the proviso "except the value x itself" means $x + \Delta x \neq x$, i.e., $\Delta x \neq 0$; otherwise $\Delta y / \Delta x$ will become meaningless.

Let us try $\delta = \epsilon/3 = \frac{1}{30}$. Then from equation (7)

$$|\Delta x| < \delta = \frac{\epsilon}{3} = \frac{1}{30}$$

$$\therefore \quad |3\Delta x| < \epsilon$$

However,

$$\left| \frac{\Delta y}{\Delta x} - 6x \right| = |6x + 3\Delta x - 6x| = |3\Delta x|$$

so that equation (7) implies

$$\left| \frac{\Delta y}{\Delta x} - 6x \right| < \epsilon$$

This means that, if the width of the interval around x is kept less than $\delta = \frac{1}{30}$, then for all values of x in this interval, except at x itself, the difference between $\Delta y / \Delta x$ and $6x$, i.e., $|\Delta y / \Delta x - 6x|$, will be less than $\epsilon = \frac{1}{10}$.

Thus we have found a δ for a given ϵ such that $|(x + \Delta x) - x| < \delta$ implies $|\Delta y / \Delta x - 6x| < \epsilon$.

We can easily see that, by repeating this process, a δ can be found for each given ϵ, no matter how small. If we make $\epsilon = \frac{1}{1000}$, for example, then $\delta = \epsilon/3 = \frac{1}{3000}$. As we make ϵ smaller, the δ that corresponds to each successively smaller ϵ also becomes smaller. Thus $|\Delta x| < \delta$ implies that $\Delta x \to 0$. Therefore, according to the definition of a limit, $6x$ is the limit of $\Delta y / \Delta x$ as $\Delta x \to 0$.

We may condense our statement and say

$$\frac{\Delta y}{\Delta x} \to 6x \quad \text{as} \quad \Delta x \to 0$$

and $6x$ is the limit of $\Delta y / \Delta x$ when $\Delta x \to 0$. Or, we may write

$$\lim_{\Delta x \to 0} \frac{\Delta y}{\Delta x} = 6x$$

and, since $\lim\limits_{\Delta x \to 0} \Delta y / \Delta x \equiv f'(x)$,

$$f'(x) = 6x$$

An alternative and simpler way of expressing the above results is as follows:
We have

$$\frac{\Delta y}{\Delta x} = 6x + 3\Delta x$$

Take the limit on both sides. Then

$$\lim_{\Delta x \to 0} \frac{\Delta y}{\Delta x} = \lim_{\Delta x \to 0} (6x + 3\Delta x) = 6x$$

The point to notice is how the difference quotient $\Delta y / \Delta x$ is transformed into a continuous function $6x + 3\Delta x$. By this transformation we can find the limit of $6x + 3\Delta x$ as $\Delta x \to 0$ by treating $\Delta x \to 0$ as if $\Delta x = 0$ without rendering it meaningless. In subsequent discussion we shall mainly use this technique.

In subsequent discussion also, we shall assume the functions to be continuous and differentiable unless otherwise stated. However, it is important to note that, even though a function may be continuous, it may not necessarily have a derivative. In Figure 3–2, the function is continuous, but there is no derivative at point A. As is seen, there are two tangents at point A.

But note carefully that, when a function has a derivative at a given point, then the function must be continuous at that point. The proof of this statement is beyond the level of this book so let us merely accept it.

So we may summarize our discussion as follows. If a function $f(x)$ has a derivative at point x_0, $f(x)$ is continuous at x_0. However, a continuous function may not necessarily have a derivative. As we defined

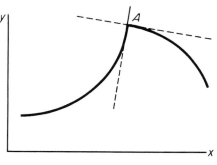

Fig. 3–2

above, a function that has a derivative $f'(x)$ at point x_0, is said to be *differentiable* at point x_0.

With these qualifications in mind, we shall assume in our subsequent discussion that the functions we deal with are differentiable.

The functions $y = f(x)$ can be classified into certain groups, and the procedure of differentiation of functions belonging to a certain group follows a definite pattern. Instead of finding a difference quotient for every problem and then finding the derivative, we can find a number of rules of differentiation which, when applied to their respective groups, will immediately give us the derivative.

3.2 Rules of differentiation

RULE 1. *Differentiation of a power of a function.*

Let $y = x^2$. What is the derivative of this function? We shall first obtain a difference quotient $\Delta y / \Delta x$ and then perform a limiting process.

$$y + \Delta y = (x + \Delta x)^2 = x^2 + 2x \cdot \Delta x + \Delta x^2$$

$$\Delta y = 2x \cdot \Delta x + \Delta x^2$$

$$\frac{\Delta y}{\Delta x} = 2x + \Delta x$$

$$\lim_{\Delta x \to 0} \frac{\Delta y}{\Delta x} = \lim_{\Delta x \to 0} (2x + \Delta x) = 2x$$

Note that we have transformed the difference quotient $\Delta y / \Delta x$ into a function $2x + \Delta x$. When $\Delta x = 0$, $\Delta y / \Delta x$ does not have any meaning. But by transforming $\Delta y / \Delta x$ into $2x + \Delta x$ we were able to find the limit by setting $\Delta x = 0$ for $2x + \Delta x$ without rendering it meaningless.

The above is usually written

$$\frac{dy}{dx} = \frac{d}{dx} f(x) = \frac{d}{dx} (x^2) = 2x$$

For the general case where $y = x^n$, we find for an increment of Δx

$$y + \Delta y = (x + \Delta x)^n$$

Using the binomial expansion, this becomes

$$y + \Delta y = x^n + \binom{n}{1} x^{n-1} (\Delta x) + \binom{n}{2} x^{n-2} (\Delta x)^2$$

$$+ \dots + \binom{n}{n-1} x (\Delta x)^{n-1} + (\Delta x)^n$$

$$\frac{\Delta y}{\Delta x} = \binom{n}{1} x^{n-1} + \binom{n}{2} x^{n-2} (\Delta x) + \dots + \binom{n}{n-1} x (\Delta x)^{n-2} + (\Delta x)^{n-1}$$

Take the limit on both sides

$$\lim_{\Delta x \to 0} \frac{\Delta y}{\Delta x} = \binom{n}{1} x^{n-1} = n x^{n-1}$$

Thus the general formula is

$$\frac{dy}{dx} = \frac{d}{dx} (x^n) = n x^{n-1}$$

Example 1. For $y = x^5$, it will be

$$\frac{dy}{dx} = \frac{d}{dx}(x^5) = 5x^{5-1} = 5x^4$$

This means that, when there is a small unit change of x, the rate of change of y is $dy/dx = 5x^4$.

Example 2. Let C be total cost and q be output, and assume $C = q^3$. The derivative of C with respect to q is

$$\frac{dC}{dq} = 3q^2$$

This shows the rate of change of total cost C with respect to a small unit change of output q; i.e., it is the marginal cost.

RULE 2. *Multiplication by a constant.*

When $y = cx^2$, where c is a constant, what is the derivative dy/dx? When procedures similar to the first rule are carried out, the result is

$$y + \Delta y = c(x + \Delta x)^2$$

$$\frac{\Delta y}{\Delta x} = 2cx + \Delta x$$

$$\lim_{\Delta x \to 0} \frac{\Delta y}{\Delta x} = \lim_{\Delta x \to 0}(2cx + \Delta x) = 2cx$$

$$= c \cdot 2x = c\frac{d}{dx}(x^2)$$

which we write

$$\frac{dy}{dx} = \frac{d}{dx}(cx^2) = c\frac{d}{dx}(x^2) = c \cdot 2x$$

In general, when $y = cu$, where u is a function of x, we have

$$\frac{dy}{dx} = c\frac{du}{dx}$$

Example 1. If $y = 3x^4$, then

$$\frac{dy}{dx} = \frac{d}{dx}(3x^4) = 3\frac{dx^4}{dx} = 3 \cdot 4x^{4-1} = 12x^3$$

Example 2. If $y = 2x^{1/2}$, then

$$\frac{dy}{dx} = 2(\tfrac{1}{2})x^{(1/2)-1} = x^{-1/2}$$

Example 3.

$$y = ax^b$$

$$\frac{dy}{dx} = a \cdot b \cdot x^{b-1}$$

RULE 3. *Derivative of a sum.*

If $y = u + v$, where $u = f(x)$ and $v = g(x)$ are functions of x, then

$$\frac{dy}{dx} = \frac{du}{dx} + \frac{dv}{dx} = f'(x) + g'(x)$$

Example.

$$y = x^2 + 3x^4$$

$$\frac{dy}{dx} = 2x + 12x^3$$

Perform this differentiation process by using the difference quotient, and prove the result to yourself.

RULE 4. *Derivative of a constant.*

Let $y = f(x) = c$, where c is a constant. Then, since y does not change, $y + \Delta y = f(x + \Delta x) = c$. The difference quotient becomes

$$\frac{(y + \Delta y) - y}{\Delta x} = \frac{f(x + \Delta x) - f(x)}{\Delta x} = \frac{c - c}{\Delta x} = 0$$

Thus, by letting $\Delta x \to 0$,

$$\frac{dy}{dx} = \frac{dc}{dx} = 0$$

That is, the derivative of a constant is zero.

Example. Let $C = a + bY$ be a linear consumption function where C is consumption, Y is income, and a and b are constants. The derivative of C with respect to Y is

$$\frac{dC}{dY} = \frac{da}{dY} + b\frac{dY}{dY}$$

$$= 0 + b = b$$

$dC/dY = b$ shows the change in C when there is a small unit change of Y.

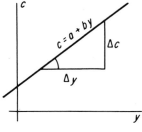

Fig. 3–3

$dC/dY = b$ also shows that the marginal propensity to consume is equal to the slope of the linear consumption function.

RULE 5. *Derivative of a product.*

Let $y = f(x)g(x)$. To find the derivative dy/dx, let $u = f(x)$ and $v = g(x)$. Then

$$y = uv$$
$$y + \Delta y = (u + \Delta u)(v + \Delta v)$$

The difference quotient becomes

$$\frac{(y + \Delta y) - y}{\Delta x} = \frac{(u + \Delta u)(v + \Delta v) - uv}{\Delta x}$$

$$\frac{\Delta y}{\Delta x} = (u + \Delta u)\frac{(v + \Delta v) - v}{\Delta x} + v\frac{(u + \Delta u) - u}{\Delta x}$$

Let $\Delta x \to 0$, and find the limit. Then

$$\frac{dy}{dx} = uv' + vu'$$

or

$$\frac{dy}{dx} = f(x)g'(x) + g(x)f'(x)$$

Example 1.

$$y = (3x^2 + 1)(x^3 + 2x)$$

$$y' = (3x^2 + 1)\frac{d}{dx}(x^3 + 2x) + (x^3 + 2x)\frac{d}{dx}(3x^2 + 1)$$

$$= 15x^4 + 21x^2 + 2$$

Check this by multiplying out the product and then differentiate according to the rule for the sum of functions of x.

Example 2. Let $y = x^6$. We know $dy/dx = 6x^5$. As an illustration of the use of the multiplication rule, let $y = x^6 = (x)(x^2)(x^3)$. Then, using the multiplication rule, we find

$$\frac{dy}{dx} = (x)(x^2)\frac{d}{dx}(x^3) + (x^2)(x^3)\frac{d}{dx}(x) + (x^3)(x)\frac{d}{dx}(x^2)$$

$$= 3x^5 + x^5 + 2x^5 = 6x^5$$

RULE 6. *Derivative of a quotient.*

Given $y = f(x)/g(x)$, find the derivative dy/dx. Let $u = f(x)$ and $v = g(x)$. Then

$$y = \frac{u}{v}$$

$$y + \Delta y = \frac{u + \Delta u}{v + \Delta v}$$

The difference quotient becomes

$$\frac{(y + \Delta y) - y}{\Delta x} = \frac{\dfrac{u + \Delta u}{v + \Delta v} - \dfrac{u}{v}}{\Delta x}$$

$$\frac{\Delta y}{\Delta x} = \frac{1}{(v + \Delta v)v}\left\{v\,\frac{(u + \Delta u) - u}{\Delta x} - u\,\frac{(v + \Delta v) - v}{\Delta x}\right\}$$

Let $\Delta x \to 0$, then the limit is

$$\frac{dy}{dx} = \frac{1}{v^2}\{vu' - uv'\}$$

or

$$y' = \frac{g(x)f'(x) - f(x)g'(x)}{[g(x)]^2}$$

Example 1.

$$y = \frac{3x^2 + 1}{x}$$

$$\therefore \quad \frac{dy}{dx} = \frac{x\dfrac{d}{dx}(3x^2 + 1) - (3x^2 + 1)\dfrac{d}{dx}(x)}{x^2}$$

$$= 3 - \frac{1}{x^2}$$

Let us check it by use of the formula for the sum.

$$y = \frac{3x^2 + 1}{x} = 3x + \frac{1}{x} = 3x + x^{-1}$$

$$\therefore \quad \frac{dy}{dx} = 3 - \frac{1}{x^2}$$

Example 2.

$$y = \frac{x}{x^2 + 1}$$

$$\frac{dy}{dx} = \frac{(x^2 + 1)\dfrac{dx}{dx} - x\dfrac{d}{dx}(x^2 + 1)}{(x^2 + 1)^2} = \frac{1 - x^2}{(x^2 + 1)^2}$$

RULE 7. *Derivative of an inverse function.*

Consider a function

(1) $$y = a + x$$

From this we find

(2) $$x = y - a$$

The characteristic of the functions (1) and (2) is that the mapping from x to y and from y to x is one to one. For each value of x, there is one and only one value of y. Function (2) is called the inverse function of (1), and (1) is the inverse function of (2).

The equation

(3) $$y = x^2$$

does not give a one-to-one mapping. That is, two different values $x_1 = 1$ and $x_2 = -1$ give the same y value, $y = 1$. A one-to-one mapping requires the condition that, when $x_1 \neq x_2$, then $f(x_1) \neq f(x_2)$. In equation (3), if we restrict x to non-negative numbers, i.e., $x \geq 0$, the mapping becomes one to one. Then we can find the inverse function of (3), which is

(4) $$x = \sqrt{y}$$

Let $y = f(x)$ have a one-to-one mapping and thus have an inverse function $x = g(y)$. Then we state without proof that

(5) $$f'(x)g'(y) = 1$$

For example, from equations (1) and (2) we find

$$\frac{dy}{dx} = 1, \qquad \frac{dx}{dy} = 1$$

Then,

$$\frac{dy}{dx}\frac{dx}{dy} = 1$$

From equations (3) and (4) we find

$$\frac{dy}{dx} = 2x, \qquad \frac{dx}{dy} = \tfrac{1}{2}y^{(1/2)-1}$$

Then

$$\frac{dy}{dx}\frac{dx}{dy} = (2x)(\tfrac{1}{2}y^{-1/2})$$

$$= (x)(x^2)^{-1/2} = 1$$

The rule given by equation (5) is helpful in finding derivatives of functions such as the inverse of the following one

$$y = x^3 + 3x$$

We observe that the mapping is one to one. Thus, theoretically we can solve for x and find the inverse function and calculate the derivative dx/dy. But, in this case, it is much simpler if we find dy/dx and note that $dx/dy = (dy/dx)^{-1}$. That is,

$$\frac{dy}{dx} = 3x^2 + 3, \quad \text{and} \quad \frac{dx}{dy} = \frac{1}{3x^2 + 3}$$

RULE 8. *Differentiation of a function of a function—the chain rule.*

This is one of the most useful rules for subsequent analysis, which we shall explain by use of an example. Let x be land, y be wheat, and z be bread. Assuming that, for every unit of x (land), we can produce 2 units of y (wheat), we have

$$y = 2x$$

For every unit of y (wheat), we can produce 15 units of z (bread), and this is shown by

$$z = 15y$$

When there is a one-unit change of x (land), how many units of change of z (bread) will there be? Obviously, by setting $x = 1$,

$$z = 15y = 15(2x) = 30x = 30$$

Let us reinterpret this with derivatives. First, dy/dx shows the change in y due to a small unit change in x and we have

$$\frac{dy}{dx} = \frac{d}{dx}(2x) = 2$$

The change in z due to a small unit change in y will be

$$\frac{dz}{dy} = \frac{d}{dy}(15y) = 15$$

Thus, the amount of change in z due to a small unit change x is

$$\frac{dz}{dx} = \frac{dz}{dy}\frac{dy}{dx} = (15)(2) = 30$$

As another example, let

$$y = 2x^2 \qquad \text{and} \qquad z = 15y^2$$

Then the amount of change in z due to a small unit change in x will be

$$\frac{dz}{dx} = \frac{dz}{dy}\frac{dy}{dx} = (30y)(4x)$$

$$= 30(2x^2)(4x) = 240x^3$$

In general, when we have

$$z = g(y) \qquad \text{and} \qquad y = f(x)$$

then,

$$\frac{dz}{dx} = \frac{dz}{dy}\frac{dy}{dx}$$

This is called the chain rule. The proof for the case of two functions can be sketched as

$$z = g(y) \qquad y = f(x)$$

Then

$$\Delta z = g(y + \Delta y) - g(y)$$

$$\Delta y = f(x + \Delta x) - f(x)$$

$$\therefore \quad \frac{\Delta z}{\Delta x} = \frac{\Delta z}{\Delta y}\frac{\Delta y}{\Delta x} = \frac{g(y + \Delta y) - g(y)}{\Delta y} \frac{f(x + \Delta x) - f(x)}{\Delta x}$$

We can see that, as $\Delta x \to 0$, then $\Delta y \to 0$ also and, as $\Delta y \to 0$, then $\Delta z \to 0$. Thus,

$$\lim_{\Delta x \to 0} \frac{\Delta z}{\Delta x} = \left(\lim_{\Delta y \to 0} \frac{g(y + \Delta y) - g(y)}{\Delta y} \right)\left(\lim_{\Delta x \to 0} \frac{f(x + \Delta x) - f(x)}{\Delta x} \right)$$

$$\frac{dz}{dx} = \frac{dz}{dy}\frac{dy}{dx}$$

Example 1.

$$z = y^4 + 3y^3 \qquad \text{and} \qquad y = x^2$$

Then

$$\frac{dz}{dx} = \frac{dz}{dy}\frac{dy}{dx} = (4y^3 + 9y^2)(2x)$$

$$= 8xy^3 + 18xy^2$$

$$= 8x^7 + 18x^5$$

Example 2.

$$z = (x^3 + 3x)^2$$

This can be differentiated with respect to x by factoring out the square. But instead of doing that, let us use the chain rule. For that we use a device that will put the function into a form which will enable us to use the chain rule. Let

$$y = x^3 + 3x$$

Then the original function can be written as

$$z = y^2 \quad \text{and} \quad y = x^3 + 3x$$

Thus, the derivative of z with respect to x becomes

$$\frac{dz}{dx} = \frac{dz}{dy}\frac{dy}{dx} = (2y)(3x^2 + 3)$$

$$= 2(x^3 + 3x)(3x^2 + 3)$$

$$= 6x^5 + 24x^3 + 18x$$

It is in this fashion, although under various different circumstances, that the chain rule is most frequently used. The problem is to develop the knack of spotting how to change the form of the function to enable the use of the chain rule. A little practice and experience will develop this ability.

Example 3.

$$u = (x^2 + 5x + 1)^5$$

Let $y = x^2 + 5x + 1$. Then $u = y^5$, and we find by the chain rule

$$\frac{du}{dx} = \frac{du}{dy}\frac{dy}{dx}$$

$$= \frac{d}{dy}(y^5)\frac{d}{dx}(x^2 + 5x + 1)$$

$$= 5y^4(2x + 5)$$

$$= 5(x^2 + 5x + 1)(2x + 5)$$

Example 4. Let c be total cost, q be output, and the total cost function be

$$c = (3 + 2q^2)^2$$

Then, marginal cost dc/dq will be, by letting $g = 3 + 2q^2$,

$$\frac{dc}{dq} = \frac{dc}{dg}\frac{dg}{dq} = 2(3 + 2q^2)(0 + 4q)$$

$$= 24q + 16q^3$$

This chain rule applies when there are more than two functions. For example,

$$y = f(w), \quad w = g(z), \quad z = h(x)$$

Then

$$\frac{dy}{dx} = \frac{dy}{dw}\frac{dw}{dz}\frac{dz}{dx}$$

Example 5.

$$y = 2w^2 + 1, \quad w = 3z^2, \quad z = 2x + x^3$$

Then

$$\frac{dy}{dx} = \frac{dy}{dw}\frac{dw}{dz}\frac{dz}{dx}$$

$$= \frac{d}{dw}(2w^2 + 1)\frac{d}{dz}(3z^2)\frac{d}{dx}(2x + x^3)$$

$$= (4w)(6z)(2 + 3x^2)$$

$$= 18(4x + 8x^3 + 3x^5)$$

$$= 72x^3(2 + x^2)^3(2 + 3x^2)$$

RULE 9. *Differentiation of implicit functions.*

$$y = \frac{x}{x^2 + 1}$$

is an explicit function because it expresses y directly in terms of x. When this is in the form

$$x^2 y - x + y = 0$$

it becomes an implicit function and y is said to be *defined implicitly as a function of x.* We may also say x is defined implicitly as a function of y. But, if we know what x and y represent and if x is considered the independent variable, we take the first interpretation.

The derivative of y with respect to x may be found by considering y as a function of x and differentiating term by term. Thus, in the above case it would be

$$\frac{d}{dx}(x^2 y) - \frac{d}{dx}(x) + \frac{d}{dx}(y) = 0$$

$$x^2\frac{dy}{dx} + y\frac{d}{dx}(x^2) - 1 + \frac{dy}{dx} = 0$$

$$x^2 y' + 2xy - 1 + y' = 0$$

$$y' = \frac{1 - 2xy}{x^2 + 1}$$

Example 1. Find dy/dx of the following function.

$$x^2 + xy + y - 1 = 0$$

$$\frac{d}{dx}(x^2) + \frac{d}{dx}(xy) + \frac{d}{dx}(y) - \frac{d}{dx}(1) = 0$$

$$2x + y + x\frac{dy}{dx} + \frac{dy}{dx} - 0 = 0$$

$$\frac{dy}{dx}(x + 1) = -(2x + y)$$

$$\frac{dy}{dx} = -\frac{2x + y}{x + 1}$$

Example 2.

$$xy + (x + y + 1)^3 = 0$$

$$\frac{d}{dx}(xy) + \frac{d}{dx}(x + y + 1)^3 = 0$$

$$y + x\frac{dy}{dx} + 3(x + y + 1)^2\frac{d}{dx}(x + y + 1) = 0$$

$$y + x\frac{dy}{dx} + 3(x + y + 1)^2\left(1 + \frac{dy}{dx} + 0\right) = 0$$

$$\frac{dy}{dx}[x + 3(x + y + 1)^2] = -[y + 3(x + y + 1)^2]$$

$$\frac{dy}{dx} = -\frac{y + 3(x + y + 1)^2}{x + 3(x + y + 1)^2}$$

RULE 10. *Higher derivatives.*

$$y = x^5 + x^3 + x^2$$

Then $y' = dy/dx = 5x^4 + 3x^2 + 2x$ is called the *first derivative*. But, as can be seen, y' is also a function of x. Thus, we can differentiate again.

$$y'' = \frac{d}{dx}(y') = 20x^3 + 6x + 2$$

is called the *second derivative*. This process may be continued, and we can get derivatives of higher order. In general, the notation for the nth derivative is

$$y^{(n)} \quad \text{or} \quad f^{(n)}(x) \quad \text{or} \quad \frac{d^n y}{dx^n}$$

Example.

$$y = x^6 + x^4 + x$$

Find the third derivative of y with respect to x.

$$y' = 6x^5 + 4x^3 + 1$$
$$y'' = 30x^4 + 12x^2$$
$$y''' = 120x^3 + 24x$$

Problems

1. Find the derivatives of the following functions.

(a) $y = x^4$ (b) $y = x^6$

(c) $y = x^{n+1}$ (d) $y = x^{n+m}$

(e) $y = x^{n/m}$ (f) $y = x^{-1}$

(g) $y = x^{-m}$

2. Find the derivatives.

(a) $y = 3x^4$ (b) $y = 6x^5$

(c) $y = 3x^n$ (d) $y = ax^{m+1}$

(e) $y = (a + b)x^{a-b+1}$ (f) $y = mx^{n/m+1}$

3. Find the derivatives.

(a) $y = x^3 + x^4$ (b) $y = 2x^2 + 3x^4$

(c) $y = 3x^{m+1} + 4x^m$ (d) $y = x^2 - x$

(e) $y = x^2 + 2$ (f) $y = x^3 + ax + b$

4. Find the derivatives.

(a) $y = x^5(2x^2 + 1)$ (b) $y = (x^5 + x^2)(x^3 + x)$

(c) $y = (ax^2 + bx)(cx^4 + dx^3)$ (d) $y = \dfrac{x^2 + 1}{x^3}$

(e) $y = \dfrac{x^3}{x^2 + 1}$ (f) $y = \dfrac{3x + 2}{4x^2 + 3}$

5. Find the derivative of the inverse function.

(a) $y = x^3 + 3$ (b) $y = x^2 + x, \; x > 0$

(c) $y = x^4 - 2x^2, \; x > 0$

6. Find the derivative of the function z with respect to x.

(a) $y = x^2 + 3x, \; z = y^2 + 1$ (b) $y = 4x, \; z = y^2$

(c) $y = x^2, \; z = \dfrac{1}{y^2}$ (d) $x = t + 1, \; z = t^2 + 1$

(e) $x = \dfrac{1}{t^2}, \; z = t^2$ (f) $z = w^2 + 1, \; w = y^2 + 1,$

$$y = x^2 + 1$$

(g) $z = 3t^2 + t, \; t = y^3 + y^2, \; y = x$

7. Find du/dx by using the chain rule technique.

(a) $u = f(x^2 + 3x)^3$
(b) $u = (4x^3 + 1)^{1/2}$
(c) $u = (x^2 + 1)^{1/2} + (x^2 + 1)^2$
(d) $u = \sqrt[3]{x^3 + 2x^2 + 3}$
(e) $u = (t^2 + 1)^{1/2}, t = (x^2 + 1)^{1/3}$

8. Find dy/dx.

(a) $2x - 3y = 6$ (b) $2x^2 + 3xy = 3$
(c) $xy = 6$ (d) $x^2y = 6$
(e) $xy + y^2 = 4$ (f) $x^2 + 2xy + y^2 = 4$

9. Find the third derivative of y.

(a) $y = 3x^6 + 2x^4 + x^3$ (b) $y = 4x^5 + 3x + 5$
(c) $y = x^4 + x^2 + x$

3.3 Differentials

The derivative was defined as

$$\lim_{\Delta x \to 0} \frac{(y + \Delta y) - y}{(x + \Delta x) - x} = \lim_{\Delta x \to 0} \frac{\Delta y}{\Delta x} = \frac{dy}{dx}$$

In our graph, we have a quotient QT/PT and the point Q gradually approaches the point P. Then, the numerator and denominator of the quotient QT/PT becomes smaller and smaller. Note that we are not saying the quotient becomes smaller, but that QT and PT become smaller. The extreme situation is where Q finally reaches the point P. The value of this quotient when Q reaches P was called the *derivative* of y with respect to x. This process was called a limiting process and the derivative is a limit. We explained that theoretically dy/dx was not to be considered a quotient once Q reaches P,

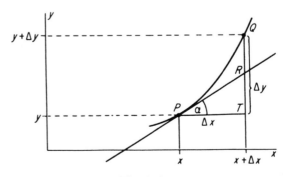

Fig. 3–4

but a symbol expressing the result of a limiting process. But, from a practical and less rigorous point of view, we may *interpret dy/dx* as a quotient. That is, dy/dx can be thought of as showing the change in y when there is a very small unit change in x.

Once we interpret it in this fashion, we may ask: How much of a change will there be in y when there is a small change in x? Let the change in y be Δy and the change in x be Δx. Since we have interpreted the derivative dy/dx as the change in y due to a small unit change in x, the change in y when there is a change of Δx will be

$$\Delta y = \frac{dy}{dx} \Delta x$$

We shall write dy for Δy and dx for Δx. Then

$$dy = \frac{dy}{dx} dx$$

This dy is called the *differential* of y.

Let us now interpret this graphically. We know that $\Delta x = PT$. We also know that the derivative dy/dx is the slope of the curve at P, and from our graph we can show this as

$$\frac{dy}{dx} = \frac{RT}{PT}$$

Thus,

$$\frac{dy}{dx} \Delta x = \frac{RT}{PT} PT = RT$$

We have set $\Delta y = QT$. We see that $(dy/dx) \Delta x = RT$. Thus, when we set

$$\Delta y = \frac{dy}{dx} \Delta x$$

as we did above to define the differential, we have $QT = RT$. However, the graph shows that

$$QT = RT + QR$$

and there is a discrepancy of

$$QR = QT - RT$$

But as Q approaches P, this discrepancy QR becomes very insignificant and may be disregarded.

When we disregard QR, we are using the straight line PR as an approximate substitute for the curve PQ. Thus, taking the differential of y can be thought of as using a *linear approximation* for the curve (or function).

Using general notation, let us write

$$y = f(x)$$

Then the differential of y is

$$dy = f'(x)\,dx$$

where $f'(x)$ is the derivative of $y = f(x)$. This is the differential of y of the first order. In the next section we shall consider differentials of higher orders.

There are several characteristics of this differential formula that we shall be using in later discussion that must be clearly kept in mind. The first is that in the equation

$$\Delta y = \frac{dy}{dx}\,\Delta x$$

the Δx is an *arbitrary* increment in x. This may be understood from Figure 3–4, where $\Delta x = PT$. This $\Delta x = PT$ may be any small increment.

The second characteristic is that, when x is an independent variable, this arbitrary increment Δx may be treated as a constant.

The third characteristic, which is simply a terminology problem is that Δx is called the differential of x and that Δy is called the differential of y. This Δy, however, is clearly defined by the above formula and is *not* arbitrary.

Example 1.

$$y = x^2 + 3$$

What is the change in y when there is a small change in x? This can be obtained by finding the differential of y.

$$dy = \frac{dy}{dx}\,dx$$

where

$$\frac{dy}{dx} = \frac{d}{dx}(x^2 + 3) = 2x$$

$$\therefore \quad dy = 2x\,dx$$

For example, let $x = 2$ change to $x = 2.05$. Then $\Delta x = 0.05$. Thus,

$$dy = 2x\,\Delta x = (2)(2)(0.05) = 0.2$$

When x changes from 2 to 2.05, the amount of change in y will be approximately 0.2.

Example 2. Let x be labor and y, the product that labor produces. Let us assume the relationship is

$$y = 3x^2 - 2x$$

Then, when we increase labor by a small amount, how much change will there be of the product y? For this we find the differential of y.

$$dy = \frac{dy}{dx}\, dx$$

$$= \frac{d}{dx}\,(3x^2 - 2x)\, dx$$

$$= (6x - 2)\, dx$$

Example 3.

$$y = x$$

$$dy = \frac{d}{dx}\,(x)\, dx = dx$$

Example 4.

$$y = k \qquad \text{a constant}$$

$$dy = \frac{d}{dx}\,(k)\, dx$$

$$= 0\, dx = 0$$

That is, the differential of a constant is zero.

Differential of higher orders

On page 88, we found higher-order derivatives. In similar fashion we may easily find higher-order differentials. Suppose we have

$$y = f(x)$$

Then the first-order differential is

$$dy = f'(x)\, dx$$

where, as mentioned above, the differential dx shows an arbitrary increment of x and may be considered a constant.

Since dx is considered a constant, the dy is clearly a function of $f'(x)$. Hence, finding the differential of dy will be a problem of finding the differential of $f'(x)$. The differential of $f'(x)$ is

$$d(f'(x)) = \left(\frac{d}{dx}\, f'(x)\right) dx$$

$$= f''(x)\, dx$$

Hence the differential of dy will be

$$d(dy) = d^2y = d[f'(x)\, dx]$$
$$= d[f'(x)]\, dx$$
$$= [f''(x)\, dx]\, dx$$
$$= f''(x)(dx)^2$$

The third-order differential of y will be

$$d(d^2y) = d^3y = d[f''(x)](dx)^2$$
$$= [f'''(x)\,dx](dx)^2$$
$$= f'''(x)(dx)^3$$

In general,

$$d^n y = f^{(n)}(x)(dx)^n$$

For problems in economics, we usually do not go beyond the second-order differentials.

Example 1.

$$y = x^5$$

$$dy = \frac{d}{dx}(x^5)\,dx$$

$$= 5x^4\,dx$$

$$d(dy) = d^2y = \frac{d}{dx}(dy)\,dx$$

$$= \frac{d}{dx}[5x^4\,dx]\,dx$$

$$= 20x^3(dx)^2$$

$$d(d^2y) = d^3y = \frac{d}{dx}[d^2y]\,dx$$

$$= \frac{d}{dx}[20x^3(dx)^2]\,dx$$

$$= 60x^2(dx)^3$$

Example 2.

$$y = 2x + 1$$

The point to note here is that we have a linear equation in x and y.

$$dy = \frac{d}{dx}(2x + 1)\,dx$$

$$= 2dx$$

$$d^2y = \frac{d}{dx}(dy)\,dx$$

$$= \frac{d}{dx}(2dx)\,dx$$

$$= 0\,dx = 0$$

That is, when we have a linear equation, the second-order differential $d^2y = 0$.

Example 3. In economics, the budget equation (or price line)

$$M = p_1q_1 + p_2q_2$$

is a linear equation in q_1 and q_2, which are the quantities of goods. The M is a given income, and p_1 and p_2 are given prices. The equation may be written as

$$q_1 = \frac{M - p_2q_2}{p_1}$$

where q_1 may be considered the dependent variable, and q_2, the independent variable. Then

$$dq_1 = \frac{d}{dq_2}\left[\frac{M - p_2q_2}{p_1}\right] dq_2$$

$$= -\frac{p_2}{p_1} dq_2$$

$$d^2q_1 = \frac{d}{dq_2}\left[-\frac{p_2}{p_1} dq_2\right] dq_2$$

$$= 0 \, dq_2 = 0$$

Example 4. The second-order differential of an independent variable is zero. For example, let

$$y = f(x)$$

The second-order differential of the dependent variable y was found to be

$$d^2y = f''(x)(dx)^2$$

We can also find the second-order differential of the independent variable x, which is

$$d(x) = \frac{d}{dx}(x) \, dx$$

$$= dx$$

$$d(dx) = d^2x = \frac{d}{dx}(dx) \, dx$$

But dx is considered a constant. Hence,

$$\frac{d}{dx}(dx) = 0$$

and, therefore,

$$d(dx) = d^2x = 0 \, dx = 0$$

That is, the second-order differential of an independent variable is zero. This is a very simple but frequently used result that should be remembered.

Problems

1. Find the differential of y.

   (a) $y = x^3$
   (b) $y = 2x^2$
   (c) $y = x^3 + 2x^2$
   (d) $y = 3x^3 - 2x^2$
   (e) $y = x(3x^2 - 2x^3)$
   (f) $y = (x^2 + 1)(3x^2 - 2x^3)$
   (g) $y = x + 1$
   (h) $y = k$, where k is a constant

2. Find the second-order differentials of y in Problem 1 above.

3. Find the approximate change in y when there is a small change in x in the following functions.

   (a) $y = 3x^2 + 4$, $x = 2$ changes to $x = 2.1$
   (b) $y = 3x^3 + 4x^2$, $x = 2$ changes to $x = 2.01$
   (c) $y = x(x^2 + 1)$, $x = 3$ changes to $x = 3.05$

3.4 Logarithms

We know that $10^2 = 100$; in logarithmic notation this becomes

$$\log_{10} 100 = 2$$

which we read as, "log to the base 10, of 100, is 2." Thus,

$$\log_{10} 10 = 1 \qquad \text{(since } 10^1 = 10\text{)}$$
$$\log_{10} 1000 = 3 \qquad \text{(since } 10^3 = 1000\text{)}$$

In general, $a^x = y$ in logarithmic notation becomes

$$\log_a y = x$$

If the base is 10, it is called the *common logarithm*, and in most cases the base is not explicitly written in.

In calculus, however, a base other than 10 is commonly used, i.e., the number e, which is obtained as a limit from the following process.

When $n \to \infty$, then $(1 + 1/n)^n$ approaches a limit, denoted by e.*

$$\lim_{n \to \infty} \left(1 + \frac{1}{n}\right)^n = e$$

* See Courant (1937), Vol. I, p. 43.

It is sometimes shown as

$$\lim_{h \to 0} (1 + h)^{1/h} = e$$

The number e is an irrational number and is equal to (for three decimal places)

$$e = 2.718$$

Thus, for example,

$$e^2 = 7.389, \qquad e^3 = 20.086$$

which, in terms of logarithms, is

$$\log_e 7.389 = 2, \qquad \log_e 20.086 = 3$$

Logarithms to the base e are called *natural logarithms* and in many cases are written ln 7.389 = 2 to distinguish it from the common logarithm, which is usually written log 100 = 2.

Logarithmic differentiation

CASE 1.

$$y = \log_a x$$

Let us first form the difference quotient $\Delta y / \Delta x$ as follows.

$$y + \Delta y = \log_a (x + \Delta x)$$

$$\Delta y = \log_a (x + \Delta x) - y$$

$$= \log_a (x + \Delta x) - \log_a x$$

$$= \log_a \frac{x + \Delta x}{x} = \log_a \left(1 + \frac{\Delta x}{x}\right)$$

$$\therefore \quad \frac{\Delta y}{\Delta x} = \frac{1}{\Delta x} \log_a \left(1 + \frac{\Delta x}{x}\right)$$

$$= \frac{1}{x}\left(\frac{x}{\Delta x}\right) \log_a \left[1 + \frac{1}{(x/\Delta x)}\right]$$

$$= \frac{1}{x} \log_a \left[1 + \frac{1}{(x/\Delta x)}\right]^{x/\Delta x}$$

Let us set $x/\Delta x \equiv n$. Then $\Delta x/x \equiv 1/n$; and, as $\Delta x \to 0$, $n \to \infty$. Thus,

$$\frac{\Delta y}{\Delta x} = \frac{1}{x} \log_a \left(1 + \frac{1}{n}\right)^n$$

$$\lim_{\Delta x \to 0} \frac{\Delta y}{\Delta x} = \frac{1}{x} \lim_{n \to \infty} \log_a \left(1 + \frac{1}{n}\right)^n$$

But we have just seen that

$$\lim_{n \to \infty} \left(1 + \frac{1}{n}\right)^n = e$$

Thus, the rule we seek is

$$\frac{dy}{dx} = \frac{1}{x} \cdot \log_a e$$

Using this basic formula, we derive the following rules.

CASE 2.

$$y = \ln x$$

When natural logarithms are used, the derivative becomes

$$\frac{dy}{dx} = \frac{1}{x} \ln e = \frac{1}{x}$$

CASE 3.

$$y = \log_a u$$

When u is a function of x, then the chain rule is applied, and we get

$$\frac{dy}{dx} = \frac{dy}{du}\frac{du}{dx} = \left(\frac{1}{u}\log_a e\right)\frac{du}{dx}$$

Example 1.

$$y = \log_a x^2$$

Let $u = x^2$, and apply the chain rule.

$$\frac{dy}{dx} = \frac{dy}{du}\frac{du}{dx} = \left(\frac{1}{u}\log_a e\right)(2x)$$

$$= \left(\frac{1}{x^2}\log_a e\right)(2x) = \frac{2}{x}\log_a e$$

Example 2.

$$y = \log_a (x^2 + 1)$$

Let $u = x^2 + 1$. Then

$$\frac{dy}{dx} = \frac{dy}{du}\frac{du}{dx} = \left(\frac{1}{x^2 + 1}\log_a e\right)(2x)$$

$$= \frac{2x}{x^2 + 1}\log_a e$$

CASE 4.

$$y = \log_e u = \ln u$$

where u is a function of x. Then

$$\frac{dy}{dx} = \frac{dy}{du}\frac{du}{dx} = \left(\frac{1}{u}\ln e\right)\left(\frac{du}{dx}\right)$$

$$= \frac{1}{u}\frac{du}{dx}$$

Example 1.

$$y = \ln x^2$$

Let $u = x^2$. Then

$$\frac{dy}{dx} = \frac{dy}{du}\frac{du}{dx} = \frac{1}{u}(2x) = \frac{1}{x^2}(2x) = \frac{2}{x}$$

Example 2.

$$y = \ln(x^2 + 1)$$

Let $u = x^2 + 1$. Then

$$\frac{dy}{dx} = \frac{1}{x^2 + 1}\frac{d}{dx}(x^2 + 1) = \frac{2x}{x^2 + 1}$$

Example 3.

$$y = \ln(x^2 + 1)^{1/2}$$

Let $u = x^2 + 1$. Then

$$y = \ln u^{1/2} = \tfrac{1}{2}\ln u$$

$$\frac{dy}{dx} = \frac{dy}{du}\frac{du}{dx}$$

$$= \frac{d}{du}(\tfrac{1}{2}\ln u)\frac{d}{dx}(x^2 + 1)$$

$$= \frac{1}{2}\frac{1}{u}(2x)$$

$$= \frac{x}{x^2 + 1}$$

A characteristic of logarithms is that products become sums and quotients become differences. That is,

$$\log ab = \log a + \log b, \qquad \log\frac{a}{b} = \log a - \log b$$

Using this characteristic, we can differentiate complicated functions of products and quotients by first taking the logarithms to the base e of the function.

Example 4.

$$y = x(x^2 + 1)$$

$$\ln y = \ln x + \ln (x^2 + 1)$$

$$\frac{d}{dx} \ln y = \frac{d}{dx} \ln x + \frac{d}{dx} \ln (x^2 + 1)$$

$$\frac{1}{y}\frac{dy}{dx} = \frac{1}{x} + \frac{1}{x^2 + 1}(2x) = \frac{3x^2 + 1}{x(x^2 + 1)}$$

$$\therefore \quad \frac{dy}{dx} = 3x^2 + 1$$

When using the product formula for differentiation, we get,

$$\frac{dy}{dx} = x^2 + 1 + x(2x) = 3x^2 + 1$$

This case is, of course, much simpler when differentiated in a straightforward manner as a product, but was used only to illustrate the procedure, which, in general, we may show as

$$y = f(x)$$

$$\frac{dy}{dx} = y\left\{\frac{d}{dx} \ln f(x)\right\}$$

Problems

1. Look up the following x from the common log table.

(a) $10^x = 2$	(b) $10^x = 20$
(c) $10^x = 200$	(d) $10^x = 0.2$
(e) $10^x = 0.02$	(f) $10^x = 56$
(g) $10^{1.5} = x$	(h) $10^{2.5} = x$
(i) $10^{3.12} = x$	(j) $10^{0.12} = x$
(k) $10^{0.012} = x$	(l) $10^{4.12} = x$

2. Look up the following x from the natural log table.

(a) $e^x = 2$	(b) $e^x = 20$
(c) $e^x = 1$	(d) $e^x = 5$

3. Prove the following.

(a) $e^{\ln x} = x$	(b) $e^{\ln 3x^2} = 3x^2$
(c) $e^{2 \ln 3x} = (3x)^2$	(d) $\ln e^x = x$
(e) $e^{-\ln 4} = ?$	(f) $e^{x + \ln x} = ?$

4. Differentiate the following functions.

(a) $y = \log_a x^3$ (b) $y = \log_a x$

(c) $y = \log_a (x^2 + 1)$ (d) $y = \ln x$

(e) $y = \ln x^2$ (f) $y = \ln (2x^2 + 1)$

(g) $y = \ln (2x^2 + 3x)$ (h) $y = \ln 1/x$

(i) $y = x^2 \ln x$ (j) $y = (x^2 + 1) \ln (x^2 + 1)$

5. Differentiate by logarithmic differentiation.

(a) $y = x^5(2x^2 + 1)$ (b) $y = (x^5 + x^2)(x^3 + x)$

(c) $y = (ax^2 + bx)(cx^4 + dx^3)$ (d) $y = (x^2 + 1)/x^3$

(e) $y = x^3/(x^2 + 1)$ (f) $y = (3x + 2)/(4x^2 + 3)$

3.5 Derivative of exponential functions

CASE 1. Let an exponential function be

$$y = a^x$$

To find the derivative of y with respect to x, let us apply the technique of taking logarithms to the base e and then differentiating. We have

$$\ln y = x \ln a$$

$$\frac{d}{dx} \ln y = \left(\frac{d}{dx} x\right)(\ln a) + x\left(\frac{d}{dx} \ln a\right)$$

$$\left(\frac{d}{dy} \ln y\right) \frac{dy}{dx} = \ln a + 0$$

$$\frac{1}{y} \frac{dy}{dx} = \ln a$$

$$\therefore \quad \frac{dy}{dx} = y \ln a = a^x \ln a$$

Thus, the rule we seek is

$$\frac{dy}{dx} = a^x \ln a$$

CASE 2.

$$y = a^u$$

where u is a function of x. Now, find dy/dx.

$$\ln y = u \ln a$$

$$\frac{1}{y} \frac{dy}{dx} = \frac{du}{dx} \ln a$$

$$\therefore \quad \frac{dy}{dx} = y \frac{du}{dx} \ln a$$

Example 1.

$$y = a^{x^2}$$

$$\therefore \quad \frac{dy}{dx} = (a^{x^2})(2x) \ln a = 2xa^{x^2} \ln a$$

Example 2.

$$y = a^{x^2+1}$$

$$\therefore \quad \frac{dy}{dx} = (a^{x^2+1})(2x) \ln a$$

$$= 2xa^{x^2+1} \ln a$$

Example 3.

$$y = 5^{x+1}$$

$$\frac{dy}{dx} = 5^{x+1} \frac{d}{dx}(x+1) \ln 5$$

$$= 5^{x+1} \ln 5$$

CASE 3.

$$y = e^u$$

where u is a function of x. Then

$$\frac{dy}{dx} = y \frac{du}{dx} \ln e = y \frac{du}{dx}$$

Thus, the rule we seek is

$$\frac{dy}{dx} = e^u \frac{du}{dx}$$

Example 1.

$$y = e^{x^2}$$

$$\frac{dy}{dx} = e^{x^2} \frac{dx^2}{dx} = 2xe^{x^2}$$

Example 2.

$$y = e^{-x^2/2}$$

$$\frac{dy}{dx} = e^{-x^2/2} \left[\frac{d}{dx}\left(-\frac{x^2}{2} \right) \right] = -xe^{-x^2/2}$$

Problems

Differentiate the following functions.

(a) $y = a^{x+1}$ (b) $y = a^{2x}$

(c) $y = a^{2x^2}$

(d) $y = a^{x^2+x}$

(e) $y = e^{2x}$

(f) $y = e^{x^2}$

(g) $y = e^{x^2+2x}$

(h) $y = e^{1/x}$

3.6 Cost curves

Since our main object is to learn various mathematical techniques and not economics, the illustrations will not involve economic discussions. At this early stage when the amount of mathematics at our disposal is very limited, only simple illustrations can be presented. References will be given for those interested in mathematical economics.

Several properties of cost curves will be derived to illustrate the use of derivatives in economics. Let us assume that π is the total cost and q is the quantity of output produced, and also that the cost function is given by

$$\pi = a + bq + cq^2$$

where a, b, and c are constants.

(1) Marginal cost (MC)

Marginal cost is defined as $d\pi/dq$. Thus, we have

$$\frac{d\pi}{dq} = b + 2cq$$

(2) Average cost (AC)

Average cost is shown by

$$\frac{\pi}{q} = \frac{a}{q} + b + cq$$

(3) Relation between average and marginal cost

The slope of the average cost curve is obtained by finding the derivative of π/q. Thus, we have, using the formula for the quotient,

$$\frac{d}{dq}\left(\frac{\pi}{q}\right) = \frac{1}{q}\left[\frac{d\pi}{dq} - \frac{\pi}{q}\right] = \frac{1}{q}[MC - AC]$$

Let us assume we have a u-shaped cost curve as in Figure 3–5. Then, when the average cost curve is sloping downward, $\frac{d}{dq}\left(\frac{\pi}{q}\right) < 0$, and this implies,

$$MC - AC < 0$$

which means, when AC is decreasing, $MC < AC$. At the lowest point on the average cost curve, the slope will be horizontal. That is,

$$\frac{d}{dq}\left(\frac{\pi}{q}\right) = 0$$

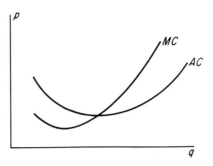

Fig. 3–5

and this means

$$MC - AC = 0$$

Thus, $MC = AC$ at the lowest point as we have drawn it. In similar fashion we may show that, when the AC curve is rising, $MC > AC$.

3.7 Demand curve

Let p be price and q be quantity. Then, the demand curve is shown as

$$q = f(p)$$

Example.

$$q = 30 - 4p - p^2$$

The total revenue R can be shown as

$$R = pq$$

(i) Elasticity of demand η

The elasticity of demand η is defined as

$$\eta = -\frac{dq/q}{dp/p} = -\frac{p}{q}\frac{dq}{dp} = -\frac{p}{q}\frac{1}{dp/dq}$$

We put a minus sign on the formula, following A. Marshall.*

Example. For the above demand curve, for $p = 3$, η is

$$q = 30 - 4p - p^2 = 9$$

$$\frac{dq}{dp} = -4 - 2p = -4 - 6 = -10$$

$$\therefore \quad \eta = -\frac{p}{q}\left(\frac{dq}{dp}\right) = -\frac{3}{9}(-10) = \frac{30}{9} = 3.3$$

* See A. Marshall (1920), mathematical appendix.

(ii) Marginal revenue

Marginal revenue (MR) is defined as dR/dq. We find

$$\frac{dR}{dq} = p + q\frac{dp}{dq} = p\left(1 + \frac{q}{p}\frac{dp}{dq}\right) = p\left(1 - \frac{1}{\eta}\right)$$

Example. For $p = 3$ and $q = 9$ we have

$$\frac{dR}{dq} = 3\left(1 - \frac{1}{30/9}\right) = 2.1$$

(iii) Relationship of AR and MR

The rate of fall of the MR curve is twice the rate of fall of the average revenue (AR) curve. As diagrammed in Figure 3–6, this means, $AF = 2AB$.

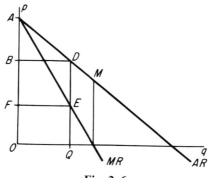

Fig. 3–6

Let us set $R = pq$. Then

$$\frac{dR}{dq} = p + q\frac{dp}{dq}$$

Let

$$p = DQ, \quad q = OQ, \quad \frac{dp}{dq} = -\frac{AB}{BD}, \quad \text{and} \quad \frac{dR}{dq} = QE$$

Now,

$$QE = \frac{dR}{dq} = DQ + OQ\left(-\frac{AB}{BD}\right)$$

$$= DQ + OQ\left(-\frac{AB}{OQ}\right)$$

$$= DQ - AB$$

$$QE = DQ - DE$$

Thus,

$$DQ - DE = DQ - AB$$
$$DE = AB = BF$$
$$AF = 2AB$$

3.8 Other illustrations

(i) Constant elasticity curves

The *constant elasticity curve* that A. Marshall* has in the mathematical appendix to his *Principles* is given by

$$qp^n = C$$

where C and n are constants. The theorem is that this curve has an elasticity of n. Let us work this out as follows.

$$q = Cp^{-n}$$

$$\frac{dq}{dp} = (-n)Cp^{-n-1}$$

$$\therefore \quad \eta = -\frac{p}{q}\frac{dq}{dp} = -\frac{p}{Cp^{-n}}(-n)Cp^{-n-1} = n$$

Thus, when, for example, $n = 1$, then

$$pq = C$$

and these demand curves (called *constant outlay curves*) are of unit elasticity throughout.

(ii) Elasticity of curves expressed in terms of logarithms

Let the demand curve be

$$q = f(p)$$

Then, by using the derivatives of logarithms,

$$\frac{d \ln q}{dp} = \frac{d \ln q}{dq}\frac{dq}{dp} = \frac{1}{q}\frac{dq}{dp}$$

Also,

$$\frac{d \ln p}{dp} = \frac{1}{p}$$

* See A. Marshall (1920), mathematical appendix.

Thus, the elasticity of the demand curve is

$$\eta = -\frac{\dfrac{d \ln q}{dp}}{\dfrac{d \ln p}{dp}} = -\frac{d(\ln q)}{d(\ln p)}$$

*(iii) Taxation problem**

Let y be income, u be total utility, and T be the amount of tax paid. Then

$$u(y) - u(y - T) = \text{constant for all } y$$

is the required condition for equal absolute sacrifice. Differentiate with respect to y. Then

$$\frac{du(y)}{dy} - \frac{du(y - T)}{dy} = 0$$

$$u'(y) - u'(y - T)\left(1 - \frac{dT}{dy}\right) = 0$$

$$1 - \frac{dT}{dy} = \frac{u'(y)}{u'(y - T)}$$

$$\frac{dT}{dy} = \frac{u'(y - T) - u'(y)}{u'(y - T)}$$

u' is the marginal utility of income, dT/dy is the change in T with respect to y that is necessary to keep equal absolute sacrifice.

Notes and References

For proofs and derivations of the various topics that have been explained heuristically, see the following references. The number of references has been limited to a few books.

3.1 Courant and Robbins (1941), pp. 414–436; Courant (Vol. I, 1937), pp. 88–109; Titchmarsh (1959), Chapter 13; Ayres (1964), Chapters 4, 5, 6.

It is customary in calculus texts to discuss the mean value theorem in order to show a relationship between the derivative and the difference quotient. It is called the *mean value theorem of differential calculus*. There is also a mean value theorem of integral calculus. We have omitted discussion of both these topics. Those interested are referred to Courant (Vol. I, 1937), p. 102 and 126.

* See Musgrave (1959), p. 100.

3.2 Allen (1938), Chapter 7; Tintner (1953), Chapter 10; Ayres (1964), Chapters 4, 5, 6.

3.3 Sokolnikoff (1939), pp. 43–45. Ayres (1964), Chapter 23.

3.4 Allen (1938), Chapters 9 and 10; Courant and Robbins (1941), pp. 442–451; Tintner (1953), Chapter 11; Titchmarsh (1959), Chapter 7; Ayres (1964), Chapter 14.

3.5 Same as 3.4.

3.6–3.7 Economic examples have been given, but with the limited amount of mathematics at our disposal, not much can be done. Instead of spending time trying to find applications at this point, it will be more economical if the student devotes himself to covering the material in the next two chapters first, since most applications use a combination of these various mathematical techniques.

Allen, R. G. D., *Mathematical Analysis for Economists*. New York: The Macmillan Company, 1938.

Ayres, F., Jr., *Calculus*, 2nd ed. New York: Schaum Publishing Co., 1964.

Kleppner, D. and Ramsey, N., *Quick Calculus, A Short Manual of Self Instruction*, New York: John Wiley and Sons, Inc., 1965.

Marshall, A., *Principles of Economics*, 8th ed. New York: The Macmillan Company, 1920.

Musgrave, R. A., *The Theory of Public Finance*. New York: McGraw-Hill Book Co., 1959.

Protter, M. H. and Morrey, C. B. Jr., *Modern Mathematical Analysis*. Massachusetts: Addison-Wesley Publishing Co., 1964.

Tintner, G., *Mathematics and Statistics for Economists*. New York: Rinehart & Co., Inc., (now Holt, Rinehart & Winston, Inc.), 1953. (This has many applied economic illustrations.)

Titchmarsh, E. C., *Mathematics for the General Reader*. New York: Doubleday & Co., Inc., 1959. (This is a paperback book written by an eminent mathematician for the general reader.)

CHAPTER 4

Functions of Several Variables

4.1 Functions of two variables

A function of one variable $y = f(x)$ was considered a mapping from one space S_1 (domain) into another space S_2 (range). We dealt with a Cartesian graph and had let S_1 be the horizontal axis and S_2 be the vertical axis. The function (rule) is shown by the curve we have drawn in Figure 4–1.

If we let S_1 be a two-dimensional Cartesian space, we have a plane as shown in Figure 4–2. Each point on this plane is an ordered pair and is mapped into the u-axis. The function (rule) that does this is now shown by the surface

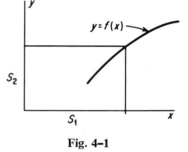

Fig. 4–1

$$u = f(x, y)$$

For example, let x be labor, y be land, and u be the wheat that is produced. The various ordered pairs of x and y on the x-y plane show the various

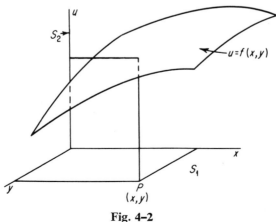

Fig. 4–2

combinations of labor and land. Let P be a point on this plane. Then, the $u = f(x, y)$ surface maps this point into the u-axis and shows how much wheat will be produced by this combination of x and y. This surface may be called the total product *surface* (in contrast to the total product *curve* for the two-dimensional space).

Another example would be one in which x is meat, y is bread, and u is utility. Then $u = f(x, y)$ is a utility surface, which shows how the various x, y combinations map into the utility axis.

When we set $y = y_0 = c$, i.e., equal to some constant, the diagram will be as shown in Figure 4–3 (a and b). We have set up a plane going through

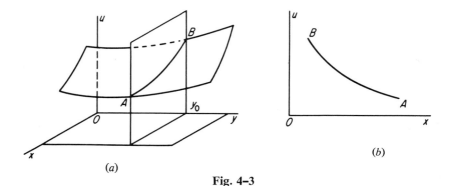

(a)

(b)

Fig. 4–3

$y = c$ and as a result have obtained a curve AB which is the intersection of this plane and the surface as shown in the two-dimensional diagram in Figure 4–3(b). This curve is the diagram of the function

$$u = f(x, c)$$

which maps the points along the line y_0 on the x-y plane into the u-axis.

The domain S_1 is sometimes called the *region*, and the points within it are called the *argument points*, or, simply, the *argument*. Figure 4–4 shows

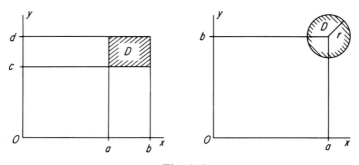

Fig. 4–4

two types of regions (domains), a rectangular region and a circular region. The rectangular region may be expressed as

$$a \leq x \leq b, \qquad c \leq y \leq d$$

and the circular region as

$$(x - a)^2 + (y - b)^2 \leq r^2$$

4.2 Partial derivatives

Assume x is labor, y is land, and u is wheat. Then, we have the functional relationship

$$u = f(x, y)$$

What will be the change in u (wheat) when there is a small change in the amount of x (labor) holding y (land) constant? What we are doing is letting $y = y_0 = c$. Then,

$$u = f(x, y_0) = f(x, c)$$

Since $y = y_0 = $ constant, u will become a function of x only. We know how to find the derivative in this case. It will be

$$\lim_{\Delta x \to 0} \frac{f(x + \Delta x, y_0) - f(x, y_0)}{(x + \Delta x) - x}$$

This derivative is denoted by

$$\frac{\partial u}{\partial x} \qquad \text{or} \qquad \frac{\partial f}{\partial x} \qquad \text{or} \qquad f_x$$

We use the letter ∂ (delta) rather than d to show that the other variables in the function have been held constant. This derivative is called the *partial derivative* of $f(x, y)$ with respect to x (labor).

Thus, the technique of differentiation to obtain the derivative with respect to one variable is, after holding the other variables constant, the same as for a single variable.

Example 1. Let us assume the u (wheat) is related to x (labor) and y (land) by

$$u = x^2 + 4xy + y^2$$

What will be the change in u (wheat) when there is a small unit change in x (labor) holding y(land) constant? For that we find the partial derivative of u with respect to x

$$\frac{\partial u}{\partial x} = 2x + 4y$$

Higher partial derivatives are obtained in the same manner as higher derivatives. For example,

$$u = x^2 + 4xy + y^2$$

$$\frac{\partial u}{\partial x} = f_x = 2x + 4y$$

$$\frac{\partial}{\partial x}\left(\frac{\partial u}{\partial x}\right) = \frac{\partial^2 u}{\partial x^2} = f_{xx} = 2$$

$$\frac{\partial}{\partial y}\left(\frac{\partial u}{\partial x}\right) = \frac{\partial^2 u}{\partial y\, \partial x} = f_{xy} = 4$$

Note that f_{xy} means that the function has been differentiated with respect to x first and then with respect to y. That is, the subscript is read from left to right. But for

$$\frac{\partial}{\partial y}\left(\frac{\partial u}{\partial x}\right) = \frac{\partial^2 u}{\partial y\, \partial x}$$

the order of finding partial derivatives is from right to left, i.e., x first and y second. Hence we read the order of differentiation from right to left. The notation extends in similar fashion to other cases.

Change of order of differentiation. In general

$$f_{xy} = f_{yx}$$

i.e., we can differentiate either with x or y first and it will make no difference when f_{xy} and f_{yx} are continuous in a region. In our example above, we have found $f_{xy} = 4$. For f_{yx}, we get

$$f_y = 4x + 2y$$
$$f_{yx} = 4$$

and

$$f_{xy} = f_{yx} = 4$$

Example 1.

$$u = 3x^3y - 5xy^4$$
$$f_x = 9x^2y - 5y^4$$
$$f_{xy} = 9x^2 - 20y^3$$
$$f_y = 3x^3 - 20xy^3$$
$$f_{yx} = 9x^2 - 20y^3$$
$$f_{xy} = f_{yx} = 9x^2 - 20y^3$$

This result may be summarized in a theorem which we state without proof.

Theorem. Assume that $f(x, y), f_x, f_y, f_{xy},$ and f_{yx} are all continuous at the point (x, y). Then

$$f_{xy} = f_{yx}$$

Example 2. An example of this theorem's use in economics is as follows: Let

$$u = q_1^2 q_2 + 3q_1 q_2^2$$

be a utility function, where u is utility and q_1 and q_2 are goods. Then

$$f_1 = 2q_1 q_2 + 3q_2^2$$

is the marginal utility of q_1.

$$f_{12} = 2q_1 + 6q_2$$

is the change in f_1 with respect to a small increment of q_2. Calculations will show that

$$f_{21} = 2q_1 + 6q_2$$

and we find

$$f_{12} = f_{21}$$

This means that the rate of change of f_1 (marginal utility of q_1) with respect to q_2 is equal to the rate of change of f_2 with respect to q_1. This result will be used later when deriving second-order conditions for utility functions.

Another result is that the order of partial differentiation is immaterial when differentiation is repeated more than two times, provided the partial derivatives are continuous in the region. For example, from Example 1 we find

$$f_{xyy} = \frac{\partial}{\partial y}(9x^2 - 20y^3) = -60y^2$$

$$f_{yxy} = \frac{\partial}{\partial y}(9x^2 - 20y^3) = -60y^2$$

$$f_y = 3x^3 - 20xy^3$$

$$f_{yy} = -60xy^2$$

$$f_{yyx} = -60y^2$$

$$\therefore \quad f_{xyy} = f_{yxy} = f_{yyx} = -60y^2$$

As an exercise, using Example 1, check that $f_{xxy} = f_{xyx} = f_{yxx}$.

4.3 Geometrical presentation of partial derivatives

Let the function be $u = f(x, y)$. Then the partial derivative of $f(x, y)$

with respect to x at the point (x_0, y_0) is

$$\lim_{\Delta x \to 0} \frac{f(x_0 + \Delta x, y_0) - f(x_0, y_0)}{(x_0 + \Delta x) - x_0} = \frac{\partial f}{\partial x}$$

$$= \lim_{\Delta x \to 0} \frac{(u + \Delta u) - u}{(x_0 + \Delta x) - x} = \lim_{\Delta x \to 0} \frac{\Delta u}{\Delta x}$$

Here we have set $y_0 = c$ (a constant). Geometrically we have a plane M that is parallel to the u-x plane (Figure 4-5). The point S is (x_0, y_0). The

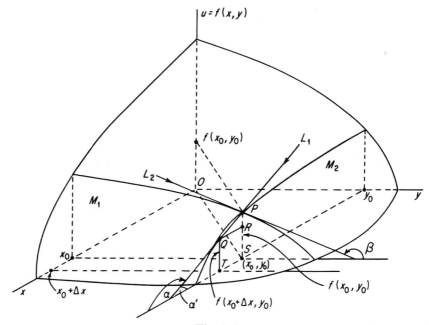

Fig. 4–5

point T is $(x_0 + \Delta x, y_0)$. Thus the limiting process can be shown as

$$\lim_{T \to S} \frac{TQ - SP}{TS} = \lim_{T \to S} \frac{-PR}{QR}$$

$$= -\tan \alpha' = \tan(180 - \alpha') = \tan \alpha$$

$$\therefore \quad f_x = \tan \alpha$$

The partial derivative of $f(x, y)$ with respect to y at the point (x_0, y_0) is shown in a similar way

$$f_y = \tan \beta$$

This geometrical presentation shows clearly that the partial derivatives of $f(x, y)$ at the point (x_0, y_0) are restricted in their direction. It was shown that $f_x = \tan \alpha$, where the direction was parallel to the x-axis. Similarly, f_y gives a direction parallel to the y-axis.

Problems

1. Find the partial derivatives f_x and f_y of the following functions.

(a) $u = 2x^2 + 3y^2$ (b) $u = x^3 + y^4$

(c) $u = x^2 + xy + y^2$ (d) $u = x^2y + xy^2$

(e) $u = 3x^2y^2 + y^2$ (f) $u = \dfrac{x^2}{y^2}$

(g) $u = \dfrac{x^2}{y^3} + \dfrac{y^2}{x^3}$ (h) $u = 3x^2 + \dfrac{x}{y}$

2. Find the partial derivatives $f_{xx}, f_{yy}, f_{yx}, f_{xy}$ of problem 1 above.

4.4 Differentials, total differential

From a practical point of view, the partial derivatives gave us a small change in $u = f(x, y)$ when there was a small unit change in x holding y constant, or vice versa. The total differential we are to discuss will give us a linear approximation of the small change in $u = f(x, y)$ when there is a small change in both x and y.

For example, let u be wheat, x be labor, and y be land. We set $u = f(x, y)$. Then, when there is a small change in x (labor) and in y (land), how much of a change will there be in u (wheat)? We have seen from our discussion of partial derivatives that $\partial u/\partial x$ will be the small change in u when there is a small unit change in x holding y constant. Thus, if x should change by Δx, then the change in u will be $(\partial u/\partial x) \Delta x$. Similarly, when there is a change in y (land) by Δy, then the change in u will be $(\partial u/\partial y) \Delta y$.

Therefore, as a first approximation we can think that the change in u due to a small change in x and y will be

$$\Delta u = \frac{\partial u}{\partial x} \Delta x + \frac{\partial u}{\partial y} \Delta y$$

Let us write $du = \Delta u$, $dx = \Delta x$, and $dy = \Delta y$. Then,

$$du = \frac{\partial u}{\partial x} dx + \frac{\partial u}{\partial y} dy$$

Or, in abbreviated form, we write

$$du = f_x \, dx + f_y \, dy$$

This is a generalization of the differential we discussed previously for $y = f(x)$, which was

$$dy = f_x \, dx$$

The du obtained above is called the *total differential* of the function $u = f(x, y)$. Instead of the symbol du, the notation df is also used.

If we have $u = f(x, y, z)$, where x is labor, y is land, and z is fertilizer, then the change in u (wheat) when there is a small change in x, y, and z will be

$$du = f_x \, dx + f_y \, dy + f_z \, dz$$

and similarly for any number of variables. This total differential is a linear approximation to the true amount of change just as in the previous case with one variable.*

As we have pointed out in Section 3.3, when x and y are independent variables, the Δx and Δy are *arbitrary* increments and may be treated as constants.

Example 1.

$$u = f(x, y) = 4x^2 + 3y^2$$

The total differential is

$$du = f_x \, dx + f_y \, dy$$

$$f_x = \frac{\partial u}{\partial x} = \frac{\partial}{\partial x}(4x^2 + 3y^2) = 8x$$

$$f_y = \frac{\partial u}{\partial y} = \frac{\partial}{\partial y}(4x^2 + 3y^2) = 6y$$

Thus,

$$du = 8x \, dx + 6y \, dy$$

Example 2. Let u be utility and x and y be goods. Then the utility function is

$$u = f(x, y)$$

When there is a small change in x and y, the corresponding change in utility is

$$du = f_x \, dx + f_y \, dy$$

where $f_x = \partial u/\partial x$ is the marginal utility with respect to good x, and $f_y = \partial u/\partial y$ is the marginal utility with respect to good y.

---

* See Courant (Vol. II, 1936), pp. 59, 68, for proof.

Example 3. Let P be the product and a and b be inputs. Then, the production function is

$$P = f(a, b)$$

A small change in a and b will bring about a small change in P that is

$$dP = f_a \, da + f_b \, db$$

where

$$f_a = \frac{\partial P}{\partial a} \qquad \text{marginal product of } a$$

$$f_b = \frac{\partial P}{\partial b} \qquad \text{marginal product of } b$$

Rules of differentiation

The rules of differentiation for differentials are exactly the same as those for derivatives. Let $g = g(x, y)$ and $h = h(x, y)$ be functions of x and y. Then we have the following rules.

RULE 1. *Differentiation of a sum.*

$$u = g + h$$
$$du = dg + dh$$

Example 1.

$$u = 3x^2 + 2y^3$$
$$du = d(3x^2) + d(2y^3)$$
$$= 6x \, dx + 6y^2 \, dy$$

Example 2. The rule for the sum may be derived by using the basic formula, as follows.

$$u = g + h$$

$$du = \frac{\partial}{\partial x}(g + h) \, dx + \frac{\partial}{\partial y}(g + h) \, dy$$

$$= \frac{\partial}{\partial x}(g) \, dx + \frac{\partial}{\partial x}(h) \, dx + \frac{\partial}{\partial y}(g) \, dy + \frac{\partial}{\partial y}(h) \, dy$$

$$= \left(\frac{\partial}{\partial x} g \, dx + \frac{\partial}{\partial y} g \, dy\right) + \left(\frac{\partial}{\partial x} h \, dx + \frac{\partial}{\partial y} h \, dy\right)$$

$$= dg + dh$$

RULE 2. *Differentiation of a product.*

$$u = gh$$
$$du = g\, dh + h\, dg$$

Example 1.

$$u = (2x^2 + y)(x + 2y^2)$$
$$du = (2x^2 + y)\, d(x + 2y^2) + (x + 2y^2)\, d(2x^2 + y)$$
$$= (2x^2 + y)\, [dx + d(2y^2)]$$
$$+ (x + 2y^2)\, [d(2x^2) + dy]$$
$$= (2x^2 + y)\, (dx + 4y\, dy)$$
$$+ (x + 2y^2)\, (4x\, dx + dy)$$
$$= (6x^2 + 8xy^2 + y)\, dx + (8x^2y + x + 6y^2)\, dy$$

Example 2. This product rule may also very easily be derived from the basic formula. Perform this derivation as an exercise.

Example 3. Let x and y be the two sides of a rectangle. Then the area will be $u = xy$. If x and y are increased by Δx and Δy, the increase in the area will be

$$(u + \Delta u) - u = (x + \Delta x)(y + \Delta y) - xy$$
$$\therefore \quad \Delta u = x\, (\Delta y) + (\Delta x)\, y + (\Delta x)(\Delta y)$$

Thus, if Δx and Δy are very small, we may omit $(\Delta x)\, (\Delta y)$ so that

$$\Delta u = x\, (\Delta y) + (\Delta x)\, y$$

In terms of the total differential formula, we have

$$du = f_x\, dx + f_y\, dy$$

$$f_x = \frac{\partial f}{\partial x} = \frac{\partial}{\partial x}(xy) = y$$

$$f_y = x$$

$$\therefore \quad du = y\, dx + x\, dy$$

	Δx	
Δy	$x\,\Delta y$	$\Delta x\,\Delta y$
y	$u = xy$ x	$y\,\Delta x$

Thus, du gives an approximation of the increase of the area if dx and dy show the small increases of x and y.

RULE 3. *Differentiation of a quotient.*

$$u = \frac{g}{h}$$

$$du = d\left(\frac{g}{h}\right) = \frac{h\, dg - g\, dh}{h^2}$$

Example 1.

$$u = \frac{x^2 + y^2}{x + y}$$

$$du = \frac{(x + y)\, d(x^2 + y^2) - (x^2 + y^2)\, d(x + y)}{(x + y)^2}$$

Numerator $= (x + y)(2x\, dx + 2y\, dy) - (x^2 + y^2)(dx + dy)$

$$= (x^2 - y^2 + 2xy)\, dx + (-x^2 + y^2 + 2xy)\, dy$$

$$\therefore \quad du = \frac{(x^2 - y^2 + 2xy)\, dx - (x^2 - y^2 - 2xy)\, dy}{(x + y)^2}$$

RULE 4. *The chain rule.*

$$z = z(u)$$
$$u = u(x)$$

Then the differential of z is

$$dz = d(z(u)) = \frac{d}{du}\,(z)\, du$$

But note that du is not an arbitrary increment of u but a differential of u, and we find

$$du = d(u(x)) = \frac{d}{dx}\,(u)\, dx$$

Hence

$$dz = \left[\frac{d}{du}\,(z)\right]\left[\frac{d}{dx}\,(u)\, dx\right]$$

Example 1.

$$z = u^2 + 1$$
$$u = x^2 + 2$$

$$dz = \left[\frac{d}{du}\,(u^2 + 1)\right]\left[\frac{d}{dx}\,(x^2 + 2)\, dx\right]$$

$$= (2u)(2x)\, dx$$

$$= 4(x^2 + 2)x\, dx$$

Example 2.

$$z = u^2 + 1$$
$$u = x^2 + y^2$$
$$dz = f'(u)\, du = 2u\, du$$

But

$$du = d(x^2 + y^2) = 2x\, dx + 2y\, dy$$

Hence

$$dz = 2u(2x\ dx + 2y\ dy)$$
$$= 2(x^2 + y^2)(2x\ dx + 2y\ dy)$$
$$= 4(x^3 + xy^2)\ dx + 4(x^2y + y^3)\ dy$$

Example 3.

$$z = (x^2 + y^2)^{1/2}$$

Let

$$u = x^2 + y^2$$

Then

$$z = u^{1/2}$$
$$dz = f'(u)\ du = \tfrac{1}{2}u^{-1/2}\ du$$
$$du = 2x\ dx + 2y\ dy$$
$$dz = \tfrac{1}{2}(x^2 + y^2)^{-1/2}(2x\ dx + 2y\ dy)$$

Example 4.

$$z = \frac{1}{\sqrt{x^2 - y^2}}$$

Let

$$u = x^2 - y^2$$

$$z = \frac{1}{\sqrt{u}} = u^{-1/2}$$

$$dz = f'(u)\ du = -\tfrac{1}{2}u^{-3/2}\ du$$
$$du = 2x\ dx - 2y\ dy$$
$$dz = -\tfrac{1}{2}(x^2 - y^2)^{-3/2}(2x\ dx - 2y\ dy)$$

RULE 5. *Differential of* $y = e^x$.

$$dy = d(e^x) = \frac{d}{dx}\ (e^x)\ dx = e^x\ dx$$

Example 1.

$$y = e^{x^2+1}$$

$$dy = d(e^{x^2+1}) = \frac{d}{du}\ (e^u)\frac{du}{dx}\ dx$$

$$= e^u \frac{d}{dx}\ (x^2 + 1)\ dx$$

$$= 2xe^{x^2+1}\ dx$$

Example 2.

$$z = e^{x^2+y^2} = e^u$$

$$dz = \frac{d}{du} e^u \, du = e^u \, du$$

$$du = d(x^2 + y^2) = 2x \, dx + 2y \, dy$$

$$dz = e^{x^2+y^2}(2x \, dx + 2y \, dy) = 2xe^{x^2+y^2} \, dx + 2ye^{x^2+y^2} \, dy$$

RULE 6. *Differentiation of* $y = \log x$.

$$dy = d(\log x) = \left(\frac{d}{dx} \log x\right) dx = \frac{1}{x} dx$$

When $y = \log u$, where $u = f(x)$, we may apply rule 4 and find

$$dy = \left(\frac{d}{du} \log u\right)\left(\frac{d}{dx} u\right) dx$$

$$= \frac{1}{u} f'(x) \, dx$$

Example 1.

$$y = \log (x^2 + 1)$$

Let $u = x^2 + 1$. Then

$$dy = d(\log u) = \left[\frac{d}{du} \log u\right]\left[\frac{d}{dx} (x^2 + 1)\right] dx$$

$$= \left(\frac{1}{u}\right)(2x) \, dx = \frac{2x}{x^2 + 1} \, dx$$

Example 2.

$$z = \log (x^2 + y^2)$$

Let $u = x^2 + y^2$. Then

$$dz = \left(\frac{d}{du} \log u\right) du = \frac{1}{u} du$$

The du is the differential of u. Hence

$$du = d(x^2 + y^2) = 2x \, dx + 2y \, dy$$

Thus

$$dz = \frac{1}{u} du = \frac{1}{x^2 + y^2} (2x \, dx + 2y \, dy)$$

$$= \frac{2x}{x^2 + y^2} dx + \frac{2y}{x^2 + y^2} dy$$

Problems

1. Find the total differential of the following functions.

(a) $u = 4x^3 + 2y^2$

(b) $u = x^2 - 3y$
(c) $u = 2x^2y^3$
(d) $u = x^2y^3 + x^3y^2$
(e) $u = (x^2 + y)(2x - y^2)$

(f) $u = \dfrac{x}{x^2 + y^2}$

(g) $u = \dfrac{x^2 - y^2}{x^2 + y^2}$

(h) $z = 2u^2 - u$
    $u = 3x + x^2$
(i) $z = 1 - u^2$
    $u = 2x^2 - 2y^2$
(j) $z = 2u^{1/2}$
    $u = 3x^2 + y^2$
(k) $z = (3x^2 + y^2)^{1/2}$
(l) $z = (x^2y + xy^2)^{-1/2}$
(m) $y = e^{x^2-1}$
(n) $y = me^{(x-a)/\sigma^2}$
(o) $y = \log (x^2 - 2y)$
(p) $y = \log \sqrt{x^2 + 1}$

2. Given a utility function

$$u = f(q_1, q_2)$$

where u is utility and q_1 and q_2 are commodities, find du.

3. Given a production function

$$q = f(x_1, x_2)$$

where q is output and x_1 and x_2 are inputs, find dq.

4. Given a production function

$$P = kL^\alpha C^\beta$$

where P is product, L is labor, C is capital, and k, α, and β are constants, find dP.

5. Given the production function

$$V = (\beta K^{-\rho} + \alpha L^{-\rho})^{-1/\rho}$$

where V is output (value added), K is capital, L is labor, and α, β, and ρ are constants, find dV.

6. Given the production function

$$V = \gamma[\delta K^{-\rho} + (1 - \delta)L^{-\rho})^{-1/\rho}$$

where V is output, K is capital, L is labor, and γ, δ, and ρ are constants, find dV.

7. (a) Let $u = xy$. If x were to increase from 2.00 to 2.01 and y were to increase from 3.00 to 3.01, give an approximation of the increase in u. Draw a diagram and explain.

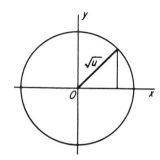

(b) Let $u = x^2 + y^2$. This is an equation for a circle with radius $\sqrt{u}$ as shown in the accompanying figure. Let x increase from 2.00 to 2.01, and let y increase from 3.00 to 3.01. What will be the approximate increase in the radius?

4.5 Second and higher-order differentials

The one-variable case of higher-order differentials were considered in Section 3.3. We found, given a function

$$y = f(x)$$

where x is an independent variable, that the nth-order differential was

$$d^n y = f^{(n)}(x)\,(dx)^n$$

We may now, with the use of partial derivatives, extend this result to 2 or more independent variables. We shall first consider cases where the variables are independent variables and then cases where they are dependent variables.

The second- and higher-order differentials are frequently used in economics in minimizing and maximizing problems, as we shall see in Chapters 5 and 11. Let us start our discussion with the 2-variable case.

(*i*) *Two-variable case—independent variables*

Suppose we have a function

(1) $u = f(x, y)$

where x and y are independent variables. Then the first-order differential du, which is also written as df, is

(2) $df = f_x\,dx + f_y\,dy$

as we have already obtained in the previous section.

The second-order differential is obtained by finding the differential of df, which is

$$d^2f = d(df) = \frac{\partial}{\partial x}(df)\,dx + \frac{\partial}{\partial y}(df)\,dy$$

$$= \frac{\partial}{\partial x} (f_x \, dx + f_y \, dy) \, dx + \frac{\partial}{\partial y} (f_x \, dx + f_y \, dy) \, dy$$

$$= \left[f_{xx} \, dx + f_x \frac{\partial}{\partial x} \, dx + f_{xy} \, dy + f_y \frac{\partial}{\partial x} (dy) \right] dx$$

$$+ \left[f_{xy} \, dx + f_x \frac{\partial}{\partial y} (dx) + f_{yy} \, dy + f_y \frac{\partial}{\partial y} (dy) \right] dy$$

But, since dx and dy are considered constants,

$$\frac{\partial}{\partial x} (dx) = 0, \quad \frac{\partial}{\partial x} (dy) = 0, \quad \frac{\partial}{\partial y} (dx) = 0, \quad \frac{\partial}{\partial y} (dy) = 0$$

Thus,

$$d^2f = (f_{xx} \, dx + f_{xy} \, dy) \, dx + (f_{xy} \, dx + f_{yy} \, dy) \, dy$$
$$= f_{xx} \, dx^2 + 2f_{xy} \, dx \, dy + f_{yy} \, dy^2$$

We notice that the form of the equation is similar to $(a + b)^2 = a^2 + 2ab + b^2$. Thus, using symbolic notation we can set

$$d^2f = (f_x \, dx + f_y \, dy)^2$$

with the understanding that this expands into the above form.

It turns out that, in general,

$$d^nf = (f_x \, dx + f_y \, dy)^n$$

For example,

$$d^3f = (f_x \, dx + f_y \, dy)^3$$
$$= f_{xxx} \, dx^3 + 3f_{xxy} \, dx^2 \, dy + 3f_{xyy} \, dx \, dy^2 + f_{yyy} \, dy^3$$

For most applications, we shall use the second-order differential. Noticing the symmetry between the x and y, we can write this as

$$d^2f = f_{xx} \, dx^2 + f_{xy} \, dx \, dy$$
$$+ f_{yx} \, dy \, dx + f_{yy} \, dy^2$$

This notation is also used when we have three or more variables, as we shall see in Section (ii). We shall also discuss this form of equation (a quadratic form) when we get to vectors and matrices.

Alternative derivation. The technique we have used above is to use repeatedly the basic formula for differentials to obtain the second-order differential. Let us now derive these results by an alternative procedure using the rules of differentiation. This alternative procedure will be easier to use, especially when the number of variables increases.

The first-order differential was

$$df = f_x \, dx + f_y \, dy$$

Then the second-order differential is

(3) $$d^2f = d(df) = d(f_x\,dx + f_y\,dy)$$

Using the rule for differentiating a sum, we find

(4) $$d^2f = d(f_x\,dx) + d(f_y\,dy)$$

Since x and y are independent variables, the dx and dy may be considered constants. Also note carefully that the partial derivatives

$$f_x = \frac{\partial}{\partial x} f(x, y) \quad \text{and} \quad f_y = \frac{\partial}{\partial y} f(x, y)$$

are functions of x and y. Keeping these points in mind, let us consider the first term on the right-hand side. We have

$$d(f_x\,dx) = d(f_x)\,dx$$

$$= \left(\frac{\partial}{\partial x} f_x\,dx + \frac{\partial}{\partial y} f_x\,dy\right) dx$$

$$= (f_{xx}\,dx + f_{xy}\,dy)\,dx$$

In similar fashion the second term becomes

$$d(f_y\,dy) = d(f_y)\,dy$$

$$= \left(\frac{\partial}{\partial x} f_y\,dx + \frac{\partial}{\partial y} f_y\,dy\right) dy$$

$$= (f_{xy}\,dx + f_{yy}\,dy)\,dy$$

Substituting these results in (4) gives us

$$d^2f = (f_{xx}\,dx + f_{xy}\,dy)\,dx + (f_{xy}\,dx + f_{yy}\,dy)\,dx$$
$$= f_{xx}\,dx^2 + f_{yy}\,dy^2 + 2f_{xy}\,dx\,dy$$

Example 1. Given the following function, find the second-order differential

$$u = x^2 + xy$$

$$du = f_x\,dx + f_y\,dy$$

$$d^2u = f_{xx}(dx)^2 + f_{yy}(dy)^2 + 2f_{xy}\,dx\,dy$$

$$f_x = \frac{\partial}{\partial x}(x^2 + xy) = 2x + y$$

$$f_y = \frac{\partial}{\partial y}(x^2 + xy) = x$$

$$f_{xx} = \frac{\partial}{\partial x}(2x + y) = 2$$

$$f_{xy} = \frac{\partial}{\partial x}(fy) = \frac{\partial}{\partial x}(x) = 1$$

$$f_{yx} = \frac{\partial}{\partial y}(fx) = \frac{\partial}{\partial y}(2x + y) = 1$$

$$f_{yy} = \frac{\partial}{\partial y}(x) = 0$$

Thus, we get

$$du = (2x + y)\, dx + x\, dy$$
$$d^2u = 2(dx)^2 + 0(dy)^2 + 2(1)\, dx\, dy$$
$$= 2(dx)^2 + 2dx\, dy$$

(*ii*) *Three or more variable case.*

When we have a function with three variables, $u = f(x, y, z)$, then,

$$df = du = f_x\, dx + f_y\, dy + f_z\, dz$$

By a process similar to that in section (i) we find

$$d^2f = (f_x\, dx + f_y\, dy + f_z\, dz)^2$$
$$= f_{xx}\, dx^2 + f_{xy}\, dx\, dy + f_{xz}\, dx\, dz$$
$$+ f_{yx}\, dy\, dx + f_{yy}\, dy^2 + f_{yz}\, dy\, dz$$
$$+ f_{zx}\, dz\, dx + f_{zy}\, dz\, dy + f_{zz}\, dz^2$$

In general,

$$d^nf = (f_x\, dx + f_y\, dy + f_z\, dz)^n$$

and, when $u = f(x, y, z, \ldots)$ we have

$$df = du = f_x\, dx + f_y\, dy + f_z\, dz + \ldots$$

For the second-order differentials, we may write

$$d^2f = (f_x\, dx + f_y\, dy + f_z\, dz + \ldots)^2$$
$$= f_{xx}\, dx^2 + f_{xy}\, dx\, dy + f_{zz}\, dx\, dz + \ldots$$
$$+ f_{yx}\, dy\, dx + f_{yy}\, dy^2 + f_{yz}\, dy\, dz + \ldots$$
$$+ d_{zy}\, dz\, dx + f_{zy}\, dz\, dy + f_{zz}\, dz^2 + \ldots$$
$$+ \ldots$$

and, for higher-order differentials,

$$d^nf = (f_x\, dx + f_y\, dy + f_z\, dz + \ldots)^n$$

(iii) One-variable case—dependent variables

The one-variable case with an independent variable was considered in Section (*i*), and we found that, when given a function

$$y = f(x)$$

the *n*th-order differential was

$$d^n y = f^{(n)}(x)\,(dx)^n$$

where x is the independent variable. In this section let us consider

(1) $$y = f(u)$$

(2) $$u = F(x)$$

where u is a function of x and hence is not an independent variable. Then

$$dy = d(f(u)) = f'(u)\,du$$

and du is not an independent variable. Hence, when we take the second-order differential of y, we get

$$
\begin{aligned}
d^2 y &= d(dy) = d[f'(u)\,du] \\
&= f'(u)\,d(du) + du\,d[f'(u)] \\
&= f'(u)\,d^2u + du\,f''(u)\,du \\
&= f'(u)\,d^2u + f''(u)\,(du)^2
\end{aligned}
$$

where d^2u is the second-order differential of u and by using (2) may be shown as

$$d^2u = F''(x)\,(dx)^2$$

Note that, when u is an independent variable and does not depend on x, du becomes an arbitrary increment (i.e., a constant), and hence $d^2u = 0$. Then d^2y becomes

$$d^2 y = f''(u)\,(du)^2$$

which is in accordance with our previous results.

Let us now extend this dependent-variable process to a two-variable case.

Example 1. Find d^2y

$$y = u + u^2$$

$$u = x^2 + 1$$

$$dy = f'(u)\,du$$

$$dy = f'(u)\,d^2u + f''(u)\,(du)^2$$

$$f'(u) = \frac{\partial}{\partial u}(u + u^2) = 1 + 2u$$

$$f''(u) = \frac{\partial}{\partial u}(1 + 2u) = 2$$

$$du = \frac{\partial}{\partial x}(x^2 + 1)\,dx = 2x\,dx$$

$$d^2u = \frac{\partial}{\partial x}(2x\,dx)\,dx = 2(dx)^2$$

$$\therefore \quad d^2y = (1 + 2u)\,2(dx)^2 + 2(2x\,dx)^2$$
$$= (1 + 2x^2 + 2)\,2(dx)^2 + 8x^2\,(dx)^2$$
$$= (12x^2 + 6)(dx)^2$$

Example 2.

$$y = (x^2 + 1)^{1/2}$$
$$u = x^2 + 1$$
$$y = u^{1/2}$$
$$dy = f'(u)\,du$$
$$d^2y = f'(u)\,d^2u + f''(u)\,(du)^2$$
$$f'(u) = \frac{\partial}{\partial u}(u^{1/2}) = \tfrac{1}{2}u^{-1/2}$$
$$f''(u) = (\tfrac{1}{2})(-\tfrac{1}{2})u^{-3/2}$$
$$= -\tfrac{1}{4}u^{-3/2}$$
$$du = 2x\,dx$$
$$d^2u = 2(dx)^2$$
$$\therefore \quad d^2y = \tfrac{1}{2}u^{-1/2}\,2(dx)^2 + (-\tfrac{1}{4}u^{-3/2})(2x\,dx)^2$$
$$= (u^{-1/2} - u^{-3/2}x^2)\,(dx)^2$$
$$= \frac{1}{\sqrt{(x^2 + 1)^3}}\,(dx)^2$$

(iv) Two-variable case—dependent variables

In many economic problems the variables x and y of a function

(1) $$u = f(x, y)$$

are not independent. For example, assume that (1) is a utility function, where x and y are commodities and we have in addition a budget equation

(2) $$M = p_x x + p_y y$$

where M is income and p_x and p_y are prices of x and y, respectively. Then x and y are related by equation (2) and are not independent. As we shall see in Chapter 5, a frequent problem in economics is to find the conditions that will maximize u (utility) and one of the conditions that we need to meet for this is that $d^2u < 0$. That is, the second-order differential of u needs to be negative. (We shall consider the meaning of this in Chapter 5.) Our concern here is: What is d^2u when x and y are not independent?

By using the rules of differentiation, this may easily be solved. For the first-order differential we have

(3) $$du = f_x\, dx + f_y\, dy$$

which is the same as when x and y were independent. It turns out, as we shall explain on page 137, that equation (3) *holds whether or not x and y are independent.* In our present case, let us assume x is dependent on y and from (2) we can show this explicitly as follows:

(4) $$x = \frac{M - p_y y}{p_x}$$

As is seen, we have a linear function of x and y.

Since x is not an independent variable, the dx in (3) is not an arbitrary increment of x but a differential of x.

Hence, when taking the differential of du, we find

$$d(du) = d^2u = d(f_x\, dx) + d(f_y\, dy)$$

$$= f_x\, d(dx) + d(f_x)\, dx + f_y\, d(dy) + d(f_y)\, dy$$

$$= f_x\, d^2x + \left(\frac{\partial}{\partial x} f_x\, dx + \frac{\partial}{\partial y} f_x\, dy\right) dx$$

$$+ f_y \cdot 0 + \left(\frac{\partial}{\partial x} f_y\, dx + \frac{\partial}{\partial y} f_y\, dy\right) dy$$

$$= f_x\, d^2x + f_{xx}\, (dx)^2 + f_{yy}\, (dy)^2 + 2f_{xy}\, dx\, dy$$

Recall that the second-order differential of an independent variable is zero, and thus $d(dy) = d^2y = 0$. Hence, $f_y\, d(dy) = 0$ and drops out.

Also recall that, when x and y are linearly related, the second-order differentials are zero. Thus, $d^2x = 0$. This may be easily checked from (4). We have

$$dx = -\frac{p_y}{p_x}\, dy$$

$$d^2x = 0\, dy = 0$$

Hence, we may summarize our results as follows: Given

(5) $$u = f(x, y)$$

(6) $$\phi(x, y) = 0$$

where x and y are not independent, d^2u is

(7) $$d^2u = f_x\, d^2x + f_{xx}\, (dx)^2 + f_{yy}\, (dy)^2 + 2f_{xy}\, dx\, dy$$

In addition, when (6) is a linear relation, then $d^2x = 0$ and d^2u becomes

(8) $$d^2u = f_{xx}\, (dx)^2 + f_{yy}\, (dy)^2 + 2f_{xy}\, dx\, dy$$

which is the same result as when x and y were independent.

Example 1. Given a utility function and budget constraint

$$u = q_1 q_2$$
$$M = p_1 q_1 + p_2 q_2$$

find d^2u. Since q_1 and q_2 are not independent, we have, assuming q_1 to be the dependent variable,

$$d^2u = f_1\, d^2q_1 + f_{11}\, (dq_1)^2 + f_{22}\, (dq_2)^2 + 2f_{12}\, dq_1\, dq_2$$

The various terms on the right-hand side of the equation are found as follows.

$$q_1 = \frac{M - p_2 q_2}{p_1}$$

$$dq_1 = \frac{d}{dq_2}\left(\frac{M - p_2 q_2}{p_1}\right) dq_2 = \frac{-p_2}{p_1}\, dq_2$$

$$d^2q_1 = \frac{d}{dq_2}\left(-\frac{p_2}{p_1}\, dq_2\right) dq_2$$

$$= 0 \cdot dq_2 = 0$$

$$f_1 = \frac{\partial u}{\partial q_1} = q_2 \qquad f_{11} = \frac{\partial}{\partial q_1}\, q_2 = 0$$

$$f_{12} = \frac{\partial}{\partial q_2}\, q_2 = 1$$

$$f_2 = q_1 \qquad f_{22} = \frac{\partial}{\partial q_2}\, q_1 = 0$$

Hence, we find

$$d^2u = 0 + 0 + 0 + 2(1) \, dq_1 \, dq_2 = 2dq_1 \, dq_2$$

Example 2. Given

$$u = x^2 + xy$$

and a side relation

$$xy = k$$

find *du* and *d²u*. For *du* we find

$$du = f_x \, dx + f_y \, dy$$

$$f_x = \frac{\partial u}{\partial x} = \frac{\partial}{\partial x}(x^2 + xy) = 2x + y$$

$$f_y = \frac{\partial}{\partial y}(x + yx) = x$$

$$\therefore \quad du = (2x + y)\, dx + x \, dy$$

For the second-order differential, we have, considering *x* the dependent and *y* the independent variable,

$$d^2u = f_x \, d^2x + f_{xx} \, (dx)^2 + f_{yy} \, (dy)^2 + 2f_{xy} \, dx \, dy$$

To find *d²x*, let us set

$$x = ky^{-1}$$

$$dx = \frac{\partial}{\partial y}(ky^{-1})\, dy = -ky^{-2}\, dy$$

$$d^2x = \frac{\partial}{\partial y}(-ky^{-2}\, dy)\, dy = 2ky^{-3}\, (dy)^2$$

$$f_{xx} = \frac{\partial}{\partial x}(2x + y) = 2$$

$$f_{xy} = \frac{\partial}{\partial x}(f_y) = \frac{\partial}{\partial x}(x) = 1$$

$$f_{yy} = 0$$

$$\therefore \quad d^2u = 2ky^{-3}\, (dy)^2 + 2(dx)^2 + 2(1)\, dx \, dy + 0\, (dy)^2$$

$$= 2ky^{-3}\, (dy)^2 + 2(dx)^2 + 2dx \, dy$$

(v) *Three-variable case—dependent variables*

Suppose we have a function and side relation with three variables

$$u = f(x, y, z)$$
$$\phi(x, y, z) = 0$$

Then the first- and second-order differentials may be obtained in exactly the same manner as the two-variable case. We have

$$du = f_x \, dx + f_y \, dy + f_z \, dz$$
$$d^2u = f_x \, d^2x + f_{xx} \, (dx)^2 + f_{yy} \, (dy)^2 + f_{zz} \, (dz)^2$$
$$+ \, 2f_{xy} \, dx \, dy + 2f_{xz} \, dx \, dz + 2f_{yz} \, dy \, dz$$
$$= f_x \, d^2x + (f_x \, dx + f_y \, dy + f_z \, dz)^2$$

As can be seen, this can be generalized to n-variable case. As an exercise, work out the details of d^2u.

Problems

1. Find the first- and second-order differentials for the following.

(a) $u = xy$ (b) $u = x^2 + y^2$
(c) $u = x^2 + 2xy + y^2$ (d) $u = f(x, y, z)$

2. Find the second-order differentials of the following functions.

(a) $u = 2x^2 - xy$
(b) $u = x^3y^2 - 3x^2y^3$
(c) $u = x^2 + xy^2 + z^3$
(d) $u = x^2y^2 + y^2z^2$
(e) $y = 2u^2 - 1$, where $u = x^2 - 1$
(f) $y = u^2 - 2u$, where $u = 2x^2 + x$
(g) $y = (x^2 - 1)^{1/2}$
(h) $y = (x^2 + x)^{-1/2}$
(i) $u = x^2 + y^2$, where $M = ax + by$
(j) $u = x^2y^2$, where $ax + by = 0$
(k) $u = xyz$, where $ax + by + cz = 0$
(l) $u = q_1q_2 + q_2q_3 + q_3q_1$, where $p_1q_1 + p_2q_2 + p_3q_3 = M$, where p_1, p_2, and p_3 are given prices and M is given income.

3. Find the first- and second-order differentials of the following functions.

(a) $y = 1 + u^2$ (b) $y = 2u + 3u^2$
   $u = 1 + x^2$ $u = x - x^2$
(c) $u = x^2 + y^2$ (d) $u = x^2 + xy$
   $x + 3y = k$ $x - ky = 0$
(e) $u = q_1^2 + q_1q_2$ (f) $u = x^2 + y^2 + z^2$
   $M = p_1q_1 + p_2q_2$ $x + 2y + 3z = k$
(g) $u = q_1q_2q_3$,
   $M = aq_1q_2 + bq_1q_3 + cq_2q_3$

4.6 Functions of functions—total derivative

(i) Total derivative—two variable case

So far, when we considered $u = f(x, y)$, the x and y were independent variables that were also independent of each other. We now consider the case where x and y are not independent variables. Let them be dependent variables of other functions, say,

$$x = g(t), \qquad y = h(t)$$

where t is the independent variable. Thus u is a function of x and y; x and y are functions of t. The question is: What is the derivative of u with respect to t? That is, what is du/dt?

Let us use an example to illustrate. Let u be wheat that is produced, x be labor, and y be land. Now the amount of labor x and land y, will, let us assume, depend on the amount of money t that is made available. Thus when there is a small increase in t, it will bring about an increase in x and y, which in turn will bring about an increase in u. How much of a change in the amount of u will a small unit change in t bring about? We shall express this by du/dt.

We know that $\partial u/\partial x$ is the change in u due to a small unit change in x holding y constant. Furthermore, dx/dt will be the change in x due to a small unit change in t. Thus, $\dfrac{\partial u}{\partial x}\dfrac{dx}{dt}$ will be the amount of change in u due to a small unit change in t that is transmitted through x. Likewise, $\dfrac{\partial u}{\partial y}\dfrac{dy}{dt}$ will be the amount of change in u due to a small unit change in t that is transmitted through y. Therefore, the change in u due to a small unit change in t will be the sum of these two effects, which we shall write

(1)
$$\frac{du}{dt} = \frac{\partial u}{\partial x}\frac{dx}{dt} + \frac{\partial u}{\partial y}\frac{dy}{dt}$$

and may also be expressed as

(2)
$$\frac{du}{dt} = f_x \frac{dx}{dt} + f_y \frac{dy}{dt}$$

This du/dt is called the *total derivative* of u with respect to t.*

Example 1. Find the total derivative of u with respect to t:

$$u = x^2 + y^2, \qquad x = t^2, \qquad y = t^2 + 1$$

$$\frac{du}{dt} = f_x \frac{dx}{dt} + f_y \frac{dy}{dt}$$

---

* See Smail (1949), pp. 424–427, and other references at the end of this chapter.

$$f_x = \frac{\partial u}{\partial x} = 2x, \qquad f_y = \frac{\partial u}{\partial y} = 2y$$

$$\frac{dx}{dt} = 2t, \qquad \frac{dy}{dt} = 2t$$

$$\frac{du}{dt} = 2x2t + 2y2t = 4tx + 4ty$$

Example 2.

$$u = x^2 + y^2$$
$$y = 2x$$

Find du/dx. Let us set

$$y = 2t, \qquad x = t$$

$$\frac{du}{dt} = f_x \frac{dx}{dt} + f_y \frac{dy}{dt}$$

$$= 2x(1) + 2y(2)$$

$$= 2x + 4y$$

But $x = t$. Thus,

$$\frac{du}{dx} = 2x + 4y$$

Example 3. We may show the result of Example 2 in the following manner: Since $x = t$, we have

(3)
$$\frac{du}{dx} = f_x \frac{dx}{dx} + f_y \frac{dy}{dx}$$

$$= f_x + f_y \frac{dy}{dx}$$

which is the general result when x and y are not independent.

This shows that the change in u due to an increment of x is the sum of two effects. The first is f_x, which is the change in u when there is an increment in x, holding y constant; the second is the change in u due to an increment in y, which in turn is due to the change in x. The student should firmly grasp this chain of reasoning because it has wide applications. We shall consider it again in more detail in Section (iv) below.

We may also find du/dy as follows.

(4)
$$\frac{du}{dy} = f_x \frac{dx}{dy} + f_y \frac{dy}{dy}$$

$$= f_x \frac{dx}{dy} + f_y$$

From our example, we have

$$x = \tfrac{1}{2}y$$

$$\frac{du}{dy} = 2x(\tfrac{1}{2}) + 2y$$

$$= x + 2y$$

Problems

1. Find the total derivative of u with respect to t.

(a) $u = x^2 + y^2, x = t^3, y = t^3 + 3$
(b) $u = x^2 + xy + y^2, x = t^3 + 3, y = t^3$
(c) $u = x^2 + xy + y^3, x = t^3, y = t^3 + t^2$
(d) $u = x^2y + xy^2, x = 1 - t^2, y = 1 + t^2$
(e) $u = f(x, y, z), x = g(t), y = h(t), z = k(t)$

2. Consider $v = \pi r^2 h$ where r is the radius, h is the height of a cylinder. The v is the volume. Let $r = t^2, h = t^2$, where t is time; i.e., r and h increase by the square of time. Then what will be the rate of increase in the volume of the cylinder per unit of time?

(ii) Three or more variables case

Formula (2) holds for more than two variables. If we have

$$u = f(x, y, z, ...)$$

where,

$$x = g(t), \qquad y = h(t), \qquad ...$$

then,

(5)
$$\frac{du}{dt} = f_x \frac{dx}{dt} + f_y \frac{dy}{dt} + f_z \frac{dz}{dt} + ...$$

(iii) Two or more independent variables case

If we have

$$u = f(x, y), \qquad x = g(t_1, t_2), \qquad y = h(t_1, t_2)$$

then,

$$\frac{\partial u}{\partial t_1} = f_x \frac{\partial x}{\partial t_1} + f_y \frac{\partial y}{\partial t_1}$$

(6)
$$\frac{\partial u}{\partial t_2} = f_x \frac{\partial x}{\partial t_2} + f_y \frac{\partial y}{\partial t_2}$$

where $\partial u / \partial t_1$ is the total derivative of u with respect to t_1 holding t_2 constant. In general,

$$u = f(x, y, z, \ldots)$$
$$x = g(t_1, t_2, \ldots)$$
$$y = h(t_1, t_2, \ldots)$$
$$z = k(t_1, t_2, \ldots)$$
$$\ldots$$

then,

$$\frac{\partial u}{\partial t_1} = f_x \frac{\partial x}{\partial t_1} + f_y \frac{\partial y}{\partial t_1} + f_z \frac{\partial z}{\partial t_1} + \ldots$$

$$\frac{\partial u}{\partial t_2} = f_x \frac{\partial x}{\partial t_2} + f_y \frac{\partial y}{\partial t_2} + f_z \frac{dz}{\partial t_2} + \ldots$$

Example 1.

$$u = x^2 + y^2, \qquad x = t^2 + s^2, \qquad y = t^2 - s^2$$

$$\frac{\partial x}{\partial t} = 2t, \qquad \frac{\partial u}{\partial x} = 2x$$

$$\frac{\partial y}{\partial t} = 2t, \qquad \frac{\partial u}{\partial y} = 2y$$

$$\therefore \quad \frac{\partial u}{\partial t} = f_x \frac{\partial x}{\partial t} + f_y \frac{\partial y}{\partial t}$$

$$= (2x)(2t) + (2y)(2t) = 4xt + 4yt$$

Student: Find $\partial u / \partial s$.

Example 2.

$$u = x^2 + 2y^2 + 3z^2, \qquad x = t^2 + 2s^2 + 3v^2$$
$$y = t^2 - 2s^2 - v^2, \qquad z = 2t^2 + s^2 - 2v^2$$

$$\frac{\partial u}{\partial t} = f_x \frac{\partial x}{\partial t} + f_y \frac{\partial y}{\partial t} + f_z \frac{dz}{\partial t}$$

$$= (2x)(2t) + (4y)(2t) + (6z)(4t)$$

$$= (4x + 8y + 24z)t$$

Student: Find $\partial u / \partial s$ and $\partial u / \partial v$.

Example 3. A very important result may be obtained from our present case, that is: Given

(7)
$$u = f(x, y)$$

the differential of u is

(8)
$$du = f_x \, dx + f_y \, dy$$

regardless of whether x and y are independent or dependent. Since we have already seen that (8) holds when x and y are independent, what we shall do in this example is to show that the differential du of (8) also holds when x and y are not independent.

Given the function (7), suppose we have

$$x = g(t_1, t_2)$$
$$y = h(t_1, t_2)$$

Then

$$\frac{\partial u}{\partial t_1} = f_x \frac{\partial x}{\partial t_1} + f_y \frac{\partial y}{\partial t_1}$$

$$\frac{\partial u}{\partial t_2} = f_x \frac{\partial x}{\partial t_2} + f_y \frac{\partial y}{\partial t_2}$$

Multiplying the first equation by dt_1 and the second equation by dt_2, we find

$$\frac{\partial u}{\partial t_1} dt_1 = f_x \frac{\partial x}{\partial t_1} dt_1 + f_y \frac{\partial y}{\partial t_1} dt_1$$

$$\frac{\partial u}{\partial t_2} dt_2 = f_x \frac{\partial x}{\partial t_2} dt_2 + f_y \frac{\partial y}{\partial t_2} dt_2$$

Add the two equations. Then the left-hand side becomes

$$\frac{\partial u}{\partial t_1} dt_1 + \frac{\partial u}{\partial t_2} dt_2$$

Since

$$u = f(x, y) = f\,[g(t_1, t_2), h(t_1, t_2)] = F(t_1, t_2)$$

we may set this equal

$$du = df = u_1 \, dt_1 + u_2 \, dt_2$$

As for the right-hand side, we get by adding the two equations,

$$f_x \left[\frac{\partial x}{\partial t_1} dt_1 + \frac{\partial x}{\partial t_2} dt_2 \right] + f_y \left[\frac{\partial y}{\partial t_1} dt_1 + \frac{\partial y}{\partial t_2} dt_2 \right]$$

But

$$dx = \frac{\partial x}{\partial t_1} \, dt_1 + \frac{\partial x}{\partial t_2} \, dt_2$$

$$dy = \frac{\partial y}{\partial t_1} \, dt_1 + \frac{\partial y}{\partial t_2} \, dt_2$$

Hence, substituting these in the above equation, the right-hand side becomes

$$f_x \, dx + f_y \, dy$$

Thus, putting the right-hand side and left-hand side together, we get

$$df = f_x \, dx + f_y \, dy$$

which is simply the differential of $u = f(x, y)$.

Note carefully that the x and y are not independent variables in our present case, but are dependent on t_1 and t_2. Hence, we may conclude that *the differential formula we derived earlier for independent variables also holds for dependent variables.*

(iv) When y is a function of x

This case was considered briefly in Example 3 on page 134, but let us reconsider it here in more detail.

Consider

$$u = f(x, y)$$

$$x = g(t), \qquad y = h(t)$$

Suppose we let $t = x$. Then

$$y = h(t) = h(x)$$

Hence, only x will be the independent variable. Then, using formula (2) of Section (i) but replacing t with x, we find

(9)
$$\frac{du}{dx} = f_x \frac{dx}{dx} + f_y \frac{dy}{dx}$$

$$= f_x + f_y \frac{dy}{dx}$$

The interpretation of this result is that the change in u is due to two sources. The first is the change in x with the other variables held constant and is expressed by f_x. However, since y is dependent on x, a change in x will cause a change in y. Hence, the second source of the change in u is due to the change in x transmitted through the intermediate variable y. This is expressed by $f_y(dy/dx)$.

Example 1.

$$u = x^2 + xy$$
$$y = 2x + 1$$

Then the total derivative of u with respect to x will be

$$\frac{du}{dx} = f_x + f_y \frac{dy}{dx}$$

$$= \frac{\partial}{\partial x}(x^2 + xy) + \frac{\partial}{\partial y}(x^2 + xy)\frac{\partial}{\partial x}(2x + 1)$$

$$= (2x + y) + 2x = 6x + 1$$

Example 2. Let

$$u = f(q_1, q_2)$$
$$p_1 q_1 + p_2 q_2 = M$$

where u is a utility function with goods q_1 and q_2. M is income, and p_1 and p_2 are the prices of q_1 and q_2. This second equation is usually called the *budget equation*. Find the marginal utility of q_1, i.e., du/dq_1, and then also find d^2u/dq_1^2, which shows the rate of change of du/dq_1.

We may consider q_2 as a function of q_1 because of the budget equation. Then q_1 is the independent variable, and we may find du/dq_1 as

$$\frac{du}{dq_1} = f_1 + f_2 \frac{dq_2}{dq_1}$$

Let us now find dq_2/dq_1. From the budget equation

$$q_2 = \frac{M - p_1 q_1}{p_2}$$

$$\frac{dq_2}{dq_1} = \frac{-p_1}{p_2}$$

Hence

$$\frac{du}{dq_1} = f_1 - \frac{p_1}{p_2} f_2$$

The d^2u/dq_1^2 is discussed in Section *(ix)*.

Example 3. Given

$$q = f(x_1, x_2)$$
$$C = r_1 x_1 + r_2 x_2$$

where in the first equation q is output and x_1 and x_2 are inputs and it is a production function. In the second equation the C is total cost and r_1 and r_2

are input prices. Find dq/dx_1, which is the marginal product of input x_1. Because of the cost equation, we may consider x_1 as a function of x_2. Then

$$\frac{dq}{dx_1} = f_1 + f_2 \frac{dx_2}{dx_1}$$

The value of dx_2/dx_1 may be easily found from the cost equation. Student: Find dx_2/dx_1, and complete the calculations.

Problems

1. Find the total derivative du/dx of the given functions.

(a) $u = x^3 + y^3$, $y = x^2$
(b) $u = x^2y + xy^2$, $y = x^2 + x$
(c) $u = x^2 + 2x + y^2$, $y = 1/x$
(d) $u = x^2 - y^2$, $y = \ln x^2$

2. Find the partial derivatives $\partial u/\partial t$, $\partial u/\partial s$ of the following functions.

(a) $u = x^3 + y^3$, $x = t^2 - s^2$, $y = t^2 + s^2$
(b) $u = x^2y + xy^2$, $x = t^2s$, $y = ts^2$

(v) *When y and z are functions of x*

Consider

$$u = f(x, y, z)$$
$$y = g(x)$$
$$z = h(x)$$

where x is the independent variable and y and z are the dependent variables. This is merely an extension of the case in Section (*iv*) and may be found by applying the results of the case in Section (*ii*) by replacing t with x. Then the total derivative of u with respect to x will be

$$\text{(10)} \qquad \frac{du}{dx} = f_x + f_y \frac{dy}{dx} + f_z \frac{dz}{dx}$$

The interpretation is similar to that of result in Section (*iv*). The only difference has been the addition of $f_z(dz/dx)$ which shows the effect of x on u via the intermediate variable z.

As is seen, the results of Sections (*iv*) and (*v*) are general

$$u = f(x, y, z, \ldots)$$
$$y = g(x)$$
$$z = g(x)$$
$$\ldots$$

(11)
$$\frac{du}{dx} = f_x + f_y \frac{dy}{dx} + f_z \frac{dz}{dx} + \dots$$

(vi) When z is a function of x and y

Let us now consider

$$u = f(x, y, z)$$
$$z = g(x, y)$$

That is, z is dependent on 2 independent variables x and y. This form of relation appears frequently in economics in the following form: We are given

$$u = f(q_1, q_2, q_3)$$
$$M = p_1 q_1 + p_2 q_2 + p_3 q_3$$

where u is the utility function dependent on q_1, q_2, and q_3. The 3 quantities of goods are, however, not independent, because they are related to each other by the budget equation, where M is income and p_1, p_2, and p_3 are prices which are given. Hence, we may consider, for example, q_3 dependent on q_1 and q_2.

Or we may have an equation

$$x^2 + 2xy - yz = 0$$

which may be expressed as

$$f(x, y, z) = 0$$

As is seen, we may consider any two of the variables, say, x and y independent, which will mean that z is a dependent variable depending on x and y.

Let us now show how $\partial u/\partial x$ and $\partial u/\partial y$ may be obtained. Note that we now write $\partial u/\partial x$ and not du/dx because we have 2 independent variables x and y. The $\partial u/\partial x$ means the partial of u with respect to x, holding the other variables constant.

Using the results of Section *(iii)*, we have

$$\frac{\partial u}{\partial x} = f_x + f_z \frac{\partial z}{\partial x}$$

which shows the change in u due to a change in the independent variable x, with the other variables held constant. We may ask: What variables are being held constant? For $\partial u/\partial x$, we may consider u a function of the 2 independent variables x and y. That is,

$$u = f(x, y, z) = f[x, y, g(x, y)] = F(x, y)$$

Hence, $\partial u/\partial x$ will be the change in u with respect to a change in x, holding y constant. The implication is that z is not held constant, and this is because z is dependent on x. Hence, we should naturally expect the change in x to cause a change in z, which in turn will effect u. This effect will appear on the right-hand side, as we shall see. Let us now consider the terms on the right-hand side.

The first term f_x is the partial derivative of $f(x, y, z)$, with respect to x, holding the other variables constant. In this case, the y and z are both held constant. In the second term $f_z(\partial z/\partial x)$, the f_z is the partial derivative with respect to z, holding x and y both constant. The $\partial z/\partial x$ is the change in z holding y constant. Hence, the term $f_z(\partial z/\partial x)$ shows the change in f due to the change in x, transmitted through z.

It is important to note how the u of $\partial u/\partial x$ on the left-hand side is considered a function of x and y, whereas the f of f_x and f_z on the right-hand side is considered functions of x, y, and z.

The partial of u with respect to y is obtained in similar fashion;

$$\frac{\partial u}{\partial y} = f_y + f_z \frac{\partial z}{\partial y}$$

Example 1. Given

$$u = x^2 + xy + y$$
$$z = 3x - 4y$$

Find $\partial u/\partial x$ and $\partial u/\partial y$.

$$\frac{\partial u}{\partial x} = f_x + f_z \frac{\partial z}{\partial x}$$

$$f_x = \frac{\partial}{\partial x}(x^2 + xy + yz) = 2x + y + 0$$

$$f_z = \frac{\partial}{\partial z}(x^2 + xy + yz) = y$$

$$\frac{\partial z}{\partial x} = \frac{\partial}{\partial x}(3x - 4y) = 3$$

$$\therefore \quad \frac{\partial u}{\partial x} = (2x + y) + 3y = 2x + 4y$$

Student: Find $\partial u/\partial y$.

Example 2. Given

$$x^2 + xy + yz = 0$$

Find $\partial z/\partial x$.

To solve this problem we note that $\partial z/\partial x$ is on the right-hand side of the total derivative formula $\partial u/\partial x$. Hence, by interpreting the given equation as having x and y as the independent variables and z as the dependent variable, we may find an equation which includes $\partial z/\partial x$. Solving this equation for

$\partial z/\partial x$ will give us the desired results. So let us set

$$u = f(x, y, z) = x^2 + xy + yz = 0$$

Then,

$$\frac{\partial u}{\partial x} = f_x + f_z \frac{\partial z}{\partial x}$$

$$= (2x + y) + y\left(\frac{\partial z}{\partial x}\right) = 0$$

$$\therefore \quad \frac{\partial z}{\partial x} = -\frac{2x + y}{y}$$

To find $\partial y/\partial x$, we may consider x and z the independent variables and y the dependent variable. To find $\partial x/\partial y$, we may consider y and z the independent variables and x the dependent variable, and so forth.
Student: Find $\partial y/\partial x$, $\partial x/\partial y$, and $\partial x/\partial z$

Problems

1. Given the following functions, find du/dx.

(a) $u = x^2 + y^2 + z^2$
$\quad y = x + 1$
$\quad z = 3x + 1$

(b) $u = xy + yz + zx$
$\quad y = 2x + 1$
$\quad z = x^2 + 3$

(c) $u = x^2 + y^2 + z^2$
$\quad z = 4x + y$

(d) $u = 3x^2y + yz$
$\quad z = x^2 + xy + y^2$

2. Given a utility function and budget constraint

$$u = q_1q_2 + q_2q_3 + q_3q_1$$
$$M = p_1q_1 + p_2q_2 + p_3q_3$$

Find du/dq_1. Note that q_1, q_2, and q_3 are goods; p_1, p_2, and p_3 are the given prices; M is the given income; and u is utility.

3. Given a production function and constraint

$$q = 3x_1^3 + 2x_2^2 + x_3$$
$$c = F + r_1x_1 + r_2x_2 + r_3x_3$$

Find dq/dx_1 (marginal product of x_1). Here x_1, x_2, and x_3 are inputs: r_1, r_2, and r_3 are input prices; and F is fixed cost.

(vii) Higher-order derivatives (I)

Let us now show how the second-order derivatives may be found. We shall discuss 3 cases, and it is the third case that will be useful in economic problems. The first two cases are the prerequisites for the third case. Suppose we have

$$u = f(x, y)$$
$$x = g(t), \qquad y = h(t)$$

where t is the independent variable. We wish to find du/dt and d^2u/dt^2. The du/dt we know is

(12)
$$\frac{du}{dt} = f_x \frac{dx}{dt} + f_y \frac{dy}{dt}$$

To find d^2u/dt^2, we apply the total derivative formula to (12). The point to note is that this differentiation process will involve repeated use of the chain rule. We have

$$\frac{d^2u}{dt^2} = \frac{\partial}{\partial x}\left[f_x \frac{dx}{dt} + f_y \frac{dy}{dt}\right]\frac{dx}{dt} + \frac{\partial}{\partial y}\left[f_x \frac{dx}{dt} + f_y \frac{dy}{dt}\right]\frac{dy}{dt}$$

Let us find the first and second terms on the right-hand side separately.

$$\text{First term} = \frac{\partial}{\partial x}\left[f_x \frac{dx}{dt} + f_y \frac{dy}{dt}\right]\frac{dx}{dt}$$

$$= \left[f_{xx} \frac{dx}{dt} + f_x \frac{\partial}{\partial x}\left(\frac{dx}{dt}\right) + f_{yx} \frac{dy}{dt} + f_y \frac{\partial}{\partial x}\left(\frac{dy}{dt}\right)\right]\frac{dx}{dt}$$

Two terms in this equation need special attention. One is

$$f_x \frac{\partial}{\partial x}\left(\frac{dx}{dt}\right) = f_x \frac{d}{dt}\left(\frac{dx}{dt}\right)\frac{dt}{dx} = f_x \frac{d^2x}{dt^2}\frac{dt}{dx}$$

As is seen, $\partial/\partial x$ requires that dx/dt be differentiated with respect to x, holding y constant. Hence we have applied the chain rule and obtained the above result. The second is

$$f_y \frac{\partial}{\partial x}\left(\frac{dy}{dt}\right) = f_y(0)$$

In this case, since $\dfrac{\partial}{\partial x}$ means we are holding y constant, the $\dfrac{\partial}{\partial x}(dy/dt) = 0$.

Hence the first term on the right-hand side becomes

$$f_{xx}\left(\frac{dx}{dt}\right)^2 + f_x \frac{d^2x}{dt^2}\frac{dt}{dx}\frac{dx}{dt} + f_{yx}\frac{dy}{dt}\frac{dx}{dt} = f_{xx}\left(\frac{dx}{dt}\right)^2 + f_x \frac{d^2x}{dt^2} + f_{yx}\frac{dy}{dt}\frac{dx}{dt}$$

The second term on the right-hand side is found in similar manner. It will be

$$f_{xy}\frac{dx}{dt}\frac{dy}{dt} + f_x(0) + f_{yy}\left(\frac{dy}{dt}\right)^2 + f_y \frac{d^2y}{dt^2}$$

Hence the second-order derivative is

(13) $$\frac{d^2u}{dt^2} = f_{xx}\left(\frac{dx}{dt}\right)^2 + f_{yy}\left(\frac{dy}{dt}\right)^2 + 2f_{xy}\frac{dx}{dt}\frac{dy}{dt} + f_x\frac{d^2x}{dt^2} + f_y\frac{d^2y}{dt^2}$$

Example 1.

$$u = x^2 + xy + y^2$$
$$x = t^3 + 1$$
$$y = t - t^3$$
$$\frac{du}{dt} = f_x\frac{dx}{dt} + f_y\frac{dy}{dt}$$
$$f_x = 2x + y, \qquad f_y = x + 2y$$
$$\frac{dx}{dt} = 3t^2, \qquad \frac{d^2x}{dt^2} = 6t$$
$$\frac{dy}{dt} = 1 - 3t^2, \qquad \frac{d^2y}{dt^2} = -6t$$

$$\frac{du}{dt} = (2x + y)3t^2 + (x + 2y)(1 - 3t^2)$$

$$\frac{d^2u}{dt^2} = f_{xx}\left(\frac{dx}{dt}\right)^2 + f_{yy}\left(\frac{dy}{dt}\right)^2 + 2f_{xy}\frac{dx}{dt}\frac{dy}{dt} + f_x\frac{d^2x}{dt^2} + f_y\frac{d^2y}{dt^2}$$

$$= 2(3t^2)^2 + 2(1 - 3t^2)^2 + 2(1)(3t^2)(1 - 3t^2)$$
$$+ (2x + y)6t + (x + 2y)(-6t)$$
$$= 30t^4 - 12t^2 + 6t + 2$$

Example 2.

$$u = x^2 + xy + y^2$$
$$x = 2t + 1$$
$$y = t - 3$$
$$\frac{dx}{dt} = 2 \qquad \frac{d^2x}{dt^2} = 0$$
$$\frac{dy}{dt} = 1 \qquad \frac{d^2y}{dt^2} = 0$$

$$\frac{d^2u}{dt^2} = 2(2)^2 + 2(1)^2 + 2(0)\frac{dx}{dt}\frac{dy}{dt} + f_x(0) + f_y(0)$$

$$= 8 + 2 = 10$$

When the $x = h(t)$ and $y = h(t)$ are linear equations, the second-order derivatives are $d^2x/dt^2 = 0$ and $d^2y/dt^2 = 0$, and the result is simply

(14) $$\frac{d^2u}{dt^2} = f_{xx}\left(\frac{dx}{dt}\right)^2 + f_{yy}\left(\frac{dy}{dt}\right)^2 + 2f_{xy}\frac{dx}{dt}\frac{dy}{dt}$$

(viii) Higher-order derivatives (II)

Let us now extend the results of the previous section to the case of two independent variables t_1 and t_2. That is,

$$u = f(x, y)$$
$$x = g(t_1, t_2)$$
$$y = h(t_1, t_2)$$

Then,

$$\frac{\partial u}{\partial t_1} = f_x\frac{\partial x}{\partial t_1} + f_y\frac{\partial y}{\partial t_2}$$

$$\frac{\partial^2 u}{\partial t_1^2} = \frac{\partial}{\partial x}\left(f_x\frac{\partial x}{\partial t_1} + f_y\frac{\partial y}{\partial t}\right)\frac{\partial x}{\partial t_1} + \frac{\partial}{\partial y}\left(f_x\frac{\partial x}{\partial t_1} + f_y\frac{\partial y}{\partial t_1}\right)\frac{\partial y}{\partial t_1}$$

Let us now work out the first and second terms on the right-hand side separately.

$$\text{First term} = \left[f_{xx}\frac{\partial x}{\partial t_1} + f_x\frac{\partial}{\partial x}\left(\frac{\partial x}{\partial t_1}\right) + f_{yx}\frac{\partial y}{\partial t_1} + f_y\frac{\partial}{\partial x}\frac{\partial y}{\partial t_1}\right]\frac{\partial x}{\partial t_1}$$

$$= f_{xx}\left(\frac{\partial x}{\partial t_1}\right)^2 + f_x\frac{\partial}{\partial t_1}\left(\frac{\partial x}{\partial t_1}\right)\frac{\partial t_1}{\partial x}\frac{\partial x}{\partial t_1} + f_{yx}\frac{\partial y}{\partial t_1}\frac{\partial x}{\partial t_1} + f_y(0)\frac{\partial x}{\partial t_1}$$

$$= f_{xx}\left(\frac{\partial x}{\partial t_1}\right)^2 + f_x\frac{\partial^2 x}{\partial t_1^2} + f_{yx}\frac{\partial x}{\partial t_1}\frac{\partial y}{\partial t_1}$$

$$\text{Second term} = \left[f_{xy}\frac{\partial x}{\partial t_1} + f_x\frac{\partial}{\partial y}\left(\frac{\partial x}{\partial t_1}\right) + f_{yy}\frac{\partial y}{\partial t_1} + f_y\frac{\partial}{\partial y}\left(\frac{\partial y}{\partial t_1}\right)\right]\frac{\partial y}{\partial t_1}$$

$$= f_{xy}\frac{\partial x}{\partial t_1}\frac{\partial y}{\partial t_1} + f_x(0)\frac{\partial y}{\partial t_1} + f_{yy}\left(\frac{\partial y}{\partial t_1}\right)^2 + f_y\frac{\partial}{\partial t_1}\left(\frac{\partial y}{\partial t_1}\right)\frac{\partial t_1}{\partial y}\frac{\partial y}{\partial t_1}$$

$$= f_{xy}\frac{\partial x}{\partial t_1}\frac{\partial y}{\partial t_1} + f_{yy}\left(\frac{\partial y}{\partial t_1}\right)^2 + f_y\frac{\partial^2 y}{\partial t_1^2}$$

Substituting these results in the original equation, we find

(15) $$\frac{\partial^2 u}{\partial t_1^2} = f_{xx}\left(\frac{\partial x}{\partial t_1}\right)^2 + f_{yy}\left(\frac{\partial y}{\partial t_1}\right)^2 + 2f_{xy}\frac{\partial x}{\partial t_1}\frac{\partial y}{\partial t_1} + f_x\frac{\partial^2 x}{\partial t_1^2} + f_y\frac{\partial^2 y}{\partial t_1^2}$$

(ix) Higher-order derivatives (III)

Let us now consider

$$u = f(x, y)$$
$$y = g(x)$$

where, as is seen, the x is the independent variable and y is the dependent variable. This is the type of situation which will be most useful in economics. For example, suppose we have

$$u = f(x, y)$$
$$M = p_x x + p_y y$$

where u is utility; x and y are goods; p_x and p_y are given prices; and M is given income. Then, as is seen, x and y are not independent. We may write

$$y = \frac{M - p_x x}{p_y}$$

and consider x the independent variable and y the dependent variable. Then du/dx is the marginal utility of x, and d^2u/dx^2 is the rate of change of du/dx. Let us now find du/dx. We have, in general,

$$\frac{du}{dx} = f_x + f_y \frac{dy}{dx}$$

The d^2u/dx^2 becomes, in general,

$$\frac{d^2u}{dx^2} = \frac{\partial}{\partial x}\left(\frac{\partial u}{\partial x}\right) + \frac{\partial}{\partial y}\left(\frac{\partial u}{\partial x}\right)\frac{dy}{dx}$$

$$= \frac{\partial}{\partial x}\left(f_x + f_y \frac{dy}{dx}\right) + \frac{\partial}{\partial y}\left(f_x + f_y \frac{dy}{dx}\right)\frac{dy}{dx}$$

$$= f_{xx} + f_{xy}\frac{dy}{dx} + f_y\frac{\partial}{\partial x}\left(\frac{dy}{dx}\right) + \left(f_{xy} + f_{yy}\frac{dy}{dx} + f_y\frac{\partial}{\partial y}\left(\frac{dy}{dx}\right)\right)\frac{dy}{dx}$$

$$= f_{xx} + f_{xy}\frac{dy}{dx} + f_y\frac{d^2y}{dx^2} + f_{xy}\frac{dy}{dx} + f_{yy}\left(\frac{dy}{dx}\right)^2 + f_y(0)\frac{dy}{dx}$$

$$\text{(16)} \qquad = f_{xx} + f_{yy}\left(\frac{dy}{dx}\right)^2 + 2f_{xy}\frac{dy}{dx} + f_y\frac{d^2y}{dx^2}$$

Example 1. Find du/dx and d^2u/dx^2

$$u = x^2 + 2y^2$$
$$y = 4x - 1$$

$$\frac{du}{dx} = f_x + f_y \frac{dy}{dx}$$

$$\frac{d^2u}{dx^2} = f_{xx} + f_{yy}\left(\frac{dy}{dx}\right)^2 + 2f_{xy}\frac{dy}{dx} + f_y\frac{d^2y}{dx^2}$$

$$\frac{dy}{dx} = 4, \qquad \frac{d^2y}{dx^2} = 0$$

$$f_x = 2x, \qquad f_{xx} = 2$$

$$f_y = 4y, \qquad f_{yy} = 4, \qquad f_{xy} = 0$$

$$\therefore \quad \frac{du}{dx} = 2x + 4y(4) = 2x + 16y$$

$$\frac{d^2u}{dx^2} = 2 + 4(4)^2 + 2(0)4 + 0 = 66$$

As a check we may find

$$\frac{d}{dx}\left(\frac{du}{dx}\right) = 2 + 16\frac{dy}{dx}$$

$$= 2 + 16(4) = 66 = \frac{d^2u}{dx^2}$$

Example 2.

$$u = x^2y + 3xy^2$$

$$y = 4x^2 - x$$

$$\frac{du}{dx} = f_x + f_y\frac{dy}{dx}$$

(17) $$= (2xy + 3y^2) + (x^2 + 6xy)(8x - 1)$$

$$\frac{d^2u}{dx^2} = f_{xx} + f_{yy}\left(\frac{dy}{dx}\right)^2 + 2f_{xy}\frac{dy}{dx} + f_y\frac{d^2y}{dx^2}$$

$$= 2x + 6x(8x - 1)^2 + 2(2x + 6y)(8x - 1) + (x^2 + 6xy)8$$

$$= 384x^3 - 56x^2 + 4x + 144xy - 12y$$

As a check, differentiate (17) with respect to x, and show that it equals the result we found above by use of formula (16).

Example 3. Let

$$u = f(q_1, q_2)$$

$$p_1q_1 + p_2q_2 = M$$

be a utility function and budget constraint. Find du/dq_1 and d^2u/dq_1^2. We have

$$q_2 = \frac{M - p_1 q_1}{p_2}$$

and we may consider q_1 the independent variable and q_2 the dependent variable. Then,

$$\frac{du}{dq_1} = f_1 + f_2 \frac{dq_2}{dq_1}$$

$$\frac{d^2u}{dq_1^2} = f_{11} + f_{22}\left(\frac{dq_2}{dq_1}\right)^2 + 2f_{12}\frac{dq_2}{dq_1} + f_2 \frac{d^2q_2}{dq_1^2}$$

Let us find dq_2/dq_1 and d^2q_2/dq_1^2.

$$\frac{dq_2}{dq_1} = \frac{d}{dq_1}\left(\frac{M - p_1 q_1}{p_2}\right) = -\frac{p_1}{p_2}$$

$$\frac{d^2q_2}{dq_1^2} = 0$$

Thus

$$\frac{du}{dq_1} = f_1 + f_2\left(-\frac{p_1}{p_2}\right)$$

$$\frac{d^2u}{dq_1^2} = f_{11} + f_{22}\left(-\frac{p_1}{p_2}\right)^2 + 2f_{12}\left(-\frac{p_1}{p_2}\right) + 0$$

Let us now extend this result to

$$u = f(x, y, z)$$
$$z = g(x, y)$$

We find

$$\frac{du}{dx} = f_x \frac{\partial x}{\partial x} + f_y \frac{\partial y}{\partial x} + f_z \frac{\partial z}{\partial x}$$

$$= f_x + f_y(0) + f_z \frac{\partial z}{\partial x}$$

(18) $$= f_x + f_z \frac{\partial z}{\partial x}$$

$$\frac{d^2u}{dx^2} = \frac{\partial}{\partial x}\left(f_x + f_z \frac{\partial z}{\partial x}\right)\frac{\partial x}{\partial x} + \frac{\partial}{\partial y}\left(f_x + f_z \frac{\partial z}{\partial x}\right)\frac{\partial y}{\partial x}$$

$$+ \frac{\partial}{\partial z}\left(f_x + f_z \frac{\partial z}{\partial x}\right)\frac{\partial z}{\partial x}$$

$$= \left(f_{xx} + f_{xz}\frac{\partial z}{\partial x} + f_z \frac{\partial}{\partial x}\left(\frac{\partial z}{\partial x}\right) \right)$$

$$+ \left(f_{xy} + f_{yz}\frac{\partial z}{\partial x} + f_z \frac{\partial}{\partial y}\left(\frac{\partial z}{\partial x}\right) \right)\frac{\partial y}{\partial x}$$

$$+ \left(f_{xz} + f_{zz}\frac{\partial z}{\partial x} + f_z \frac{\partial}{\partial z}\left(\frac{\partial z}{\partial x}\right) \right)\frac{\partial z}{\partial x}$$

But $\partial y/\partial x = 0$ and $\dfrac{\partial}{\partial z}\left(\dfrac{\partial z}{\partial x}\right) = 0$. Thus

$$\frac{d^2u}{dx^2} = f_{xx} + f_{xz}\frac{\partial z}{\partial x} + f_z \frac{\partial^2 z}{\partial x^2}$$

$$+ f_{xz}\frac{\partial z}{\partial x} + f_{zz}\left(\frac{\partial z}{\partial x}\right)^2$$

(19) $$= f_{xx} + f_{zz}\left(\frac{\partial z}{\partial x}\right)^2 + 2f_{xz}\frac{\partial z}{\partial x} + f_z \frac{\partial^2 z}{\partial x^2}$$

In similar fashion we find

(20) $$\frac{du}{dy} = f_y + f_z \frac{\partial z}{\partial y}$$

(21) $$\frac{d^2u}{dy^2} = f_{yy} + f_{zz}\left(\frac{\partial z}{\partial y}\right)^2 + 2f_{yz}\frac{\partial z}{\partial y} + f_z \frac{\partial^2 z}{\partial y^2}$$

Example 1. Find du/dx and d^2u/dx^2.

$$u = x^2 + y^2 + z^2$$

$$z = 3x - 2y$$

$$\frac{du}{dx} = f_x + f_z \frac{\partial z}{\partial x}$$

$$= 2x + 2z(3) = 2x + 6z$$

$$\frac{d^2u}{dx^2} = f_{xx} + f_{zz}\left(\frac{\partial z}{\partial x}\right)^2 + 2f_{xz}\frac{\partial z}{\partial x} + f_z \frac{\partial^2 z}{\partial x^2}$$

$$= 2 + 2(3)^2 + 2(0)3 + 2z(0)$$

$$= 20$$

Student: Find du/dy and d^2u/dy^2.

Problems

1. Given the following functions, find du/dt and d^2u/dt^2.

(a) $u = 2x^2 - xy + 3y^2$
$x = t + 1$
$y = 2t - 1$

(b) $u = 3x^2 - 4xy - y^2$
$x = t^2 + 1$
$y = 3t^2 - t$

(c) $u = x^2y - 4xy^2$
$x = 3t^3 + t^2$
$y = t - t^3$

2. Find du/dq_1, d^2u/dq_1^2.

$u = f(q_1, q_2, q_3)$
$M = p_1q_1 + p_2q_2 + p_3q_3$

3. Given the following functions, find $\partial u/\partial t_1$ and $\partial^2u/\partial t^2$.

(a) $u = 2x^2 - xy + 3y^2$
$x = t_1^2 + 2t_2^2$
$y = 2t_1^2 - t_2^2$

(b) $u = x^2y - 3xy^2$
$x = 2t_1t_2 - t_2$
$y = t_1 - 3t_1t_2$

4. Find $\partial^2u/\partial t_1^2$ for the following function.

$u = f(x, y, z)$
$x = g(t_1, t_2)$
$y = h(t_1, t_2)$
$z = k(t_1, t_2)$

4.7 Implicit functions

In many cases relationships between variables are given in implicit form. For example, let x and y be inputs and u be output. Then, the transformation function that changes inputs into outputs can be written in abstract form as

(1) $$f(x, y, u) = 0$$

where x, y, and u are not independent. The marginal product of input x, i.e., $\partial u/\partial x$ may be of interest. How may this be obtained?

If we could set

(2) $$u = g(x, y)$$

then, finding $\partial u/\partial x$ would be simple. But in many cases, (2) may be hard to obtain. For example, suppose (1) is

$$x^2 + xy + yu + u^2 = 0$$

Then, expressing this in the form of (2) is difficult.

Fortunately, instead of this straightforward way, we may find $\partial u/\partial x$ in two alternative ways. One is to use the results of the previous section, and a second is to use the method of undetermined coefficients. Let us start with the first method.

METHOD 1. Suppose we have an implicit function

(1) $$f(x, y, u) = 0$$

and we wish to find $\partial u/\partial x$ and $\partial u/\partial y$. For this let us first set (1) as

(2) $$W = f(x, y, u) = 0$$

and consider u as dependent on x and y. Then, conceptually we may write

(3) $$u = g(x, y)$$

Using the results of the previous section concerning total derivatives, let us find

(4) $$\frac{\partial W}{\partial x} = f_x + f_u \frac{\partial u}{\partial x} = 0$$

$$\therefore \quad \frac{\partial u}{\partial x} = -\frac{f_x}{f_u}$$

which is what we seek. The $\partial u/\partial y$ is found in similar manner as

$$\frac{\partial u}{\partial y} = -\frac{f_y}{f_u}$$

Example 1. Suppose we have the implicit function

$$x^2 + xy + yu + u^2 = 0$$

Find $\partial u/\partial x$ and $\partial u/\partial y$. We have

$$\frac{\partial u}{\partial x} = -\frac{f_x}{f_u}$$

where

$$f_x = \frac{\partial}{\partial x}(x^2 + xy + yu + u^2) = 2x + y$$

$$f_u = y + 2u$$

$$\frac{\partial u}{\partial x} = -\frac{2x + y}{y + 2u}$$

Student: Find $\partial u/\partial y$.

Let us summarize these results for a 4 variable case.

$$W = f(x, y, z, u) = 0$$

For $\partial u/\partial x$, we have

$$\frac{\partial W}{\partial x} = f_x + f_u \frac{\partial u}{\partial x} = 0$$

$$\therefore \quad \frac{\partial u}{\partial x} = -\frac{f_x}{f_u}$$

In similar manner

$$\frac{\partial u}{\partial y} = -\frac{f_y}{f_u}$$

$$\frac{\partial y}{\partial x} = -\frac{f_x}{f_y}$$

METHOD 2. Suppose we have the implicit function

$$f(x, y, z, u) = 0$$

and we wish to find, for example, $\partial u/\partial x$. Let us set the function as

$$W = f(x, y, z, u) = 0$$

and also assume we can set

$$u = g(x, y, z)$$

From our discussion of total differentials we can set

$$dW = f_x \, dx + f_y \, dy + f_z \, dz + f_u \, du = 0$$

We also have

$$du = g_x \, dx + g_y \, dy + g_z \, dz$$

Thus, by substituting du in the above equation

$$f_x \, dx + f_y \, dy + f_z \, dz + f_u(g_x \, dx + g_y \, dy + g_z \, dz) = 0$$

$$(f_x + f_u g_y) \, dx + (f_y + f_u g_y) \, dy + (f_z + f_u g_z) \, dz = 0$$

Since we have considered u the dependent variable and x, y, and z the independent variables, no restrictions have been placed on the values of x, y, and z. A solution for this equation when x, y, and z can take on any values will be for the coefficients of dx, dy, and dz all to be zero. Thus, we get

$$f_x + f_u g_x = 0$$
$$f_y + f_u g_y = 0$$
$$f_z + f_u g_z = 0$$

Then we can find the desired terms $\partial u/\partial x$, $\partial u/\partial y$, and $\partial u/\partial z$ as follows:

$$\frac{\partial u}{\partial x} = g_x = -\frac{f_x}{f_u}, \qquad \frac{\partial u}{\partial y} = g_y = -\frac{f_y}{f_u}, \qquad \frac{\partial u}{\partial z} = g_z = -\frac{f_z}{f_u}$$

This can be generalized to more than four variables.

Example 2. Given the implicit function $x^2 y - x + y = 0$, find dy/dx.
Let

$$u = f(x, y) = x^2 y - x + y = 0$$
$$y = g(x)$$

Then,

$$du = f_x\, dx + f_y\, dy = 0$$
$$dy = g_x\, dx$$

Thus,

$$f_x\, dx + f_y g_x\, dx = 0$$
$$(f_x + f_y g_x)\, dx = 0$$

Setting the coefficient of dx equal to *zero*, we find

$$f_x + f_y g_x = 0 \qquad \text{or} \qquad g_x = -\frac{f_x}{f_y}$$

But we know that

$$f_x = 2xy - 1, \qquad f_y = x^2 + 1$$

Thus, our solution is

$$\frac{dy}{dx} = g_x = -\frac{2xy - 1}{x^2 + 1}$$

Example 3. Given $x^2 - y^2 - z^2 = 0$, find $\partial z/\partial x$.
Let us set

$$f(x, y, z) = x^2 - y^2 - z^2 = 0$$
$$z = g(x, y)$$

Then we have from our theorem

$$\begin{cases} f_x + f_z g_x = 0 \\ f_y + f_z g_y = 0 \end{cases}$$

$$f_x = 2x, \qquad f_z = -2z$$

$$\therefore \quad g_x = \frac{\partial z}{\partial x} = -\frac{2x}{-2z} = \frac{x}{z}$$

Student: Find $\partial z/\partial y$, $\partial y/\partial x$, and $\partial y/\partial z$.

Example 4. The constant outlay curve is an implicit function of prices p and quantities q and is shown as $pq = c$, where c is a constant. Let us find dq/dp by our present method and also by an alternative. Set

$$u = f(p, q) = pq - c = 0$$
$$q = g(p)$$

Then, the differentials are

$$du = f_p \, dp + f_q \, dq = 0$$
$$dq = g_p \, dp$$

By substitution we find

$$f_p \, dp + f_q g_p \, dp = 0$$

$$\therefore \quad g_p = -\frac{f_p}{f_q}$$

But we know that

$$f_p = \frac{\partial f}{\partial p} = q, \qquad f_q = \frac{\partial f}{\partial q} = p$$

Thus,

$$\frac{dq}{dp} = g_p = -\frac{q}{p}$$

Checking this result, let $q = cp^{-1}$. Then

$$\frac{dq}{dp} = -cp^{-2} = -\frac{c}{p^2} = -\frac{c}{p}\frac{1}{p} = -\frac{q}{p}$$

because $q = c/p$. Thus, it checks.

Example 5. Let u be utility and x and y be goods. Then the utility function is shown as $u = f(x, y)$. Assume u is constant. This is when we are considering a specific indifference curve where all different combinations of x and y on that curve give us the same utility. Set

$$V = F(x, y) = f(x, y) - u = 0$$
$$y = g(x)$$

The slope of the indifference curve $dy/dx = g_x$ can be found by

$$g_x = -\frac{F_x}{F_y} = -\frac{f_x}{f_y}$$

But

$$\frac{\partial u}{\partial x} = f_x \ldots \qquad \text{marginal utility of } x$$

$$\frac{\partial u}{\partial y} = f_y \ldots \qquad \text{marginal utility of } y$$

Thus the slope of the indifference curve is

$$\frac{dy}{dx} = -\frac{f_x}{f_y} = -\frac{\text{marginal utility of } x}{\text{marginal utility of } y}$$

a well-known result.*

4.8 Higher-order differentiation of implicit functions

Let us assume we have a function $f(x, y) = 0$. Then we know that

$$\frac{dy}{dx} = -\frac{f_x}{f_y}$$

Let us now find the second derivative d^2y/dx^2.

$$\frac{d^2y}{dx^2} = \frac{d}{dx}\left(\frac{dy}{dx}\right) = \frac{d}{dx}\left(-\frac{f_x}{f_y}\right)$$

$$= -\frac{f_y\dfrac{d}{dx}(f_x) - f_x\dfrac{d}{dx}(f_y)}{f_y^2}$$

Using the total derivative formula, we can work out the numerator as follows:

$$\frac{d}{dx}(f_x) = \frac{\partial}{\partial x}(f_x)\frac{dx}{dx} + \frac{\partial}{\partial y}(f_x)\frac{dy}{dx}$$

$$= f_{xx} + f_{xy}\frac{dy}{dx}$$

$$= f_{xx} + f_{xy}\left(-\frac{f_x}{f_y}\right)$$

$$= f_{xx} - f_{xy}\frac{f_x}{f_y}$$

Similarly,

$$\frac{d}{dx}(f_y) = f_{xy} - f_{yy}\frac{f_x}{f_y}$$

Substituting these results in the numerator, we find

$$\text{Numerator} = \left(f_{xx} - f_{xy}\frac{f_x}{f_y}\right)f_y - \left(f_{xy} - f_{yy}\frac{f_x}{f_y}\right)f_x$$

* See Hicks, J. R., *Value and Capital*, Chapter 1. New York: Oxford University Press, Inc., 1939.

$$= f_{xx}f_y - f_{xy}f_x - f_{xy}f_x + f_{yy}\frac{f_x^2}{f_y}$$

$$= f_{xx}f_y - 2f_{xy}f_x + f_{yy}\frac{f_x^2}{f_y}$$

$$= \frac{1}{f_y}(f_{xx}f_y^2 - 2f_{xy}f_xf_y + f_{yy}f_x^2)$$

Thus, the second-order derivative becomes

$$\frac{d^2y}{dx^2} = -\frac{f_{xx}f_y^2 + f_{yy}f_x^2 - 2f_{xy}f_xf_y}{f_y^3}$$

Example. Let u be an index of utility, x be meat, and y be bread. Then we can set $u = f(x, y)$. Let us hold u constant and find the differential of u. Since u is constant,

$$du = f_x\, dx + f_y\, dy = 0$$

$$\frac{dy}{dx} = -\frac{f_x}{f_y}$$

This may be interpreted as showing the amount of y (bread) that will be changed (in this case decreased) when there is a small unit increase of x (meat) to keep u constant; f_x and f_y are ordinal marginal utilities. In economics dy/dx is defined as the marginal rate of substitution between x and y. Since it is common to consider marginal utilities as positive, we have $f_x > 0$ and $f_y > 0$. Thus, $dy/dx < 0$.

Now, what is the rate of change? Is the rate increasing or decreasing? For this we need to find the second derivative, i.e., d^2y/dx^2. But we have just found it in our discussion above, i.e.,

$$\frac{d^2y}{dx^2} = -\frac{1}{f_y^3}(f_{xx}f_y^2 - 2f_{xy}f_xf_y + f_{yy}f_x^2)$$

Thus, the sign of d^2y/dx^2 will depend on whether or not what is contained in the parentheses is positive or negative. If it is negative, then $d^2y/dx^2 > 0$. This means, geometrically, that the curvature of the (indifference) curve is convex toward the origin. We shall have occasion to discuss this again.

Problems

1. Find dy/dx by use of implicit differentiation.

(a) $x^2y - x + 2y = 0$ (b) $x^2 - xy - 2x + 3 = 0$
(c) $x^2 - xy + y^2 = 0$ (d) $x^2 - y^2 = 0$
(e) $x^3 + 4xy = y^3 = 0$ (f) $x^2 + y^2 = r^2$

2. Find $\partial z/\partial x$ and $\partial z/\partial y$ of the following functions.

(a) $x^2 - y^2 + z^2 = 0$ (b) $x^2 + y^2 + 2z^2 - 6 = 0$

(c) $x^2 + 3y^2 + z^2 = 12$ (d) $xy - yz + zx = 0$

(e) $x^2 - 2xy + z^2 = 0$

(f) The mass of a rectangular solid is $xyz = v$. If the mass v were kept constant, what would be the change in z when there is a small change in x, i.e., find $\partial z/\partial x$.

3. Find d^2y/dx^2 for (a), (b), and (c) of Problem 1.

4. Given the utility function

$$u = q_1 q_2$$

where q_1 and q_2 are commodities and u is utility, hold u constant and find d^2q_2/dq_1^2. Explain the meaning of d^2q_2/dq_1^2.

5. Given the implicit function

$$f(x, y, z) = 0$$

assume we can set

$$z = g(x, y)$$

Find $\partial z/\partial x$ and $\partial^2 z/\partial x^2$.

4.9 Homogeneous functions

(i) Homogeneous functions—Definition

A special type of function that is used frequently in economics is the homogeneous function. Let us first illustrate it by use of an example. Let

$$f(x, y) = x^2 - y^2$$

If we replace x with tx and y with ty in this function, where t is a positive constant, then,

$$f(tx, ty) = (tx)^2 - (ty)^2 = t^2(x^2 - y^2)$$
$$= t^2 f(x, y)$$

If the function is

$$f(x, y) = x^3 - y^3$$

then

$$f(tx, ty) = t^3 f(x, y)$$

By induction we see that, if we have

$$f(x, y) = x^n - y^n$$

then

$$f(tx, ty) = t^n f(x, y)$$

Other examples of homogeneous functions are

$$f(x, y) = x^2 + xy - 3y^2$$

then

$$f(tx, ty) = t^2 f(x, y)$$
$$f(x, y) = x^3 + 3x^2 y - 3xy^2 + y^3$$

and then

$$f(tx, ty) = t^3 f(x, y)$$

When we have a function that behaves in this fashion, i.e.,

$$f(tx, ty) = t^h f(x, y)$$

we call $f(x, y)$ a *homogeneous function of degree h*. A type of homogeneous function used frequently in economics is that of degree zero.

Example 1.

$$f(x, y, z) = \frac{x}{z} + \frac{y}{z}$$

Thus, we have

$$f(tx, ty, tz) = \frac{tx}{tz} + \frac{ty}{tz} = \frac{x}{z} + \frac{y}{z}$$
$$= f(x, y, z) = t^0 f(x, y, z)$$

Example 2.

$$f(x, y, z) = \frac{x^2}{yz} + \frac{y^2}{xz} + \frac{z^2}{xy}$$

Then,

$$f(tx, ty, tz) = \frac{t^2 x^2}{t^2 yz} + \frac{t^2 y^2}{t^2 xz} + \frac{t^2 z^2}{t^2 xy}$$
$$= t^0 f(x, y, z)$$

Example 3. Let q be quantity, p be price, and y be income. The demand function is shown as

$$q = f(p, y) = \frac{y}{kp}$$

where k is a constant. Then,

$$f(tp, ty) = \frac{ty}{ktp} = \frac{y}{kp} = t^0 f(p, y)$$

Thus,

$$q = f(p, y) = f(tp, ty)$$

which means, when prices p and income y change in the same proportion t, that there will be no change in demand q (there is no money illusion).

Example 4. The Cobb-Douglas production function* is shown as

$$P = bL^k C^{1-k}$$

where P is the amount of product, L is labor, C is capital, and b and k are constants. We shall write this in functional form as

$$P = f(L, C)$$

Then,

$$f(tL, tC) = b(tL)^k (tC)^{1-k} = tbL^k C^{1-k} = tf(L, C)$$

i.e., the production function is a homogeneous function of degree 1. This means that, if labor and capital are doubled ($t = 2$), for example, then product P will also double.

Let us next find the marginal product due to labor.

$$\frac{\partial P}{\partial L} = bkL^{k-1}C^{1-k}$$

In functional form, this is

$$f_L = f_L(L, C) = bkL^{k-1}C^{1-k}$$

Let us check its homogeneity.

$$\begin{aligned}
f_L(tL, tC) &= bk(tL)^{k-1}(tC)^{1-k} \\
&= bkt^{k-1+1-k}L^{k-1}C^{1-k} \\
&= t^0 bkL^{k-1}C^{1-k} = t^0 f_L(L, C)
\end{aligned}$$

i.e., the marginal product of labor is homogeneous of degree zero. This means that, when labor and capital are doubled, the marginal product of labor does not change (but recall the product doubles). Similarly, it can be easily checked to see that the marginal product of capital is also homogeneous of degree zero.

Example 5. Let q_i be the quantity consumed and q_i^0 be the initial endowment of a consumer. Then,

$$E_i = q_i - q_i^0$$

is the excess demand for Q_i. Let

$$u = u(q_1, q_2, q_3)$$

be the utility function. (We consider only three goods for simplicity.) This is shown in terms of the excess demand function as

$$u = u(E_1 + q_1^0, E_2 + q_2^0, E_3 + q_3^0)$$

* Douglas, P. H., *Theory of Wages.* New York: Macmillan Co., 1934.

Let y be income, then,

$$y = p_1 q_1 + p_2 q_2 + p_3 q_3 = p_1(E_1 + q_1^0) + p_2(E_2 + q_2^0) + p_3(E_3 + q_3^0)$$

The consumer wishes to maximize his utility U subject to his income y. The conditions for the maximum to be achieved are

$$\frac{\partial u}{\partial E_1} - \lambda p_1 = 0$$

$$\frac{\partial u}{\partial E_2} - \lambda p_2 = 0$$

$$\frac{\partial u}{\partial E_3} - \lambda p_3 = 0$$

$$p_1 E_1 + p_2 E_2 + p_3 E_3 + p_1 q_1^0 + p_2 q_2^0 + p_3 q_3^0 - y = 0$$

These conditions will be derived in the next chapter, so, for the moment, let us accept them as given. We have four equations and four unknowns, λ, E_1, E_2, and E_3. This means we can find the unknowns in terms of prices and the initial quantities which are known.

This process can be shown as follows: From the third equation we find

$$\lambda = \frac{1}{p_3} \frac{\partial u}{\partial E_3}$$

Substituting this in the first two equations and combining these two with the fourth equation, we have

$$\frac{\partial u}{\partial E_1} - \frac{1}{p_3} \frac{\partial u}{\partial E_3} p_1 = 0$$

$$\frac{\partial u}{\partial E_2} - \frac{1}{p_3} \frac{\partial u}{\partial E_3} p_2 = 0$$

$$p_1 E_1 + p_2 E_2 + p_3 E_3 + p_1 q_1^0 + p_2 q_2^0 + p_3 q_3^0 - y = 0$$

Thus, we have three unknowns E_1, E_2, and E_3, which, when solved, will be in terms of the given prices p_1, p_2, p_3 and q_1^0, q_2^0, q_3^0 as follows:

$$E_1 = E_1(p_1, p_2, p_3, q_1^0, q_2^0, q_3^0)$$
$$E_2 = E_2(p_1, p_2, p_3, q_1^0, q_2^0, q_3^0)$$
$$E_3 = E_3(p_1, p_2, p_3, q_1^0, q_2^0, q_3^0)$$

The excess demand functions are homogeneous of degree zero, i.e., if prices change proportionately, there will be no change in excess demand. To put it another way, only the relative prices affect excess demand. We shall show this as follows: Let the prices increase by t times. Then,

$$ty = tp_1q_1 + tp_2q_2 + tp_3q_3$$

The conditions for a maximum will become

$$\frac{\partial u}{\partial E_1} - \lambda tp_1 = 0$$

$$\frac{\partial u}{\partial E_2} - \lambda tp_2 = 0$$

$$\frac{\partial u}{\partial E_3} - \lambda tp_3 = 0$$

$$t(p_1E_1 + p_2E_2 + p_3E_3 + p_1q_1^0 + p_2q_2^0 + p_3q_3^0) - ty = 0$$

From the third equation we find

$$\lambda t = \frac{1}{p_3} \frac{\partial u}{\partial E_3}$$

Thus, the first and second equations become

$$\frac{\partial u}{\partial E_1} - \frac{1}{p_3} \frac{\partial u}{\partial E_3} p_1 = 0$$

$$\frac{\partial u}{\partial E_2} - \frac{1}{p_3} \frac{\partial u}{\partial E_3} p_2 = 0$$

and also from the fourth equation, dividing through by t,

$$p_1E_1 + p_2E_2 + p_3E_3 + p_1q_1^0 + p_2q_2^0 + p_3q_3^0 - y = 0$$

Thus from these three equations we find

$$E_i = E_i(p_1, p_2, p_3, q_1^0, q_2^0, q_3^0), \qquad i = 1, 2, 3$$

Even though we increased the prices by t times, we have obtained the same excess demand functions, and they are homogeneous of degree zero.

(ii) Properties of the homogeneous function (I)

Let us look at several other properties of the homogeneous function. Consider a homogeneous function of degree h

$$u = f(x, y)$$

(1)
$$f(tx, ty) = t^h f(x, y)$$

Since t can be any value, let $t = 1/x$. Then,

$$(2) \qquad f(tx, ty) = f\left(1, \frac{y}{x}\right) = \phi\left(\frac{y}{x}\right)$$

That is, $f(tx, ty)$ becomes a function ϕ which has as its variable y/x. Also

$$(3) \qquad t^h f(x, y) = \left(\frac{1}{x}\right)^h f(x, y)$$

Thus, from equations (2) and (3),

$$(4) \qquad f(x, y) = x^h \phi\left(\frac{y}{x}\right)$$

That is, if $f(x, y)$ is a homogeneous function of degree h, it can be shown as equation (4).

In general, if

$$u = f(x, y, z, \ldots)$$
$$f(tx, ty, tz, \ldots) = t^h f(x, y, z, \ldots)$$

then,

$$f(x, y, z, \ldots) = x^h \phi\left(\frac{y}{x}, \frac{z}{x}, \ldots\right)$$

$$= y^h \psi\left(\frac{x}{y}, \frac{z}{y}, \ldots\right)$$

$$= z^h \mu\left(\frac{x}{z}, \frac{y}{z}, \ldots\right)$$

Example 1. Consider a homogeneous equation of degree 3.

$$f(x, y) = x^2 y - xy^2$$

Then,

$$f(x, y) = x^3 \left(\frac{y}{x} - \frac{y^2}{x^2}\right) = x^3 \phi\left(\frac{y}{x}\right)$$

where

$$\phi\left(\frac{y}{x}\right) = \frac{y}{x} - \frac{y^2}{x^2}$$

Example 2.

$$f(x, y, z) = x^3 y^2 z - xy^5 + y^3 z^3$$

This is a homogeneous function of degree 6. Then

$$f(x, y, z) = x^6 \left(\frac{y^2 z}{x^3} - \frac{y^5}{x^5} + \frac{y^3 z^3}{x^6}\right)$$

$$= x^6 \left[\left(\frac{y}{x}\right)^2 \left(\frac{z}{x}\right) - \left(\frac{y}{x}\right)^5 + \left(\frac{y}{x}\right)^3 \left(\frac{z}{x}\right)^3 \right]$$

$$= x^6 \phi \left(\frac{y}{x}, \frac{z}{x}\right)$$

Work out the cases for y and z as exercises.

Example 3. Consider a function

$$f(x, y, z) = \frac{x^3}{y^2 z} + \frac{y^3}{x^2 z}$$

A check will show that it is a homogeneous function of degree zero. We also see that

$$f(x, y, z) = \frac{x}{z} \frac{x^2}{y^2} + \frac{y}{z} \frac{y^2}{x^2}$$

$$= \frac{x}{z} \frac{x^2}{z^2} \frac{z^2}{y^2} + \frac{y}{z} \frac{y^2}{z^2} \frac{z^2}{x^2}$$

$$= \left(\frac{x}{z}\right)^3 \left(\frac{y}{z}\right)^{-2} + \left(\frac{y}{z}\right)^3 \left(\frac{x}{z}\right)^{-2}$$

$$= \phi \left(\frac{x}{z}, \frac{y}{z}\right)$$

$$= z^0 \phi \left(\frac{x}{z}, \frac{y}{z}\right)$$

Example 4. Consider an individual demand function

$$q_j = q(p_1, p_2, \ldots, p_n, \bar{q}_1, \bar{q}_2, \ldots, \bar{q}_n)$$

where p_i are prices and $\bar{q}_i$ are the initial collection of commodities. The initial position is in equilibrium and we shall assume the $\bar{q}_i$ to be given. If we assume the demand function to be a homogeneous function of degree zero, we find

$$q_j = p_n^0 \phi \left(\frac{p_1}{p_n}, \frac{p_2}{p_n}, \ldots, \frac{p_{n-1}}{p_n}\right)$$

$$= \phi \left(\frac{p_1}{p_n}, \frac{p_2}{p_n}, \ldots, \frac{p_{n-1}}{p_n}\right)$$

Assume p_n to be the *numéraire*. Then our result tells us the demand for q_j is dependent on relative prices.

(iii) Properties of homogeneous functions (II)

The next property is that if $f(x, y)$ is a homogeneous function of degree

h, the kth partial derivative of f is a homogeneous function of degree $h - k$, provided the derivative exists. As an illustration, consider a homogeneous function of degree 4

$$f(x, y) = x^2y^2 + xy^3$$

Then, the partial derivative with respect to x is

$$f_x = 2xy^2 + y^3$$

As is easily seen, this is a homogeneous function of degree $4 - 1 = 3$. Let us differentiate again.

$$f_{xx} = 2y^2$$

This is a homogeneous function of degree $4 - 2 = 2$.

Sketching the proof as follows, we know that

$$f(x, y) = x^h \phi \left(\frac{y}{x} \right)$$

and the partial derivative becomes

$$f_x = hx^{h-1}\phi + x^h \phi' \frac{\partial}{\partial x}\left(\frac{y}{x} \right)$$

$$= hx^{h-1}\phi - x^h \frac{y}{x^2} \phi' = x^{h-1}\left[h\phi - \frac{y}{x} \phi' \right]$$

Thus, we see that f_x is a homogeneous function of degree $h - 1$. By differentiating again,

$$f_{xx} = (h - 1)x^{h-2}\left(h\phi - \frac{y}{x} \phi' \right)$$

$$+ x^{h-1}\left[h\phi'\left(-\frac{y}{x^2} \right) + \frac{y}{x^2} \phi' + \frac{y}{x} \phi'' \frac{y}{x^2} \right]$$

$$= x^{h-2}\left(h^2\phi - h\phi + \frac{y^2}{x^2} \phi'' - 2\frac{y}{x} h\phi' + 2\frac{y}{x} \phi' \right)$$

Thus, f_{xx} is a homogeneous function of degree $h - 2$. When this process is continued k times, we find that the kth partial derivative of f will be a homogeneous function of degree $h - k$.

Problems

1. Show that $f(tx, ty) = t^h f(x, y)$ for the following functions.

(a) $f(x, y) = ax^2 + by^2$, $h = 2$ (b) $f(x, y) = ax^2y + bxy^2$, $h = 3$
(c) $f(x, y) = ax^3 + bx^2y + cxy^2 + dy^3$, $h = 3$

2. Given the following production function, show that it is homogeneous of degree 1.

$$V = (\beta K^{-\rho} + \alpha L^{-\rho})^{-1/\rho}$$

where K, L, and V are capital, labor, and output, respectively.

3. Using the functions in Problem 1, show that

$$f(x, y) = x^h \phi\left(\frac{y}{x}\right)$$

$$= y^h \phi\left(\frac{x}{y}\right)$$

4. Given the following functions, show that

$$f(x, y, z) = z^0 \phi\left(\frac{x}{z}\right), \left(\frac{y}{z}\right)$$

$$= y^0 \psi\left(\frac{x}{y}\right), \left(\frac{z}{y}\right)$$

$$= x^0 \mu\left(\frac{y}{x}\right), \left(\frac{z}{x}\right)$$

(a) $f(x, y, z) = \dfrac{x^3 + y^3 + z^3}{xyz}$

(b) $f(x, y, z) = x^3 + y^3 + z^3$
$$x^2y + y^2z + z^2x$$

5. Using the functions in Problem 1, show that f_x is homogeneous of degree 1 and f_{xx} is homogeneous of degree 2.

4.10 Euler's theorem

Euler's theorem is a special relationship obtained from homogeneous functions and is well known to economists in connection with marginal productivity theory, usually under the name of *adding-up theorem*.

Let $u = f(x, y)$ be a homogeneous function of degree h. Then, the following relation holds identically

$$x\frac{\partial u}{\partial x} + y\frac{\partial u}{\partial y} \equiv hu$$

This relation is proved very simply by using implicit differentiation and letting

$$f(tx, ty) = t^h f(x, y)$$

$$\frac{\partial}{\partial t}(\text{l.h.s.}) = \frac{\partial f(tx, ty)}{\partial tx}\frac{\partial tx}{\partial t} + \frac{\partial f(tx, ty)}{\partial ty}\frac{\partial ty}{\partial t}$$

$$= xf_{tx} + yf_{ty}$$

$$\frac{\partial}{\partial t}(\text{r.h.s.}) = \frac{\partial t^h}{\partial t} f(x, y) + t^h \frac{\partial f(x, y)}{\partial t}$$

$$= ht^{h-1}f(x, y) + 0$$

$$= ht^{h-1}f(x, y)$$

where l.h.s. is the left-hand side and r.h.s. is the right-hand side. Since l.h.s. = r.h.s., we have

$$xf_{tx} + yf_{ty} = ht^{h-1}f(x, y)$$

Thus, if $t = 1$, then, since t can be any number,

$$xf_x + yf_y = hf(x, y)$$

h is the degree of the equation. If we have a linear homogeneous function, then $h = 1$, and

$$xf_x + yf_y = f(x, y)$$

or

$$x\frac{\partial u}{\partial x} + y\frac{\partial u}{\partial y} = u$$

When we have a second-degree equation, it will become

$$x\frac{\partial u}{\partial x} + y\frac{\partial u}{\partial y} = 2u$$

and the same for higher degrees. Furthermore, this may be generalized for more than 2 variables, i.e.,

$$x\frac{\partial u}{\partial x} + y\frac{\partial u}{\partial y} + z\frac{\partial u}{\partial z} + \ldots = ku(x, y, z, \ldots)$$

where k is the degree of the equation.

Example 1.

$$f(x, y, z) = 3x + 2y - 4z$$

is a linear homogeneous function (degree 1). Then, according to Euler's theorem:

$$xf_x + yf_y + zf_z = 1 \times (3x + 2y - 4z)$$

Check

$$f_x = 3, \qquad f_y = 2, \qquad f_z = -4$$

Thus, the left-hand side is

$$\text{l.h.s.} = 3x + 2y - 4z = \text{r.h.s.}$$

Example 2.
$$f(x, y) = x^2 - 3y^2$$
is a homogeneous function of degree 2. Thus, the Euler theorem tells us
$$xf_x + yf_y = 2(x^2 - 3y^2)$$

Check
$$f_x = 2x, \qquad f_y = -6y$$

Thus,
$$\text{l.h.s.} = 2x^2 - 6y^2 = 2(x^2 - 3y^2) = \text{r.h.s.}$$

Example 3.
$$f(x, y) = x^3 + 2x^2y + y^3$$
is a homogeneous function of degree 3. Then, Euler's theorem tells us
$$xf_x + yf_y = 3(x^3 + 2x^2y + y^3)$$

Check
$$xf_x = x(3x^2 + 4xy) = 3x^3 + 4x^2y$$
$$yf_y = y(2x^2 + 3y^2) = 2x^2y + 3y^3$$
$$\text{l.h.s.} = 3x^3 + 6x^2y + 3y^3$$
$$= 3(x^3 + 2x^2y + y^3) = \text{r.h.s.}$$

Example 4. The *adding-up theorem* states that the product will be exhausted if factors are paid according to the marginal productivity theory. That is, if
$$q = f(a, b)$$
where q is output and a and b are inputs, then,
$$q = af_a + bf_b$$
where f_a and f_b will be the marginal products of a and b.

We shall first show how this works for a linear homogeneous production function. The Cobb-Douglas function was such a function, so let us use that.
$$P = bL^kC^{1-k} = f(L, C)$$
The adding up theorem states that
$$Lf_L + Cf_C = P$$

Check
$$\text{l.h.s.} = L(bkL^{k-1}C^{1-k}) + C(b(1 - k)L^kC^{-k})$$
$$= (k + 1 - k)bL^kC^{1-k} = bL^kC^{1-k} = \text{r.h.s.}$$

This linear function implies that average costs and, hence, marginal costs are constant. A more general case of the adding-up theorem will be discussed after we have studied maxima and minima problems.

Problems

Given the following homogeneous functions of degree h show that

$$xf_x + yf_y = hu$$

(a) $f(x, y, z) = x^2 + xy + y^2 + yz$
(b) $f(Kx, y, z) = x^2y^{-2} + y^2z^{-2} + z^2x^{-2}$
(c) $f(K, L) = (\beta K^{-\rho} + \alpha L^{-\rho})^{1/\rho}$

4.11 Partial elasticities

Let

$$q_a = f(p_a, p_b)$$

where q_a is the quantity of good A that is demanded, p_a is its price, and p_b is the price of good B. We have only the price of two goods, but it can easily be generalized to n goods.

Partial elasticities are defined as

$$\eta = - \frac{\partial q_a}{\partial p_a} \frac{p_a}{q_a}$$

This is the partial elasticity of good A with respect to p_a. Likewise, we may define the partial elasticity of good A with respect to p_b by

$$\eta = - \frac{\partial q_a}{\partial p_b} \frac{p_b}{q_a}$$

Example.

$$q_a = 50 - 5p_a - 4p_b$$

Then, elasticity with respect to p_a is

$$\eta = - \frac{\partial q_a}{\partial p_a} \frac{p_a}{q_a}$$

$$\frac{\partial q_a}{\partial p_a} = -5$$

Thus,

$$\eta = (-5) \frac{p_a}{50 - 5p_a - 4p_b}$$

At $p_a = 5$ and $p_b = 5$, we have

$$\eta = (-5) \frac{5}{50 - 25 - 20} = 5$$

Problems

Given the following demand curves, find the partial elasticities with respect to p_a, and evaluate for the given prices.

(a) $q_a = 50 - 4p_a - 5p_b, p_a = 5, p_b = 5,$
(b) $q_a = 10 - p_a + 2p_b, p_a = 3, p_b = 2$

Notes and References

For proofs and derivations of the various topics that have been explained heuristically, see the following references.

4.1–4.3 Courant (Vol. I, 1937), Chapter 10; Sokolnikoff (1939), Chapter 3; Tintner (1953), Chapter 16; Munroe (1963), Chapters 1–6; Spiegel (1963), Chapter 6; Taylor (1955), Chapters 5, 6, 7; Aleksandrov (1956), Chapter 2; Protter-Morrey (1964), Chapter 4.

4.4–4.5 Allen (1938), Chapter 8; Courant (Vol. II, 1936), pp. 59–69; and the corresponding sections in Munroe (1963), Spiegel (1963), Taylor (1955); Protter-Morrey (1964).

4.6 Allen (1938) pp. 332–334. Courant (Vol. I, 1937) pp. 472–476. Courant (Vol. II, 1936) pp. 69–74. Sokolnikoff (1939) pp. 67–71.

4.7, 4.8 Allen (1938) pp. 334–339. Courant (Vol. I, 1937) pp. 480–485. Sokolnikoff (1939) pp. 71–74, 89–91.

4.9, 4.10 Allen (1938) pp. 315–322. Sokolnikoff (1939) p. 75. Tintner (1953) Chapter 17.

4.11 For economic applications of partial derivatives, see Tintner (1953) Chapter 16. It is better to first finish the next chapter before seeking applications.

Aleksandrov, A. D., Kolmogorov, A. N., and Lavrent'ev, M. A. (ed.), Mathematics, Its Content, Methods, and Meaning. Translated by Gould, S. H., Bartha, T. Massachusetts: The M. I. T. Press, 1963.

Munroe, M. E., Modern Multidimensional Calculus. Massachusetts: Addison-Wesley Publishing Co., 1963.

Spiegel, M. R., Advanced Calculus. New York: Schaum Publishing Co., 1963.

CHAPTER 5

Maxima and Minima of Functions

5.1 Increasing and decreasing functions

Let us assume x is output and y is average cost. Furthermore, let us assume that the relation between x and y is $y = 40 - 6x + x^2$. This can be thought of as an *average cost function*. Now, the question is: Does y (average cost) increase, decrease, or stay stationary as x (output) increases? Let us first draw a graph (Figure 5–1) of this cost function, which shows that, as

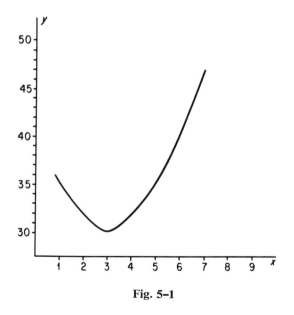

Fig. 5–1

x (output) increases, y (average cost) decreases, reaches a minimum, and then starts to increase. Graphing the first part of the function, we have Figure 5–2. A function (curve) that is downward sloping like this is called a

171

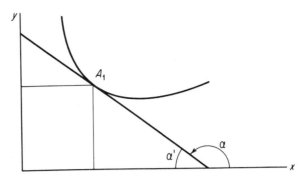

Fig. 5–2

decreasing function, i.e., the value of the function y decreases as x increases. We shall show this mathematically, selecting a point A_1 on the curve and drawing a tangent to the curve. The slope of this tangent is given by tan α. We also know that the derivative of the function at the point A_1 is equal to the slope of the curve at that point. Thus,

$$\frac{dy}{dx} = \tan \alpha$$

But we see graphically that $\alpha > 90°$. We know from trigonometry that

$$\tan \alpha = \tan (180° - \alpha') = -\tan \alpha'$$

For example, if $\alpha = 135°$, then $\alpha' = 45°$. Thus,

$$\tan 135° = \tan (180° - 45°) = -\tan 45° = -1$$

and the derivative will be equal to

$$\frac{dy}{dx} = \tan \alpha = \tan 135° = -1 < 0$$

In general, when $\alpha > 90°$, then $dy/dx < 0$. As a conclusion, we may say that $y = f(x)$ is a *decreasing* function at the point x when $f'(x) < 0$. By a similar argument we may say $y = f(x)$ is an *increasing* function at the point x when $f'(x) > 0$.

Example 1. Using our average cost function, let us find whether it is a decreasing or increasing function at the values $x = 2$ and $x = 4$.
(a) When $x = 2$, $y = 40 - 6x + x^2$

$$\frac{dy}{dx} = -6 + 2x = -6 + 4 = -2 < 0$$

Thus, at $x = 2$, it is a decreasing (cost) function. This is interpreted as follows: When x increases by a small amount, y will decrease by 2 units at the point $x = 2$.

(b) When $x = 4$,

$$\frac{dy}{dx} = -6 + 2x = -6 + 8 = 2 > 0$$

and it is an increasing function. When $f'(x) = 0$ the slope of the curve is horizontal. That is, $\tan \alpha = \tan 0° = 0$. At this point the curve is stationary. We shall present this again in connection with our discussion of maxima and minima.

Example 2.

$$y = x^2 - 4x$$

$$\therefore \quad \frac{dy}{dx} = 2x - 4$$

When $x = -1$, then $f'(x) = -6 < 0$. Thus, $y = f(x)$ is a decreasing function at the point where $x = -1$.

When $x = 2, f'(x) = 0$ and then $y = f(x)$ is stationary at $x = 2$.

When $x = 3, f'(x) = 2 > 0$, and then $y = f(x)$ is an increasing function at this point.

5.2 Convexity of curves

Consider a car that starts from a standstill position and reaches a certain speed after a certain amount of time. Let y (meters) be the distance the car has traveled and t (seconds) be time. We have the following relationship:

(1) $$y = t^2$$

Thus, when $t = 1$ second, then $y = 1$ meter; when $t = 3$ seconds, then $y = 9$ meters, and so forth. Let us differentiate with respect to t. Then,

(2) $$\frac{dy}{dt} = 2t$$

dy/dt gives the *velocity* at time t. For example, when $t = 2$, i.e., 2 seconds after the car has started, $dy/dt = 4$ meters/second, and so forth.

Let us graph equation (1). In Figure 5–3 $dy/dt = 2t$ shows the slope of this curve at various points. For example, at the point $(3, 9)$, we have

$$\frac{dy}{dt} = \tan \alpha = 2 \times 3 = 6$$

$$\therefore \quad \alpha = 80°30' \text{ (approximately)}$$

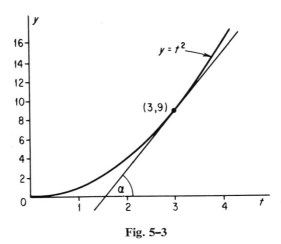

Fig. 5–3

Next, let us differentiate (2) once more

(3) $$\frac{d^2y}{dt^2} = 2$$

This gives us the change in velocity per second, i.e., the acceleration. We have 2 meters per second, per second, as acceleration. This means velocity *increases* every second by 2 meters per second. Table 5–1 summarizes this in table form.

Table 5–1

t (seconds)	0	1	2	3	4
y (meters)	0	1	4	9	16
dy/dt (meters/second)	0	2	4	6	8
d^2/dt^2 (meters/second^2)	2	2	2	2	2

We are interested in the second derivative $d^2y/dt^2 = f''(t)$. This shows the rate of change. In our present case $f''(t) = 2$ meters/second^2 and it is constant, i.e., the rate of change is the same. Thus, the velocity is *increasing* at a rate of 2 meters/second every second whether it is 1 second or 4 seconds after start.

Using this discussion, we may define several terms. The function $y = f(x)$ in Figure 5–4(a) is our present case, and we shall say y is increasing at an increasing rate. This is shown by

$$\frac{d^2y}{dx^2} = f''(x) > 0$$

The curve $y = f(x)$ lies above the tangent, and we say the curve is *concave upward* or *convex downward*.

The implication of $f''(x) > 0$ is that $f'(x) = \tan \alpha$ is increasing at the point of tangent. For $f'(x) = \tan \alpha$ to increase, α needs to increase toward 90°. This can happen only if the curve gets steeper. Thus, the curve will be convex downward as in Figure 5–4(a).

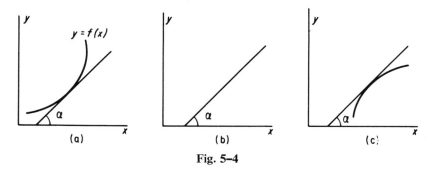

(a)   (b)   (c)

Fig. 5–4

Figure 5–4(b) shows the rate of increase of y at zero. That is,

$$\frac{d^2y}{dx^2} = f''(x) = 0$$

For example, if

$$y = 2t, \qquad \frac{dy}{dt} = 2, \qquad \frac{d^2y}{dt^2} = 0$$

there is no curvature of the curve. The curve is a straight line.

Figure 5–4(c) shows the rate of increase of y to be decreasing. This is written

$$\frac{d^2y}{dx^2} = f''(x) < 0$$

To summarize, the condition for convex downward is $f''(x) > 0$; straight line, $f''(x) = 0$; and convex upward, $f''(x) < 0$. In the special case where we have two curves tangent to each other, we can draw a tangent going through the point P where they touch, as in Figure 5–5. Then the curve APB will be above, and the curve CPD will be below, the tangent line.

If we look upon CPB as a curve and imagine the point P moving along the curve, then, when P is between C and P of the curve, $f'' < 0$ because CD is

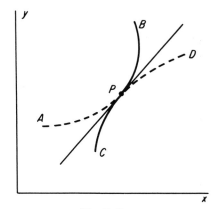

Fig. 5–5

convex upward. But, from point P up to B, since APB is convex downward, $f'' > 0$. Thus, at point P, f'' changes signs and, at that point, $f'' = 0$. This point P is called the *point of inflection* of the curve, and the tangent line is called an *inflectional tangent*.

Example 1.

$$y = x^2 - 4x, \qquad f' = 2x - 4, \qquad f'' = 2 > 0$$

Thus convex downward.

Example 2.

$$y = \tfrac{1}{2}x^4 - 3x^2, \qquad f' = 2x^3 - 6x, \qquad f'' = 6x^2 - 6$$

The point of inflection is where $f''(x) = 0$. Thus, let

$$6x^2 - 6 = 0, \qquad x^2 - 1 = 0, \qquad (x + 1)(x - 1) = 0$$

$$\therefore \quad x = 1, \qquad x = -1$$

Thus, the point of inflection will be at $x = 1$ and $x = -1$. For $x = 1$ we have

$$y = \tfrac{1}{2}x^4 - 3x^2 = -2.5$$

and one of the points of inflection is at $(1, -2.5)$.

Example 3. The point of inflection is well known to students who have studied the law of diminishing returns and the total product curve. Let

$$q = f(x_1, x_2)$$

be a production function, where q is output and x_1 and x_2 are variable inputs. Hold $x_2 = x_2^0$ constant, and let x_1 vary. Then the change in q is usually shown graphically as in Figure 5–6. The student will recall the argument that the output will increase at an increasing rate up to point A on the total product curve and, from A on, it will increase at a decreasing rate. In terms of the marginal physical product (MPP), the MPP increases up to A; then starts to decrease. This is shown by the MPP curve in the lower diagram, where the MPP reaches a maximum at A and then starts to decrease.

This point A is the point of inflection. Let us show this mathematically. From (1) we have $\partial q / \partial x_1$ as the MPP. Then since the MPP is increasing up to point A,

$$\frac{\partial}{\partial x_1} \left(\frac{\partial q}{\partial x_1} \right) > 0$$

That is, $\partial^2 q / \partial x_1^2 > 0$. Hence, in terms of the curvature argument, the total product curve up to point A is convex downward.

From point A on, the MPP increases at a decreasing rate. Hence

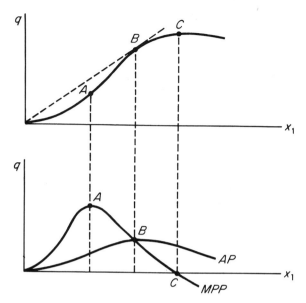

Fig. 5–6

$$\frac{\partial}{\partial x_1}\left(\frac{\partial q}{\partial x_1}\right) < 0$$

That is, $\partial^2 q/\partial x_1^2 < 0$. Hence, from point A on, the total product curve is convex upward.

Therefore, at the point A, where the sign of $\partial^2 q/\partial x_1^2$ changes from $+$ to $-$, we have

$$\frac{\partial^2 q}{\partial x_1^2} = 0$$

and A is the point of inflection.

Example 4. Given the following function, find the points of inflection.

$$y = ke^{-x^2/2}$$

We first find f' and f''.

$$f' = -xke^{-x^2/2}$$
$$f'' = -ke^{-x^2/2} + x^2ke^{-x^2/2} = (x^2 - 1)ke^{-x^2/2}$$

The point of inflection is where $f''(x) = 0$. Thus let

$$x^2 - 1 = 0$$
$$\therefore \quad x = 1 \quad \text{or} \quad -1$$

That is, the point of inflection will be at two points: $x = 1$ and $x = -1$. Figure 5–7 is a graph of this function. As is seen, it is a normal curve. The

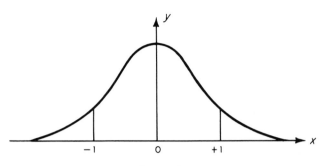

Fig. 5–7

function we have is the function of the normal curve where the mean $\mu = 0$ and the $\sigma = 1$. Hence the normal curve has points of inflection at one standard deviation from the origin on both sides as shown in the diagram.

Example 5. Given the following function

$$y = x^4 + 2x + 5$$

find the points of inflection.

$$y' = 4x^3 + 2$$

$$y'' = 12x^2$$

The $y'' = 0$ when $x = 0$. When $x \neq 0$, $y'' = 12x^2 > 0$ and is a monotone increasing function. That is, it does not change signs before and after $x = 0$. Hence, we do not have a point of inflection.

This example illustrates the basic characteristic that the point of inflection is where $f''(x)$ changes sign. The condition that $f''(x) = 0$ is derived from this basic property that the point of inflection is where $f''(x)$ changes sign, and, as the example illustrates, $f''(x) = 0$ does not necessarily imply that $f''(x)$ changes sign.

Problems

1. Determine whether the curves are rising or falling at the given points. Also find the x that gives y a stationary value. Draw a rough graph for your own visual aid.

(a) $y = 2x^2 - 6x + 2$ (1) $x = 2$,   (2) $x = 6$
(b) $y = x^3 - 3x^2$ (1) $x = 1$,   (2) $x = 4$
(c) $y = x^2 - 2x$ (1) $x = -1$,   (2) $x = 3$
(d) $y = -x^2 + 4x$ (1) $x = 1$,   (2) $x = 5$

2. Using the problems in 1 above, determine whether the curves are convex downward or convex upward.

3. Find the point (or points) of inflection, if any, on the following curves.

(a) $y = x^4 - 6x^2$
(b) $y = 3x^3 - 6x^2$
(c) $y = ce^{-x^2/2}$
(d) $y = x^4 - 4x + 1$

5.3 Maxima and minima of functions of one variable

(i) Maxima and minima of functions

Referring to Figure 5–8, we see that points on either side of B_1 in a small neighborhood are lower than B_1. Then, the function $y = f(x)$ has a maximum value at the point B_1. In a similar way we define B_2 as the point where the function $y = f(x)$ has a minimum value. The maximum and minimum values together are called the *extreme values* of the function.

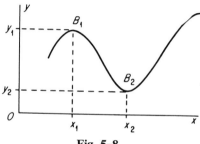

Fig. 5–8

Symbolically, this may be shown as follows: Let $\epsilon > 0$ be a small number. Then,

$$f(x_1 - \epsilon) < f(x_1), \quad f(x_1) > f(x_1 + \epsilon) \quad \dots \quad \text{maximum}$$
$$f(x_2 - \epsilon) > f(x_2), \quad f(x_2) < f(x_2 + \epsilon) \quad \dots \quad \text{minimum}$$

As can be seen, as the domain of x is enlarged, other maximum and minimum values may occur at different points. In Figure 5–9, there are two maximum points A and C and two minimum points B and E. Since point C is the highest of the maximum points, it is sometimes called a *global maximum*,

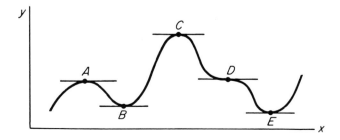

Fig. 5–9

and the other maximum points such as *A* are called *local maxima*. In similar fashion, the point *B* is a *local minimum*, and *E* is a *global minimum*.

The point *D* is a point of inflection and is neither a maximum or minimum.

Let us consider one more special case of an extreme value, although we shall not be using it in our subsequent discussion. In Figure 5–10, point *A* is

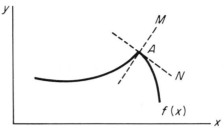

Fig. 5–10

a maximum point on a continuous curve. That is, there is no break in this curve.

At point *A*, however, we can see there are two tangents, and the function is not differentiable at the point *A*. That is, a continuous function may not be differentiable. (However, if a function is differentiable at a given point, it is continuous at that point.)

In such situations as shown in Figure 5–10, we shall not be able to determine whether it is an extreme value by the methods described in the subsequent discussions. However, since we usually do not encounter such functions in economics, we shall assume the functions are differentiable (and hence continuous) in our subsequent discussions, unless otherwise stated, and hence shall not encounter extreme points such as *A*.

(ii) Necessary and sufficient conditions for an extreme value

Assume we have two functions as shown in Figure 5–11(a) and (b). From our previous discussion we know that, when $dy/dx = 0$, the tangent to the

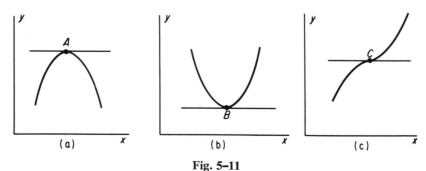

Fig. 5–11

curve at that point will be parallel to the x-axis. Let A and B be two such points, then the tangents are parallel to the x-axis. As is evident from the graph, point A is a maximum and point B a minimum. In other words, the *necessary conditions* for a certain point such as A or B to be an extreme value is that $dy/dx = 0$ at that point.

From our discussion of the convexity of curves, however, we may have a situation such as in Figure 5–11(c), where the inflectional tangent going through the point of inflection is parallel to the x-axis. Hence, at this point the $dy/dx = 0$, but C is not a maximum or minimum. In other words, the point at which $dy/dx = 0$ may be a maximum or minimum or a point such as C. Hence, this $dy/dx = 0$ is a necessary condition but is not a sufficient condition for an extreme value.

Therefore, two questions arise: (1) How may we be certain that we do not have a point of inflection such as in Figure 5–11(c), and (2) how do we tell whether it is a maximum or minimum? For this we can use our knowledge of the curvature of curves. Looking at Figure 5–12, we see that, for the left side

Fig. 5–12

of the curve, we have an increasing curve, i.e., $dy/dx > 0$. But we also see that it is increasing at a decreasing rate. That is, $d^2y/dx^2 < 0$, and thus the slope dy/dx must gradually approach zero.

Looking on the right side of the curve, we see it is a decreasing curve. Thus $dy/dx < 0$. But we see it is decreasing at an increasing rate. Since $dy/dx < 0$, this means that $d^2y/dx^2 < 0$. Putting the two sides together, the curvature of this curve is shown by $d^2y/dx^2 < 0$. So, when we have a point that satisfies

$$\frac{dy}{dx} = 0, \qquad \frac{d^2y}{dx^2} < 0$$

we must have a maximum.

In a similar manner, we find that, when

$$\frac{dy}{dx} = 0, \qquad \frac{d^2y}{dx^2} > 0$$

we must have a minimum.

We can see that, when $dy/dx = 0$ and either $d^2y/dx^2 > 0$ or $d^2y/dx^2 < 0$, we must have a minimum or maximum, respectively. Hence these are sufficient conditions for the occurrence of an extreme value. But do they cover all maximum and minimum points? That is, are there maximum and minimum points where $dy/dx = 0$ and $d^2y/dx^2 = 0$? The answer is: Yes; when $dy/dx = 0$ and $d^2y/dx^2 = 0$, we may have a maximum or minimum or neither. The proof of this statement may be found in the references listed at the end of the chapter, so let us accept it.

Therefore, when we have $dy/dx = 0$ and $d^2y/dx^2 \gtrless 0$, the point is an extreme value, but there is a possibility that other extreme values may exist. Hence this condition is a sufficient condition but not a necessary and sufficient condition for the occurrence of an extreme value.

To obtain the necessary and sufficient conditions, we need $dy/dx = 0$ and $d^2y/dx^2 \gtrless 0$, and in addition we have to qualify the $d^2y/dx^2 = 0$ so that it only includes extreme values. This way of defining necessary and sufficient conditions for an extreme value becomes rather complicated and hence is usually not used. This is especially so because there is a simpler way of presenting the necessary and sufficient conditions for extreme values. This alternative method of defining extreme values is given below.

Furthermore, in economics, the problems of maximum and minimum are usually clear cut and can be effectively analyzed by the sufficient conditions without resorting to the more stringent necessary and sufficient conditions. Problems such as maximum utility, maximum profits, minimum cost, and so forth, may be effectively analyzed with the sufficient conditions.

In economics, the $dy/dx = 0$ is usually called the first-order condition for the occurrence of extreme values; and the $d^2y/dx^2 \gtrless 0$ is usually called the second-order condition. As we shall illustrate later, the second-order condition becomes important in economics because various economic laws are derived from these conditions.

To clarify the terminology, let us summarize as follows:

In general:

	Maximum	Minimum
necessary condition	$dy/dx = 0$	$dy/dx = 0$
sufficient condition	$dy/dx = 0$	$dy/dx = 0$
	$d^2y/dx^2 < 0$	$d^2y/dx^2 > 0$

In economics:

	Maximum	Minimum
first-order condition	$dy/dx = 0$	$dy/dx = 0$
second-order condition	$d^2y/dx^2 < 0$	$d^2y/dx^2 > 0$

Example 1. Our cost function was

$$y = 40 - 6x + x^2$$

Then, the necessary condition for this to have an extreme value is

$$\frac{dy}{dx} = -6 + 2x = 0$$

$$\therefore \quad x = 3$$

Now, is the value of y a maximum or minimum at $x = 3$? For this we determine the second derivative to find the curve. This is

$$\frac{d^2y}{dx^2} = 2 > 0$$

Thus, the curve is convex downward, and the function has a minimum value at $x = 3$, i.e., at $x = 3$ we have the minimum average cost, which is

$$y = 40 - 6x + x^2 = 40 - 6 \times 3 + 3^2 = 31$$

Example 2. Examine the following function for its maximum or minimum.

$$y = 2x - 3x^2$$

First-order condition

$$y' = 2 - 6x = 0$$

$$\therefore \quad x = \tfrac{1}{3}$$

Second-order condition

$$y'' = -6 < 0$$

Thus y is a maximum at $x = \tfrac{1}{3}$ and its value is

$$y = 2(\tfrac{1}{3}) - 3(\tfrac{1}{3})^2 = \tfrac{2}{3} - \tfrac{1}{3} = \tfrac{1}{3}$$

Example 3. Examine the following function for its maximum or minimum.

$$y = 2x^2 - x^3$$

First-order condition

$$y' = 4x - 3x^2 = 0$$

$$x(4 - 3x) = 0$$

$$\therefore \quad x = 0 \quad \text{or} \quad x = \tfrac{4}{3}$$

Second-order condition

$$y'' = 4 - 6x$$

When $x = 0$,

$$y'' = 4 - 6(0) = 4 > 0$$

Hence y is minimum at $x = 0$, and the value of the function is

$$y = 2x^2 - x^3 = 2(0)^2 - (0)^3 = 0$$

When $x = \frac{4}{3}$,

$$y'' = 4 - 6(\tfrac{4}{3}) = -4 < 0$$

Hence y is maximum at $x = \frac{4}{3}$, and the value of the function is

$$y = 2(\tfrac{4}{3})^2 - (\tfrac{4}{3})^3 = \tfrac{32}{27}$$

(ii) Maxima and minima—an alternative approach

An alternative way of finding the conditions for the occurrence of an extreme value is to consider the change of signs of $f(x)$. The characteristics of this approach are that it does not rely on d^2y/dx^2 and that it gives us the necessary and sufficient conditions for the occurrence of an extreme value. Let us give a heuristic explanation of this approach.

Suppose we have a continuous function $f(x)$, as shown in Figure 5–13.

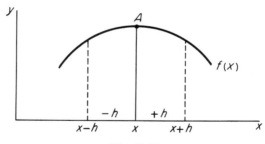

Fig. 5–13

Then this approach claims: If the derivative $f'(x)$ changes sign on passing through A, then point A will be an extreme value. Let us analyze this claim as follows.

Suppose, on the left side of A, the $f'(x) > 0$ and, on the right side of A, the $f'(x) < 0$. Next, let us take a small deviation $h > 0$, where, to the left of A, it is shown by $-h$ and, to the right, it is shown by $+h$. Then between $x - h$ and x we have, since on the left side we assumed $f'(x) > 0$,

$$\lim_{-h \to 0} \frac{f(x - h) - f(x)}{-h} > 0$$

and between x and $x + h$, since we assumed $f'(x) < 0$, we have

$$\lim_{+h \to 0} \frac{f(x + h) - f(x)}{h} < 0$$

Hence, since $h > 0$ and $-h < 0$, the numerators of the above inequalities become

$$f(x - h) - f(x) < 0$$
$$f(x + h) - f(x) < 0$$

That is,

$$f(x) > f(x - h)$$
$$f(x) > f(x + h)$$

This simply means that $f(x)$ is larger than the values on either side of it. Hence $f(x)$ is at a maximum at point A. This may be summarized as follows:

$f(x)$ has a maximum if the $f'(x)$ changes from positive to negative.

In similar manner,

$f(x)$ has a minimum if $f'(x)$ changes from negative to positive.

It turns out that these conditions are necessary and sufficient for the occurrence of a maximum or minimum.

We also note that, since $f'(x)$ changes sign from positive to negative, or vice versa, when passing through the point, the $f'(x)$ must be zero at that point. That is, $f'(x) = 0$ at the extreme point.

As mentioned above, this approach was explained mainly to get a better understanding of the conditions for the occurrence of an extreme value. We shall mainly use the first- and second-order conditions that we obtained above in subsequent discussions.

Example 4. Given

$$y = x^5 + 5x^3 + 5$$

find the extreme values of y, if any, where x is assumed to be a real variable.

$$y' = 5x^4 + 15x^2$$

Hence

$$5x^4 + 15x^2 = 0$$
$$x^2(x^2 + 3) = 0$$

Since x is a real variable, $x^2 + 3 \neq 0$. Hence, $x = 0$.

For $x = 0$ to be a point of extreme value, $y' = f'(x)$ must change signs upon passing through $x = 0$. But

$$\text{For } x > 0 \qquad y' = 5x^4 + 15x^2 > 0$$
$$\text{For } x < 0 \qquad y' = 5x^4 + 15x^2 > 0$$

Thus $x = 0$ is not a point of extreme value.

Let us check to see whether this function has a point of inflection. We find

$$y'' = 20x^3 + 30x$$
$$20x^3 + 30x = 0$$
$$x(2x^2 + 3) = 0$$

Since x is a real variable, $2x^2 + 3 \neq 0$. Hence $x = 0$. To check whether $x = 0$ is a point of inflection, we need to check the sign of $f''(x)$ as it passes through $x = 0$. Hence

For $x < 0$ $f''(x) = 20x^3 + 30x = x(20x^2 + 30) < 0$

For $x > 0$ $f''(x) > 0$

Hence, $x = 0$ is a point of inflection.

From Figure 5–14, we can see that there is no extreme value, but that $x = 0$ is a point of inflection. As is seen, the slope is $\tan \alpha = 20$ at $x = -1$ and $+1$, and the rate of change of the slope is $f'' = -50$ (i.e., decreasing) at $x = -1$; and is $f'' = 50$ (i.e., increasing) at $x = +1$.

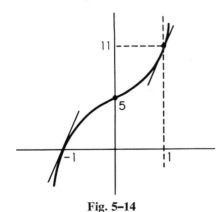

Fig. 5–14

$$y = x^5 + 5x^3 + 5$$

x	-1	0	1
y	-1	5	11
y'	20	0	20
y''	-50	0	50

Problems

1. Using the functions in Problems 1 and 3 of pages 178–179, find the extreme values, and show whether they are maximum or minimum.

2. Find the extreme values of the following functions, and determine whether they are maximum or minimum.

(a) $y = x^4 - 6x^2 - 8x + 10$

(b) $y = x^2 - 6x$ (draw a diagram)

(c) $y = x + \dfrac{1}{x}$ (draw a diagram)

(d) $y = e^{-x^2}$

(e) $y = xe^{-x^2}$

(f) $y = x^3 e^{-x}$

3. Divide 24 into two parts, each being a positive real number, such that the product is a maximum.

4. Given

$$y = (2 - x)^2 + (3 - x)^2 + (4 - x)^2$$

show that y is a minimum when x is equal to the arithmetic mean of 2, 3, and 4.

5. Given a demand function

$$p = \frac{36}{q - 36} + 12$$

where p is price and q is quantity, find the maximum revenue $R = pq$. Draw a graph of this demand function.

5.4 Maxima and minima of functions of two or more variables

We shall only discuss the functions of two independent variables since the functions of more than two variables are analogous.

(i) Definition of maxima and minima of functions of two variables

Let

$$u = f(x, y)$$

Then, instead of a curve we have a surface as in Figure 5–15. The idea of maxima and minima here can be explained in a similar way to that of the one-variable case. If ϵ and η are small positive numbers and $u = f(x, y)$ is a continuous function, then the maximum of the function at (x_0, y_0) is defined as

$$f(x_0 - \epsilon, y_0 - \eta) < f(x_0, y_0), \qquad f(x_0, y_0) > f(x_0 + \epsilon, y_0 + \eta)$$

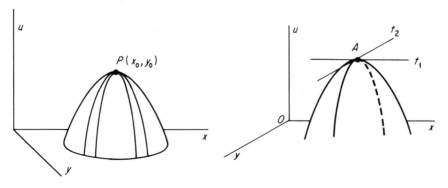

Fig. 5–15   Fig. 5–16

and the minimum is defined as

$$f(x_0 - \epsilon, y_0 - \eta) > f(x_0, y_0), \qquad f(x_0, y_0) < f(x_0 + \epsilon, y_0 + \eta)$$

where $f(x_0, y_0)$ is the maximum or minimum value of the function respectively.

(ii) Necessary conditions for an extreme value

The necessary and sufficient conditions for an extreme value of $u = f(x, y)$ may be explained in similar fashion. Assume we have a surface as shown in Figure 5–16, where A is at the maximum point. If we cut the surface by two planes going through the point A, each surface being parallel to the u-y and u-x planes, we shall obtain the two tangents t_1 and t_2, as in the diagram. The tangent t_1 is obtained when the value of y is held constant and the partial derivative of the function is zero. That is,

$$\frac{\partial u}{\partial x} = 0$$

Likewise, t_2 is obtained when x is held constant and

$$\frac{\partial u}{\partial y} = 0$$

Thus, in our present case, we need the two partial derivatives set equal to zero for the necessary conditions. That is,

$$\frac{\partial u}{\partial x} = 0, \qquad \frac{\partial u}{\partial y} = 0$$

(iii) Sufficient conditions

But as in the one-variable case, the first partial derivatives' being equal to zero is a necessary condition but not a sufficient condition for the occurrence of an extreme value. When we have extreme values, then $f_x = 0$ and $f_y = 0$; but, when we have $f_x = 0$ and $f_y = 0$, the point may or may not be an extreme value. The point may be a *saddle point*, as shown in Figure 5–17.

What are the conditions we need in addition to $f_x = 0$ and $f_y = 0$ to distinguish between maximum, minimum, and saddle points? Let us consider this problem heuristically.

We know that, when $d^2y/dx^2 < 0$, the curvature is convex upward, as when we had a maximum for the one-variable case. Looking at Figure 5–16 and observing the two cuts by the vertical surfaces, we see that the two curves projected on these cuts are also convex upward. Thus, we have

$$\frac{\partial^2 u}{\partial x^2} < 0, \qquad \frac{\partial^2 u}{\partial y^2} < 0$$

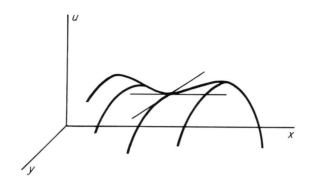

Fig. 5–17

It turns out that, when given the necessary conditions $f_x = 0$ and $f_y = 0$, it will be sufficient for $u = f(x, y)$ to have a maximum when

$$\frac{\partial^2 u}{\partial x^2} < 0, \qquad \frac{\partial^2 u}{\partial y^2} < 0$$

and

$$\frac{\partial^2 u}{\partial x^2} \frac{\partial^2 u}{\partial y^2} > \left(\frac{\partial^2 u}{\partial x \, \partial y} \right)^2$$

For the occurrence of a minimum, the sufficient conditions will be

$$f_x = 0, \qquad f_y = 0$$

$$\frac{\partial^2 u}{\partial x^2} > 0, \qquad \frac{\partial^2 u}{\partial y^2} > 0$$

$$\frac{\partial^2 u}{\partial x^2} \frac{\partial^2 u}{\partial y^2} > \left(\frac{\partial^2 u}{\partial x \, \partial y} \right)^2$$

The above are the sufficient conditions for the extreme value we seek. In addition, we have the following two situations: If $f_x = 0, f_y = 0$, and

$$\frac{\partial^2 u}{\partial x^2} \frac{\partial^2 u}{\partial y^2} < \left(\frac{\partial^2 u}{\partial x \, \partial y} \right)^2$$

we have a saddle point. And, when

$$\frac{\partial^2 u}{\partial x^2} \frac{\partial^2 u}{\partial y^2} = \left(\frac{\partial^2 u}{\partial x \, \partial y} \right)^2$$

we have no information. We shall discuss the sufficient conditions again in Chapter 11. For the present let us take them as given.[*]

* See Courant (Vol. II, 1936), pp. 183–209, for proof.

In economics the $f_x = 0$ and $f_y = 0$ are called *first-order conditions*, and the conditions involving f_{xx}, f_{yy}, f_{xy} are called *second-order conditions*. In many cases the nature of the problem indicates whether a maximum or minimum is to be expected, and thus only the first-order conditions may be considered. In economics, however, these second-order conditions become important for deriving economic laws. This is illustrated in Chapter 11.

Example 1.

$$u = x^3 + x^2 - xy + y^2 + 4$$

We first obtain

$$\frac{\partial u}{\partial x} = 3x^2 + 2x - y = 0, \qquad \frac{\partial u}{\partial y} = -x + 2y = 0$$

Solve simultaneously

$$3x^2 + 2x - y = 0$$
$$-x + 2y = 0$$

We have $x = 2y$. Substitute this in the first equation. Then,

$$3(2y)^2 + 2(2y) - y = 0$$
$$y(12y + 3) = 0$$
$$y = 0 \quad \text{or} \quad y = -\tfrac{1}{4}$$

When $y = 0$

$$x = 2y = 0$$

When $y = -\tfrac{1}{4}$

$$x = 2y = -\tfrac{1}{2}$$

Thus, we have two points $(0, 0)$ and $(-\tfrac{1}{2}, -\tfrac{1}{4})$ obtained from the necessary conditions.

We now check whether these values satisfy the maximum or minimum conditions. We have

$$\frac{\partial^2 u}{\partial x^2} = 6x + 2, \qquad \frac{\partial^2 u}{\partial y^2} = 2, \qquad \frac{\partial^2 u}{\partial x \, \partial y} = -1$$

For $(0, 0)$, we have

$$\frac{\partial^2 u}{\partial x^2} = 6(0) + 2 = 2 > 0, \qquad \frac{\partial^2 u}{\partial y^2} = 2 > 0$$

$$\frac{\partial^2 u}{\partial x^2} \frac{\partial^2 u}{\partial y^2} = 2 \cdot 2 = 4 > \left(\frac{\partial^2 u}{\partial x \, \partial y}\right)^2 = (-1)^2 = 1$$

Thus, $(0, 0)$ satisfies the conditions for a minimum value. The minimum value at the point $(0, 0)$ is

$$u = x^3 + x^2 - xy + y^2 + 4 = 4$$

For $(-\frac{1}{2}, -\frac{1}{4})$, we have

$$\frac{\partial^2 u}{\partial x^2} = 6(-\frac{1}{2}) + 2 = -1, \qquad \frac{\partial^2 u}{\partial y^2} = 2$$

$$\frac{\partial^2 u}{\partial x^2} \frac{\partial^2 u}{\partial y^2} - \left(\frac{\partial^2 u}{\partial x \partial y}\right)^2 = (-1)2 - (-1) = -3 < 0$$

Thus, $(-\frac{1}{2}, \frac{1}{4})$ gives us a saddle point.

We can summarize the conditions for the occurrence of an extreme value as follows:

<table>
<tr><td align="center">maximum</td><td align="center">minimum</td></tr>
<tr>
<td align="center">$f_x = 0, \qquad f_y = 0$
$f_{xx} < 0, \qquad f_{yy} < 0$
$f_{xx}f_{yy} - (f_{xy})^2 > 0$</td>
<td align="center">$f_x = 0, \qquad f_y = 0$
$f_{xx} > 0, \qquad f_{yy} > 0$
$f_{xx}f_{yy} - (f_{xy})^2 > 0$</td>
</tr>
<tr><td align="center">saddle point</td><td align="center">no information</td></tr>
<tr>
<td align="center">$f_x = 0, \qquad f_y = 0$
$f_{xx}f_{yy} - (f_{xy})^2 < 0$</td>
<td align="center">$f_x = 0, \qquad f_y = 0$
$f_{xx}f_{yy} - (f_{xy})^2 = 0$</td>
</tr>
</table>

Example 2. Find the extreme values of u.

$$u = x^3 + y^3 - 3x - 27y + 24$$

First-order conditions

$$f_x = 3x^2 - 3 = 0, \qquad x^2 - 1 = 0$$
$$f_y = 3y^2 - 27 = 0, \qquad y^2 - 9 = 0$$
$$\therefore \quad (1, 3), \quad (1, -3), \quad (-1, 3), \quad (-1, -3)$$

Second-order conditions

$$f_{xx} = 9x$$
$$f_{yy} = 9y$$
$$f_{xy} = 0$$

$(1, 3)$ case

$$f_{xx} = 9x = 9 > 0$$
$$f_{yy} = 9y = 27 > 0$$
$$f_{xx}f_{yy} - (f_{xy})^2 = 243 - 0 = 243 > 0$$

Thus u is minimum at $(1, 3)$.

$(1, -3)$ case

$$f_{xx} = 9x = 9 > 0$$
$$f_{yy} = 9y = -27 < 0$$
$$f_{xx}f_{yy} - (f_{xy})^2 = 9(-27) - 0 < 0$$

Thus we have a saddle point at $(1, -3)$.

$(-1, 3)$ case

$$f_{xx} = 9x = -9 < 0$$
$$f_{yy} = 9y = 27 > 0$$
$$f_{xx}f_{yy} - (f_{xy})^2 = (-9)27 - 0 < 0$$

Thus we have a saddle point at $(-1, 3)$.

$(-1, -3)$ case

$$f_{xx} = 9x = -9 < 0, \qquad f_{yy} = 9y = -27 < 0$$
$$f_{xx}f_{yy} - (f_{xy})^2 = (-9)(-27) - 0 > 0$$

Thus u is maximum at $(-1, -3)$.

(iv) Necessary and sufficient conditions using differentials

We have investigated the necessary and sufficient conditions, respectively, for the occurrence of extreme values for a function with two variables, using partial derivatives. In economics, however, many of the problems involve more than two variables. For example, we may consider demand theory or production theory or the theory of exchange with n variables. In such cases the method we have been using becomes cumbersome and complicated. This is especially so because, as has been mentioned several times, it is frequently necessary to investigate the implications of the second-order conditions. A question that naturally arises is: Is there an alternative way in which we can investigate maximum and minimum problems involving many variables, that will be easier to handle?

Fortunately there is an alternative approach using differentials which is easier to use, especially for second-order conditions. The added advantages of this alternative approach are that (1) we can easily apply the results of matrix algebra to it, as we shall see in Chapter 11, and (2) it links up with the Lagrange multiplier technique, which we shall discuss shortly. In this section, however, we shall confine our discussion to a simple 2 variable case and acquire an introductory acquaintance with this method.

Consider a function $u = f(x, y)$. The necessary condition for this to have an extreme value is

(1) $$du = df = f_x \, dx + f_y \, dy = 0$$

The rationale is that, at the point of extreme values, the tangents are parallel to the x-y plane and the value of u is stationary. Thus, $du = 0$.

This condition is consistent with our previous necessary conditions $f_x = 0$ and $f_y = 0$. We may argue that, since dx and dy can be any value and $du = 0$, then the condition for (1) to hold will be $f_x = 0$ and $f_y = 0$.

What are the additional conditions we need in order to determine the occurrence of a maximum or minimum? We shall argue heuristically that it is related to the rate of change of du. Keeping in mind that u varies in a three-dimensional space, we may think that $d^2u > 0$ means that u is increasing (decreasing) at an increasing (decreasing) rate. If we can imagine the surface of a bowl representing u, then, as we go down the slope of the bowl, the u is decreasing at a decreasing rate. Then as we start up the other side, the u is increasing at an increasing rate. And the bottom of the bowl is where we have a minimum. Thus, when

$$du = 0 \quad \text{and} \quad d^2u > 0$$

we have the sufficient condition for a minimum.

In similar manner, when

$$du = 0 \quad \text{and} \quad d^2u < 0$$

we have the sufficient condition for a maximum.

These necessary and sufficient conditions, respectively, need to be derived with the use of what is known as *Taylor's formula*. (We shall discuss Taylor's formula in Chapter 7). Let us for the moment accept these conditions for the occurrence of extreme values, and refer the student to the references at the end of the chapter for a formal proof.

What happens if $d^2u = 0$? We shall merely state that it becomes necessary to investigate d^3u. But, since we never encounter such a situation in economics, we shall confine our discussion to the following two cases.

maximum	minimum
$du = 0$	$du = 0$
$d^2u < 0$	$d^2u > 0$

where d^2u is

$$d^2u = f_{xx}\, dx^2 + f_{yy}\, dy^2 + 2f_{xy}\, dx\, dy$$

Confining ourselves to these two cases, we may now ask: How do these conditions correspond with the conditions we derived in the previous subsection? We have already seen that the necessary condition $du = 0$ implies that

$$f_x = 0, \quad f_y = 0$$

and hence corresponds to the previous necessary conditions.

As for the sufficient conditions, the $du = 0$ is as we have just explained.

The second-order condition d^2u we have seen was

$$d^2u = f_{xx}\,dx^2 + f_{yy}\,dy^2 + 2f_{xy}\,dx\,dy$$

Note that the form of this is similar to a quadratic

$$ax^2 + 2hxy + by^2$$

This can be changed to

$$ax^2 + 2hxy + by^2 = a\left(x + \frac{h}{a}\,y\right)^2 + \frac{ab - h^2}{a}\,y^2$$

Thus, if this function is to be positive, we must have

$$a > 0, \qquad ab - h^2 > 0$$

In terms of the differentials obtained, we have the following correspondence

$$a \to f_{xx}, \qquad (ab - h^2) \to [f_{xx}f_{yy} - (f_{xy})^2]$$

For $d^2u > 0$, we need

$$f_{xx} > 0, \qquad f_{xx}f_{yy} - (f_{xy})^2 > 0$$

Thus, the sufficient condition for a minimum $du = 0$ and $d^2u > 0$ becomes in terms of partial derivatives

$$f_x = 0, \qquad f_y = 0$$
$$f_{xx} > 0, \qquad f_{xx}f_{yy} - (f_{xy})^2 > 0$$

This is the same as we had obtained previously. Note that

$$f_{xx} > 0, \qquad f_{xx}f_{yy} - (f_{xy})^2 > 0 \quad \text{implies} \quad f_{yy} > 0$$

In similar manner, the sufficient condition for a maximum $du = 0$ and $d^2u < 0$ becomes

$$f_x = 0, \qquad f_y = 0$$
$$f_{xx} < 0, \qquad f_{yy} < 0$$
$$f_{xx}f_{yy} - (f_{xy})^2 > 0$$

(v) *More than two variables case*

It is now easy to see that, when there are a large number of variables, this alternative method is easier to use than the first method. For 3 variables we have

$$u = f(x, y, z)$$
$$du = f_x\,dx + f_y\,dy + f_z\,dz$$
$$d^2u = f_{xx}\,dx^2 + f_{yy}\,dy^2 + f_{zz}\,dz^2 + 2f_{xy}\,dx\,dy + 2f_{xz}\,dx\,dz + 2f_{yz}\,dy\,dz$$

The sufficient conditions for a maximum require that $du = 0$ and $d^2u < 0$.

The first-order condition $du = 0$ leads to

$$f_x = 0, \qquad f_y = 0, \qquad f_z = 0$$

and is obtained by similar reasoning as for 2 variables case.

As for the second-order condition, we can see that it is a quadratic, just as was the second-order condition for 2 variables case. Hence, the problem is to determine the sign of this quadratic. We shall show, in Chapter 11, how this sign may be determined with the help of determinants and matrices. And with the help of matrices and determinants, we can very easily extend our analysis to n variables. For the moment, we can say that, when we have many variables, the sufficient conditions for the occurrence of an extreme value are

first order	second order	
$du = 0$	$d^2u < 0$	minimum
$du = 0$	$d^2u < 0$	maximum

Example 3.

$$u = x^3 + y^3 - 3x - 27y + 24$$

First-order conditions

$$du = f_x\,dx + f_y\,dy$$
$$= (3x^2 - 3)\,dx + (3y^2 - 27)\,dy = 0$$
$$3x^2 - 3 = 0, \qquad \therefore \quad x^2 - 1 = 0$$
$$3y^2 - 27 = 0, \qquad \therefore \quad y^2 - 9 = 0$$

Second-order conditions

$$d^2u = f_{xx}\,dx^2 + f_{yy}\,dy^2 + 2f_{xy}\,dx\,dy$$
$$f_{xx} = 9x, \qquad f_{yy} = 9y, \qquad f_{xy} = 0$$
$$\therefore \quad d^2u = 9x\,dx^2 + 9y\,dy^2 + 0$$

$(1, 3)$ case

$$d^2u = 9dx^2 + 27dy^2 > 0 \qquad \text{Thus, minimum}$$

$(1, -3)$ case

$$d^2u = 9dx^2 - 27dy^2$$

$(-1, 3)$ case

$$d^2u = -9dx^2 + 27dy^2$$

$(-1, -3)$ case

$$d^2u = -9dx^2 - 27dy^2 < 0 \qquad \text{Thus, maximum}$$

As is seen, when using the differential method, we cannot determine the $(-1, 3)$ and $(1, -3)$ case.

Problems

1. Examine the functions for maximum or minimum.

(a) $u = 2x^2 + y^2 - 4x + 8y$
(b) $u = 3x^2 + y^3 - 3xy$
(c) $u = x^2 + y^2 + xy + 10x + 10y$
(d) $u = 2x^2 + 2y^2 + 9 - 6x - 6y - 2xy$
(e) $u = 4x + 2y - x^2 - y^2$
(f) $u = x^2 - 2xy + 2y^2$

2. Let $x + y + z = 24$ and $u = xyz$. Find x, y, and z (positive numbers) that will maximize u.

4. Examine the functions for maximum or minimum.

(a) $z = x^2 - 2xy + y^2$
(b) $z = x^2 - y^2 + xy$
(c) $z = xy$
(d) $z = x^3 - y^3$

5.5 Maxima and minima with subsidiary conditions—Lagrange multiplier method

Suppose we have a utility function and a budget constraint

$$u = f(x, y)$$
$$p_x x + p_y y = M$$

where u is utility, x and y are goods, p_x and p_y are prices which are given, and M is income which is also given. The problem we usually deal with in economics is: How much of x and y should the consumer buy and in what proportions to maximize his utility? As is seen, since income is given, if the consumer buys more of x, he will have to buy less of y. Most of the economic problems concerning maximum and minimum are of this nature where there is a constraint placed on the variables. And as a result, the variables x and y are not independent. That is, if a certain amount of x is bought, then the amount of y that can be bought is automatically determined, and vice versa

There are various ways of solving this type of problem, one of which is the Lagrange multiplier method, which we shall discuss in this section. Alternative methods will be discussed in the subsequent sections. All of these methods are most useful in economic analysis. Let us start with the simple 2-variable case.

(i) Two variables case

Consider $u = f(x, y)$, where the variables x and y are not independent of each other but are connected by some function

$$\phi(x, y) = 0$$

which is called a *subsidiary condition*. Under such conditions, what are the conditions for the extreme values of the function $u = f(x, y)$? For example, let

$$u = f(x, y) = x^2 - y^2 + xy + 5x$$

Assume that x and y are related by

$$\phi(x, y) = x - 2y = 0$$

We wish to find the extreme value of u subject to the condition that $x - 2y = 0$.

Let us approach the problem backwards. We know that, when x and y are independent variables, a necessary condition for $u = f(x, y)$ to have an extreme value is $du = 0$. In our present case, however, x and y are *not* independent variables. Hence, a question arises: When x and y are not independent variables, may we still consider $du = 0$ as a necessary condition for the occurrence of an extreme value? The answer is yes, and this will be explained in Example 2.

We have seen in Chapter 4 that, regardless of whether x and y are independent, the total differential formula holds. Thus

$$(1) \qquad du = f_x \, dx + f_y \, dy = 0$$

is a necessary condition for the occurrence of an extreme value whether or not x and y are independent. When x and y were independent, a necessary condition for (1) to hold was that $f_x = 0$ and $f_y = 0$. But now x and y are *not* independent, and hence we cannot claim $f_x = 0$ and $f_y = 0$ as a necessary condition for (1) to hold. What shall we do?

Let us consider the following line of thought. Can we, from the side relation, find

$$(2) \qquad y = g(x)$$

and consider x the independent variable and y the dependent variable? In our present illustration we have

$$y = \tfrac{1}{2}x$$

and clearly we can interpret x and y in this manner. We shall assume for our subsequent discussions that we can rewrite the side relations $\phi(x, y) = 0$ in the form of (2). Hence, if we can eliminate dy from (1), we shall have only the independent variable dx left and this will enable us to find the necessary condition.

In order to eliminate the dy from (1), we first find

$$d\phi = \phi_x \, dx + \phi_y \, dy = 0$$

Let us assume that, at the point of extreme values, the $\phi_y \neq 0$. Then, multiplying both sides by f_y/ϕ_y gives us

$$\frac{f_y}{\phi_y}\, \phi_x\, dx + f_y\, dy = 0$$

Subtracting this from (1), we find

$$du = f_x\, dx + f_y\, dy = 0$$

$$\frac{f_y}{\phi_y}\, \phi_x\, dx + f_y\, dy = 0$$

$$\overline{}$$

$$du = \left(f_x - \frac{f_y}{\phi_y}\, \phi_x\right) dx = 0$$

But, since dx is an independent variable, the necessary condition for $du = 0$ to hold is

$$f_x - \frac{f_y}{\phi_y}\, \phi_x = 0$$

This may be rewritten as

(3) $$\frac{f_x}{\phi_x} = \frac{f_y}{\phi_y}$$

Hence, equation (3) is a necessary condition for $du = 0$, subject to $\phi(x, y) = 0$, to hold. And this $du = 0$ is a necessary condition for the occurrence of an extreme value. Therefore, (3) is a necessary condition for the occurrence of an extreme value when there is a side relation.

Let us set this (3) as

$$\frac{f_x}{\phi_x} = \frac{f_y}{\phi_y} = -\lambda$$

where λ is some constant. This becomes

$$f_x + \lambda\phi_x = 0$$
$$f_y + \lambda\phi_y = 0$$

We also have

$$\phi(x, y) = 0$$

From these three equations, we solve for x_0, y_0, and λ, and the (x_0, y_0) we obtain will be the x, y that gives us an extreme value. Thus, if we reverse what we have done and find the equations directly by some method and then solve for x, y, and λ, we shall be able to find the extreme value of the function.

This is easily done by setting

$$z = f(x, y) + \lambda\phi(x, y)$$

Then find

$$\frac{\partial z}{\partial x} = 0, \qquad \frac{\partial z}{\partial y} = 0, \qquad \frac{\partial z}{\partial \lambda} = 0$$

We see that this becomes

$$f_x + \lambda \phi_x = 0$$
$$f_y + \lambda \phi_y = 0$$
$$\phi(x, y) = 0$$

as is required.

Using our example, we have

$$z = (x^2 - y^2 + xy + 5x) + \lambda(x - 2y)$$

Thus,

$$\frac{\partial z}{\partial x} = 2x + y + 5 + \lambda = 0$$

$$\frac{\partial z}{\partial y} = x - 2y - 2\lambda = 0$$

$$\frac{\partial z}{\partial \lambda} = x - 2y = 0$$

Solving these three equations, we find

$$x = -2, \qquad y = -1, \qquad \lambda = 0, \qquad u = -5$$

The astute reader has probably noted that we needed the assumption that $\phi_y \neq 0$ at the extreme value. For this Lagrange multiplier technique to work, at least one of ϕ_x and ϕ_y must not be zero. The reason for this requires explanations beyond the level of this book and hence will be omitted. However, the functions used in economics are usually assumed to be continuous and differentiable, and the Lagrange multiplier technique may be used without fear that ϕ_x and ϕ_y are both zero.

Example 1. Let

(1) $\qquad\qquad u = xy$

be a production function, where x and y are inputs. Then for different values of u we get a set of isoquants, as shown in the graph of Figure 5–18. Now let

(2) $\qquad\qquad 2x + y = 6$

be a budget constraint. That is, the firm is given, say, $6, and the price of input x is $2

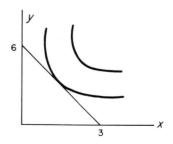

Fig. 5–18

and the price of y is \$1. How much of x and y should be bought to obtain maximum output u? Equation (2) may be rewritten as

$$y = 6 - 2x$$

which is easier to interpret. The 6 is the y intercept, and -2 is the slope. When $x = 0$, then $y = 6$; and, when $y = 0$, then the $x = 3$. Hence we have drawn the budget line (2) as shown in the figure. Our problem geometrically is to find the highest curve that is tangent to this isocost line.

For this we set

$$z = xy + \lambda(2x + y - 6)$$

$$\frac{\partial z}{\partial x} = y + 2\lambda = 0$$

$$\frac{\partial z}{\partial y} = x + \lambda = 0$$

$$\frac{\partial z}{\partial \lambda} = 2x + y - 6 = 0$$

Solving these equations for x, y, and λ, we find $x = \frac{2}{3}$, $y = \frac{4}{3}$, and $\lambda = -\frac{2}{3}$. Hence the maximum value we seek is

$$u = xy = \frac{2}{3}\left(\frac{4}{3}\right) = \frac{8}{9}$$

Note that we have stated that u is a maximum value by observation of the graph. The way to determine whether we have a maximum or minimum is explained below.

Example 2. Let p_1 and p_2 be the prices of commodities q_1 and q_2 that a consumer buys, M be the amount of money he has, and the utility function be $u = u(q_1, q_2)$ which he wishes to maximize subject to

$$M = p_1 q_1 + p_2 q_2$$

Using the Lagrange multiplier method, set

$$z = u(q_1, q_2) + \lambda(M - p_1 q_1 - p_2 q_2)$$

$$\frac{\partial z}{\partial q_1} = u_1 - \lambda p_1 = 0$$

$$\frac{\partial z}{\partial q_2} = u_2 - \lambda p_2 = 0$$

Thus, from these two equations we find

$$\lambda = \frac{u_1}{p_1} = \frac{u_2}{p_2}$$

where u_1, for example, is the marginal utility of q_1. This gives us the necessary condition for consumer equilibrium. This necessary condition is sometimes called the *law of equi-marginal utilities*.

Example 3. Let us now explain the following result that we used in our discussion above, i.e., given

$$u = f(x, y, z)$$

a necessary condition for the occurrence of an extreme value is

$$du = 0$$

regardless of whether the variables x, y, and z are independent. We have already discussed the condition with independent variables. We shall now show that it is also true when the variables are *not* independent. This type of problem usually appears in the form in which we are given a constraint

$$\phi(x, y, z) = 0$$

The result is an important one that is used frequently in economics. The following explanation is rather long, but the student should read it as an exercise in total derivatives and differentiation.

Suppose we have a function

(1) $$u = f(x, y, z)$$

with a side relation (or, we may say, subsidiary condition, or constraint)

(2) $$\phi(x, y, z) = 0$$

Suppose we may regard x and y as the independent variables and z as the dependent variable and write

(3) $$z = g(x, y)$$

Then, substituting (3) in (1) gives us

(4) $$u = f[x, y, g(x, y)]$$

and u is a function of two *independent* variables. We know that the necessary condition for an extreme value is in this case that

(5) $$\frac{\partial u}{\partial x} = 0, \qquad \frac{\partial u}{\partial y} = 0$$

Note carefully that u has been considered a function of x and y only in the present context. We shall use f when we want to consider the function a function of x, y, and z.

These partial derivatives become

(6) $$\frac{\partial u}{\partial x} = \frac{\partial f}{\partial x}\frac{\partial x}{\partial x} + \frac{\partial f}{\partial y}\frac{\partial y}{\partial x} + \frac{\partial f}{\partial z}\frac{\partial z}{\partial x} = 0$$

(7)
$$\frac{\partial u}{\partial y} = \frac{\partial f}{\partial x}\frac{\partial x}{\partial y} + \frac{\partial f}{\partial y}\frac{\partial y}{\partial y} + \frac{\partial f}{\partial z}\frac{\partial z}{\partial y} = 0$$

Since x and y are considered independent variables, when taking the partial of u with respect to x, i.e., $\partial u/\partial x$, we are holding y constant. Hence, $\partial y/\partial x = 0$. But, since we assumed z is a function of x and y, i.e., $z = g(x, y)$, the $\partial z/\partial x$ does not necessarily vanish. Similarly, for the $\partial u/\partial y$ case, the $\partial z/\partial y$ does not necessarily vanish. Therefore (6) and (7) become

(8)
$$\frac{\partial u}{\partial x} = \frac{\partial f}{\partial x} + \frac{\partial f}{\partial z}\frac{\partial z}{\partial x} = 0$$

(9)
$$\frac{\partial u}{\partial y} = \frac{\partial f}{\partial y} + \frac{\partial f}{\partial z}\frac{\partial z}{\partial y} = 0$$

This is the necessary condition for u to have an extreme value that was given in (5), expressed in a different form.

Let us next find the total differential of u. Since u is considered a function of two independent variables x and y, we get

(10)
$$du = \frac{\partial y}{\partial x}dx + \frac{\partial u}{\partial y}dy$$

Let us substitute (7) and (8) in (10). Then

(11) $$\frac{\partial u}{\partial x}dx + \frac{\partial u}{\partial y}dy = \frac{\partial f}{\partial x}dx + \frac{\partial f}{\partial y}dy + \frac{\partial f}{\partial z}\left(\frac{\partial z}{\partial x}dx + \frac{\partial z}{\partial y}dy\right) = 0$$

Thus the values of (x, y) that make (7) and (8) zero will make (11) equal to zero. That is, the values of (x, y) that give u an extreme value will make (11) equal to zero. Hence (11) is a necessary condition for the occurrence of an extreme value.

But the third term on the right-hand side in parentheses is, since $z = g(x, y)$,

$$dz = \frac{\partial z}{\partial x}dx + \frac{\partial z}{\partial y}dy$$

Substituting this in (11) gives us

(12)
$$\frac{\partial f}{\partial x}dx + \frac{\partial f}{\partial y}dy + \frac{\partial f}{\partial z}dx = 0$$

Hence equation (12) is a necessary condition for u to have an extreme value. But this is simply the differential of y, when u is considered a function of the 3 variables x, y, and z. That is,

(13)
$$du = \frac{\partial f}{\partial x}dx + \frac{\partial f}{\partial y}dy + \frac{\partial f}{\partial z}dx = 0$$

Hence a necessary condition for

$$u = f(x, y, z)$$

to have an extreme value when given a constraint

$$\phi(x, y, z) = 0$$

will be

$$du = 0$$

which is the result we seek.

There are several points that should be kept in mind. One is that, when we wrote $\partial u/\partial x = 0$ and $\partial u/\partial y = 0$, this u was considered a function of the two independent variables x and y, whereas, when we wrote $\partial f/\partial x$, $\partial f/\partial y$, and $\partial f/\partial z$, the f was considered a function of the 3 variables x, y, and z, which are not independent. Hence the $\partial f/\partial x$, $\partial f/\partial y$, and $\partial f/\partial z$ may not be zero.

Recall also that (12) held regardless of whether the x, y, and z are independent.

(*ii*) *Three variables case*

For three variables

$$u = f(x, y, z)$$

with the constraint

$$\phi(x, y, z) = 0$$

we set

$$u = f(x, y, z) + \lambda\phi(x, y, z)$$

$$\frac{\partial u}{\partial x} = f_x + \lambda\phi_x = 0$$

$$\frac{\partial u}{\partial y} = f_y + \lambda\phi_y = 0$$

$$\frac{\partial u}{\partial z} = f_z + \lambda\phi_z = 0$$

$$\frac{\partial u}{\partial \lambda} = \phi(x, y, z) = 0$$

These are the necessary conditions for an extreme value. Solving for x, y, z, and λ gives us the desired point.

The first three conditions are in many cases shown as

$$\frac{f_x}{\phi_x} = \frac{f_y}{\phi_y} = \frac{f_z}{\phi_z} = -\lambda$$

(iii) Two subsidiary conditions

If we have a function $u = f(x, y)$ with two subsidiary conditions

$$\phi(x, y) = 0$$
$$\psi(x, y) = 0$$

then we set it up as follows

$$z = f(x, y) + \lambda\phi(x, y) + \mu\psi(x, y)$$

By setting the partial derivatives equal to zero,

$$\frac{\partial z}{\partial x} = f_x + \lambda\phi_x + \mu\psi_x = 0$$

$$\frac{\partial z}{\partial y} = f_y + \lambda\phi_y + \mu\psi_y = 0$$

Then, we solve these two equations with the two subsidiary conditions for x, y, λ, and μ.

In similar fashion this can be extended to other general cases.*

Example 4.

$$u = f(x, y) = x^2 - y^2 + xy + 5x$$

Find the extreme value of the function, subject to

$$x - 2y = 0$$
$$x + y = -3$$

Solution.

$$z = (x^2 - y^2 + xy + 5x) + \lambda(x - 2y) + \mu(x + y + 3)$$

$$\frac{\partial z}{\partial x} = 2x + y + 5 + \lambda + \mu = 0$$

$$\frac{\partial z}{\partial y} = -2y + x - 2\lambda + \mu = 0$$

$$2x + y + \lambda + \mu = -5$$
$$x - 2y - 2\lambda + \mu = 0$$
$$x - 2y = 0$$
$$x + y = -3$$

$$\therefore \quad x = -2, \qquad y = -1, \qquad \lambda = \tfrac{5}{3}, \qquad \mu = \tfrac{10}{3}$$

$$\therefore \quad u = 4 - 1 + 2 - 10 = -5$$

* See Courant (Vol. II, 1936), pp. 194–202, for proof.

The extreme value will be $u = -5$. We do not yet know whether this is a maximum or minimum.

As we have seen in the above examples, we need to investigate the second-order conditions to determine whether we have a maximum or minimum. When given

$$u = f(x, y, z)$$

subject to

$$\phi(x, y, z) = 0$$

the second-order condition for a maximum is obtained as follows. Set

$$w = f(x, y, z) + \lambda\phi(x, y, z)$$

Then the second-order condition for a maximum is

(14) $$d^2w < 0$$

(15) $$\phi_x \, dx + \phi_y \, dy + \phi_z \, dz = 0$$

where dx, dy, and dz are not all zero.

For a minimum, we have

$$d^2w > 0$$

$$\phi_x \, dx + \phi_y \, dy + \phi_z \, dz = 0$$

The d^2w becomes, for a maximum,

$$d^2w = w_{xx} \, dx^2 + w_{yy} \, dy^2 + w_{zz} \, dz^2 + 2w_{xy} \, dx \, dy$$
$$+ \, 2w_{yz} \, dy \, dz + 2w_{zx} \, dz \, dx < 0$$

As is seen this is a quadratic. Hence the problem becomes one of finding the conditions for this quadratic to be negative, subject to (15) above.

We can see that, for example,

$$w_{xy} = f_{xy} + \lambda\phi_{xy}$$

and hence with a large amount of algebraic work, we could find these conditions. However, when using matrix algebra, this is a relatively simple task. So let us postpone this discussion until Chapter 11.

Problems

1. (a) Find the minimum of $u = 2x^2 - 6y^2$ under the condition that $x + 2y = 4$. What is the value of u?

   (b) Find the maximum of $u = x^2 + 3xy - 5y^2$, given $2x + 3y = 6$. What is the value of u?

   (c) Find the minimum of $u = 6x^2 + y^2$, given $4x - y = 1$. What is the value of u?

   (d) Find the minimum of $u = x^2 + xy + y^2 + 3z^2$, given $x + 2y + 4z = 60$. What is the value of u?

   (e) Let the utility function be $u = q_1 q_2$. Let prices be $p_1 = 1$ and $p_2 = 3$, and income be $M = 15$ (i.e., $p_1 q_1 + p_2 q_2 = 15$). Find q_1 and q_2 that will maximize u.

2. Given the function

$$u = x^2 + y^2$$

subject to the linear constraint

$$x + y = 1$$

find the point where u is minimum and also the minimum value of u. Sketch a graph of the result.

3. Given the function

$$u = x^2 + y^2 + z^2$$

and a linear constraint

$$x + y + z = 1$$

find the point where u is maximum and also the value of u. Explain in words the geometric interpretation of the result.

4. Given the production function

$$q = f(x_1, x_2)$$

and the linear constraint

$$C = r_1 x_1 + r_2 x_2 + F$$

find the first-order conditions for a maximum q (output), given C (budget), where x_1 and x_2 are inputs, r_1 and r_2 are input prices, and F is fixed cost.

5. Given a cost function

$$C = r_1 x_1 + r_2 x_2 + F$$

and a constraint

$$q = f(x_1, x_2)$$

find the first-order condition for a minimum C (cost), given q (output). Let

$$C = r_1 x_1 + r_2 x_2 + F = H(x_1, x_2)$$

and find the first-order conditions.

5.6 Maxima and minima with subsidiary conditions (II)

An alternative way of finding the first- and second-order conditions, respectively, for a function with a side relation will be given because this alternative method has the advantage that we can easily apply the methods of matrix algebra.

In this section, however, we shall explain the method in a straightforward algebraic way in order to understand the principle involved.

Suppose we have

$$(1) \qquad\qquad u = f(x, y, z)$$

$$(2) \qquad\qquad \phi(x, y, z) = 0$$

Then, the x, y, z are not independent and so we cannot use the results we have already obtained for the case where the variables are independent. Those results were, for a maximum,

$$du = 0, \qquad d^2u < 0$$

Hence it is natural to ask ourselves: Is there a way of transforming (1) and (2) so that we can apply these results of the independent variables case?

The answer is yes, and it is performed as follows. Suppose (2) can be written as

$$(3) \qquad\qquad z = g(x, y)$$

Then, substituting this in (1) gives us

$$(4) \qquad\qquad u = f[x, y, g(x, y)]$$

We may treat x and y as the independent variables and z as the dependent variable. Then (4) is a function with 2 *independent* variables, and hence we may apply the results we already know for the independent variables case. Let us now show how this is worked out.

We know that for (4) to have an extreme value, we need

$$du = 0, \qquad d^2u \gtrless 0$$

because x and y are independent variables. So let us first find $du = 0$ as a function of x and y only. We know that

$$du = f_x\, dx + f_y\, dy + f_z\, dz$$

We wish to eliminate dz so that du will become a function of dx and dy only. To eliminate dz from du, we shall use the following relation obtained from the side relation:

$$d\phi = \phi_x\, dx + \phi_y\, dy + \phi_z\, dz = 0$$

Assuming $\phi_z \neq 0$, we multiply $d\phi$ by f_z/ϕ_z and subtract this from du. Since $d\phi = 0$, this subtraction does not change du. We have

$$du = f_x\,dx + f_y\,dy + f_z\,dz$$

$$\frac{f_z}{\phi_z}\,d\phi = \phi_x\frac{f_z}{\phi_z}\,dx + \phi_y\frac{f_z}{\phi_z}\,dy + f_z\,dz = 0$$

$$\therefore \quad du - \frac{f_z}{\phi_z}\,d\phi = \left(f_x - \phi_x\frac{f_z}{\phi_z}\right)dx + \left(f_y - \phi_y\frac{f_z}{\phi_z}\right)dy$$

But, since

$$\frac{f_z}{\phi_z}\,d\phi = \frac{f_z}{\phi_z}\,(0) = 0$$

we get

(5) $$du = \left(f_x - \phi_x\frac{f_z}{\phi_z}\right)dx + \left(f_y - \phi_y\frac{f_z}{\phi_z}\right)dy$$

As can be seen, we have eliminated dz, and we are left with the 2 independent variables dx and dy. This equation (5) is the differential of (4), and, since it contains only 2 independent variables, we may apply our previous results of the independent variables case. That is, for (4) to have an extreme value, we need (5) to be zero:

(6) $$du = \left(f_x - \phi_x\frac{f_z}{\phi_z}\right)dx + \left(f_y - \phi_y\frac{f_z}{\phi_z}\right)dy = 0$$

But, since dx and dy are independent, a necessary condition for this to hold is

$$f_x - \phi_x\frac{f_z}{\phi_z} = 0$$

$$f_y - \phi_y\frac{f_z}{\phi_z} = 0$$

And this leads to

(7) $$\frac{f_x}{\phi_x} = \frac{f_y}{\phi_y} = \frac{f_z}{\phi_z}$$

which is the necessary condition for u to have an extreme value

As can be seen, this is the same result we obtained by the Lagrange multiplier method.

Let us now find the second-order conditions $d^2u \gtrless 0$. We find

$$d^2u = f_z\,d^2z + f_{xx}\,dx^2 + f_{yy}\,dy^2 + f_{zz}\,dz^2$$
$$+ 2f_{xy}\,dx\,dy + 2f_{xz}\,dx\,dz + 2f_{yz}\,dy\,dz$$

Recall that the term $f_z\,d^2z$ is included because z is the dependent variable.

To transform this into a form with only independent variables, we need to eliminate dz. And for this we shall first eliminate d^2z, using the second-order differential $d^2\phi$, and then eliminate dz, using the first-order differential $d\phi$. So let us first find $d^2\phi$. We get

$$(8) \quad d^2\phi = \phi_z \, d^2z + \phi_{xx} \, dx^2 + \phi_{yy} \, dy^2 + \phi_{zz} \, dz^2$$
$$+ \, 2\phi_{xy} \, dx \, dy + 2\phi_{xz} \, dx \, dz + 2\phi_{yz} \, dy \, dz$$

In order to eliminate d^2z from d^2u, we shall multiply $d^2\phi$ by f_z/ϕ_z and subtract from d^2u. We have

$$\frac{f_z}{\phi_z} \, d^2\phi = f_z \, d^2z + \frac{f_z}{\phi_z} \, \phi_{xx} \, dx^2 + \frac{f_z}{\phi_z} \, \phi_{yy} \, dy^2 + \frac{f_z}{\phi_z} \, \phi_{zz} \, dz^2$$
$$+ \, 2\phi_{xy} \frac{f_z}{\phi_z} \, dx \, dy + 2\phi_{xz} \frac{f_z}{\phi_z} \, dx \, dz + 2\phi_{yz} \frac{f_z}{\phi_z} \, dy \, dz$$

Hence

$$(9) \quad d^2u - \frac{f_z}{\phi_z} \, d^2\phi = d^2u = \left(f_{xx} - \frac{f_z}{\phi_z} \, \phi_{xx} \right) dx^2 + \left(f_{yy} - \frac{f_z}{\phi_z} \, \phi_{yy} \right) dy^2$$
$$+ \left(f_{zz} - \frac{f_z}{\phi_z} \, \phi_{zz} \right) dz^2 + 2 \left(f_{xy} - \frac{f_z}{\phi_z} \, \phi_{xy} \right) dx \, dy$$
$$+ 2 \left(f_{xz} - \frac{f_x}{\phi_x} \, \phi_{xz} \right) dx \, dz + 2 \left(f_{yz} - \frac{f_z}{\phi_z} \, \phi_{yz} \right) dy \, dz$$

Having eliminated d^2z, our next step is to eliminate dz from (9) so that d^2u will become a function of dx and dy only. And for this we use the side relation

$$(10) \qquad\qquad d\phi = \phi_x \, dx + \phi_y \, dy + \phi_z \, dz = 0$$

We may rewrite this as

$$(11) \qquad\qquad dz = -\frac{1}{\phi_z} (\phi_x \, dx + \phi_y \, dy)$$

Substituting this in the d^2u of (9) will eliminate dz and give us d^2u with the 2 independent variables dx and dy only. Then we may apply our previous results of the case where the variables are independent and claim that, when $d^2u < 0$, we shall have a maximum.

As is seen, when (11) is substituted in (9), the d^2u will become quite a complicated equation. To avoid this, we may write: When

$$d^2u < 0$$

subject to

$$dz = -\frac{1}{\phi_z} (\phi_x \, dx + \phi_y \, dy)$$

we shall have a maximum. That is, instead of combining the two formulas into one complicated formula, we have left them uncombined. Or, more simply, we may write: When

$$d^2u < 0$$

subject to

$$d\phi = \phi_x \, dx + \phi_y \, dy + \phi_z \, dz = 0$$

we shall have a maximum.

Let us summarize our results up to this point. When we have

$$u = f(x, y, z)$$

$$\phi(x, y, z) = 0$$

a necessary condition for u to have an extreme value is

$$du = 0, \qquad d\phi = 0$$

A sufficient condition for u to have an extreme value is

maximum		minimum	
$du = 0$		$du = 0$	
$d\phi = 0$	first-order conditions	$d\phi = 0$	first-order conditions
$d^2u < 0$		$d^2u > 0$	
$d\phi = 0$	second-order conditions	$d\phi = 0$	second-order conditions

As is seen, we have written $d\phi = 0$ twice, first, to be used with $du = 0$ and, second, to be used with $d^2u \gtrless 0$. This repetition of expression is not necessary, so we shall simply write as our final result

maximum	minimum
$du = 0$	$du = 0$
$d^2u < 0$	$d^2u > 0$
$d\phi = 0$	$d\phi = 0$

We now have to go one step further. We have the second-order conditions as

$$d^2u \gtrless 0$$

$$d\phi = 0$$

The question now is: What must be the relations between $f_{xx}, f_{yy}, f_{zz}, \ldots, \phi_{zz}$ for this second-order condition to hold? Recall that for $u = f(x, y)$, where

x and y were independent, we had

$$f_{xx} < 0, \qquad f_{yy} < 0$$
$$f_{xx}f_{yy} - (f_{xy})^2 > 0$$

for the occurrence of a maximum. It will turn out that we shall obtain similar conditions for our present case. We may work out the conditions for the two variables by simple algebra, but for three or more variables the algebra becomes too complicated. Hence we shall postpone an answer to this question until Chapter 11, where it will be treated with the help of matrix algebra. So let us for the moment be satisfied with an understanding of how the first- and second-order conditions, respectively, were obtained.

One additional point should be mentioned. In many cases in economics, the first-order conditions are obtained by the Lagrange multiplier method because of its ease of calculation, and the second-order conditions are obtained by the alternative method, which we have just mentioned above, with the help of matrix algebra.

Let us summarize our results and illustrate with examples.

First-order conditions

$$du = 0$$
$$d\phi = 0$$

which leads to

$$\frac{f_x}{\phi_x} = \frac{f_y}{\phi_y} = \frac{f_z}{\phi_z}$$

Second-order conditions. Assume that z is the dependent variable

$$z = g(x, y)$$

then

$$d^2u = f_z \, d^2z + f_{xx} \, dx^2 + f_{yy} \, dy^2 + f_{zz} \, dz^2$$
$$+ 2f_{xy} \, dx \, dy + 2f_{yz} \, dy \, dz + 2f_{zx} \, dz \, dx$$

Check the sign of d^2u subject to

$$d\phi = \phi_x \, dx + \phi_y \, dy + \phi_z \, dz = 0$$

Example 1. Given

(1) $$u = x^2 + y^2$$

subject to

(2) $$x + y = 1$$

find the point at which u is maximum or minimum. Let us first look at the problem diagrammatically. Equation (1) is a set of concentric circles with the origin at $(0, 0)$ and radius $\sqrt{u}$ as shown in Figure 5–19. We have drawn 3 circles for purposes of explanation: I, the largest; II, the next largest; and III, the smallest.   Circle I cuts $x + y = 1$ at A and A';   circle II is

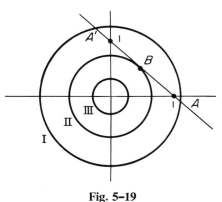

Fig. 5–19

tangent at B; and circle III does not cut $x + y = 1$. Since x and y are to satisfy equations (1) and (2), it must be a point common to the circle and the straight line. Hence the circles must be larger than II. We can easily see that there are an infinite number of circles intersecting $x + y = 1$ and, also, that II is the smallest. Hence, diagrammatically, we observe that we wish to find the u that is minimum, i.e., we wish to find the smallest circle, which means finding the point B.

Now let us find point B mathematically.

First-order conditions. First set

$$\phi(x, y) = x + y - 1 = 0$$

Then the first-order conditions are

$$du = 0$$
$$d\phi = 0$$

which lead to

$$\frac{f_x}{\phi_y} = \frac{f_y}{\phi_y}$$

In our present case this is

$$\frac{2x}{1} = \frac{2y}{1}$$

or

$$x = y$$

In addition we have the linear constraint (2). There are 2 variables x and y and two equations. Hence, solving for x and y gives us

$$x = \tfrac{1}{2}, \qquad y = \tfrac{1}{2}$$

We now have to check whether this point is a maximum or minimum point.

Second-order conditions. The second-order conditions were

$$d^2u \lessgtr 0$$
$$d\phi = 0$$

Let us check d^2u. In order to find d^2u, we must be careful to note that x and y are not independent variables. Let us assume that x is the dependent variable and y the independent variable. Then

$$d^2u = f_x\, d^2x + f_{xx}\, dx^2 + f_{yy}\, dy^2 + 2f_{xy}\, dx\, dy$$
$$= 2x\, d^2x + 2dx^2 + 2dy^2 + 0dx\, dy$$

But, since the relation between x and y is linear,

$$x = 1 - y$$
$$dx = -dy$$
$$\therefore \quad d^2x = 0$$

Thus

$$d^2u = 2dx^2 + 2dy^2$$

and, clearly, $d^2u > 0$ for all values of x and y. Hence, point B is a minimum.

As is seen, because we had only 2 variables and because they were linearly related, we were able to determine the sign of d^2u very easily. As the variables increase and the relation is not linear, it will be much easier to use determinants and matrices, which are explained in Chapter 11.

Let us actually find point B geometrically. Since $x + y = 1$, we have a straight line with a $45°$ angle as shown in Figure 5–20. Then point B, where the circle is tangent to $x + y = 1$, is obtained by drawing a line from 0 perpendicular to $x + y = 1$. And clearly B is the midpoint. Hence, C and D will be midpoints, and thus point B is $(\frac{1}{2}, \frac{1}{2})$. The u is $u = (\frac{1}{2})^2 + (\frac{1}{2})^2 = \frac{1}{2}$.

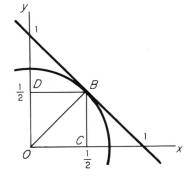

Fig. 5–20

Example 2. Let us try the analysis with 3 variables.

(1) $u = x^2 + y^2 + z^2$

(2) $x + y + z = 1$

Find the maximum or minimum of u subject to (2). Here we have a sphere in 3-dimensional space and a linear plane, instead of a circle and a line. We can easily guess from the previous example that the point will be a minimum.

First-order conditions. Set

$$\phi(x, y, z) = x + y + z - 1 = 0$$

Then

$$du = 0$$
$$d\phi = 0$$

leads to

$$\frac{f_x}{\phi_x} = \frac{f_y}{\phi_y} = \frac{f_z}{\phi_z}$$

which is

$$\frac{2x}{1} = \frac{2y}{1} = \frac{2z}{1}$$

or

$$x = y = z$$

Hence, we have two equations

$$x = y \quad \text{and} \quad x = z$$

and the linear constraint (2). Solving for x, y, and z gives us

$$x = \tfrac{1}{3}, \qquad y = \tfrac{1}{3}, \qquad z = \tfrac{1}{3}$$

as the extreme point.

Second-order conditions.

$$d^2u \lessgtr 0$$
$$d\phi = 0$$

Assume

$$x = 1 - y - z$$

Then

$$d^2u = f_x \, d^2x + f_{xx} \, dx^2 + f_{yy} \, dy^2 + f_{zz} \, dz^2 + 2f_{xy} \, dx \, dy + 2f_{xz} \, dx \, dz$$
$$+ 2f_{yz} \, dy \, dz$$
$$= 2x(0) + 2dx^2 + 2dy^2 + 2dz^2 + 2(0)dx \, dy + 2(0)dx \, dz + 2(0)dy \, dz$$
$$= 2dx^2 + 2dy^2 + 2dz^2$$

Hence, we check whether

$$d^2u = 2dx^2 + 2dy^2 + 2dz^2$$

is positive or negative, subject to

$$x + y + z = 1$$

But, clearly, $d^2u > 0$ for all values of $x, y,$ and z. Hence, point $(\tfrac{1}{3}, \tfrac{1}{3}, \tfrac{1}{3})$ is a minimum point.

Example 3.

(1) $u = xy$

(2) $2x + y = 6$

Find the extreme value of u subject to (2).

First-order conditions. Let

$$\phi(x, y) = 2x + y - 6$$

Then the first-order conditions are

$$du = 0$$
$$d\phi = 0$$

which lead to

$$\frac{f_x}{\phi_x} = \frac{f_y}{\phi_y}$$

This is

$$\frac{y}{2} = \frac{x}{1}$$

or

$$y = 2x$$

From this result and (2), we find $x = \frac{3}{2}$ and $y = 3$.

Second-order conditions. Let

(3) $$y = 6 - 2x$$
$$d^2u = f\, d^2y + f_{xx}\, dx^2 + f_{yy}\, dy^2 + 2f_{xy}\, dx\, dy$$
$$= x(0) + 0dx^2 + 0dy^2 + 2(1)dx\, dy$$
$$= 2dx\, dy$$

But from (3)

$$dy = -2dx$$

Thus

$$d^2u = 2dx(-2dx) = -4dx^2 < 0$$

for all values of x and y. Hence point $(\frac{3}{2}, 3)$ is a maximum point.

Example 4. Given the utility function

$$u = f(q_1, q_2, q_3)$$

and budget constraint

$$M = p_1 q_1 + p_2 q_2 + p_3 q_3$$

where prices p_1, p_2, and p_3 are given and income M is given, find the first- and second-order conditions for u to be a maximum.

First-order conditions. Let

$$\phi(q_1, q_2, q_3) = u - p_1 q_1 - p_2 q_2 - p_3 q_3$$

Then the first-order conditions are

$$du = 0 \quad \text{and} \quad d\phi = 0$$

which lead to

$$\frac{f_1}{\phi_1} = \frac{f_2}{\phi_2} = \frac{f_3}{\phi_3}$$

The f_i are marginal utilities. Also, $\phi_i = p_i$. Thus

$$\frac{f_1}{p_1} = \frac{f_2}{p_2} = \frac{f_3}{p_3}$$

which is the law of equi-marginal utilities.

Second-order conditions. Let

$$q_1 = g(q_2, q_3)$$

Then

$$d^2u = f_1\, d^2q_1 + f_{11}\, dq_1^2 + f_{22}\, dq_2^2 + f_{33}\, dq_3^2$$
$$+ 2f_{12}\, dq_1\, dq_2 + 2f_{13}\, dq_1\, dq_3 + 2f_{23}\, dq_2\, dq_3$$

Since the q_i are linearly related,

$$d^2q_1 = 0$$

Thus we need to determine the sign of

$$d^2u = f_{11}\, dq_1^2 + f_{22}\, dq_2^2 + f_{33}\, dq_3^2$$
$$+ 2f_{12}\, dq_1\, dq_2 + 2f_{13}\, dq_1\, dq_3 + 2f_{23}\, dq_2\, dq_3$$

Hence the problem of determining the sign of d^2u becomes a problem of determining the sign of the quadratic on the right-hand side. This problem is discussed in Chapter 11.

As is seen in Example 4, the first-order conditions become

$$\frac{f_1}{\phi_1} = \frac{f_2}{\phi_2} = \frac{f_3}{\phi_3}$$

and the second-order conditions become

$$d^2u = f_1\, d^2x_1 + f_{11}\, dx_1^2 + f_{22}\, dx_2^2 + f_{33}\, dx_3^2 + 2f_{12}\, dx_1\, dx_2$$
$$+ 2f_{13}\, dx_1\, dx_3 + 2f_{23}\, dx_2\, dx_3$$
$$= f_1\, d^2x + \text{(a quadratic)}$$

In economics, most of the constraints $\phi(x_1, x_2, x_3) = 0$ are linear and, as a result, $d^2x_1 = 0$. Then

$$d^2u = \text{a quadratic}$$

and the problem of determining the sign of d^2u becomes a problem of determining the sign of a quadratic. As mentioned above, this problem will be discussed fully in Chapter 11. This is an important problem in economics because from these second-order conditions we derive important economic laws such as the law of demand.

Problems*

1. Using the questions in Problem 1 on page 206, find the first- and second-order conditions by the differential method, and determine the extreme points.

2. Using the data of Problem 4 on page 206, find the first- and second-order conditions by the differential method, and discuss the results.

3. Using the data of Problem 5 on page 206, find the first- and second-order conditions by the differential method, and discuss the results.

5.7 Combining the Lagrange multiplier method and the differential method

In Section 5.6 we mentioned that very frequently in economics the first-order conditions are obtained by the Lagrange multiplier method, while the second-order conditions are obtained by the differential method. The reason for obtaining the first-order conditions by the Lagrange multiplier method is its ease. The reason for obtaining the second-order conditions by the differential method is that this method may be analyzed by matrix algebra. Let us briefly summarize the results of the Lagrange multiplier method and the differential method.

Suppose we have

$$u = f(x, y, z)$$
$$\phi(x, y, z) = 0$$

Let us find the first-order conditions by the Lagrange multiplier method and then by the differential method.

First-order conditions. Lagrange multiplier method

$$w = f(x, y, z) + \lambda\phi(x, y, z)$$

$$\frac{\partial w}{\partial x} = f_x + \lambda\phi_x = 0$$

$$\frac{\partial w}{\partial y} = f_y + \lambda\phi_y = 0$$

$$\frac{\partial w}{\partial z} = f_z + \lambda\phi_z = 0$$

First-order conditions. Differential method

$$dw = d(f + \lambda\phi)$$
$$= f_x\,dx + f_y\,dy + f_z\,dz + \lambda\phi_x\,dx + \lambda\phi_y\,dy + \lambda\phi_z\,dz = 0$$
$$(f_x + \lambda\phi_x)\,dx + (f_y + \lambda\phi_y)\,dy + (f_z + \lambda\phi_z)\,dz = 0$$

We may consider the undetermined multiplier λ the dependent variable and x, y, z independent variables. Hence, the necessary conditions for the equation to be zero are that the coefficients of dx, dy, dz be equal to zero. That is,

$$f_x + \lambda\phi_x = 0$$
$$f_y + \lambda\phi_y = 0$$
$$f_z + \lambda\phi_z = 0$$

and, as is seen, these are the same conditions as those obtained by the Lagrange multiplier method.

Second-order conditions. Differential method

$$d^2z = d(df + \lambda\,d\phi)$$

In most cases in economic problems, the constraint ϕ is linear. Then

$$d(d\phi) = 0$$

Hence, d^2z becomes

$$d^2z = d(df + \lambda\,d\phi)$$
$$= d^2f + 0$$
$$= f_x\,d^2x + f_{xx}\,dx^2 + f_{yy}\,dy^2 + f_{zz}\,dz^2$$
$$+ 2f_{xy}\,dx\,dy + 2f_{xz}\,dx\,dz + 2f_{yz}\,dy\,dz$$

But, when ϕ is linear, $d^2x = 0$. Hence, by using the notation on page 213,

$$d^2z = (f_x\,dx + f_y\,dy + f_z\,dz)^2$$

which is the same result as in Section 5.6.

Example 1. Given the utility function

$$u = f(q_1, q_2, q_3)$$

and the budget constraint

$$M = p_1q_1 + p_2q_2 + p_3q_3$$

where q_i are quantities, p_i are prices which are given, and M is income, find the first- and second-order conditions for maximum utility.

First-order conditions. Using the Lagrange multiplier method

$$z = f + \lambda(M - p_1q_1 - p_2q_2 - p_3q_3)$$

$$\frac{\partial z}{\partial q_1} = f_1 - \lambda p_1 = 0$$

$$\frac{\partial z}{\partial q_2} = f_2 - \lambda p_2 = 0$$

$$\frac{\partial z}{\partial q_3} = f_3 - \lambda p_3 = 0$$

$$\therefore \quad \frac{f_1}{p_1} = \frac{f_2}{p_2} = \frac{f_3}{p_3} = \lambda$$

Second-order conditions. Using the differential method, we find, since the constraint is linear,

$$d^2u = (f_1\, dq_1 + f_2\, dq_2 + f_3\, dq_3)^2$$
$$= f_{11}\, d^2q_1 + f_{22}\, d^2q_2 + f_{33}\, d^2q_3 + 2f_{12}\, dq_1\, dq_2 + 2f_{13}\, dq_1\, dq_3 + 2f_{23}\, dq_2\, dq_3$$

For maximum utility we need $d^2u < 0$. Hence we need to find the conditions for the right-hand side of the above equation to be less than zero (i.e., negative). This is discussed in Chapter 11.

Example 2. Given a production function

$$q = f(x_1, x_2, x_3)$$

and a budget constraint

$$C = r_1 x_1 + r_2 x_2 + r_3 x_3 + F$$

find the first- and second-order conditions for maximum output. Here x_i are inputs, r_i are input prices and given, F is fixed cost, and C is total cost which is given.

First-order conditions.

$$z = f + \lambda(C - F - r_1 x_1 - r_2 x_2 - r_3 x_3)$$

$$\frac{\partial z}{\partial x_1} = f_1 - \lambda r_1 = 0$$

$$\frac{\partial z}{\partial x_2} = f_2 - \lambda r_2 = 0$$

$$\frac{\partial z}{\partial x_3} = f_3 - \lambda r_3 = 0$$

which may be shown as

$$\frac{f_1}{r_1} = \frac{f_2}{r_2} = \frac{f_3}{r_3}$$

The f_i are MPP and this equation shows the law of equi-marginal productivities.

Second-order conditions. Using the differential method, since the cost constraint is linear, we find

$$d^2q = (f_1\, dx_1 + f_2\, dx_2 + f_3\, dx_3)^2$$

$$= f_{11}\, dx_1^2 + f_{22}\, dx_2^2 + f_{33}\, dx_3^2 + 2f_{12}\, dx_1\, dx_2 + 2f_{13}\, dx_1\, dx_3 + 2f_{23}\, dx_2\, dx_3$$

For maximum q, we need $d^2q < 0$. Hence we need to find the conditions for the right-hand side of the above equation to be negative. This is discussed in Chapter 11.

Example 3. Given a cost function

$$C = r_1 x_1 + r_2 x_2 + F$$

and a production function which serves as a constraint

$$q = f(x_1, x_2)$$

find the first- and second-order conditions for minimum cost.

First-order condition. Set the cost function as

$$C = r_1 x_1 + r_2 x_2 + F = h(x_1, x_2)$$

Then by the Lagrange multiplier method

$$z = h(x_1, x_2) + \lambda[q - f(x_1, x_2)]$$

$$\frac{\partial z}{\partial x_1} = r_1 + \lambda(-f_1) = 0$$

$$\frac{\partial z}{\partial x_2} = r_2 + \lambda(-f_2) = 0$$

$$\frac{\partial z}{\partial \lambda} = q - f(x_1, x_2) = 0$$

$$\therefore \quad \frac{f_1}{r_1} = \frac{f_2}{r_2} = \frac{1}{\lambda}$$

express the first-order conditions, which is the law of equi-marginal productivity.

Second-order conditions. Using the differential method, this is

$$d^2C < 0$$

subject to

$$d\phi(x_1, x_2) = 0$$

where

$$\phi(x_1, x_2) = q - f(x_1, x_2) = 0$$

Calculations will show that

$$d^2C = r_1\, d^2x_1$$

$$d^2\phi = -f_1\, d^2x_1 - f_{11}f_1^2 - f_{22}\, dx_2^2 - 2f_{12}\, dx_1\, dx_2 = 0$$

From $d^2\phi$, we find d^2x_1, and substituting this d^2x_1 into d^2C gives us

$$d^2C = -\frac{r_1}{f_1}\,[f_{11}\, dx_1^2 + f_{22}\, dx_2^2 + 2f_{12}\, dx_1\, dx_2] > 0$$

Since $r_1 > 0$ and $f_1 > 0$, we need

$$f_{11}\, dx_1^2 + f_{22}\, dx_2^2 + 2f_{12}\, dx_1\, dx_2 < 0$$

for $d^2C < 0$, i.e., for C to be minimum.

Problem

Work out the calculation details of Example 3.

5.8 Competitive equilibrium of a firm

As an illustration of finding the conditions for a maximum, we shall discuss how a firm will maximize its profits in pure competition. When we have pure competition, the demand curve for a firm is horizontal. Graphically, it is as in Figure 5–21. Let p be price and q be output. As we see, p is

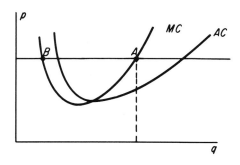

Fig. 5–21

given in pure competition. Let R be revenue. Then,

$$R = pq$$

The marginal revenue is

$$\frac{dR}{dq} = p + q\,\frac{dp}{dq}$$

But, since p is given as a constant in this case, we have

$$\frac{dR}{dq} = p$$

Thus, $MR = p = AR$ as we have drawn it in our diagram.

Now, let C be total cost. Then profits π will be

$$\pi = R - C$$

For maximum profits we need

$$\frac{d\pi}{dq} = 0, \qquad \frac{d^2\pi}{dq^2} < 0$$

From our necessary condition we get

$$\frac{d\pi}{dq} = \frac{dR}{dq} - \frac{dC}{dq} = 0$$

This means

$$MR - MC = 0$$

Thus, the necessary condition for maximum profits is $MR = MC$. But, as the diagram shows, we have two points A and B. Which one should it be? The sufficient condition gives us

$$\frac{d^2\pi}{dq^2} = \frac{d^2R}{dq^2} - \frac{d^2C}{dq^2} < 0$$

i.e.,

$$\frac{d^2R}{dq^2} < \frac{d^2C}{dq^2}$$

This means that the rate of increase of MR must be smaller than the rate of increase of MC when there is a small increase in q. Graphically, when the MR curve is steeper (downward) than the MC curve, this condition is fulfilled. To put it another way, the MC curve should cut the MR curve from below. In our graph, the point B is ruled out and the equilibrium point that satisfies the necessary and sufficient conditions will be A.

5.9 Monopoly price and output

Assume a monopolist has demand and cost curves as in Figure 5–22. We know from elementary economics that his profits π will be maximum when $MC = MR$ and prices will be p_1 and output OA, as in the diagram. Let us illustrate this with a simple example. Let the demand curve be

$$q = 400 - 20p$$

and average cost be

$$AC = 5 + \frac{q}{50}$$

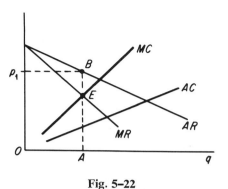

Fig. 5–22

Then, total cost will be

$$C = 5q + \frac{q^2}{50}$$

and profits

$$\pi = R - C$$

Conditions for maximum profits are

$$\frac{d\pi}{dq} = \frac{dR}{dq} - \frac{dC}{dq} = MR - MC = 0$$

From dC/dq we get

$$\frac{dC}{dq} = \frac{d}{dq}\left(5q + \frac{q^2}{50}\right) = 5 + \frac{q}{25}$$

For dR/dq, let us first change the demand function as follows:

$$p = 20 - \frac{q}{20}$$

Then,

$$R = pq = 20q - \frac{q^2}{20}$$

Thus,

$$\frac{dR}{dq} = 20 - \frac{q}{10}$$

and we have

$$20 - \frac{q}{10} = 5 + \frac{q}{25}$$

so that

$$q = 107 \text{ (approximately)}$$

We can find $p = 14.6$ (approximately), and maximum profits will be $\pi = 799$. The sufficient condition is

$$\frac{d^2R}{dq^2} = \frac{d}{dq}\left(20 - \frac{q}{10}\right) = -\frac{1}{10}$$

$$\frac{d^2C}{dq^2} = \frac{d}{dq}\left(5 + \frac{q}{25}\right) = \frac{1}{25}$$

$$\therefore \quad \frac{d^2\pi}{dq^2} = \frac{d^2R}{dq^2} - \frac{d^2C}{dq^2} = -\frac{1}{10} - \frac{1}{25} < 0$$

Thus, the sufficient condition is satisfied.

5.10 Discriminating monopolist

When the monopolist can sell his products in two markets that are economically isolated and when the demand elasticities are different, he can maximize his profits by charging different prices in each market. Let us assume he sells q_1 in market I and q_2 in market II. Let $R(q_1)$ and $E(q_2)$ be the revenue from each market, which are functions of what they sell in each market. Total cost is given by $C(q_1 + q_2)$. The profits π are

$$\pi = R(q_1) + R(q_2) - C(q_1 + q_2)$$

For the monopolist to maximize π, we have

$$\frac{\partial \pi}{\partial q_1} = 0, \quad \frac{\partial \pi}{\partial q_2} = 0$$

Let us set $q = q_1 + q_2$. Then, the above becomes, letting $q = q_1 + q_2$,

$$\frac{dR}{dq_1} - \frac{dC}{dq} = 0$$

i.e., $MR_1 = MC$

$$\frac{dR}{dq_2} - \frac{dC}{dq} = 0$$

i.e., $MR_2 = MC$

Thus, the conditions for π to be maximum are

$$MR_1 = MR_2 = MC$$

That is, the MR of each market must be equal to each other and also equal to the MC of the total output.

We have seen previously that $MR = p\left(1 - \frac{1}{\eta}\right)$. Thus, if we let η_1 and η_2 be the elasticity in each market, then, since $MR_1 = MR_2$,

$$p_1\left(1 - \frac{1}{\eta_1}\right) = p_2\left(1 - \frac{1}{\eta_2}\right)$$

where p_1 and p_2 are the prices in each market. Thus,

$$\frac{p_1}{p_2} = \frac{1 - (1/\eta_2)}{1 - (1/\eta_1)}$$

Since η ranges from 0 to $+\infty$, if $\eta_1 > \eta_2$, i.e., if demand is more elastic in market I, we get

$$\frac{p_1}{p_2} < 1$$

This means that the monopolist will charge a lower price in market I (elastic market) and the ratio of the prices is related to the elasticities in the above form.

5.11 Equilibrium conditions for a producer

Assume a producer buys inputs a and b to produce output q. We show the production function by

$$q = f(a, b)$$

Furthermore, assume the prices of the inputs are p_a and p_b. Let his budget be M. Then,

$$p_a a + p_b b = M$$

Thus, the problem is to produce the maximum amount of q (output), given the budget constraint. Let us set

$$z = f(a, b) + \lambda[M - p_a a - p_b b]$$

$$\frac{\partial z}{\partial a} = f_a - \lambda p_a = 0$$

$$\frac{\partial z}{\partial b} = f_b - \lambda p_b = 0$$

$$\frac{\partial z}{\partial \lambda} = M - p_a a - p_b b = 0$$

If we find a and b from these equations, that will be the amount of input that should be purchased to produce the maximum amount of q (output). We usually show these conditions by

$$\frac{f_a}{p_a} = \frac{f_b}{p_b} = \lambda$$

where f_a and f_b are the marginal physical products of a and b. This is the well-known *law of equi-marginal productivity*, and, when we follow it, we get the *least-cost combination* of inputs.

5.12 Adding-up theorem

Let us discuss the adding-up theorem again in a more general form. Assume we have

$$q = f(a, b)$$
$$C = p_a a + p_b b$$
$$\pi = pq - C$$

where q is output, p is the price of the product, a, b are inputs, p_a, p_b are prices of inputs, C is total cost, and π is profits. The conditions for maximum profits are

$$\frac{\partial \pi}{\partial a} = \frac{\partial (pq)}{\partial a} - \frac{\partial C}{\partial a} = 0$$

$$\frac{\partial \pi}{\partial b} = \frac{\partial (pq)}{\partial b} - \frac{\partial C}{\partial b} = 0$$

Next we find

$$\frac{\partial pq}{\partial a} = p\frac{\partial q}{\partial a} + q\frac{\partial p}{\partial a} = p\frac{\partial q}{\partial a} + q\frac{\partial p}{\partial q}\frac{\partial q}{\partial a}$$

$$= \frac{\partial q}{\partial a} p\left[1 + \frac{q}{p}\frac{\partial p}{\partial q}\right]$$

$$= \frac{\partial q}{\partial a} \times MR \qquad (MR = \text{marginal revenue})$$

$$= f_a \times MR$$

$f_a = \partial q / \partial a$ is the marginal product of input a. The $f_a \times MR$ is the marginal revenue product of a (MRP_a). Thus, we have

$$MRP_a = pf_a\left[1 - \frac{1}{\eta}\right]$$

$$= (VMP \text{ of } a)\left[1 - \frac{1}{\eta}\right]$$

where $(VMP \text{ of } a) = pf_a$ is the value of the marginal product of a, and η is the elasticity of demand.

On the other hand,

$$\frac{\partial C}{\partial a} = p_a + a\frac{\partial p_a}{\partial a} = p_a\left[1 + \frac{a}{p_a}\frac{\partial p_a}{\partial a}\right]$$

$$= p_a\left[1 + \frac{1}{e_a}\right]$$

where e_a is the elasticity of supply of input a and p_a is the price of input a. Thus, we can set it as the average factor cost (afc) of a. Since we have

$$\frac{\partial(pq)}{\partial a} - \frac{\partial C}{\partial a} = 0$$

i.e., $\partial(pq)/\partial a = \partial C/\partial a$, we get

$$(afc\ of\ a)\left(1 + \frac{1}{e_a}\right) = mfc_a = MRP_a = VMP_a\left(1 - \frac{1}{\eta}\right)$$

This will be the condition for maximum profits with respect to input a and also to input b.

When we have pure competition in the commodity market and factor market, then $e = \infty$ and $\eta = \infty$. Thus, for a given input we have

$$afc = mfc = MRP = VMP$$

Next let us derive the *adding-up theorem*. We have just derived the relationship

$$p_a\left(1 + \frac{1}{e_a}\right) = MRP_a = MR \times f_a$$

Thus,

$$p_a = MR\frac{f_a}{k_a}$$

where $k_a = 1 + 1/e_a$. In the same manner p_b will be found. Thus,

$$pq = p_a a + p_b b$$

$$= MR\left(\frac{f_a}{k_a}a + \frac{f_a}{k_b}b\right)$$

$$\therefore\quad q = \frac{MR}{p}\left(\frac{f_a}{k_a}a + \frac{f_b}{k_b}b\right)$$

This is the general form of the adding-up theorem. If we assume pure competition in the commodity market, $MR = p$ and, thus,

$$q = \frac{f_a}{k_a}a + \frac{f_b}{k_b}b$$

If we assume pure competition in the factor market, then $e = \infty$ and $k_a = k_b = 1$. Thus,

$$q = af_a + bf_b$$

5.13 Method of least squares

Fig. 5–23

As another application, let us discuss the *method of least squares*. As is well known, we have a set of data y_i $(i = 1, 2, ..., n)$ to which we fit a straight line

$$y_c = a + bx$$

such that

$$\sum_{i=1}^{n} (y_i - y_c)^2 = \text{minimum}$$

where we sum over all the points. Let

$$f(a, b) = \sum (y_i - y_c)^2 = \sum [y_i - (a + bx)]^2$$

The problem is to find the values of the coefficients a and b such that $f(a, b)$ will be a minimum. For this we need $f_a = 0$, $f_b = 0$ as the necessary conditions. For ease of calculations, let

$$z = y - (a + bx)$$

Thus,

$$f(a, b) = \sum z_i^2$$

Thus,

$$\frac{\partial f}{\partial a} = \sum \frac{\partial z^2}{\partial a}$$

$$= \sum \frac{\partial z^2}{\partial z} \frac{\partial z}{\partial a}$$

$$= \sum 2z(0 - 1 - 0)$$

$$\sum 2z = 0, \quad \text{or} \quad \sum z = 0$$

$$\sum [y - (a + bx)] = 0$$

$$\sum y - \sum a - \sum bx = 0$$

$$\therefore \quad \sum y = \sum a + b \sum x$$

Likewise

$$f_b = \sum (2z)(-x) = 0$$

$$\sum xz = 0$$

$$\sum xy - \sum ax - b \sum x^2 = 0$$

$$\therefore \quad \sum xy = a \sum x + b \sum x^2$$

Thus, by solving the two equations

$$\sum y = na + b \sum x$$
$$\sum xy = a \sum x + b \sum x^2$$

we find a and b that minimize $f(a, b)$. These equations are called the *normal equations* associated with the method of least squares.

Problem

Find the normal equations that will minimize

(a) $f(a, b, c) = \sum [y - (a + bx + cx^2)]^2$

(b) $f(a, b, c, ...) = \sum [y - (a + bx + cx^2 + ...)]^2$

Notes and References

For proofs and derivations of the various topics that have been explained heuristically, see the following references.

5.1–5.3 Allen (1938), Chapter 14; Courant (Vol. I, 1937), pp. 158–167; Courant and Robbins (1941), pp. 341–345; Smail (1949), pp. 64–85; Sokolnikoff (1939), pp. 315–317, explains maxima and minima by using Taylor's formula (we discuss Taylor's formula in Chapter 7); Tintner (1953), Chapter 15.

5.4 Allen (1938), Chapter 19, uses Taylor's formula for explanation; Courant (Vol. II, 1936), pp. 183–209; Sokolnikoff (1939), pp. 321–326 also uses Taylor's formula for explanation; Tintner (1953), pp. 166–169; Protter, Morrey (1964), Chapter 4; Munroe (1963), Chapter 6.

5.5–5.7 Allen (1938), Chapter 19; Courant (Vol. II, 1936), pp. 183–209; Sokolnikoff (1939), pp. 327–334. Maxima and minima techniques are used extensively in economics. This topic will be taken up again in Chapter 11 with the help of matrices. "Mathematical Appendix A" of Samuelson (1947) discusses the maxima and minima problem but should read after Chapter 11 of this book has been finished.

5.8–5.12 With this background, a fairly large amount of mathematical economics literature should become accessible. Henderson and Quandt (1958), Davis

(1941), Lange (1959), Hicks (1935), Samuelson (1949), Chapter 4, Allen (1960), Allen (1967), Kooros (1965), Cohen and Cyert (1965), Chiang (1967), provide many illustrations.

Allen, R. G. D., *Macro-Economic Theory*. New York: St. Martin's Press, 1967.

————— *Mathematical Economics*. St. Martin's Press, 1960.

Chiang, A. C., *Fundamental Methods of Mathematical Economics*. N.Y.: McGraw-Hill Book Company, 1967.

Cohen, K. J. and Cyert, R. M., *Theory of the Firm*. Englewood Cliffs, N.J.: Prentice-Hall, Inc., 1965.

Davis, H. T., *The Theory of Econometrics*. Bloomington, Ind.: Principia Press, Inc., 1941.

Henderson, J. M. and Quandt, R. E., *Microeconomic Theory, A Mathematical Approach*. New York: McGraw-Hill Book Company, 1958.

Hicks, J. R., "The Theory of Monopoly," *Econometrica*, Vol. 3, pp. 1–20, 1935.

Kooros, A., *Elements of Mathematical Economics*. Boston: Houghton Mifflin Co., 1965.

Lange, O., *Introduction to Econometrics*. New York: Pergamon Press, Inc., 1959.

Samuelson, P. A., *Foundations of Economic Analysis*. Cambridge, Mass.: Harvard University Press, 1947.

CHAPTER 6

Integration

The first limiting process discussed was differentiation. From a geometrical standpoint, differentiation was a study of the tangent to a curve. The second limiting process we take up is integration. In geometrical terms, this will be a study of area under a curve. Analytically speaking, however, integration and differentiation do not depend on geometry. A geometrical interpretation is used only to help foster intuition.

6.1 Riemann integral

Assume a continuous function $y = f(x)$ as shown in Figure 6–1. The

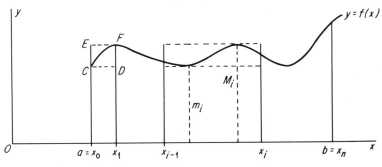

Fig. 6–1

domain of the function is the closed interval $[a, b]$ which may be considered a set of points. Assume the values of $y = f(x)$ are finite. We are interested in calculating the area under the curve $y = f(x)$ between a and b.

Let us divide the interval $[a, b]$ into equal or unequal subintervals and set

$$a = x_0 < x_1 < x_2 < \ldots < x_n = b$$

Looking at the strip between x_0 and x_1, we can find an approximation to the

231

area under the curve by either the rectangles

$$R_1 = x_0 C D x_1 \quad \text{or} \quad R_1' = x_0 E F x_1$$

and R_1 and R_1' can be calculated by

$$R_1 = (x_1 - x_0) f(x_0)$$
$$R_1' = (x_1 - x_0) f(x_1)$$

Let the area under the curve be R_1''. Then we can see from Figure 6–1 that

$$R_1 < R_1'' < R_1'$$

This was because x_0 and x_1 were picked so that $f(x_0)$ would be the smallest and $f(x_1)$ would be the largest $f(x)$ value in (x_0, x_1).

In general, if we take an interval (x_{i-1}, x_i), as in Figure 6–1, from all the values that $f(x)$ can take in this interval we can find an upper bound M_i and a lower bound m_i as shown. Then, $M_i(x_i - x_{i-1})$ would give the upper bound of the area, and $m_i(x_i - x_{i-1})$, the lower bound of the area.

Let us carry this operation out for all of the intervals, first for the m_i, then for the M_i. Thus,

$$z = m_1(x_1 - x_0) + m_2(x_2 - x_1) + \ldots + m_n(x_n - x_{n-1})$$

Let $(x_i - x_{i-1}) = \Delta x_i$. Then we can abbreviate the above as follows.

$$z = \sum_{i=1}^{n} m_i \Delta x_i$$

Likewise for the M_i we have

$$Z = \sum_{i=1}^{n} M_i \Delta x_i$$

If we consider $[a, b]$ a set S and all the n subintervals S_i disjoint subsets,

$$S = S_1 + S_2 + S_3 + \ldots + S_n$$

Then we can think of $(x_i - x_{i-1})$ as a measure (in our present case, length) of the set S_i (in our present case, a subinterval). Designate the measure as $\mu(S_i)$. Then the above sums can be shown as

$$z = \sum m_i \mu(S_i)$$
$$Z = \sum M_i \mu(S_i)$$

which would be their most general terms. Let us call this the lower and upper sums associated with this division of the set S.

If we let m be the lower bound of the function $f(x)$ and M be the upper bound, then, obviously

$$m\mu(S) < z < Z < M\mu(S)$$

Furthermore, if we let the area under the curve be A, then

$$z < A < Z$$

We now apply the limiting process to the sums. We want to show that z and Z will tend to a limit and that the limit will be A. Obviously all we need to show is that z and Z converge to one limit.

Let us superimpose a finer division on the one we already have. It is intuitively clear that the new combined partition, which is much finer than the original, will produce new sums, where the difference between m_i and M_i in an interval (x_{i-1}, x_i) will become smaller. Let

$$Z - z = \sum (M_i - m_i)\mu(S_i)$$

Let ϵ be the largest difference between M_i and m_i. Then $\epsilon \geq M_i - m_i$. Thus,

$$Z - z = \sum (M_i - m_i)\mu(S_i) \leq \sum \epsilon\mu(S_i)$$
$$= \epsilon \sum \mu(S_i) = \epsilon(b - a)$$

ϵ will tend toward zero as the subdivision is repeated over and over again. Thus,

$$Z - z \leq \epsilon(b - a) \to 0$$

as the subdivision is repeated. This is a limiting process, and in the limit we can set

$$Z = z = A$$

When a limit is obtained, the common value is written as

$$\int_S f(x)\, dx$$

and we say $f(x)$ is integrable over S. (In our present case, over the interval $[a, b]$.)

Graphically, the process of $z \to A$ can be thought of as approaching the area under the curve from inside the curve, and $Z \to A$ as approaching it from outside. In the limit, z and Z become equal to the area under the curve A.

Thus, the integral is defined as the limit of a finite sum of numbers ($f(x)\, dx$). Integration is the process of obtaining a limit, and the integral is the limit. In our particular example, it so happens that it becomes the area under the curve.

But, for most practical purposes in economics, this "pure" attitude will be compromised, and it will be convenient to interpret $\int f(x)\, dx$ as a summation process and look upon it as the area under the curve or volume or whatever we are applying it to.

In contrast to the definite bounds of the interval, we now let $b = x$

become a variable. Then we have

$$F(x) = \int_a^x f(x)\, dx$$

We call $F(x)$ an *indefinite integral*, and we shall see that it is one of the integrals obtained by changing the lower limit a; $f(x)$ is called the *integrand*.

The geometrical interpretation of $F(x)$ is the area under the curve from a to x. The point a is fixed, but x is allowed to vary. Hence, as x moves along the x-axis, the area under the curve changes. The $F(x)$ shows the area for the different values of x.

The integrand $f(x)$ is independent of x. That is to say, the rule of mapping that is given by $f(x)$ will be the same regardless of what x is so long as x is in the domain of definition. That is, regardless of where x is on the x-axis, the curve shown by $f(x)$ in Figure 6–2 stays the same. From Figure 6–2 we

Fig. 6–2

have

$$\int_a^x f(x)\, dx = \int_a^{a_1} f(x)\, dx + \int_{a_1}^x f(x)\, dx$$

$$\int_a^{a_1} f(x)\, dx = \text{a definite integral} = \text{constant} = c$$

Let

$$\int_a^x f(x)\, dx = F(x), \qquad \int_{a_1}^x f(x)\, dx = G(x)$$

Then,

$$F(x) = G(x) + c$$

Thus, we have a whole family of indefinite integrals that differ only by constants.

The geometric interpretation is that c is the area from a to a_1; $G(x)$ is the area from a_1 to x; hence $F(x)$ is the sum of these two areas. Since the point a_1 was selected arbitrarily, we can select it at any other point. If it is put at a different point, say a_1', then we get a new constant c' and the $G(x)$ is the area from this a_1' to x and $F(x)$ is the sum of these two areas. As can be seen, geometrically we have a whole family of combinations of $G(x)$ and c that add up to $F(x)$.

6.2 Numerical methods for evaluating the integral

To obtain a better feeling for the integral $\int f(x)\, dx$ as the limit of a finite sum of $f(x)\, dx$, let us show how the integral may be approximated by two numerical methods.

(i) Rectangular rule

Suppose the integral

$$\int_a^b f(x)\, dx$$

is for the area between a and b in Figure 6–3. We can see geometrically that

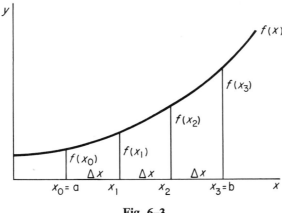

Fig. 6–3

the area may be approximated by

$$\Delta x\, f(x_0) + \Delta x\, f(x_1) + \Delta x\, f(x_2)$$

or

$$\Delta x\, f(x_1) + \Delta x\, f(x_2) + \Delta x\, f(x_3)$$

where

$$\Delta x = \frac{b - a}{n}$$

The n shows the number of subintervals, which in the present illustration is $n = 3$. This method of approximation is called the *rectangular rule*.

The $f(x_0), f(x_1),$ and $f(x_2)$, which show the heights on the left-hand side of each strip, may be expressed as

$$f(a + k\,\Delta x)$$

where $k = 0, 1, 2$. That is,

$$
\begin{aligned}
k = 0: &\quad f(a + 0\,\Delta x) = f(x_0) = y_0 \\
k = 1: &\quad f(a + 1\,\Delta x) = f(x_1) = y_1 \\
k = 2: &\quad f(a + 2\,\Delta x) = f(x_2) = y_2
\end{aligned}
$$

In similar manner, the $f(x_1)$, $f(x_2)$, and $f(x_3)$, which show the heights on the right side of each strip, may be expressed as

$$f(a + k\,\Delta x)$$

where $k = 1, 2, 3$. That is,

$$
\begin{aligned}
k = 1: &\quad f(a + 1\,\Delta x) = f(x_1) = y_1 \\
k = 2: &\quad f(a + 2\,\Delta x) = f(x_2) = y_2 \\
k = 3: &\quad f(a + 3\,\Delta x) = f(x_3) = y_3
\end{aligned}
$$

Hence, the general formula is

$$\int_a^b f(x)\,dx \approx \begin{array}{l} \Delta x\{y_0 + y_1 + y_2\} \\ \Delta x\{y_1 + y_2 + y_3\} \end{array} \qquad \begin{array}{l} \text{for the left-side heights} \\ \text{for the right-side heights} \end{array}$$

for $n = 3$ and where

$$y_k = f(a + k\,\Delta x)$$

Let us illustrate with examples.

Example 1. Find the area beneath the curve

$$y = x^2 + 1$$

from $x = 1$ to $x = 4$ (Figure 6–4). For simplicity, let us divide the interval

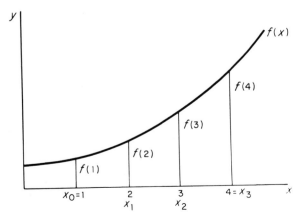

Fig. 6–4

[1, 4] into $n = 3$ subintervals. Then the length of a subinterval is

$$\Delta x = \frac{b-a}{n} = \frac{4-1}{3} = 1$$

For $k = 0, 1, 2$ (i.e., by using the heights on the left side of the strips) we get, since $a = 1$ and $\Delta x = 1$,

$$k = 0: \quad f(a + k\,\Delta x) = f[1 + 0(1)] = f(1) = y_0 = 1^2 + 1 = 2$$
$$k = 1: \quad f(a + k\,\Delta x) = f[1 + 1(1)] = f(2) = y_1 = 2^2 + 1 = 5$$
$$k = 2: \quad f(a + k\,\Delta x) = f[1 + 2(1)] = f(3) = y_2 = 3^2 + 1 = 10$$

$$\therefore \quad \int_1^4 f(x)\,dx \approx \Delta x\{y_0 + y_1 + y_2\}$$
$$= \Delta x\{f(1) + f(2) + f(3)\}$$
$$= 1(2 + 5 + 10) = 17$$

For $k = 1, 2, 3$

$$\int_1^4 f(x)\,dx \approx \Delta x\{f(2) + f(3) + f(4)\}$$
$$= 1\{5 + 10 + 17\} = 32$$

The true value is, as we shall explain in Section 6.4

$$\int_1^4 f(x)\,dx = \int_1^4 (x^2 + 1)\,dx = 24$$

As can be seen geometrically, as the subdivisions n become larger, the approximations will become closer to the true value 24. Let us try it with $n = 6$.

Example 2. Suppose the interval is subdivided by $n = 6$. Then

$$\Delta x = \frac{b-a}{n} = \frac{4-1}{6} = \frac{3}{6} = \frac{1}{2}$$

Hence, for $k = 0, 1, 2, 3, 4$, and 5, we get for $f(a + k\,\Delta x)$

$$k = 0: \quad f[1 + 0(\tfrac{1}{2})] = f(1) \quad = y_0 = 1^2 + 1 = 2$$
$$k = 1: \quad f[1 + 1(\tfrac{1}{2})] = f(1.5) = y_1 = (1.5)^2 + 1 = 3.25$$
$$k = 2: \qquad\qquad\qquad f(2.0) = y_2 = 5$$
$$k = 3: \qquad\qquad\qquad f(2.5) = y_3 = 7.25$$
$$k = 4: \qquad\qquad\qquad f(3) = y_4 = 10$$
$$k = 5: \qquad\qquad\qquad f(3.5) = y_5 = 13.25$$

Thus,

$$\int_1^4 f(x)\,dx \approx \Delta x(y_0 + y_1 + \ldots + y_5)$$
$$= \tfrac{1}{2}[2 + 3.25 + \ldots + 13.25] = 20.375$$

(ii) Trapezoidal rule

In the rectangular rule, we obtained the area of the strip by multiplying the base by the left-hand height or the right-hand height (see Figure 6–5).

 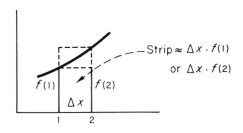

Fig. 6–5

As is seen in our present case, there is a large difference between $f(1)$ and $f(2)$ and hence the $\Delta x\, f(1)$ considerably underestimates the area of the strip while $\Delta x\, f(2)$ overestimates it.

To improve the estimate of the area of this strip, a natural thing to do would be to take the average height and multiply it by Δx. That is,

$$\text{Area of strip} \approx \Delta x \left[\frac{f(1) + f(2)}{2} \right]$$

The trapezoidal rule uses this idea. Note that, when the strip is viewed sideways, it may be roughly considered a trapezoid. Let us illustrate this technique with an example.

Example 3. Using the $y = x^2 + 1$ of Example 1, we get with the trapezoidal method

$$\int_1^4 f(x)\, dx \approx \Delta x \left[\frac{f(1) + f(2)}{2} + \frac{f(2) + f(3)}{2} + \frac{f(3) + f(4)}{2} \right]$$

$$= 1 \left(\frac{2 + 5}{2} + \frac{5 + 10}{2} + \frac{10 + 17}{2} \right)$$

$$= 24\tfrac{1}{2}$$

Since the true value is 24, this result of $24\tfrac{1}{2}$ is a substantial improvement over the previous results of 17 and 32.

The above equation may be written as

$$\int_1^4 f(x)\, dx \approx \frac{\Delta x}{2} \left[f(1) + 2f(2) + 2f(3) + f(4) \right]$$

or, in general, when we have n subintervals

$$\int_a^b f(x)\,dx \approx \frac{\Delta x}{2}\{y_0 + 2y_1 + 2y_2 + \ldots + 2y_{n-1} + y_n\}$$

Problems

1. Find the area beneath the curve

$$y = x^2 + 1$$

from $x = 1$ to $x = 4$ by the rectangular rule. Divide the interval into $n = 12$ subintervals.

2. Solve Problem 1 using the trapezoidal rule.

3. Find the area beneath the curve

$$y = 20 - x^2$$

from $x = 1$ to $x = 4$ using the (a) rectangular rule and (b) trapezoidal rule. Divide the interval into $n = 6$ subintervals.

6.3 Fundamental theorem of the calculus

We saw that differentiation was a limiting process by which we obtained the limit of a difference quotient dy/dx of a function $y = f(x)$. We also saw that integration was a limiting process by which we obtained the limit of a sum. It turns out that these two processes are the inverse of each other. This can be shown intuitively by starting with the integration process and interpreting it from the standpoint of an area.

According to the indefinite integral we discussed, the area under $y = f(x)$ of Figure 6–6 can be shown as

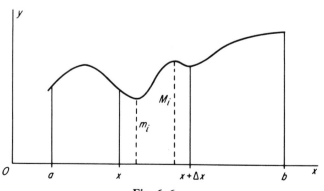

Fig. 6–6

$$F(x) = \int_a^x f(x)\,dx$$

$$F(x + \Delta x) = \int_a^{x+\Delta x} f(x)\,dx$$

$$F(x + \Delta x) - F(x) = \int_x^{x+\Delta x} f(x)\,dx$$

The area in the interval $(x, x + \Delta x)$ can be approximated, as we did in Section 6.1 by

$$m_i(\Delta x) \quad \text{and} \quad M_i(\Delta x)$$

We have

$$m_i(\Delta x) < F(x + \Delta x) - F(x) < M_i(\Delta x)$$

where m_i and M_i are, as before, the smallest and largest values of $f(x)$ in $(x, x + \Delta x)$. Thus,

$$m_i < \frac{F(x + \Delta x) - F(x)}{\Delta x} < M_i$$

If we let the interval $(x, x + \Delta x)$ become smaller, i.e., undertake a limiting process by letting $\Delta x \to 0$, then, m_i and M_i will become equal in the limit to $f(x)$, provided $f(x)$ is continuous. The difference quotient

$$\frac{F(x + \Delta x) - F(x)}{\Delta x}$$

will approach a limit $F'(x)$,

$$\lim_{\Delta x \to 0} \frac{F(x + \Delta x) - F(x)}{\Delta x} = F'(x)$$

Since m_i and M_i will approach a common limit $f(x)$ as $\Delta x \to 0$ and since $m_i \le F'(x) \le M_i$,

$$F'(x) = f(x)$$

That is, differentiation of the indefinite integral $F(x)$ at x gives us the value of the function $f(x)$ at x. This is called the *fundamental theorem of calculus*. We may state it more formally as follows: Given the indefinite integral

$$F(x) = \int_a^x f(x)\,dx$$

as a function of x, the derivative of $F(x)$ at x is equal to $f(x)$. That is,

$$F'(x) = f(x)$$

Note the following points: First, we defined the *definite* integral of $f(x)$ over the interval $[a, b]$ as the limit of a sum. We noted that this definite integral was dependent on the lower and upper limits of integration, i.e., a and b. Second, to show the relation of the definite integral and its limits, we let the upper limit b become $b = x$, i.e., a variable. The definite integral then became a function of $b = x$, and we called it an *indefinite* integral. Since it has become a function of x, we could differentiate it with respect to x. Thirdly, this led to the result that the derivative of the indefinite integral

$$F(x) = \int_a^x f(x)\, dx$$

i.e., $F'(x)$, is equal to $f(x)$ at x, or $F'(x) = f(x)$.

Although $F(x)$ is an integral, to emphasize its relation with $f(x)$ and also that it is a function of x, it is preferably called *a* (not *the*) *primitive function* of $f(x)$. It can be seen that $f(x)$ will have a whole family of primitive functions

$$G(x) = F(x) + c$$

where c is some constant. When we differentiate, we have

$$G'(x) = F'(x) = f(x)$$

a result already obtained in Section 6.1.

Let us illustrate this with an example. Suppose we have a function

$$y = 2 + x^2$$

which is shown in Figure 6–7, and we are interested in the area under the curve from 1 to 4.

This function may be written as

$$y = 2 + x^2 = f(x)$$

Then the area is shown by

$$F(x) = \int_1^x f(x)\, dx = \int_1^x (2 + x^2)\, dx$$

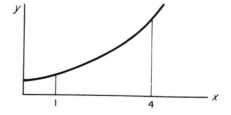

Fig. 6–7

The primitive function of $f(x) = 2 + x^2$ is a function $F(x)$ such that $F'(x) = f(x) = 2 + x^2$.

Hence, to find $F(x)$, we need to find a function that when differentiated will give us $f(x) = 2 + x^2$. How do we find $F(x)$? For this simple problem, we know enough calculus to guess that

(1) $$F(x) = 2x + \tfrac{1}{3}x^3$$

should give us

$$F'(x) = f(x) = 2 + x^2$$

Let us check.

$$F'(x) = \frac{d}{dx}(2x + \tfrac{1}{3}x^3) = 2 + x^2$$

Hence (1) is a primitive function of $f(x)$. Notice that we said *a* primitive function. We did not say *the* primitive function. This is because

$$F(x) = 2x + \tfrac{1}{3}x^3 + 1$$
$$F(x) = 2x + \tfrac{1}{3}x^3 + 2$$
$$\cdots$$

are also primitive functions of $f(x)$. We can get as many as we want by simply adding a constant. Hence we may express all of these primitive functions by

$$F(x) + c$$

where c is a constant.

Let us give one more example.

Example 1. Suppose we have

$$F(x) = \int_a^x f(x)\, dx = \int_a^x (2x + x^3)\, dx$$

Find the primitive function of $f(x) = 2x + x^3$. Our problem is to find a function $F(x)$ such that $F'(x) = 2x + x^3$. Let us guess it. We guess

$$F(x) = x^2 + \tfrac{1}{4}x^4$$

We may check our guess by

$$F'(x) = \frac{d}{dx}(x^2 + \tfrac{1}{4}x^4) = 2x + x^3$$

and it checks. Hence the primitive function we seek is

$$G(x) = F(x) + c = x^2 + \tfrac{1}{4}x^4 + c$$

We may summarize our discussion as follows. Given

$$F(x) = \int_a^x f(x)\, dx$$

Then,

$$\frac{d}{dx} F(x) = F'(x) = \frac{d}{dx}\left\{ \int_a^x f(x)\, dx \right\} = f(x)$$

The fundamental theorem has shown us that differentiation and integration of a function $f(x)$ are the inverse of each other. When the process of integrating $f(x)$ is differentiated, the process is reversed and we obtain the original situation $f(x)$. It also shows us a method of evaluating the definite integral. Let us explain this second point.

Let $f(x)$ be a continuous function in the interval (a, b). Then the definite integral over (a, b) will be

$$\int_a^b f(x)\, dx$$

Let $F(x)$ be a primitive function of $f(x)$. Then,

$$F(x) = \int_a^x f(x)\,dx$$

We have just seen from the *fundamental theorem* that

$$G(x) = F(x) + c$$

where c is a constant. Thus, we obtain

$$G(x) = \int_a^x f(x)\,dx + c$$

Let $x = a$. Then,

$$G(a) = \int_a^a f(x)\,dx + c = c$$

Thus,

$$F(x) = G(x) - c = G(x) - G(a)$$

$$\therefore \quad \int_a^x f(x)\,dx = G(x) - G(a)$$

Let $x = b$. Then,

$$\int_a^b f(x)\,dx = G(b) - G(a)$$
$$= \{F(b) + c\} - \{F(a) + c\}$$
$$= F(b) - F(a)$$

Thus, we obtain the following result: If $f(x)$ is a continuous function in (a, b) and

$$F(x) = \int_a^x f(x)\,dx$$

is an indefinite integral of $f(x)$, the value of the definite integral $\int_a^b f(x)$ is

$$\int_a^b f(x)\,dx = F(b) - F(a)$$

In words this simply means that the value of the definite integral is obtained by first finding the primitive function $F(x)$ and then substituting in this primitive function the values a and b and finding $F(b) - F(a)$. Let us illustrate with two examples.

Example 2. Using the function of the illustration above, we have

$$\int_1^4 (2 + x^2)\,dx$$

A primitive function $F(x)$ of $f(x) = 2 + x^2$ was found to be

$$F(x) = 2x + \tfrac{1}{3}x^3$$

Hence, the value of the definite integral is

$$F(4) - F(1) = \{2(4) + \tfrac{1}{3}(4)^3\} - \{2(1) + \tfrac{1}{3}(1)^3\} = 27$$

This 27 is the area under the curve from 1 to 4.

Example 3. The other illustration we had was

$$\int_a^b (2x + x^3)\, dx$$

A primitive function of $f(x) = 2x + x^3$ was

$$F(x) = x^2 + \tfrac{1}{4}x^4$$

Hence, the value of the integral is

$$F(b) - F(a) = \{b^2 + \tfrac{1}{4}b^4\} - \{a^2 + \tfrac{1}{4}a^4\}$$

In the next section we shall consider this problem of evaluating the integrals in a more systematic way.

The student may have noticed that all of the discussions up to this point assumed the function $f(x)$ to be continuous. The theory of integration we have explained is what is called the *Riemann integral* originated by German mathematician Bernhard Riemann (1826 to 1866). There are other theories of integration that consider cases where $f(x)$ may be discontinuous. One is the Stieltjes integral, and another is the Lesbegue integral.

Unless otherwise stated we shall be using the Riemann integral. Then we shall write

$$\int_a^b f(x)\, dx$$

and call this the definite integral of $f(x)$ with respect to x from $x = a$ to $x = b$. The a and b are called the *lower and upper limits of integration*. This can be interpreted to mean that, when the integral is evaluated, we shall get a definite numerical answer. In the cases we discussed, we got the area under the curve between a and b.

6.4 Techniques of integration

When discussing the derivative, we saw how derivatives could be evaluated by using the definition. But we also saw how tedious the calculations were, and as a result adopted various convenient rules for differentiation. As for the evaluation of the integral, we can follow the steps in the definition and construct a finite sum and evaluate it by a limiting process. But, as in the case of derivatives, we can adopt various convenient rules that will facilitate our calculations.

The evaluation of many integrals is not easy. Various tables of standard forms of integrals have been compiled to help in applied mathematics. We shall discuss only three such standard forms. We shall first state the standard form, give a few examples, and then interpret its meaning in geometric terms. It should be noted again that the integral does not depend on such geometric interpretation, but rather, when certain conditions are satisfied, the integrals can be interpreted geometrically.

RULE 1. *The power formula.*

$$\int x^n \, dx = \frac{x^{n+1}}{n+1}, \qquad n \neq -1$$

Example 1.

(1)
$$\int x^3 \, dx = \frac{x^4}{4} + c$$

Check

$$\frac{d}{dx}\left(\frac{x^4}{4} + c\right) = x^3$$

(2)
$$\int x^a \, dx = \frac{x^{a+1}}{a+1} + c$$

Check

$$\frac{d}{dx}\left(\frac{x^{a+1}}{a+1} + c\right) = x^a$$

(3)
$$\int 3x^2 \, dx = \frac{3x^3}{3} + c = x^3 + c$$

Check

$$\frac{d}{dx}(x^3 + c) = 3x^2$$

(4)
$$\int dx = x + c$$

Check

$$\frac{d}{dx}(x + c) = 1$$

(5)
$$\int h \, dx = hx + c$$

Check

$$\frac{d}{dx}(hx + c) = h$$

Example 2. Let

$$y = f(x) = h \qquad a \le x \le b$$
$$= 0 \qquad \text{otherwise}$$

Graphically, this is a straight line, as in Figure 6–8. Then, the integral of y will be

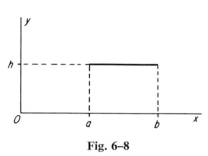

Fig. 6–8

$$\int y \, dx = \int h \, dx = hx + c$$

Now we wish to find the integral of y between a and b. For that we write

$$\int_a^b y \, dx = \int_a^b h \, dx$$

and this is the definite integral of the single-valued and continuous function $y = f(x) = h$ between a and b. As we have explained, this will be the area under the straight line $y = h$.

How is this definite integral evaluated? This will be done as follows.

$$\int_a^b h \, dx = hx \Big|_a^b = hb - ha = h(b - a)$$

As can be seen $h(b - a)$ is the area of the rectangle under the straight line $y = h$ between a and b.

Example 3. Let us now try a function that goes through the origin as in Figure 6–9. This function is shown by $y = Bx$, where B is the slope of the

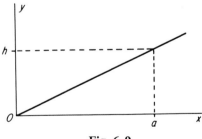

Fig. 6–9

curve and $B = h/a$. The integral of $y = Bx$ over $(0, a)$ will be

$$\int_0^a y \, dx = \int_0^a Bx \, dx = B \frac{x^2}{2} \Big|_0^a = B \frac{a^2}{2} - 0 = B \frac{a^2}{2}$$

But, since $B = h/a$, we have

$$B\frac{a^2}{2} = \frac{h}{a}\frac{a^2}{2} = \frac{ha}{2} = \text{area of triangle}$$

Example 4. Let us now find the area of the trapezoid in Figure 6–10. The

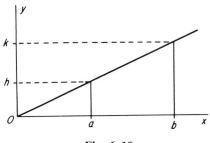

Fig. 6–10

function for this straight line is $y = Bx$, where $B = h/a = k/b$. Then the integral of y over (a, b) is

$$\int_a^b y\,dx = \int_a^b Bx\,dx = B\frac{x^2}{2}\Big|_a^b = B\frac{b^2}{2} - B\frac{a^2}{2} = \frac{kb}{2} - \frac{ha}{2}$$

Now $kb/2$ is the triangle over $(0, b)$, and $ha/2$ is the triangle over $(0, a)$. Thus, the difference of the two triangles gives us the trapezoid.

Example 5. Let us now have a function $y = x^2$, as shown in Figure 6–11.

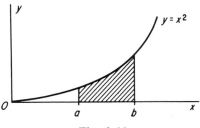

Fig. 6–11

Then the area under this curve between a and b will be

$$\int_a^b y\,dx = \int_a^b x^2\,dx = \frac{x^3}{3}\Big|_a^b = \frac{1}{3}(b^3 - a^3)$$

As is seen by these examples, this power formula is very easy to use. This would suggest that, when we have a complicated integrand, if by some means we could transform it into the power formula, the integration process would be simplified.

Let us first present several simple examples, then show how this transformation may be obtained by observation, and then present its theory.

Example 6.

$$\int (x + 1)^2 \, dx$$

To transform this into the power formula, we set

$$u = x + 1$$

and, using differentials, we know that

$$du = d(x + 1) = dx$$

Hence, the integral becomes

$$\int (x + 1)^2 \, dx = \int u^2 \, du = \frac{u^3}{3} + c$$

Substituting the $u = x + 1$ back in, we get

$$\int (x + 1)^2 \, dx = \frac{(x + 1)^3}{3} + c$$

Example 7.

$$\int (x^2 + 1)^2 x \, dx \qquad x > 0$$

Set

$$u = x^2 + 1$$

Then

$$du = d(x^2 + 1) = 2x \, dx$$

We note that $x \, dx$ is in the integral. Hence, using this $du = 2x \, dx$, we set

$$x \, dx = \tfrac{1}{2} du$$

Substituting $u = x^2 + 1$ and $x \, dx$ in the integral gives us

$$\frac{1}{2} \int u^2 \, du = \frac{1}{2} \frac{u^3}{3} + c$$

$$= \frac{1}{2} \frac{(x^2 + 1)^3}{3} + c$$

Example 8.

$$\int \sqrt{x} \, dx \qquad x > 0$$

Set

$$u = \sqrt{x} = x^{1/2}$$

Then

$$du = \tfrac{1}{2}x^{-1/2} \, dx$$

Thus

$$dx = 2x^{1/2} \, du = 2\sqrt{x} \, du = 2u \, du$$

Substituting these back in the integral gives us

$$\int \sqrt{x} \, dx = \int u2u \, du = 2 \int u^2 du$$

$$= 2\frac{u^3}{3} + c = \frac{2(\sqrt{x})^3}{3} + c$$

$$= \frac{2}{3} x^{3/2} + c$$

Check

$$\frac{d}{dx}\left(\frac{2}{3} x^{3/2} + c\right) = \frac{2}{3}\frac{3}{2} x^{(3/2)-1} = x^{1/2} = \sqrt{x}$$

This technique which we have used in Examples 6, 7, and 8 is called the *method of substitution* and is widely used. In simple cases, the transformation may be spotted by observation, and the transformation may be carried out mentally. In Examples 6 and 7 we may write by observation

$$\int (x + 1)^2 \, dx = \int (x + 1)^2 \, d(x + 1)$$

$$= \int u^2 \, du = \frac{u^3}{3} + c$$

$$\int (x^2 + 1)^2 x \, dx = \tfrac{1}{2} \int (x^2 + 1)^2 \, d(x^2 + 1)$$

$$= \tfrac{1}{2} \int u^2 \, du = \frac{1}{2}\frac{u^3}{3} + c$$

For Example 8, however, we need

$$\int \sqrt{x} \, dx = 2 \int (\sqrt{x})^2 \, d(\sqrt{x})$$

$$= 2 \int u^2 \, du = 2\frac{u^3}{3} + c$$

and this is not easy to spot. For this example, it is easier if we use the method of substitution systematically. Since this will be the case in a number of other problems, let us explain the formal steps of the method of substitution.

Let us use Example 7 and illustrate the process. We had

(1) $$\int f(x)\,dx = \int (x^2 + 1)^2 x\,dx \qquad x > 0$$

Hence

(2) $$f(x) = (x^2 + 1)^2 x$$

We set

(3) $$u = x^2 + 1$$

which may be shown as

(4) $$u = u(x)$$

and, since $x > 0$, we have

(5) $$x = \sqrt{u - 1}$$

and a one-to-one correspondence. Then $f(x)$ becomes

(6) $$f(x) = u^2\sqrt{u - 1}$$
$$= h(u)$$

The dx was found by differentiating (4)

(7) $$du = \frac{du}{dx}\,dx$$
$$= 2x\,dx$$

We shall assume that the relation between u and x is one to one and that $du/dx \neq 0$. Then

(8) $$dx = \frac{dx}{du}\,du = \frac{1}{2x}\,du = \frac{1}{2\sqrt{u-1}}\,du$$

Substituting (6) and (8) in $f(x)\,dx$ gives us

$$f(x)\,dx = h(u)\frac{dx}{du}\,du$$

which in our example is

$$(x^2 + 1)^2 x\,dx = u^2\sqrt{u-1}\,\frac{1}{2\sqrt{u-1}}\,du$$
$$= \tfrac{1}{2}u^2\,du$$

Hence the integral becomes

$$\int (x^2 + 1)x\,dx = \int \tfrac{1}{2}u^2\,du = \frac{1}{2}\frac{u^3}{3} + c$$

which is what we previously obtained.

Let us summarize this result as follows. Given the indefinite integral

$$\int f(x)\, dx$$

we may set

$$f(x) = h(u)$$

where

$$u = u(x)$$

Assuming that u and x have a one-to-one correspondence and that $du/dx \neq 0$, then

(9) $$\int f(x)\, dx = \int h(u) \frac{dx}{du}\, du$$

where

$$\frac{dx}{du} = \frac{1}{du/dx}$$

By substituting $u = u(x)$ in the result of (9), we shall obtain our answer in terms of x.

Let us solve Example 8 once again with this theorem.

Example 9.

$$\int \sqrt{x}\, dx \qquad x > 0$$

$$u = \sqrt{x} = x^{1/2}$$

$$\frac{du}{dx} = \frac{1}{2} x^{-1/2}$$

$$\frac{dx}{du} = \frac{1}{du/dx} = 2x^{1/2} = 2u$$

$$\therefore \quad \int \sqrt{x}\, dx = \int h(u) \frac{dx}{du}\, du$$

$$= \int u(2u)\, du = 2 \int u^2\, du = 2 \frac{u^3}{3} + c$$

$$= \tfrac{2}{3} x^{3/2} + c$$

Example 10.

$$\int (x^3 + 5)^2 3x^2\, dx \qquad x > 0$$

$$u = x^3 + 5$$

$$\frac{du}{dx} = 3x^2$$

$$\frac{dx}{du} = \frac{1}{3x^2}$$

$$\therefore \quad \int (x^3 + 5)^2 3x^2 \, dx = \int h(u) \frac{dx}{du} \, du = \int u^2 3x^2 \frac{1}{3x^2} \, du$$

$$= \int u^2 \, du = \frac{u^3}{3} + c = \frac{(x^3 + 5)^3}{3} + c$$

Example 11.

$$\int \frac{x^2 \, dx}{(x^3 + 5)^2} \qquad x > 0$$

$$u = x^3 + 5$$

$$\frac{du}{dx} = 3x^2, \qquad \frac{dx}{du} = \frac{1}{3x^2}$$

$$\int \frac{x^2 \, dx}{(x^3 + 5)^2} = \int h(u) \frac{dx}{du} \, du$$

$$= \int \frac{x^2}{u^2} \frac{1}{3x^2} \, du$$

$$= \frac{1}{3} \int \frac{1}{u^2} \, du = \frac{1}{3}(-u^{-1}) + c$$

$$= \frac{-1}{3}(x^3 + 5)^{-1} + c$$

Example 12.

$$\int x\sqrt{x^2 + 1} \, dx \qquad x > 0$$

$$u = x^2 + 1$$

$$\frac{du}{dx} = 2x$$

$$\int x\sqrt{x^2 + 1} \, dx = \int h(u) \frac{dx}{du} \, du$$

$$= \int x\sqrt{u} \frac{1}{2x} \, du$$

$$= \tfrac{1}{2} \int \sqrt{u} \, du$$

$$= \frac{1}{2} \frac{u^{3/2}}{(3/2)} + c$$

$$= \tfrac{1}{3}(x^2 + 1)^{3/2} + c$$

Example 13. The previous examples dealt with *indefinite* integrals. Let us now show how a *definite* integral is evaluated. The new problem is to determine the lower and upper limits of integration for the transformed integral. Using the integral of Example 10, suppose we wish to find

$$\int_1^2 (x^3 + 5)^2 3x^2 \, dx$$

Using the result of Example 10, we have

$$\int_1^2 (x^3 + 5)^2 3x^2 \, dx = \int_\alpha^\beta u^2 \, du$$

where

$$u = x^3 + 5$$

As is seen, we need to find the α and β for the transformed integral. We find

$$x = 1: \qquad u = 1^3 + 5 = 6$$
$$x = 2: \qquad u = 2^3 + 5 = 13$$

Hence, the definite integral becomes

$$\int_6^{13} u^2 \, du = \frac{u^3}{3} \Big|_6^{13} = \frac{13^3 - 6^3}{3}$$

In terms of x we have

$$\int_1^2 (x^3 + 5)^2 3x^2 \, dx = \frac{(x^3 + 5)^3}{3} \Big|_1^2 = \frac{13^3 - 6^3}{3}$$

RULE 2. *Logarithmic Formula.* We have seen that, when $y = \ln x$, the derivative of y is

$$\frac{dy}{dx} = \frac{1}{x}$$

Thus, we shall define (without explanation)

$$\int \frac{1}{x} \, dx = \ln x + c$$

For our present purpose, we shall always assume that $x > 0$. Graphically, the function $y = 1/x$ is as shown in Figure 6–12, the area between (a, b) being the shaded part. This is shown by

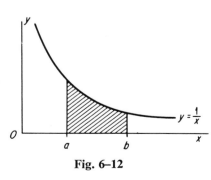

Fig. 6–12

$$\int_a^b \frac{1}{x} \, dx = \ln x \Big|_a^b = \ln b - \ln a$$

In general the logarithmic formula is

$$\int \frac{1}{u}\, du = \ln u + c$$

where u is a function of x and we assume $u(x) > 0$.

Examples.

(1) $$\int \frac{2}{x}\, dx = 2 \ln x + c$$

Check

$$\frac{d}{dx} (2 \ln x + c) = \frac{2}{x}$$

(2) $$\int \frac{1}{x+1}\, dx = \int \frac{d(x+1)}{x+1} = \ln (x+1) + c$$

Check

$$\frac{d}{dx} \ln (x+1) = \frac{1}{x+1}$$

(3) $$\int \frac{x}{x^2+1}\, dx = \frac{1}{2} \int \frac{d(x^2+1)}{x^2+1} = \frac{1}{2} \ln (x^2+1) + c$$

Check

$$\frac{d}{dx} \left(\frac{1}{2} \ln (x^2+1) + c \right) = \frac{1}{2} \frac{1}{x^2+1} 2x = \frac{x}{x^2+1}$$

As is seen, the substitution method has been used in (2) and (3) above.

RULE 3. *Exponential Formula.* We have seen that, when $y = e^x$, then

$$\frac{dy}{dx} = e^x$$

Thus, we can expect that

$$\int y\, dx = \int e^x\, dx = e^x + c$$

and, in general, the standard formula is

$$\int e^u\, du = e^u + c$$

where $u = u(x)$. Since, when $y = a^u$, we have

$$\frac{dy}{du} = a^u \ln a$$

the standard form for the integral will be

$$\int a^u\, du = \frac{a^u}{\ln a} + c$$

Examples.

(1)
$$\int e^{x+3} \, dx = \int e^{x+3} \, d(x + 3) = e^{x+3} + c$$

Check
$$\frac{d}{dx} (e^{x+3} + c) = e^{x+3}$$

(2)
$$\int e^{2x} \, dx = \frac{1}{2} \int e^{2x} \, d(2x) = \frac{1}{2} e^{2x} + c$$

Check
$$\frac{d}{dx} \left(\frac{1}{2} e^{2x} + c \right) = e^{2x}$$

(3)
$$\int e^{-3x+1} \, dx = -\frac{1}{3} \int e^{-3x+1} \, d(-3x + 1) = -\frac{1}{3} e^{-3x+1} + c$$

Check
$$\frac{d}{dx} \left(-\frac{1}{3} e^{-3x+1} + c \right) = e^{-3x+1}$$

(4)
$$\int a^{2x+3} \, dx = \frac{1}{2} \int a^{2x+3} \, d(2x + 3) = \frac{1}{2} \frac{a^{2x+3}}{\ln a} + c$$

Check
$$\frac{d}{dx} \left(\frac{1}{2} \frac{a^{2x+3}}{\ln a} + c \right) = \frac{1}{2 \ln a} (a^{2x+3} \ln a) \times 2 = a^{2x+3}$$

We list some important fundamental rules of the technique of integration. Observation of Figure 6–13 should help the student to grasp the meaning intuitively.

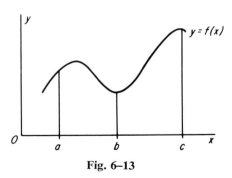

Fig. 6–13

RULE 1.

$$\int_a^b f(x) \, dx = -\int_b^a f(x) \, dx, \qquad a \neq b$$

Rule 2.

$$\int_a^b f(x)\,dx + \int_b^c f(x)\,dx = \int_a^c f(x)\,dx, \qquad a < b < c$$

Rule 3.

$$\int_a^b cf(x)\,dx = c\int_a^b f(x)\,dx$$

where c is a constant.

Rule 4. When $f(x) = g(x) + h(x)$, then

$$\int_a^b f(x)\,dx = \int_a^b g(x)\,dx + \int_a^b h(x)\,dx$$

Rule 5.

$$\int_{-a}^a f(x)\,dx = 2\int_0^a f(x)\,dx$$

when $f(x)$ is an even function.

$$\int_{-a}^a f(x)\,dx = 0$$

when $f(x)$ is an odd function.

$$f(-x) = f(x) \qquad \text{is an even function, e.g., } x^{2n}$$
$$f(-x) = -f(x) \qquad \text{is an odd function, e.g., } x^{2n+1}$$

Problems

1. Evaluate the following integrals, then differentiate your results and check your answers.

(a) $\displaystyle\int x^4\,dx$ (b) $\displaystyle\int x^{n+1}\,dx$

(c) $\displaystyle\int x^a\,dx$ (d) $\displaystyle\int (x^a + x^b)\,dx$

(e) $\displaystyle\int (x^{a+b} - x^{c+d})\,dx$ (f) $\displaystyle\int \frac{1}{x^3}\,dx$

(g) $\displaystyle\int \frac{1}{x^n}\,dx$ (h) $\displaystyle\int 2\,dx$

(i) $\displaystyle\int (a + 2)\,dx$ (j) $\displaystyle\int e^x(e^x + 2)\,dx$

(k) $\displaystyle\int e^x(e^x + 2)^2\,dx$ (l) $\displaystyle\int e^{2x}\,dx$

2. Draw graphs of the following functions, and find the area under the curves according to the data given.

(a) $y = 5$, $2 \le x \le 6$
(b) $y = 2x$, $2 \le x \le 6$
(c) $y = 3 + 2x$, $2 \le x \le 6$
(d) $y = 3x^2$, $2 \le x \le 6$

3. Evaluate the following integrals.

(a) $\int \dfrac{1}{x} dx$

(b) $\int \dfrac{1}{x+1} dx$

(c) $\int \dfrac{3}{x+3} dx$

(d) $\int \dfrac{2}{2-x} dx$

(e) $\int \dfrac{x}{x^2+1} dx$

(f) $\int \dfrac{2x}{x^2-3} dx$

(g) $\int \dfrac{2x+1}{x^2+x} dx$

(h) $\int \dfrac{2x-2}{x^2-2x+3} dx$

(i) $\int \dfrac{x+3}{x+5} dx$

(j) $\int \dfrac{x-2}{x+5} dx$

Hint: $\dfrac{x+3}{x+5} = 1 - \dfrac{2}{x+5}$

(k) $\int \dfrac{e^x}{e^x+1} dx$

(l) $\int \dfrac{3e^x}{2e^x-1} dx$

4. Evaluate the following integrals. Differentiate the results for a check.

(a) $\int e^x \, dx$

(b) $\int e^{2x} \, dx$

(c) $\int e^{-x} \, dx$

(d) $\int xe^{x^2} \, dx$

(e) $\int xe^{-x^2} \, dx$

(f) $\int e^{3x+2} \, dx$

(g) $\int ae^{-mt} \, dt$

(h) $\int ate^{-mt^2} \, dt$

(i) $\int (e^x - e^{-x}) \, dx$

(j) $\int (e^x - e^{-x})^2 \, dx$

(k) $\int a^x \, dx$

(l) $\int 3^x \, dx$

(m) $\int 3^{2x+1} \, dx$

(n) $\int a^x e^x \, dx$

Hint: $a^x e^x = (ae)^x$

(o) $\int x3^{x^2}\,dx$ (p) $\int x^2 3^{x^3}\,dx$

(q) $\int x^4 3^{x^5+1}\,dx$ (r) $\int x3^{-x^2}\,dx$

(s) $\int \dfrac{x}{4^{x^2}}\,dx$ (t) $\int \dfrac{x}{e^{x^2}}\,dx$

6.5 Improper integrals

So far we have considered only continuous functions for the integrand and the value of the function was finite in the intervals (a, b). Secondly, we assumed that (a, b) was a finite interval. When the integral under consideration has an integrand that can take on infinite values or when the interval (a, b) is not a finite interval, i.e., when $a = \infty$ or $b = \infty$ or both, then we have an improper integral.

(i) Improper integrals with discontinuous integrand

If the integrand $f(x)$ is continuous in (a, b) but takes on an infinite value at either a or b, then we approach the problem as follows: Assume $f(x)$ to

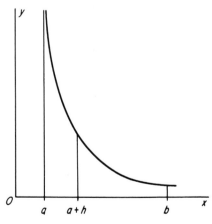

Fig. 6–14

be continuous in $a < x \le b$, but that

$$\lim_{x \to a} f(x) = \infty \quad \text{or} \quad \lim_{h \to 0} f(x) = \infty$$

Then, if

$$\lim_{h \to 0} \int_{a+h}^{b} f(x)\,dx$$

has a limit, we say the improper integral converges and

$$\int_a^b f(x)\, dx = \lim_{h \to 0} \int_{a+h}^b f(x)\, dx, \qquad (h > 0)$$

The definition is similar when $f(x)$ takes on an infinite value at b.

When there is an infinite jump discontinuity at c, where $a < c < b$, we split the integral into two improper integrals and define as

$$\int_a^b f(x)\, dx = \int_a^c f(x)\, dx + \int_c^b f(x)\, dx$$

If each improper integral on the right side converges to a limit, then the value of the integral will be the sum of the two improper integrals.

Example 1. $\int_0^b \dfrac{1}{x^2}\, dx$. When $x \to 0$, then, $1/x^2 \to \infty$. Thus, we evaluate

as

$$\int_0^b \frac{1}{x^2}\, dx = \lim_{h \to 0} \int_h^b \frac{1}{x^2}\, dx = \lim_{h \to 0} \left(-\frac{1}{x} \right)\Big|_h^b$$

$$= \lim_{h \to 0} \left(-\frac{1}{b} + \frac{1}{h} \right) \to \infty$$

Thus, the integral diverges.

Example 2. $\int_{-1}^{+1} \dfrac{1}{x^2}\, dx$. As x varies from -1 to $+1$, it will take a value 0 which will make $1/x^2 \to \infty$. Thus, we split the integral into two parts

$$\int_{-1}^0 \frac{1}{x^2}\, dx \qquad \text{and} \qquad \int_0^1 \frac{1}{x^2}\, dx$$

Then these become

$$\int_{-1}^0 \frac{1}{x^2}\, dx = \lim_{h \to 0} \int_{-1}^{-h} \frac{1}{x^2}\, dx = \lim_{h \to 0} \left(-\frac{1}{x} \right)\Big|_{-1}^{-h}$$

$$= \lim_{h \to 0} \left(\frac{1}{h} - 1 \right) \to \infty$$

$$\int_0^1 \frac{1}{x^2}\, dx = \lim_{h \to 0} \int_h^1 \frac{1}{x^2}\, dx = \lim_{h \to 0} \left(-1 + \frac{1}{h} \right) \to \infty$$

Thus, the integral diverges.

Example 3. $\int_3^5 \dfrac{dx}{\sqrt{x-3}}$. When $x = 3$, the denominator of the integral becomes zero. Thus, set

$$\int_3^5 \frac{dx}{\sqrt{x-3}} = \lim \int_{3+h}^5 \frac{dx}{\sqrt{x-3}}$$

Using a table of integrals, we can find that this becomes

$$\lim_{h\to 0} \int_{3+h}^5 \frac{dx}{\sqrt{x-3}} = \lim_{h\to 0} 2\sqrt{x-3} \Big|_{3+h}^5$$

$$= \lim_{h\to 0} [2\sqrt{5-3} - 2\sqrt{3+h-3}]$$

$$= 2\sqrt{2}$$

(ii) Improper integrals with infinite limits

In the second case, where a or b or both are infinite, we say, for example, $\int_a^\infty f(x)\,dx$ *converges* if $\lim_{t\to +\infty} \int_a^t f(x)\,dx$ has a limit. Otherwise, if it does not have a limit, it is *divergent*. What is being done is first to find the value of $\int_a^t f(x)\,dx$ and then let $t \to \infty$ and find the limit. The same is true when the lower limit b is infinite.

There is also the case in which both the upper and lower limits are infinite. An example is the integral of the normal distribution curve. Another important example of an improper integral is the *gamma function*.

Example 1.

$$\int_a^\infty \frac{dx}{x^2} = \lim_{b\to\infty} \int_a^b x^{-2}\,dx = \lim_{b\to\infty} \left(\frac{x^{-1}}{-1}\right)\Big|_a^b$$

$$= \lim_{b\to\infty} \left(-\frac{1}{b} + \frac{1}{a}\right) = \frac{1}{a}$$

Example 2. The *normal distribution curve* (Figure 6–15) is a bell-shaped

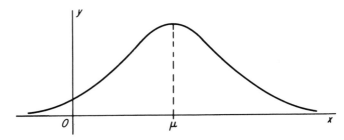

Fig. 6–15

curve that is symmetrical around the mean μ. The function is given by

$$n(x) = \frac{1}{\sqrt{2\pi\sigma}} e^{-(x-\mu)^2/2\sigma^2}, \qquad -\infty < x < \infty$$

where σ is the standard deviation. As is well known, x varies from $-\infty$ to $+\infty$.

We also know from elementary statistics that the area under the normal curve is unity. That is,

$$\int_{-\infty}^{\infty} n(x)\, dx = 1$$

which is an improper integral. It can easily be proved that the integral from $-\infty$ to $+\infty$ will be one.*

Example 3. The improper integral

$$\Gamma(\alpha) = \int_0^{\infty} x^{\alpha-1} e^{-x}\, dx, \qquad \alpha > 0$$

is called the gamma function, and the symbol Γ (gamma) is usually used to designate this special function.

When $\alpha > 0$, this function converges for all values of α and has the following characteristics, which we give without proof.

$$\Gamma(\alpha) = \int_0^{\infty} x^{\alpha-1} e^{-x}\, dx, \qquad \alpha > 0$$

then,

$$\Gamma(\alpha + 1) = \int_0^{\infty} x^{\alpha} e^{-x}\, dx = \alpha\Gamma(\alpha)$$

Let $\alpha = 1$. Then,

$$\Gamma(1) = \int_0^{\infty} e^{-x}\, dx = \lim_{h \to \infty} \int_0^h e^{-x}\, dx$$

$$= \lim_{h \to \infty} (-e^{-x}) \Big|_0^h = \lim_{h \to \infty} (-e^{-h} + e^0) = 1$$

Next, if $\alpha' = \alpha + 1$, then,

$$\Gamma(\alpha + 2) = \Gamma(\alpha' + 1) = \alpha'\Gamma(\alpha') = (\alpha + 1)\Gamma(\alpha + 1)$$
$$= (\alpha + 1)\alpha\Gamma(\alpha)$$

This process can be repeated, and we obtain

$$\Gamma(\alpha + n) = (\alpha + n - 1)(\alpha + n - 2) \ldots (\alpha + 1)\alpha\Gamma(\alpha)$$

* See Mood (1963), p. 123.

Let $\alpha = 1$, then

$$\Gamma(n + 1) = n(n - 1)(n - 2) \dots 2(1)\Gamma(\alpha)$$
$$\therefore \quad \Gamma(n + 1) = n!$$

The gamma function in statistics provides the *gamma distribution*. For example, a particular form of the gamma distribution gives us the chi-square distribution.*

6.6 Multiple integrals

When we had a function $y = f(x)$, we defined the integral as $\int_S f(x)\, dx$, where S was the set of points given by the interval (a, b). We can interpret this as the limit of the sum $\Sigma f(x)\, dx$, where dx can be looked upon as indicating a subset of S.

As is seen, when S is an interval, dx can be interpreted as a small sub-interval S_i.

We can now extend this kind of thinking to the two dimensions. Let us assume we have a continuous function $u = f(x, y)$. Then we can define the integral of $f(x, y)$ as

$$\int_S f(x, y)\, dx\, dy$$

In this case our set S is a two-dimensional set, i.e., a region in a plane as shown in Figure 6–16.

Similar to the one-dimensional case, we can find lower and upper sums

$$z = \sum m_i \mu(S_i)$$
$$Z = \sum M_i \mu(S_i)$$

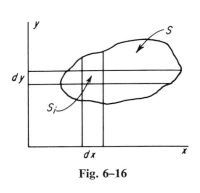

Fig. 6–16

In this case m_i and M_i are the lower and upper bounds of the function $f(x, y)$ defined in a two-dimensional subregion S_i of S. The term $\mu(S_i)$ is the measure (in this case, area) of this subregion S_i. For one dimension it was an interval when we were considering the Riemann integral. Here for two dimensions, we can consider it the product of two intervals, i.e., an area. Let us call this area a *two-dimensional interval*. By use of this terminology we can call a three-dimensional subregion, which will be a volume, a *three-dimensional*

---

* See Mood (1963), Chaps. 6 and 10, and Sokolnikoff and Sokolnikoff (1941), p. 272.

interval. If we are dealing with n-dimensions, we shall have an n-dimensional interval.

Thus, we can interpret $z = \Sigma\, m_i \mu(S_i)$ geometrically as a cylinder between the xy-plane and the $u = f(x, y)$ surface, as shown in Figure 6–17. Then the process of integration can be thought of as finding the volume of mass between the surface u and the xy-plane over the region defined by $u = f(x, y)$ on the xy-plane.

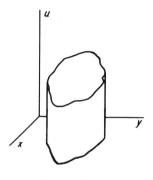

Fig. 6–17

But aside from such geometrical interpretations, we shall describe the integral as follows: Undertake a limiting process by subdividing the regions into smaller and smaller subregions until $Z - z$ becomes arbitrarily small. Then we can eventually set $Z = z$ as the common value reached after the limiting process. This limit of a finite sum is defined as the integral, and we shall denote it as

$$\int_S f(x, y)\, dx\, dy$$

This can be extended to a more general case. The integral for a function $f(x_1, x_2, \ldots, x_n)$ is defined as

$$\int_S f(x_1, \ldots, x_n)\, dx_1, \ldots, dx_n$$

which is also written as

$$\underbrace{\int \cdots \int}_{n} f(x_1, \ldots, x_n)\, dx_1, \ldots, dx_n$$

6.7 Evaluation of multiple integrals

(1) $$\int_0^1 \int_0^x (x^2 + y^2)\, dy\, dx$$

We evaluate this by first evaluating

$$\int_0^x (x^2 + y^2)\, dy = \left.(x^2 y + \tfrac{1}{3}y^3)\right|_0^x = x^3 + \tfrac{1}{3}x^3 = \tfrac{4}{3}x^3$$

Then

$$\int_0^1 \tfrac{4}{3}x^3\, dx = \tfrac{4}{3} \cdot \left.\tfrac{1}{4}x^4\right|_0^1 = \tfrac{4}{3} \cdot \tfrac{1}{4} \cdot 1 - 0 = \tfrac{1}{3}$$

As can be seen, we first treat x as a *parameter* and y as the variable of the first integration. Then we integrate with respect to x. Integrals such as (1) are called the iterated (or repeated) double integral.

6.8 Total cost, marginal cost

Let x be output and the total cost function be

$$f(x) = 100 + 3x + 4x^2 + 5x^3$$

Then, the marginal cost is

$$f'(x) = \frac{df(x)}{dx} = 3 + 8x + 15x^2$$

We can reverse the procedure and, if given the marginal cost function, determine the total cost function. We know $f(x) = \int f'(x)\, dx$. Thus,

$$f(x) = \int (3 + 8x + 15x^2)\, dx$$

$$= 3x + \tfrac{1}{2}(8x^2) + \tfrac{1}{3}(15x^3) + c$$

$$= 3x + 4x^2 + 5x^3 + c$$

We can determine the c if we have an additional condition. Let it be that $f(0) = 100$. Thus,

$$f(0) = 3(0) + 4(0) + 5(0) + c = 100$$

$$c = 100$$

$$\therefore\ f(x) = 100 + 3x + 4x^2 + 5x^3$$

Problems

1. Evaluate the following integrals.

(a) $\int_1^2 \int_x^{2x} dy\, dx$

(b) $\int_0^1 \int_x^{x^2} (x + 2)\, dy\, dx$

(c) $\int_0^1 \int_{3y}^{y^2} xy\, dx\, dy$

(d) $\int_0^1 \int_y^{2y} (x + y)\, dx\, dy$

(e) $\int_0^x \int_{3y}^{y^2} xy\, dx\, dy$

(f) $\int_0^1 \int_{-y}^{3y} x\, dx\, dy$

2. Given the marginal cost function $f'(x)$, find total cost $f(x)$.

(a) $f'(x) = 2 + x + x^2$
$f(0) = 50$
(c) $f'(x) = 10 - 2x$
$f(0) = 50$

(b) $f'(x) = 2 + 5/x$
$f(1) = 15$

3. Given the marginal propensity to consume $dC/dy = f'(y)$, find $C = f(y)$.

(a) $f'(y) = 0.680 - 0.0012y$
$f(0) = 0.128$
(b) $f'(y) = -0.23(1/y_0)$, where y_0 is constant
$f(0) = 117.96$

6.9 Law of growth

(i) Geometric progression

Let a be a population that doubles itself every time period. Then we have a geometric progression

$$a, \quad a \cdot 2, \quad a \cdot 4, \quad a \cdot 8, \quad \ldots$$

or

$$a, \quad ar, \quad ar^2, \quad ar^3, \quad \ldots, \quad ar^t, \quad \ldots$$

where $r = 2 \; (= 200\%)$ is the relative increase per time period. This geometric progression can be shown as

$$y = ar^t = a \cdot 2^t$$

or $y = a(1 + i)^t$, where $i = 1$ in our present case. This is the familiar compound interest formula, in which usually y is the value of capital at time t, a is the initial value of capital, and i is the rate of interest. In our present case, $i = 1 \; (= 100\%)$ is the *rate of increase*.

Note the difference between r and i. To distinguish the two, i will be called the *rate of increase* and r, the *coefficient of growth*.

(ii) Compound interest formula

Effective rate of interest—i. In terms of capital values, the compound interest formula is

$$P_t = P_0(1 + i)^t$$

P_t: value of capital at time t
P_0: initial value of capital
t: number of years
i: effective rate of interest

The initial capital is compounded annually, and the rate of interest is i, which will be called the effective rate of interest.

Nominal rate of interest—j. Instead of compounding on an annual basis, assume the compounding takes place four times a year. For example, let

$i = 8\%$, $P_0 = \$100$. Then, on an annual basis, it becomes

$$P_t = \$100(1 + 0.08) = \$108$$

When it is compounded four times a year, it becomes

$$P_t = \$100\left(1 + \frac{0.08}{4}\right)^4 = \$108.2432$$

Thus, the rate of interest on an annual basis is 8.2432% rather than 8%. Noting this difference, let us define as follows: When

$$1 + i = \left(1 + \frac{j}{m}\right)^m$$

this j will be called the nominal rate of interest. Here $1 + i$ is the total amount of investment of $1 after one year when the effective interest rate is i and the compounding is on an annual basis, and $(1 + j/m)^m$ is the total amount of investment of $1 after one year when it is compounded m times per year. The rate of interest j which equates the two is called the *nominal rate of interest*. As can be seen from our example, $i = 8\%$ and j will be less than 8%. From the formula defining j, we find

$$j = m[(1 + i)^{1/m} - 1]$$

The total amount of investment P_t will be

$$P_t = P_0\left(1 + \frac{j}{m}\right)^{mt}$$

The force of interest—δ. The nominal rate was defined by

$$1 + i = \left(1 + \frac{j}{m}\right)^m$$

Thus, j will differ depending on m. When $m \rightarrow \infty$, i.e., the compounding is continuous (or instantaneous), j is called the *force of interest* and it will be denoted by δ to distinguish it from the other interest terms. Thus, we have

$$1 + i = \lim_{m \to \infty} \left(1 + \frac{\delta}{m}\right)^m$$

$$= \lim_{m \to \infty} \left[\left(1 + \frac{\delta}{m}\right)^{m/\delta}\right]^{\delta} = e^{\delta}$$

The total amount of investment is, then,

$$P_t = P_0 e^{\delta t}$$

This is the compound interest formula for continuous compounding, where

$$\delta = \ln(1 + i)$$

What is the rate of increase of P_t in relation to time t? It is

$$\frac{dP_t}{dt} = P_0 \delta e^{\delta t} = \delta P_t$$

Since δ is a constant, P_t increases at a rate proportional to P_t itself.

Let us now reverse the process and show that, when a function increases at a rate proportional to itself, it will be an exponential function.

(iii) Exponential law

Let $y = y(t)$ be a function that increases at a rate proportional to itself. Then this means the rate of increase dy/dt will be

(1)
$$\frac{dy}{dt} = ry$$

where r is a constant.

From equation (1) we obtain

$$\frac{1}{y} dy = r\, dt$$

Integrating both sides, we have

$$\int_0^t \frac{1}{y} dy = \int_0^t r\, dt$$

$$\ln y(t) \Big|_0^t = rt \Big|_0^t$$

$$rt = \ln y(t) - \ln y(0) = \ln \frac{y(t)}{y(0)}$$

Let $y(0) = 1$. Then,

$$y(t) = e^{rt}$$

Thus, a function y which increases at a rate proportional to itself is an exponential function. Let us next generalize it.

It turns out that the constant r corresponds to the force of interest δ of Section (ii), which is what we expected.

(iv) Exponential law—generalized

We are now interested in r as a function of t. Thus, (1) becomes

$$\frac{dy}{dt} = r(t)y$$

and

$$\int_0^t \frac{1}{y}\, dy = \int_0^t r(t)\, dt$$

$$y(t) = y(0)e^{\int_0^t r(t)\,dt}$$

which is the *generalized exponential law*.

This can be approached in an alternative manner. Let P_t be the capital value at time t. P_t is a function of time t. Thus, set $P_t = f(t)$. Then the relative increase of P_t from t to $t + \Delta t$ is

$$\frac{f(t + \Delta t) - f(t)}{f(t)}$$

The rate of increase of this relative increase is shown by

$$\frac{f(t + \Delta t) - f(t)}{\Delta t f(t)}$$

Let us set this equal to $r(t)$, and let $\Delta t \to 0$. Then,

$$r(t) = \lim_{\Delta t \to 0} \frac{f(t + \Delta t) - f(t)}{\Delta t f(t)} = \lim \frac{f(t + \Delta t) - f(t)}{\Delta t} \frac{1}{f(t)}$$

$$= \frac{1}{f(t)} \frac{df(t)}{dt}$$

Thus,

$$r(t)\, dt = \frac{1}{f(t)}\, df(t)$$

Integrate both sides over 0 to t. Then,

$$\int_0^t r(t)\, dt = \int_0^t \frac{1}{f(t)}\, df(t) = \ln f(t)\Big|_0^t = \ln \frac{f(t)}{f(0)}$$

Assume $f(0) = P_0 = 1$. Then,

$$f(t) = e^{\int_0^t r(t)\,dt}$$

i.e.,

(2) $$P_t = e^{\int_0^t r(t)\,dt}$$

which gives us the value of capital at time t when: (1) The rate of the relative increase $r(t)$ changes with t (i.e., a function of t), (2) the compounding is continuous, and (3) $P_0 = 1$.

If we assume $r(t) = r$ constant, then,

$$P_t = e^{\int_0^t r\, dt} = e^{rt}$$

which is the result we obtained in Section (iii).

Problem

Prove that, when the initial capital is P_0, the formula becomes (r constant)

$$P^t = P_0 e^{rt}$$

(v) *Present value of P_t*

The present value of P_t is from equation (2)

$$P_0 = P_t e^{-\int_0^t r(t)\, dt}$$

Let $t > t_1 > 0$. Then what is the value of P_t at time t_1? It can be shown that

(3)
$$P_{t_1} = P_t e^{-\int_{t_1}^t r(t)\, dt}$$

Problem

Prove the result shown in equation (3).

(vi) *Summary*

(a) $P_t = P_0(1 + i)^t$, P_0 compounded annually at the effective interest rate i.

(b) $P_t = P_0(1 + j/m)^{mt}$, P_0 compounded m times per year, j being the nominal rate.

(c) $P_t = P_0 e^{\delta t}$, P_0 compounded continuously, δ being the force of interest.

(d)
$$\frac{dy}{dt} = r(t)y$$

$$\therefore \quad y(t) = y(0) e^{\int_0^t r(t)\, dt}$$

(e) i $=$ effective rate

$j = m[(1 + i)^{1/m} - 1] =$ nominal rate

$\delta = \ln (1 + i)$ $=$ force of interest

$1 + i$ $=$ coefficient of growth

(vii) Present value of capital

Discounting. From the compound interest formula, the initial value P_0 will be

$$P_0 = P_t(1 + i)^{-t}$$

where i is the annual rate of interest. This process of finding the value of an investment P_t at some earlier time, say $t = 0$, is called *discounting*.

For continuous compounding, P_0 will be

$$P_0 = P_t e^{-\delta t}$$

where δ is the force of interest.

Value of a capital asset. Let $y_0, y_1, y_2, \ldots$ be the expected yield of a capital asset. Then the present value of the capital asset will be, assuming continuous compounding,

$$C = \int_0^t y_t e^{-rt} dt$$

If we assume that $y_t = f(t) = y = $ constant, (for example, rent), then C becomes

$$C = \int_0^t y e^{-rt} dt = y \int e^{-rt} dt$$

$$= y\left(-\frac{1}{r} e^{-rt}\right)\Big|_0^t = y\left(-\frac{1}{r} e^{-rt}\right) - y\left(-\frac{1}{r}\right)$$

$$= \frac{y}{r}(1 - e^{-rt})$$

Thus, the present value of capital, C, will be

$$C = \frac{y}{r}(1 - e^{-rt})$$

If $t \to \infty$, then $C = y/r$.

Problem

Show that the accumulated value of a constant income stream will be

$$V = \frac{y}{r}(e_{rt} - 1)$$

6.10 Domar's model of public debt and national income*

Y = national income

D = public debt

a = national income at beginning

α = fraction of national income borrowed by government

r = relative annual rate of growth of national income

t = time (in years)

Let Y_t be income at time t. Then we have seen in the previous section that, if Y_t grows continuously at a constant rate of r,

$$Y_t = Y_0 e^{rt} = a e^{rt}$$

since $Y_0 = a$. Thus, the debt at time t will be

$$D_t = D_0 + \int_0^t \alpha Y_t \, dt = D_0 + \alpha \int_0^t a e^{rt} \, dt$$

$$= D_0 + \alpha a \frac{1}{r} (e^{rt} - 1)$$

The ratio of debt to income becomes

$$\frac{D_t}{Y_t} = \frac{D_0}{Y_t} + \frac{\alpha a}{r Y_t} (e^{rt} - 1)$$

$$= \frac{D_0}{a e^{rt}} + \frac{\alpha}{r} (1 - e^{-rt})$$

Thus, if we let $t \to \infty$,

$$\lim_{t \to \infty} \frac{D_t}{Y_t} = \lim_{t \to \infty} \frac{D_0}{a e^{rt}} + \lim_{t \to \infty} \frac{\alpha}{r} (1 - e^{-rt})$$

$$= 0 + \frac{\alpha}{r} = \frac{\alpha}{r}$$

and the ratio approaches α/r.

* E. D. Domar, "The Burden of Debt and the National Income," *American Economic Review*, Vol. 34 (Dec., 1944). See also Notes and References at end of this chapter.

Problem

Assume income increases at an absolute annual rate of b. That is, $Y_t = a + bt$. Show that in this case the ratio of debt to national income approaches ∞.*

$$\lim_{t \to \infty} \frac{D}{Y} = \infty$$

6.11 Domar's capital expansion model †

(*i*) *Equilibrium rate of increase* $\alpha\sigma$

Let P be productive capacity, Y be national income, and I be investment. Let v be the net value added due to the new investments. Then,

$$s = \frac{v}{I} \quad \text{or} \quad v = Is$$

is the *potential output of these new projects*. The potential social average investment productivity σ is defined as

$$\sigma = \frac{dP/dt}{I}$$

Assume s and σ are constant. Then,

$$\frac{dP}{dt} = \sigma I(t)$$

Next, let α be the marginal propensity to save. Then,

$$\frac{dY}{dI} = \frac{1}{\alpha}$$

Thus,

$$\frac{dY}{dt} = \frac{dI}{dt}\frac{1}{\alpha}$$

Equilibrium is obtained when supply is equal to demand. That is,

$$P_0 = Y_0$$

---

* See *op. cit.*, Domar's Essay.

† E. D. Domar, "Capital Expansion, Rate of Growth, and Employment," *Econometrica*, Vol. 14 (April, 1946). See also Notes and References at end of this chapter.

It will remain in equilibrium when

$$\frac{dP}{dt} = \frac{dY}{dt}$$

Substituting in our results above, we have

$$I\sigma = \frac{dI}{dt}\frac{1}{\alpha}$$

Thus we have

$$\alpha\sigma \; dt = \frac{1}{I} \; dI$$

Integrate both sides from time 0 to t

$$\int_0^t \alpha\sigma \; dt = \int_0^t \frac{1}{I(t)} \; dI(t)$$

$$\alpha\sigma t \Big|_0^t = \ln I(t) - \ln I(o)$$

$$\alpha\sigma t = \ln \frac{I(t)}{I(o)}$$

$$\therefore \quad I(t) = I(o)e^{\alpha\sigma t}$$

Thus, $\alpha\sigma$ is the relative rate of increase of I that maintains full employment. Domar illustrates by letting $\alpha = 12\%$, $\sigma = 30\%$. Then $\alpha\sigma = 3.6\%$ per year. (This is the force of interest.) The $\alpha\sigma$ is called the *equilibrium rate*.

(ii) When actual rate and equilibrium rate are not equal

Domar considers two cases where the actual rate r (constant) is not equal to $\alpha\sigma$. He assumes $I/Y = \alpha$ and $P/k = s$, where k is capital. Only the case where $\sigma = s$ will be considered.

Capital $k(t)$ at time t will be

$$k = k_0 + \int_0^t I_0 e^{rt} \; dt = k_0 + \frac{I_0}{r}(e^{rt} - 1)$$

As t becomes large, e^{rt} becomes large and k_0 relatively small. Thus k will approach

$$k \to \frac{I_0}{r} e^{rt}$$

which implies that k will also grow at a rate approaching r.

Problem

Note that $Y = \dfrac{I}{\alpha} = \dfrac{1}{\alpha} I_0 e_{rt}$. Using this, prove that

$$\lim_{t \to \infty} \frac{Y}{k} = \frac{r}{\alpha}$$

What does this imply?*

6.12 Capitalization

Let $Y_1 = Y_2 = Y_3 = \ldots = Y$ be a constant stream of yield from a capital good, for example, land. The present value of Y_t is

$$Y_t e^{-rt}$$

where r is a constant rate of interest. Thus, the present value of the capital good is

$$\int_0^\infty Y_t e^{-rt}\, dt = Y \int_0^\infty e^{-rt}\, dt$$

$$= \frac{Y}{r} \int_0^\infty e^{-rt}\, d(rt) = \frac{Y}{r} \left(-e^{-rt} \right) \Big|_0^\infty = \frac{Y}{r}$$

Thus the present value of the capital good is Y/r, which we usually call *capitalization*.

6.13 Pareto distribution

Vilfredo Pareto in his *Cours d'economic politique* (1897) gave the following hypothesis concerning income distribution: The distribution of income is given by the following empirical law

$$N = ax^{-b}$$

where N is the number of incomes greater than the income level x, a is a constant, and b is an exponent that has a value of 1.5. We shall not discuss this law but show some results that can be derived mathematically.

(i) *The total number of income recipients between income levels* y_1 *and* y_2

$$\int_{y_1}^{y_2} ax^b\, dx = a \left(\frac{1}{-b+1} \right) \left(\frac{1}{x^{b-1}} \right) \Big|_{y_1}^{y_2}$$

$$= \frac{a}{-b+1} [y_1^{-b+1} - y_2^{-b+1}]$$

* See E. D. Domar, "Capital Expansion, Rate of Growth, and Employment," *Econometrica*, Vol. 14 (April, 1946).

(*ii*) *Total amount of income over income level y*

$$N = ax^{-b}$$

Let

$$\therefore \quad dN = f_x \, dx = a(-b)x^{-b-1} \, dx$$

$$N \, dx = -dN = abx^{-b-1} \, dx$$

where dN is the small change in the number of people when there is an increase in income. As the level of income increases, there is a decrease. Thus, we have $-dN$. The total income at level x is

$$xN \, dx = abx^{-b} \, dx$$

Total income over y will be

$$\int_y^\infty xN \, dx = \int_y^\infty abx^{-b} \, dx = \frac{ab}{b-1} \, y^{1-b}$$

Problem

Using the results above, show that the average income over y is

$$\bar{y} = \frac{b}{b-1} y$$

Notes and References

Integration is a very difficult topic and no attempt has been made to give rigorous proofs of the various results that have been presented. For further study on an elementary level, see Courant and Robbins (1941) pp. 398–416; Titchmarsh (1959), Chapter 14; Courant (Vol. I, 1937), Chapters 2, 3, and 4 and pp. 486–500; Kleppner-Ramsey (1965), Chapter 3. For advanced treatment of the multiple integral see Courant (Vol. II, 1936), Chapter 4 and Appendix; Sokolnikoff (1939), Chapters 4, 5, 10.

The generalization of the Riemann integral is the Riemann-Stieltjes integral. References for this are Rudin (1953), Chapter 6; Thielman (1953), Chapter 9; Bartle (1964), Chapter 22.

For further studies of integration, it is necessary to study set theory more extensively. This will lead into measure theory and then into Lebesgue-Stieltjes integration. Lebesgue-Stieltjes integrals are used in such topics as mathematical statistics and game theory. Those interested are referred to Thielman (1953), Chapters 8,9; McShane (1944); Munroe (1953); Cramer (1951); Riesz and Sz.-Nagy (1955); Hartman and Mikusinski (1961).

For techniques of integration, see a standard elementary calculus textbook like Smail (1949), Chapters 11, 12, 13, 15, 20.

6.5 Discussion of the normal distribution can be found in Mood and Graybill (1963), Chapter 6; Fraser (1958), pp. 68–71; Courant (Vol. I, 1937), p. 496. The Gamma function is discussed in Sokolnikoff and Sokolnikoff (1941), pp. 272–276. The distribution can be found in Mood (1963), pp. 123–126 and pp. 226–227 for chi-square distribution.

6.9 Discussion of law of growth or law of organic growth can be found in elementary calculus texts, such as Smail (1949), pp. 270–272. Also see Allen (1938), pp. 401–408; Courant and Robbins (1941), pp. 454–457; and Davis (1941), Chapter 13.

6.10–6.11 The illustrations were taken from articles by Domar. Domar's (1957) book is a compilation of articles he has written. See in particular his articles "The Burden of Debt and the National Income" (reprinted from *AER*, 1944, pp. 798–827) and "Capital Expansion, Rate of Growth, and Employment" (reprinted from *Econometrica*, 1946, pp. 137–147). Also see Allen (1957), pp. 64–69, Section 3.3, "Harrod-Domar Growth Theory."

6.12 Pareto's curve of income distribution is discussed in Lange (1959), pp. 185–205, and Davis (1941), pp. 23–25.

Allen, R. G. D., *Mathematical Economics*. New York: St. Martin's Press, Inc., 1957.

Cramer, H., *Mathematical Methods of Statistics*. Princeton, N.J.: Princeton University Press, 1951.

Domar, E. D., *Essays in the Theory of Economic Growth*. New York: Oxford University Press, Inc., 1957.

Fraser, D. A. S., *Statistics, An Introduction*. New York: John Wiley & Sons, Inc., 1958.

Halmos, P. R., *Measure Theory*. Princeton, N.J.: D. Van Nostrand Co., Inc., 1950.

Hartman, S. and Mikusinski, J., *The Theory of Lebesgue Measure and Integration*. Translated by L. F. Boron. New York: Pergamon Press, 1961.

Hoel, P. G., *Introduction to Mathematical Statistics*, 2nd ed. New York: John Wiley & Sons, Inc., 1954.

McShane, E. J., *Integration*. Princeton, N.J.: Princeton University Press, 1944.

Mood, A. M. and Graybill, F. A., *Introduction to the Theory of Statistics*, 2nd ed. New York: McGraw-Hill Book Company, 1963.

Munroe, M. E., *Introduction to Measure and Integration*. Reading, Mass.: Addison-Wesley Publishing Co., Inc., 1953.

Riesz, F. and Sz.-Nagy, B., *Functonal Analysis*. Translated by L. F. Boron. New York: Fredric Ungar Publishing Co., 1955.

Rudin, W., *Principles of Mathematical Analysis*. New York: McGraw-Hill Book Company, 1953.

Sokolnikoff, I. S. and Sokolnikoff, E. S., *Higher Mathematics for Engineers and Physicists*. New York: McGraw-Hill Book Company, 1941.

CHAPTER 7

Series

In this chapter we shall discuss series, and several other topics which we shall need in subsequent discussions.

7.1 Series

Consider an infinite sequence $a_1, a_2, a_3, \ldots$. Let

$$s_1 = a_1, \qquad s_2 = a_1 + a_2, \qquad s_3 = a_1 + a_2 + a_3, \qquad \ldots$$

Then we have a new sequence, $s_1, s_2, s_3, \ldots$. If this sequence approaches a limit S, then

$$S = \lim_{n \to \infty} s_n$$

Thus,

$$\lim_{n \to \infty} s_n = \sum_{n=1}^{\infty} a_n = a_1 + a_2 + a_3 + \ldots$$

which is the sum of the terms of an infinite sequence, is called a *series*. When s_n approaches a limit S as $n \to \infty$, we say the series is *convergent*. S is called the *sum of the series*. When it does not converge, we say the series is *divergent*.

The problem is thus to determine whether or not a series is convergent. For this let us use the Cauchy test mentioned in Chapter 2.

We have a sequence $s_1, s_2, s_3, \ldots s_n$. Let $\rho(s_1, s_2)$, $\rho(s_2, s_3)$, and so forth be the distance between the two s_i. If $\rho(s_m, s_{m+1})$ becomes smaller as m becomes larger, we will finally reach a point where beyond that point s_m the distance between the two points and some point further ahead, say $s_n (n > m)$, will be arbitrarily small. That is,

$$\rho(s_m, s_n) < \epsilon$$

for sufficiently large m and n where ϵ is an arbitrarily small positive number. This is the Cauchy sequence we have in Chapter 2 which we know converges to a limit (say S).

The distance $\rho(s_m, s_n)$ can be shown as

$$|s_n - s_m| = |a_1 + a_2 + \ldots + a_m + a_{m+1} + \ldots + a_n$$
$$-(a_1 + \ldots + a_m)|$$
$$= |a_{m+1} + a_{m+2} + \ldots + a_n|$$

We have thus found the conditions necessary for a series to converge. But the practical problem of finding the limit, i.e., the sum (or value) of the series remains. Various methods are used to find the sum of series. Let us illustrate this process by several examples.

7.2 Geometric series

Let a be a constant and $0 < r < 1$. Then

$$a + ar + ar^2 + \ldots + ar^m + \ldots$$

is a geometric series. Since a is a constant, let us set $a = 1$ for simplicity and consider

$$1 + r + r^2 + \ldots + r^n + \ldots$$

Let us perform the following "trick"

$$s_n = 1 + r + r^2 + \ldots + r^{n-1}$$
$$rs_n = r + r^2 + r^3 + \ldots + r^n$$
$$\therefore \quad s_n - rs_n = 1 - r^n$$
$$\therefore \quad s_n = \frac{1 - r^n}{1 - r} = \frac{1}{1 - r} - \frac{r^n}{1 - r}$$

Since $0 < r < 1$, $\lim_{n \to \infty} r^n = 0$. Thus,

$$\lim_{n \to \infty} s_n = \frac{1}{1 - r}$$

and

(1)
$$1 + r + r^2 + \ldots = \frac{1}{1 - r}$$

The multiplier in economics uses this series. When the marginal propensity to consume is $0 < \alpha < 1$, the income propagation process is given by

$$1 + \alpha + \alpha^2 + \ldots = \frac{1}{1 - \alpha}$$

If $\alpha = 0.8$, then the multiplier is $1/(1 - 0.8) = 5$. The principle of credit expansion of banks also uses this series.

Problems

1. Given the geometric progression 2, 4, 8, 16, ... find s_4. (Use formula)

2. Let α be the marginal propensity to consume. $0 < \alpha < 1$. Find the value of
$$\alpha + \alpha^2 + \alpha^3 + \dots$$

7.3 Taylor's theorem

(i) *Expansion of a function*

Consider a function

(1) $$y = x^2$$

as shown in Figure 7–1. The value of the function at x is

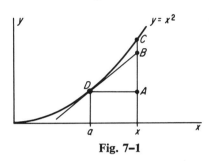

$$f(x) = \overline{xC}$$

Let us now select a point a and draw in a tangent as shown. Then the function $f(x)$ at the point x can be shown as

$$f(x) = \overline{xC} = xA + AB + BC$$

where xA is equal to $f(a)$, AB is equal to $f'(a) \cdot AD = f'(a)(x - a)$. Thus,

Fig. 7–1

$$f(x) = f(a) + f'(a)(x - a) + BC$$

where we shall call BC the remainder. What we have shown is that the function $y = f(x) = x^2$ can be expressed in terms of $f(x)$ and its derivatives at another point a. We shall say the function $f(x)$ has been expanded about the point $x = a$, and a is called the *center of expansion*.

Let us now approach it algebraically and generalize the result. Let $f(x)$ be

(2) $$f(x) = a_0 + a_1x + a_2x^2 + \dots + a_nx^n$$

Differentiating the function with respect to x

$$f'(x) = a_1 + 2a_2x + 3a_3x^2 + \dots + na_nx^{n-1}$$
$$f''(x) = 2a_2 + 2 \times 3 \times a_3x + \dots + (n - 1)na_nx^{n-2}$$

and so forth. Let $x = 0$. Then,

$$f(0) = a_0$$
$$f'(0) = a_1$$
$$f''(0) = 2a_2 = 2!\, a_2$$
$$f'''(0) = 2 \times 3 \times a_3 = 3!\, a_3$$

and so forth. Thus, substituting these values back into (2), we obtain

(3)
$$f(x) = f(0) + f'(0)x + \frac{1}{2!}f''(0)x^2$$

$$+ \dots + \frac{1}{n!}f^{(n)}(0)x^n$$

This is called a *Taylor series*, although later we shall show it in other forms. The function $f(x)$ has been expanded around 0.

Let us apply this to our function $y = x^2$ which can be shown as

$$y = x^2 = a_0 + a_1 x + a_2 x^2$$

where $a_0 = 0$, $a_1 = 0$, $a_2 = 1$. The corresponding Taylor series is

$$f(x) = f(0) + f'(0)x + \frac{1}{2!}f''(0)x^2$$

$$f(0) = a_0 = 0, \qquad f'(0) = a_1 = 0, \qquad f''(0) = 2a_2 = 2$$

Substituting these values,

$$f(x) = 0 + 0x + \frac{1}{2!} \times 2 \times x^2 = x^2$$

which is as we expect.

Let us expand another function

(4)
$$y = 5 + 3x + 8x^2$$

Then, we see that

$$f(0) = 5, \qquad f'(0) = 3, \qquad f''(0) = 16$$

Thus,

$$f(x) = f(0) + f'(0)x + \frac{1}{2!}f''(0)x^2$$

$$= 5 + 3x + \tfrac{1}{2} \times 16x^2 = 5 + 3x + 8x^2$$

Let us now expand (4) around point a instead of zero. For this let $x = a + h$ or $x - a = h$. The derivatives of (4) are

$$f(x) = 5 + 3x + 8x^2$$
$$f'(x) = 3 + 16x$$
$$f''(x) = 16$$

Since we have set $x = a + h$,

$$f(x) = f(a + h) = 5 + 3(a + h) + 8(a + h)^2$$
$$f'(x) = 3 + 16(a + h)$$
$$f''(x) = 16$$

Next, let us set

$$f(x) = f(a + h) = g(h)$$

where in $g(h)$, h is considered the variable. Then,

$$g(h) = 5 + 3(a + h) + 8(a + h)^2$$

Differentiate $g(h)$ with respect to h. Then,

$$g'(h) = 3 + 16(a + h)$$
$$g''(h) = 16$$

and we can see that

$$f(x) = g(h), \qquad f'(x) = g'(h), \qquad f''(x) = g''(h)$$

Since $x = a + h$, if we let $h = 0$, then $x = a$, and what we have derived becomes

(5) $$f(a) = g(0), \qquad f'(a) = g'(0), \qquad f''(a) = g''(0)$$

Next, let us expand $g(h)$ around 0. Then,

$$g(h) = g(0) + hg'(0) + \frac{h^2}{2!} g''(0)$$

Substituting the results (5) into this equation we find

$$f(x) = g(h) = f(a) + hf'(a) + \frac{h^2}{2!} f''(a)$$

Thus, we have shown how $f(x)$ can be expanded around a point a, where $a = x - h$.

Letting $h = x - a$, our result becomes

(6) $$f(x) = f(a) + (x - a)f'(a) + \frac{(x - a)^2}{2!} f''(a)$$

Let us apply this to our function

$$y = 5 + 3x + 8x^2$$
$$f(a) = 5 + 3a + 8a^2$$
$$f'(a) = 3 + 16a$$
$$f''(a) = 16$$
$$f(x) = f(a) + (x - a)f'(a) + \frac{(x - a)^2}{2!} f''(a)$$

$$= (5 + 3a + 8a^2) + (x - a)(3 + 16a) + \tfrac{1}{2}(x - a)^2 16$$
$$= 5 + 3x + 8x^2$$

We have illustrated how $f(x)$ expanded around a point a by Taylor's series is equal to the original function.

Generalizing the results, let

$$f(x) = c_0 + c_1 x + c_2 x^2 + \ldots + c_n x^n$$

Expand this function around the point a by Taylor's series. Then,

(7) $$f(x) = f(a) + (x - a)f'(a) + \frac{(x - a)^2}{2!} f''(a) + \ldots + \frac{(x - a)^n}{n!} f^{(n)}(a)$$

(ii) Taylor's formula with a remainder

So far we have applied Taylor's theorem to polynomials and showed how a function can be expanded around a given point. Let us now consider an arbitrary function. Taylor's theorem (which we give without proof) states that a function $f(x)$ can be expanded around a point a as follows

(8) $$f(x) = f(a) + (x - a)f'(a) + \frac{1}{2!}(x - a)^2 f''(a)$$

$$+ \ldots + \frac{1}{(n - 1)!}(x - a)^{n-1} f^{(n-1)}(a) + R_n$$

where R_n is called the *remainder*.

When R_n becomes very small as n becomes large, then,

$$f(a) + (x - a)f'(a) + \frac{1}{2!}(x - a)^2 f''(a) + \ldots + \frac{1}{(n - 1)!}(x - a)^{n-1} f^{(n-1)}(a)$$

will be a good *polynomial approximation* to the function $f(x)$. Thus, an important mathematical problem is to show the form of R_n and how it behaves when n becomes large. Lagrange's form of the remainder is

$$R_n = \frac{1}{n!}(x - a)^n f^{(n)}(\xi)$$

where ξ is between x and a.

A special case of Taylor's Theorem is where $a = 0$. Then,

$$f(x) = f(0) + xf'(0) + \frac{1}{2!} x^2 f''(0)$$

$$+ \ldots + \frac{1}{(n - 1)!} x^{n-1} f^{n-1}(0) + R_n$$

$$R_n = \frac{1}{n!} x^n f^{(n)}(\xi)$$

where ξ is between 0 and x. This is sometimes called *Maclaurin's theorem*.

What we wish to do now is to tie this in with our series discussion. But before that, a few illustrations of the expansions will be given.

Example 1. Expansion of e^x

$$f(x) = e^x \qquad\qquad f(0) = 1$$

$$f'(x) = e^x \qquad\qquad f'(0) = 1$$

$$\vdots \qquad\qquad\qquad \vdots$$

$$f^{n-1}(x) = e^x \qquad\qquad f^{n-1}(0) = 1$$

$$f^n(x) = e^x \qquad\qquad f^n(0) = 1$$

$$\therefore \quad e^x = 1 + x + \frac{1}{2!}x^2 + \dots + \frac{1}{(n-1)!}x^{n-1} + R_n$$

$$R_n = \frac{1}{n!}x^n e^\xi$$

Example 2. $\ln(1+x)$

$$f(x) = \ln(1+x) \qquad\qquad f(0) = \ln(1+0) = 0$$

$$f'(x) = (1+x)^{-1} \qquad\qquad f'(0) = 1$$

$$f''(x) = -(1+x)^{-2} \qquad\qquad f''(0) = -1$$

$$f'''(x) = 2(1+x)^{-3}, \quad f'''(0) = 2!, \quad \frac{1}{3!}f'''(0) = \frac{1}{3}$$

$$\vdots$$

$$f^n(x) = (-1)^{n-1}(n-1)!\,(1+x)^{-n}, \quad \frac{1}{n!}f^n(0) = (-1)^{n-1}\frac{1}{n}$$

$$\therefore \quad \ln(1+x) = 0 + 1x - \frac{1}{2}x^2 + \frac{1}{3}x^3 + \dots + R_n$$

$$R_n = (-1)^{n-1}\frac{1}{n}x^n(1+\xi)^{-n}$$

$$\therefore \quad \ln(1+x) = x - \frac{x^2}{2} + \frac{x^3}{3} - \frac{x^4}{4} + \dots + (-1)^{n-2}\frac{x^{n-1}}{n-1} + R_n$$

$$R_n = (-1)^{n-1}\frac{x^n}{n}(1+\xi)^{-n}$$

where ξ is between 0 and x.

Example 3. The results of expansions of several functions are given

(1) $$\sin x = x - \frac{x^3}{3!} + \frac{x^5}{5!} - \dots + \frac{x^{n-1}}{(n-1)!} \sin\left[\frac{1}{2}(n-1)\pi\right] + R_n$$

$$R_n = \frac{x^n}{n!} \sin\left(\xi + \frac{1}{2}n\pi\right)$$

(2) $$\cos x = 1 - \frac{x^2}{2!} + \frac{x^4}{4!} + \dots + \frac{x^{n-1}}{(n-1)!} \cos\left[\frac{1}{2}(n-1)\pi\right] + R_n$$

$$R_n = \frac{x^n}{n!} \cos\left(\xi + \frac{1}{2}n\pi\right)$$

Problems

1. Expand the following functions by Taylor's formula, around $a = 0$

(a) e^{-x}

(b) $\ln(2 + x)$

(c) $\sqrt{x}$

2. Expand the following function by Taylor's formula around a.

(a) e^{-x}, $a = 2$

(b) $\sqrt{x}$, $a = 1$

7.4 Taylor series

From Section 7.3 we have

$$f(x) = f(0) + xf'(0) + \frac{1}{2!}x^2f''(0) + \dots + \frac{1}{(n-1)!}x^{n-1}f^{n-1}(0) + R_n$$

$$= s_n + R_n$$

where s_n is the sum of the first n terms. Thus, as $n \to \infty$, s_n can be considered an infinite series. Furthermore, if $R_n \to 0$ as $n \to \infty$, then $s_n \to f(x)$. Thus, we shall state the *infinite series*

(1) $$f(0) + xf'(0) + \dots + \frac{1}{(n-1)!}x^{n-1}f^{n-1}(0) + \dots$$

converges to the function $f(x)$ if $R_n \to 0$ as $n \to \infty$ where R_n is the Lagrange remainder, provided all the derivatives exist.

This was the special case of the Taylor series where $a = 0$. It can also be expressed for $a \neq 0$. Then the series will be

(2) $$f(a) + (x-a)f'(a) + \dots + \frac{1}{(n-1)}(x-a)^{n-1}f^{n-1}(a) + \dots$$

which will converge to $f(x)$ when $R_n \to 0$ as $n \to \infty$, provided all the derivatives exist.

Let us now apply this to the exponential function.

7.5 Exponential series

We know that

(1) $$e^x = 1 + x + \frac{x^2}{2!} + \frac{x^3}{3!} + \ldots + \frac{x^{n-1}}{(n-1)!} + R_n$$

$$R_n = \frac{1}{n!} e^\xi x^n$$

If we can show that $R_n \to 0$ as $n \to \infty$, then the series

(2) $$1 + x + \frac{x^2}{2!} + \ldots + \frac{x^{n-1}}{(n-1)!} + \ldots$$

will converge to e^x.

First, let us show that the series (1) converges. Take the ratio of two consecutive terms. Then,

$$\left(\frac{x^n}{n!}\right) \div \left(\frac{x^{n-1}}{(n-1)!}\right) = \frac{x}{n}$$

If we let n become large, it will after some point become larger than x. Let that point be n_0. Then, for $n > n_0$

$$\left|\frac{x}{n}\right| < 1$$

Let

$$\frac{x^{n_0}}{n_0!} = b_0, \qquad \frac{x^{n_0+1}}{(n_0+1)!} = b_1, \ldots$$

for brevity. Then,

$$\left|\frac{b_1}{b_0}\right| = \left|\frac{x}{n_0}\right| < q < 1$$

$$\left|\frac{b_2}{b_1}\right| = \left|\frac{x}{n_0+1}\right| < \left|\frac{x}{n_0}\right| < q$$

and so forth. Thus,

$$|b_1| < q\, |b_0|$$

$$|b_2| < q\, |b_1| < q^2\, |b_0|$$

$$\vdots$$

$$|b_n| < q^n\, |b_0|$$

Thus, for that part of the series beyond n_0, we have

$$b_0 + b_1 + b_2 + b_3 + \ldots + b_n + \ldots < b_0[1 + q + q^2 \ldots + q^n + \ldots]$$

Since $q < 1$, the geometric series $1 + q + q^2 \ldots$ converges. Thus, we conclude that series (1) converges.

The second step is to show that the general term in this series approaches 0 as $n \to \infty$. But we know that this is a necessary condition for the series to converge. Thus,

$$\lim_{n \to \infty} \left| \frac{x^n}{n!} \right| = 0$$

The third step is to show that $R_n \to 0$ as $n \to \infty$. We know that

$$R_n = \frac{x^n}{n!} e^{\xi}$$

where ξ is between 0 and x. Since e^{ξ} is bounded, and since $x^n/n! \to 0$ as $n \to \infty$, R_n will also approach zero and, $R_n \to 0$ as $n \to \infty$.

Thus, from our discussion in Section 7.4, we conclude that the infinite series (2) will converge to $f(x) = e^x$.

Using this result we can calculate e, where $x = 1$.

$$e = 1 + 1 + \frac{1}{2!} + \frac{1}{3!} + \ldots$$
$$= 2.7182 \ldots$$

7.6 Taylor's theorem for several independent variables

Consider a function $f(x, y)$ that has continuous partial derivatives at the point (x, y) and $(x + h, y + k)$ where h and k are sufficiently small numbers. We wish to expand the function $f(x + h, y + k)$ around the point (x, y). This will be (without proof)

$$f(x + h, y + k) = f(x, y) + df + \frac{1}{2!} d^2f + \ldots + \frac{1}{n!} d^n f + R_n$$

where

$$R_n = \frac{1}{(n + 1)!} d^{n+1}(x + \theta h, y + \theta k), \qquad 0 < \theta < 1$$

The df's show the differentials of $f(x, y)$. Thus,

$$df = f_x dx + f_y dy = hf_x + kf_y$$
$$d^2f = h^2 f_{xx} + 2hk f_{xy} + k^2 f_{yy}$$

and so forth as we have seen in Section 4.5.

In applications we are usually interested in the difference,

$$f(x + h, y + k) - f(x, y).$$

For example, let p_1^0, p_2^0 be equilibrium values and p_1, p_2 be small deviations from the equilibrium values. Let $D(p_1, p_2)$ be the demand function. Then,

$$D(p_1, p_2) - D(p_1^0, p_2^0) = df + \frac{1}{2!}d^2f + \dots$$

where

$$df = (p_1 - p_1^0)f_{p_1} + (p_2 - p_2^0)f_{p_2}$$
$$d^2f = (p_1 - p_1^0)^2 f_{p_1 p_1} + 2(p_1 - p_1^0)(p_2 - p_2^0)f_{p_1 p_2}$$
$$+ (p_2 - p_2^0)^2 f_{p_2 p_2}$$

If we assume that $(p_1 - p_1^0)$ and $(p_2 - p_2^0)$ are very small deviations, then $(p_1 - p_1^0)^2$, $(p_2 - p_2^0)^2$ will be smaller and in many cases can be neglected. Then the excess demand can be shown as

$$D(p_1, p_2) - D(p_1^0, p_2^0) = (p_1 - p_1^0)f_{p_1} + (p_2 - p_2^0)f_{p_2}$$

where f_{p_1} is the change in demand due to a small change of p_1 holding p_2 constant, and vice versa for f_{p_2}.

This can be generalized to any number of variables.

7.7 Complex numbers

(i) Complex numbers

Let a and b be two real numbers. Then $c = a + bi$ where $i = \sqrt{-1}$ is called a complex number. $c = a + bi$ will be interpreted to mean a pair of ordered numbers (a, b). Thus, the complex number $d = (b, a) = b + ai$ is different from c.

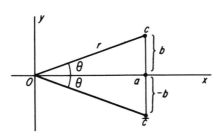

Fig. 7–2

Complex numbers, which we defined as an ordered pair, can be shown geometrically on a complex (or Gaussian) plane as in Figure 7–2. The x-axis is called the *real axis*. The complex number $c = a + bi$ is shown by the point c that has the coordinates $x = a, y = b$.

Next, let the angle of the point c be θ and the distance from the origin be r as in Figure 7–2. Then,

$$\sin \theta = \frac{b}{r} \qquad \therefore \quad r \sin \theta = b$$

$$\cos \theta = \frac{a}{r} \qquad \therefore \quad r \cos \theta = a$$

$$c = a + bi = r(\cos \theta + i \sin \theta)$$

θ is called the *amplitude* of the complex number c. r is called the *modulus* of c, which is also written $|c|$. We can see that

$$r^2(\sin^2 \theta + \cos^2 \theta) = a^2 + b^2$$

$$\therefore \quad r^2 = a^2 + b^2$$

The *conjugate* complex number $\bar{c}$ is

$$\bar{c} = a - bi = r(\cos \theta - i \sin \theta)$$

It is shown as $\bar{c}$ in Figure 7–2. The product of a complex number with its conjugate is

$$c\bar{c} = (a + ib)(a - ib) = a^2 - i^2 b^2 = a^2 + b^2$$

Thus,

$$r^2 = c\bar{c} = |c|^2$$

Example 1. Find the roots of

$$x^2 + 1 = 0$$

$$x^2 = -1$$

$$\therefore \quad x = \pm \sqrt{-1} = \pm i$$

Thus, $r_1 = i$, $r_2 = -i$. In terms of our definition

$$r_1 = i = a + bi$$

where

$$a = 0, b = 1, \text{ and}$$

$$r_2 = -i = a + bi$$

where

$$a = 0, b = -1.$$

Example 2.

$$x^2 + x + 1 = 0$$

The roots are

$$x = \frac{1}{2}(-1 \pm \sqrt{1 - 4}) = \frac{1}{2}(-1 \pm i\sqrt{3})$$

$$x_1 = -\frac{1}{2} + i\frac{\sqrt{3}}{2} = a + bi$$

$$x_2 = -\frac{1}{2} - i\frac{\sqrt{3}}{2} = a - bi$$

where $a = -\frac{1}{2}$, $b = \sqrt{3}/2$.

In terms of trigonometric functions,

$$x_1 = r(\cos\theta + i\sin\theta)$$
$$x_2 = r(\cos\theta - i\sin\theta)$$

where

$$r = \sqrt{a^2 + b^2} = \sqrt{(-\tfrac{1}{2})^2 + (\sqrt{3}/2)^2} = 1$$

$$\theta = \tan^{-1}\frac{b}{a} = \tan^{-1}(-\sqrt{3})$$

We know that $\tan\theta = -\sqrt{3}$, or

$$\sqrt{3} = -\tan\theta = \tan(180 - \theta)$$

From trigonometric tables we find

$$180 - \theta = 60°$$
$$\theta = 120°$$

Problems

1. Expand the function $f(x + h, y + k, z + m)$ around the point (x, y, z) by Taylor's formula, for the first three terms only.

2. Given the conjugate complex number $c = 1 + i$, $\bar{c} = 1 - i$, change this into a polar coordinate system.

(ii) *De Moivre's theorem*

Using the results in section (i) we have

$$c_1 = a_1 + b_1 i = r_1(\cos\theta_1 + i\sin\theta_1)$$
$$c_2 = a_2 + b_2 i = r_2(\cos\theta_2 + i\sin\theta_2)$$

Thus,

$$c_1 c_2 = r_1 r_2 [\cos(\theta_1 + \theta_2) + i\sin(\theta_1 + \theta_2)]$$

Thus, if $c_1 = c_2$, then,

$$c_1 c_2 = c_1^2 = r_1^2 [\cos 2\theta_1 + i\sin 2\theta_1]$$

We can repeat this process. Then,

$$c^n = r^n[\cos n\theta + i\sin n\theta]$$

But,

$$c^n = r^n[\cos\theta + i\sin\theta]^n$$

Thus,

$$(\cos\theta + i\sin\theta)^n = \cos n\theta + i\sin n\theta$$

This is known as *De Moivre's theorem* and will be used when discussing cyclical fluctuations in connection with difference equations.

(iii) *Euler formulas*

We have seen that

$$e^x = 1 + x + \frac{x^2}{2!} + \frac{x^3}{3!} + \dots$$

$$e^{-x} = 1 - x + \frac{x^2}{2!} - \frac{x^3}{3!} + \dots$$

Thus,

$$e^{ix} = 1 + ix + \frac{(ix)^2}{2!} + \frac{(ix)^3}{3!} + \dots$$

$$e^{-ix} = 1 - ix + \frac{(ix)^2}{2!} - \frac{(ix)^3}{3!} + \dots$$

Thus,

$$e^{ix} + e^{-ix} = 2\left[1 + \frac{(ix)^2}{2!} + \frac{(ix)^4}{4!} + \frac{(ix)^6}{6!} + \dots \right]$$

$$= 2\left[1 - \frac{x^2}{2!} + \frac{x^4}{4!} - \frac{x^6}{6!} + \dots \right]$$

But we have seen that (p. 171)

$$\cos x = 1 - \frac{x^2}{2!} + \frac{x^4}{4!} - \frac{x^6}{6!} + \dots$$

Thus,

$$\cos x = \frac{e^{ix} + e^{-ix}}{2}$$

Next, we find that

$$e^{ix} - e^{-ix} = 2i\left(x - \frac{x^3}{3!} + \frac{x^5}{5!} - \dots \right)$$

But,

$$\sin x = x - \frac{x^3}{3!} + \frac{x^5}{5!} - \dots$$

Thus,

$$\sin x = \frac{e^{ix} - e^{-ix}}{2i}$$

or

$$i \sin x = \frac{e^{ix} - e^{-ix}}{2}$$

Thus,

$$\cos x + i \sin x = e^{ix}$$

$$\cos x - i \sin x = e^{-ix}$$

These formulas are called *Euler relations*.

(iv) *Trigonometric functions*

We list here several trigonometric formulas for reference.

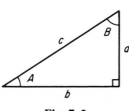

Fig. 7–3

$$\sin A = \frac{a}{c}$$

$$\cos A = \frac{b}{c}$$

$$\tan A = \frac{a}{b} = \frac{\sin A}{\cos A}$$

$$\cot A = \frac{b}{a}$$

Signs of functions. We shall list frequently used relations concerning signs of functions. They can be interpreted geometrically with the aid of Figure 7–4.

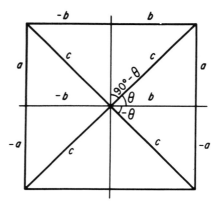

Fig. 7–4

$$\sin (-\theta) = -\sin \theta, \qquad \sin (90 - \theta) = \cos \theta$$
$$\cos (-\theta) = \cos \theta, \qquad \cos (90 - \theta) = \sin \theta$$
$$\tan (-\theta) = -\tan \theta, \qquad \tan (90 - \theta) = \cot \theta$$

$$\sin (90 + \theta) = \cos \theta, \qquad \sin (180 + \theta) = -\sin \theta$$
$$\cos (90 + \theta) = -\sin \theta, \qquad \cos (180 + \theta) = -\cos \theta$$
$$\tan (90 + \theta) = -\cot \theta, \qquad \tan (180 + \theta) = \tan \theta$$

$$\sin (180 - \theta) = \sin \theta, \qquad \sin (n\,360 \pm \theta) = \pm\sin \theta$$
$$\cos (180 - \theta) = -\cos \theta, \qquad \cos (n\,360 \pm \theta) = \cos \theta$$
$$\tan (180 - \theta) = -\tan \theta, \qquad \tan (n\,360 \pm \theta) = \pm\tan \theta$$

Problem

Check these relations geometrically using Figure 7–4. Let $\theta = 45°$.

Identities.

$$\sin^2 \theta + \cos^2 \theta = 1$$
$$\sin (\alpha + \beta) = \sin \alpha \cos \beta + \cos \alpha \sin \beta$$
$$\sin (\alpha - \beta) = \sin \alpha \cos \beta - \cos \alpha \sin \beta$$
$$\cos (\alpha + \beta) = \cos \alpha \cos \beta - \sin \alpha \sin \beta$$
$$\cos (\alpha - \beta) = \cos \alpha \cos \beta + \sin \alpha \sin \beta$$

Problems

Prove the following relations:

1. $\sin 2\theta = 2 \sin \theta \cos \theta$

2. $\cos 2\theta = \cos^2 \theta - \sin^2 \theta$

3. $\cos 2\theta = 1 - 2 \sin^2 \theta = 2 \cos^2 \theta - 1$

7.8 Inequalities

Rules concerning inequalities sometimes prove to be tricky to deal with for the less experienced. This is especially so when absolute values of numbers are involved. Since inequalities play an important role in higher mathematics, a few elementary rules will be given.

(i) Sum of two absolute numbers

The sum of the absolute values of the numbers a and b is greater than or equal to the absolute value of the sum of a and b. That is

$$|a + b| \leq |a| + |b|$$

Examples.

(a)
$$a = 1, \qquad b = 2$$

then,

$$|a + b| = |a| + |b| = 1 + 2 = 3$$

(b)
$$a = 1, \qquad b = -2$$

then,

$$|a + b| = |1 - 2| = 1$$
$$|a| + |b| = |1| + |-2| = 1 + 2 = 3$$
$$\therefore \ \ |a + b| < |a| + |b|$$

(ii) Difference of two absolute numbers

The difference of the absolute values of the numbers a and b is less than or equal to the absolute value of the sum of a and b. That is

$$|a + b| \geq |a| - |b|$$

Examples.

(a)
$$a = 1, \qquad b = 2.$$
$$|a + b| = 3, \qquad |a| - |b| = 1 - 2 = -1$$
$$\therefore \quad |a + b| > |a| - |b|$$

(b)
$$a = 1, \quad b = -2.$$
$$|a + b| = |1 - 2| = 1$$
$$|a| - |b| = |1| - |-2| = 1 - 2 = -1$$
$$\therefore \quad |a + b| > |a| - |b|$$

(c)
$$a = -1, \qquad b = 2.$$
$$|a + b| = |-1 + 2| = 1$$
$$|a| - |b| = |-1| - |2| = -1$$
$$\therefore \quad |a + b| > |a| - |b|$$

(d)
$$a = 2, \qquad b = -1.$$
$$|a + b| = |2 - 1| = 1$$
$$|a| - |b| = |2| - |-1| = 1$$
$$\therefore \quad |a + b| = |a| - |b|$$

(iii) Multiplication by a negative number

Multiplication by a negative number reverses the direction of the inequality. For example, consider
$$3 > -2$$

Multiply both sides by -1. Then,
$$-3 < 2$$

(iv) Schwartz's inequality

Let $a_1, a_2,$ and b_1, b_2 be any real numbers. Set

$$x_i = \frac{|a_i|}{\sqrt{a_1^2 + a_2^2}}, \qquad y_i = \frac{|b_i|}{\sqrt{b_1^2 + b_2^2}}$$

Now,

$$(x_i - y_i)^2 = x_i^2 - 2x_iy_i + y_i^2 \geq 0$$

$$\therefore \quad 2x_iy_i \leq x_i^2 + y_i^2$$

Thus,

$$2\left(\frac{|a_1|}{\sqrt{a_1^2 + a_2^2}}\right)\left(\frac{|b_1|}{\sqrt{b_1^2 + b_2^2}}\right) \leq \frac{a_1^2}{a_1^2 + a_2^2} + \frac{b_1^2}{b_1^2 + b_2^2}$$

$$2\left(\frac{|a_2|}{\sqrt{a_1^2 + a_2^2}}\right)\left(\frac{|b_2|}{\sqrt{b_1^2 + b_2^2}}\right) \leq \frac{a_2^2}{a_1^2 + a_2^2} + \frac{b_2^2}{b_1^2 + b_2^2}$$

Sum these inequalities. Then,

$$2\left(\frac{|a_1b_1| + |a_2b_2|}{\sqrt{a_1^2 + a_2^2}\sqrt{b_1^2 + b_2^2}}\right) \leq 2$$

$$\therefore \quad |a_1b_1| + |a_2b_2| \leq \sqrt{a_1^2 + a_2^2}\sqrt{b_1^2 + b_2^2}$$

Since both sides are positive, we can square both sides.

$$(a_1b_1 + a_2b_2)^2 \leq (a_1^2 + a_2^2)(b_1^2 + b_2^2)$$

This can be generalized to more variables and is called *Schwartz's inequality*.

Notes and References

7.1–7.2 See Courant (Vol. I, 1937) Chapter 8; Sokolnikoff (1939) Chapter 7; Sokolnikoff and Sokolnikoff (1941) Chapter 1. For Computational illustrations see Smail (1949) Chapter 18 and Titchmarsh (1959) Chapter 18.

7.3–7.4 See Courant (Vol. I, 1937) pp. 320–325; Smail (1949) Chapter 17 and pp. 400–401 and Sokolnikoff (1939) pp. 293–305.

7.5 See Smail (1949) p. 402 and Sokolnikoff and Sokolnikoff (1941) pp. 30–35.

7.6 See Courant (Vol. II, 1936) pp. 80–81 and Sokolnikoff (1939) 317–321. The student is also recommended to read pp. 321–326 which uses Taylor's formula to explain the conditions for maxima and minima of a function with several variables. This is also discussed in Allen (1938) Chapter 29.

7.7 Courant and Robbins (1941) pp. 88–100, Titchmarsh (1950) Chapter 10, Churchill (1948) Chapter 1 will provide an excellent introduction. Allen (1956) devotes a whole chapter (Chapter 4) to complex numbers. Complex numbers lead to complex variables and analytic functions. Economists have borrowed from electrical engineers who use this technique for model building. See Allen (1956) Chapter 9 for economic illustrations. References for complex variables are Churchill (1948), Franklin (1958), Hille (1959).

7.8 Discussion of inequalities was mainly a review, except for Schwartz inequality. The classic reference is Hardy, Littlewood, and Polya (1952). Inequalities related to matrices are discussed by Bellman (1960) Chapter 8. This is necessary for those interested in the mathematical aspects of programming. There is an excellent bibliography at the end of that chapter.

Bellman, R., *Introduction to Matrix Analysis.* New York: McGraw-Hill Book Co., Inc., 1960.

Churchill, R. V., *Introduction to Complex Variables.* New York: McGraw-Hill Book Co., Inc., 1948.

Franklin, P., *Functions of Complex Variables.* Englewood Cliffs, N.J.: Prentice-Hall, Inc., 1958.

Hardy, G. H., Littlewood, J. E., and Polya, G., *Inequalities*, 2nd ed. New York: Cambridge University Press 1952.

Hille E., *Analytic Function Theory*, Vol. I. Boston: Ginn and Co., 1959.

CHAPTER 8

Differential Equations

8.1 Introduction

Consider a functional relationship between x and y as

(1) $$y = x^2 \qquad 0 \le x \le 3$$

where x is the independent variable. Equation (1) is shown in Figure 8–1. The derivative of y will be

(2) $$\frac{dy}{dx} = 2x$$

Thus, for $x = 2$, $dy/dx = 4$, which is the slope of the curve at the point $(2, 4)$. For $x = 3$, $dy/dx = 6$, which is the slope of the curve at the point $(3, 9)$.

Let us now reverse the process. Assume we have an equation such as (2) that implicitly assumes a functional relation between x and y and includes x, y, the derivatives of y, and sometimes the differential. Such an equation is called a *differential equation*.

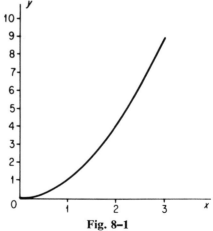

Fig. 8–1

For example, assume we wish to find the relation between total cost (y) and quantity produced (x). We know that marginal cost (dy/dx) doubles for every unit increase of production. This is shown by

$$\frac{dy}{dx} = 2x$$

The problem then is to solve this differential equation and find the relation between x (product) and y (total cost).

Now let us be more precise and ask the question: "What do we mean by a solution?" Let us illustrate as follows. Select a point, say, (1, 1) on the curve given by (1). Then the slope of the curve at (1, 1) is

$$\frac{dy}{dx} = 2x = 2$$

On the other hand, the differential equation (2) tells us that the slope at (1, 1) of a function (curve) that it implicitly assumes must be

$$\frac{dy}{dx} = 2x = 2$$

Thus, the curve given by (1) has the slope of a curve (function) that is predetermined by the differential equation (2) at the point (1, 1).

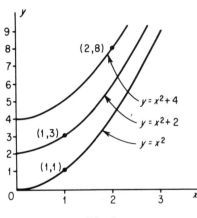

Fig. 8–2

Let us take another point (2, 8) as in Figure 8–2. Then (2) predetermines the slope of a curve as

$$\frac{dy}{dx} = 2x = 2 \times 2 = 4$$

and the question is: "Can we find a curve that passes through the point (2, 8) that has the slope 4?" If so, it would satisfy (2). The answer is yes, and the curve is given by

(3) $y = x^2 + 4$

As can be seen, when $x = 2$, then $y = 8$. Thus, the curve passes through the point (2, 8) as required.

Furthermore the slope of this curve (3) at the point (2, 8) is

$$\frac{dy}{dx} = \frac{d}{dx}(x^2 + 4) = 2x = 2 \times 2 = 4$$

as required by the differential equation (2).

Let us try another point (1, 3). The differential equation (2) requires that a curve passing through this point have a slope of

$$\frac{dy}{dx} = 2x = 2 \times 1 = 2$$

Is there such a curve? Yes, it is

(4) $y = x^2 + 2$

As can be seen, when $x = 1$, then $y = 3$. Thus, the curve (4) passes through $(1, 3)$ as required. Furthermore, the slope at $(1, 3)$ is

$$\frac{dy}{dx} = \frac{d}{dx}(x^2 + 2) = 2x = 2$$

as required by (2).

The equations (3) and (4) that we found are solutions of the differential equation (2). More specifically, by a solution of a differential equation we shall mean a function $f(x)$ that satisfies the differential equation for all values of the independent variable under consideration. In our present example this can be shown by substituting $f(x)$ in (2) as

$$f'(x) \equiv 2x$$

where the identity relation indicates that this equation must hold for all values of x that are being considered. In our present case $0 \leq x \leq 3$.

We have seen that

$$f(x) = x^2$$

$$f(x) = x^2 + 2$$

$$f(x) = x^2 + 4$$

are solutions of (2). If we selected other points in the graph, we would have been able to find other solutions which may be found as follows. Equation (2) is a very simple differential equation and, solving it, we find

$$dy = 2x \, dx$$

Integrating both sides, we get

$$y = x^2 + c$$

where c is a constant. Thus, we have a whole family of solutions. We had found three specific cases, $c = 0$, $c = 2$, and $c = 4$.

Now let us be a little more careful and ask the following questions:

(a) When we selected a point, say $(1, 3)$, how did we know a solution existed?

(b) We found one curve (function) that passed through the point $(1, 3)$ and satisfied the differential equation. Is there only one, or are there other curves that will also be solutions that pass through $(1, 3)$?

These are difficult questions and the proofs will not be given. Only the results will be explained.

The answer to these questions are: (a) yes, there *exists* a solution, and (b), there is *only one* solution. Let us state this as a theorem:

Let $y' = f(x, y)$ be a differential equation. Let the function $f(x, y)$ be continuous and its derivatives be continuous with respect to y in a region

R of the $x - y$ plane. Let (x_0, y_0) be a point in R. Then for each point (x_0, y_0):

    (a) there exists a solution $f(x)$ of the differential equation, and

    (b) there is one and only one solution such that $f(x_0) = y_0$.

This is known as the *fundamental existence theorem*.

In terms of our example, this means, if we select a point, say $(1, 3)$ in the region R (where in our case $0 \le x \le 3$), there exists a curve passing through $(1, 3)$ such that the slope of this curve will satisfy the requirements set out by the differential equation, and furthermore there will be only one such curve going through $(1, 3)$. The two characteristics given to us by the existence theorem are stated succinctly by the terms *existence* of a solution, and *uniqueness* of a solution.

The implication of the existence theorem is: If we have a differential equation and if by some method, even though it may be by reading tea leaves or gazing into a crystal ball, we find *a* solution of the differential equation, it will become *the* solution of the differential equation and we do not need to look any further. For example, in our subsequent discussion we shall use the function $y = e^{mx}$ as *a* solution of linear differential equations. The existence theorem tell us that this function is *the* solution of the differential equation, and we do not need to look for other solutions.

With this much background concerning solutions of differential equations, we shall in our subsequent discussion mainly be concerned with techniques of finding solutions.

Differential equations are broadly classified into *ordinary differential equations* and *partial differential equations*. The ordinary differential equations are those having only one independent variable and its derivatives. When the differential equation has several independent variables then the derivatives become partial derivatives and we have partial differential equations.

The *order* of a differential equation is determined by the order of the highest derivative in the equation. The *degree* of a differential equation is determined by the highest exponent of the derivatives when the equation is rationalized.

An ordinary differential equation is said to be *linear* if the dependent variable is of the first degree; i.e., the y-variable and its derivatives are of the first power only. We also say, in this case, that the y-variable and its derivatives are linearly combined. The general form of a linear differential equation is

$$h_0(x)\frac{d^n y}{dx^n} + h_1(x)\frac{d^{n-1}y}{dx^{n-1}} + \ldots + h_{n-1}(x)\frac{dy}{dx} + h_n(x)y = f(x)$$

This is an ordinary linear differential equation of order n.

If the coefficients of y and its derivatives, i.e., $h_0(x), h_1(x), \ldots h_n(x)$ are all constants, then it is called a *linear differential equation with constant coefficients*. Let $a_0, a_1, \ldots a_n$ be constants, then

$$a_0 \frac{d^n y}{dx^n} + a_1 \frac{d^{n-1} y}{dx^{n-1}} + \ldots + a_{n-1} \frac{dy}{dx} + a_n y = f(x)$$

If $f(x) = 0$, then we have a *homogeneous* linear equation with constant coefficients.

For convenience, we will classify differential equations as follows:
1. Non-linear differential equations of the first order and first degree.
   (a) variables are separable case
   (b) homogeneous differential equation
   (c) exact differential equation
2. Linear differential equation of first order.
   (a) homogeneous differential equation with constant coefficients
   (b) non-homogeneous differential equation with constant coefficients
   (c) general case
3. Linear differential equation of the second order with constant co-efficients.

8.2 Solutions

Assume we have an equation

(1) $y = x^4 + c_1 x^3 + c_2 x^2 + c_3 x + c_4$

Then, if we perform successive differentiation, we get

(2) $\dfrac{dy}{dx} = 4x^3 + 3c_1 x^2 + 2c_2 x + c_3$

(3) $\dfrac{d^2 y}{dx^2} = 12x^2 + 6c_1 x + 2c_2$

(4) $\dfrac{d^3 y}{dx^3} = 24x + 6c_1$

(5) $\dfrac{d^4 y}{dx^4} = 24$

The equation (1) is a solution of equation (5). Equation (5) is a differential equation of the 4th order, and the solution (1) has four arbitrary constants.

In general, if we have an nth order differential equation with n constants, we can eliminate the constants by n successive differentiations. And, conversely, it can be shown that a differential equation of order n will have a solution with n arbitrary constants, and it can have no more than n arbitrary constants. Such a solution is called the *general solution* of the differential equation. Thus, equation (1) is the general solution of equation (5). Depending on the value of the constants, a whole family of solutions exist. Any one of these specific solutions obtained from the general solution is called a *particular solution*.

In general, we are interested in a particular solution that fits the particular circumstances we are in. This means we must determine the values of the constants to suit our situation. This in turn is dependent on the so-called *initial conditions*.

8.3 Non-linear differential equations of the first order and first degree

In general we can only solve a very few of the various differential equations and we are restricted to linear differential equations. There are some special types of non-linear differential equations that can be solved, which are of the first order and first degree, for instance:

$$\frac{dy}{dx} = f(x, y)$$

An example of this is

$$\frac{dy}{dx} = 3xy^2$$

and, in differential form,

$$f_1(x, y)dx + f_2(x, y)\,dy = 0$$

of which an example is

$$(y^2 - x^2)\,dx - 2xy\,dy = 0$$

We will now take up certain types of easily-solved non-linear differential equations of the first order and first degree and then discuss linear differential equations.

8.4 Case I—variables separable case

If the differential equation

$$\frac{dy}{dx} = f(x, y)$$

can be put in the form

$$f_1(x)\,dx + f_2(y)\,dy = 0$$

where with dx we associate a function $f_1(x)$ which is only a function of x and with dy we associate a function $f_2(y)$ which is only a function of y, we have the *variables separable case*. This is easily integrable.

For example, solve

$$\frac{dy}{dx} = xy$$

By inspection we see we can separate the variables. Thus, we get

$$\frac{1}{y} dy - x \, dx = 0$$

We integrate and get

$$\ln y - \tfrac{1}{2}x^2 = c$$

$$y = c'e^{x^2/2} \qquad (c' = e^c)$$

where c' is an arbitrary constant. This gives an exponential curve and, as the value of the constant c' changes, we will have a family of such curves. In general, the solution will be of the form

$$g(x, y) = c$$

which will be a family of curves.

Problems

Solve the following differential equations.

1. $\dfrac{dy}{dx} = \dfrac{x}{y}$

2. $\dfrac{dy}{dx} = \dfrac{y}{x}$

3. $\dfrac{dy}{dx} = \dfrac{y}{1+x}$

4. $\dfrac{dy}{dx} = \dfrac{1+y}{1+x}$

5. $\dfrac{dy}{dx} + e^x + ye^x = 0$

6. $\dfrac{dy}{dx} = xy^2 - x$

8.5 Case II—differential equation with homogeneous coefficients

If $f(x, y)$ is a homogeneous function of degree n, then

$$f(\lambda x, \lambda y) = \lambda^n f(x, y)$$

If the differential equation

$$f_1(x, y) \, dx + f_2(x, y) \, dy = 0$$

has homogeneous coefficients, that is if $f_1(x, y)$ and $f_2(x, y)$ are homogeneous functions of the same order, then by change of variable we can reduce it to the variables separable case. Let f_1 and f_2 be of order n; i.e., of the same order. Now let

$$y = vx, \quad dy = v\, dx + x\, dv$$

Then

$$f_1(x, vx)\, dx + f_2(x, vx)(v\, dx + x\, dv) = 0$$

$$\frac{f_1(x, vx)}{f_2(x, vx)}\, dx + v\, dx + x\, dv = 0$$

Since f_1 and f_2 are homogeneous functions we can divide out the x. Thus,

$$\left(\frac{f_1(1, v)}{f_2(1, v)} + v\right) dx + x\, dv = 0$$

and we have the variables separable case which we can solve by integration.

Example. Solve

$$x^2 + 2xy\frac{dy}{dx} - y^2 = 0$$

This can be put in the form

$$(x^2 - y^2)\, dx + 2xy\, dy = 0$$

By inspection we see this has a homogeneous function of degree 2 for its coefficients. Thus, letting

$$y = vx, \qquad dy = v\, dx + x\, dv$$

$$\frac{x^2 - v^2x^2}{2x(vx)}\, dx + v\, dx + x\, dv = 0$$

$$\frac{1}{x}\, dx + 2v\frac{dv}{1 + v^2} = 0$$

We integrate and get

$$\ln x + \ln (1 + v^2) = c$$

$$\ln x\left(1 + \frac{y^2}{x^2}\right) = \ln c'$$

$$x^2 + y^2 = x\, c'$$

Problems

Solve the following differential equations.

1. $(x + y)\, dx + x\, dy = 0$.   *Ans.* $x^2 + 2xy = c$

2. $(x - y)\, dx - (x + y)\, dy = 0$.   *Ans.* $x^2 - 2xy - y^2 = c$

3. $\dfrac{x + y}{x - y} = \dfrac{dx}{dy}$.   *Ans.* $y^2 + 2xy - x^2 = c$

4. $(y^2 - x^2)\, dy + 2xy\, dx = 0$.   *Ans.* $x^2 + y^2 + cy = 0$

5. $y^2 dx = (xy - x^2)\, dy$.   *Ans.* $y + ce^{y/x} = 0$

8.6 Case III—exact differential equations

Consider a function

$$f(x, y) = x^2 y$$

The differential of this function is

$$df = \frac{\partial f}{\partial x}\, dx + \frac{\partial f}{\partial y}\, dy$$

$$= 2xy\, dx + x^2\, dy$$

Let

$$P(x, y) = 2xy, \qquad Q(x, y) = x^2$$

We know that

$$\frac{\partial P}{\partial y} = f_{xy} = 2x = f_{yx} = \frac{\partial Q}{\partial x}$$

Now let us reverse the procedure. We are given an expression

$$2xy\, dx + x^2\, dy$$

or

(1) $$P(x, y)\, dx + Q(x, y)\, dy$$

This expression is said to be the *exact differential* of some function $f(x, y)$, if the following (necessary and sufficient) condition holds

(2) $$\frac{\partial P}{\partial y} = \frac{\partial Q}{\partial x}$$

Let us check

$$\frac{\partial P}{\partial y} = \frac{\partial}{\partial y}(2xy) = 2x$$

$$\frac{\partial Q}{\partial x} = \frac{\partial}{\partial x}(x^2) = 2x$$

Thus, the condition (2) holds, and we know (1) is an exact differential of some function $f(x, y)$.

Let us now set (1) equal to zero.

(3) $$P(x, y)\, dx + Q(x, y)\, dy = 0$$
$$\therefore \quad 2xy\, dx + x^2\, dy = 0$$

This is called an *exact differential equation*.

With this much background let us argue as follows:

We are given a differential equation (3). Upon checking we find that it satisfies the condition (2). Thus, we conclude we have an exact differential equation. This means there is a function $f(x, y)$ whose differential is equal to the left side of the equation (3). Let this differential be $df(x, y)$. Then, from (3)

$$df(x, y) = 0$$

Integrating both sides we write

(4) $$f(x, y) = c$$

which is a solution of (3).

It can be shown that the solution $f(x, y)$ will be

(5) $$f(x, y) = \int P\, dx + \int \left[Q - \frac{\partial}{\partial y} \int P\, dx \right] dy$$

In our present case,

$$\int P\, dx = \int 2xy\, dx = x^2 y$$

$$\frac{\partial}{\partial y} \int P\, dx = x^2$$

$$\int \left[Q - \frac{\partial}{\partial y} \int P\, dx \right] dy = \int [x^2 - x^2]\, dy = 0$$

$$\therefore \quad f(x, y) = x^2 y + 0 + c' = x^2 y + c'$$

Thus, from (4)

$$x^2 y = c$$

which is the solution where c is an arbitrary constant.

Example. Solve the following differential equation:

$$(2x + 3y)\, dx + (3x - 2y)\, dy = 0$$

$$P = 2x + 3y, \qquad Q = 3x - 2y$$

$$\frac{\partial P}{\partial y} = 3, \qquad \frac{\partial Q}{\partial x} = 3$$

Thus, we have an exact differential equation and

$$f(x, y) = \int P \, dx + \int \left[Q - \frac{\partial}{\partial y} \int P \, dx \right] dy$$

$$\int P \, dx = \int (2x + 3y) \, dx = x^2 + 3xy$$

$$Q - \frac{\partial}{\partial y} \int P \, dx = 3x - 2y - 3x = -2y$$

$$\therefore \quad f(x, y) = x^2 + 3xy + \int (-2y) \, dy = x^2 + 3xy - y^2$$

The solution is

$$x^2 + 3xy - y^2 = c$$

Note that the exact differential equation we solved is also a differential equation with homogeneous coefficients.

Problems

Solve the following differential equations by the method discussed in Section 8.6.

1. $(2x + 3y + 1) \, dx + (3x - 2y + 1) \, dy = 0$.

2. $xy^2 \, dx + x^2y \, dy = 0$.

3. $2xy \, dx + (x^2 + 4y) \, dy = 0$.   *Ans.* $x^2y + 2y^2 = c$

8.7 Linear differential equations of the first order

So far we have discussed certain types of non-linear differential equations that were easy to solve. Let us now take up linear differential equations. The general expression is

$$\frac{dy}{dx} + Py = Q$$

where P and Q are functions of x or constants. The general solution for this equation is given by*

(1) $$y = e^{-\int P \, dx} \int e^{\int P \, dx} Q \, dx + ce^{-\int P \, dx}$$

(i) Case 1.—Homogeneous differential equation

When $Q = 0$, and P is a function of x, we have a homogeneous differential equation and the solution is, from (1).

(2) $$y = ce^{-\int P \, dx}$$

* For proof see Sokolnikoff and Sokolnikoff (1941) p. 284.

Example.

$$\frac{dy}{dx} + xy = 0$$

i.e., $P = x$, and $Q = 0$. Thus, from (2) we get

$$y = ce^{-\int x \, dx} = ce^{-x^2/2}$$

Check. Substitute this solution into the left side of the differential equation.

(ii) Case 2—Non-homogeneous differential equation

When P and Q are constants and we have a non-homogeneous differential equation with constant coefficients the solution becomes

$$y = e^{-a_1 x} \int e^{a_1 x} a_2 \, dx + ce^{-a_1 x}$$

$$= ce^{-a_1 x} + \frac{a_2}{a_1}$$

Example.

$$\frac{dy}{dx} + 3y = 4$$

$$y = ce^{-3x} + \frac{4}{3}$$

Check. Check this solution.

(iii) Case 3—General case

When P and Q are functions of x and we have the general case, the solution is equation (1).

Example.

$$\frac{dy}{dx} + \frac{1}{x} y = x$$

$$y = e^{-\ln x} \int e^{\ln x} x \, dx + ce^{-\ln x}$$

$$= \frac{x^2}{3} + \frac{c}{x}$$

Check. Work out the details of the above example, noting that $e^{\ln x} = x$. Then check the solution by substituting it in the original equation.

Problems

Solve the following linear first-order differential equations.

1. $\dfrac{dy}{dx} + 3x^2y = 0.$

2. $\dfrac{dI}{dt} - 2tI = 0.$

3. $\dfrac{dI}{dt} - 2I = k.$

4. $\dfrac{dy}{dx} + 6y = 4.$

5. $\dfrac{dy}{dx} + 2xy = 3x.$

6. $\dfrac{dP}{dc} - 3c^2P = 2P.$

8.8 Linear differential equation of second order with constant coefficient

This type of equation is expressed by

$$(1) \qquad \frac{d^2y}{dx^2} + a_1\frac{dy}{dx} + a_2y = f(x)$$

The solution is obtained in two steps. Step one is to set $f(x) = 0$ and solve

$$(2) \qquad \frac{d^2y}{dx^2} + a_1\frac{dy}{dx} + a_2y = 0$$

This is called a *homogeneous equation*, and the solution is called the *complementary function* for equation (1). Let this be y_c.

Step two is to find a *particular solution* of equation (1). Let this be y_p. Then the general solution y will be*

$$y = \text{complementary function} + \text{particular solution}$$

$$= y_c + y_p$$

Step 1. Find the general solution of the homogeneous equation: i.e., the complementary function.

The method we will be using depends on the following theorem which we give without proof.†

$$y_c = c_1y_1 + c_2y_2$$

---

* For proof see Smail, (1949), pp. 508–515, and Sokolnikoff and Sokolnikoff (1941) pp. 283–398.

† See W. Leighton (1952), Chap. 4, or Smail (1949), p. 510.

is the general solution of (2) if y_1 and y_2 are linearly independent solutions of (2) and c_1 and c_2 are arbitrary constants. By linearly independent we mean there are two arbitrary constants d_1 and d_2 ($d_1d_2 \neq 0$) such that

$$d_1y_1 + d_2y_2 = 0$$

Since (2) is a second order equation, we expect the solution to have two arbitrary constants.

The method of approach is to set

$$y = e^{mx}$$

where m is a constant and look for a solution in this form. From this we obtain

$$\frac{dy}{dx} = me^{mx}, \quad \frac{d^2y}{dx^2} = m^2e^{mx}$$

Thus, (2) becomes

$$(m^2 + a_1m + a_2)e^{mx} = 0$$

If m_1 is any root of

$$m^2 + a_1m + a_2 = 0$$

which is called the *auxiliary* or *characteristic equation*, then $y = e^{m_1x}$ will be a solution of (2). This is clear because, if we substitute $y = e^{m_1x}$ into (2), the auxiliary equation will become zero.

As can be seen, the solution of the auxiliary equation will have three cases, where the two roots are distinct, two roots are equal, and the two roots are conjugate complex numbers.

CASE 1—*Two roots distinct case.* We set the auxiliary equation equal to zero and solve

$$m^2 + a_1m + a_2 = 0$$

$$m_1, m_2 = \tfrac{1}{2}(-a_1 \pm \sqrt{a_1^2 - 4a_2})$$

where $a_1^2 > 4a_2$. Then the general solution of (2), i.e., the complementary function of (1) is

$$y_c = c_1e^{m_1x} + c_2e^{m_2x}$$

Example.

$$\frac{d^2y}{dx^2} - 5\frac{dy}{dx} + 6y = e^{2x}$$

Set:

$$\frac{d^2y}{dx^2} - 5\frac{dy}{dx} + 6y = 0$$

$$m^2 - 5m + 6 = 0$$

$$m_1 = 2, \quad m_2 = 3$$

$$\therefore \quad y_c = c_1e^{2x} + c_2e^{3x}$$

Check. Check by substituting this into the original equation.

CASE 2—*Two roots equal case.* The solution in this case takes the following form which we give without proof.*

$$y_c = c_1 e^{mx} + c_2 x e^{mx}$$

Example.

$$\frac{d^2 y}{dx^2} - 4 \frac{dy}{dx} + 4y = 0$$

$$m^2 - 4m + 4 = 0$$

$$m_1 = m_2 = 2$$

$$\therefore \ y_c = c_1 e^{2x} + c_2 x e^{2x}$$

Check: Check by substituting this into the original equation.

CASE 3—*Conjugate complex numbers.* The solution is as follows which we give without proof.†

$$y_c = e^{ax}(c_1 \cos bx + c_2 \sin bx)$$

where $m_1 = a + bi$, $m_2 = a - bi$.

Example.

$$\frac{d^2 y}{dx^2} + 2 \frac{dy}{dx} + 10y = 0$$

$$m^2 + 2m + 10 = 0$$

$$m_1, m_2 = -1 \pm 3i$$

$$a = -1, \qquad b = 3$$

$$\therefore \ y_c = e^{-x}(c_1 \cos 3x + c_2 \sin 3x)$$

Step 2. Find a particular integral of (1). The general solution for (1) was made up of two parts, the general solution y_c of the homogeneous equation (2) which was called the complementary function and the particular integral of (1), y_p, so that $y = y_c + y_p$. We now want to find y_p. The two methods used to find the particular integral are the method of *iteration* and the method of *partial fractions*. We will discuss only the method of iteration.

The method of iteration uses the following formula to find the particular integral, which we give without proof.‡

$$y_p = e^{m_1 x} \int e^{(m_2 - m_1)x} \int e^{-m_2 x} f(x) \, (dx)^2$$

where m_1 and m_2 are obtained from the auxiliary equation.

* See e.g., Smail (1949) p. 513.
† See Smail (1949) p. 514.
‡ See Sokolnikoff and Sokolnikoff (1941) p. 296.

Example 1.

$$\frac{d^2y}{dx^2} - 7\frac{dy}{dx} + 12y = e^{3x}$$

$$m^2 - 7m + 12 = 0$$

$$m_1 = 3, \qquad m_2 = 4$$

$$y_p = e^{3x} \int e^{(4-3)x} \int e^{-4x}e^{3x} \, (dx)^2$$

$$= e^{3x} \int \left[e^x \int e^{-x} \, dx \right] dx$$

$$= e^{3x} \int \left[e^x(-e^{-x}) \right] dx$$

$$= -e^{3x} \int dx = -xe^{3x}$$

$$\therefore \ y_p = -xe^{3x}$$

Check: Check the solution by substituting into original equation.

Example 2.

$$\frac{d^2y}{dx^2} - 5\frac{dy}{dx} + 6y = e^{2x}$$

$$m^2 - 5m + 6 = 0$$

$$m_1 = 2, \qquad m_2 = 3$$

$$y_p = e^{2x} \int e^{(3-2)x} \int e^{-3x}e^{2x} \, (dx)^2$$

$$= -xe^{2x}$$

Check: Work out the details and check the solution by substituting in the original equation.

Step 3. Thus the general solution of

$$\frac{d^2y}{dx^2} + a_1\frac{dy}{dx} + a_2 y = f(x)$$

will be

$$y = y_c + y_p$$

where, for instance when we have two distinct roots,

$$y_c = c_1 e^{m_1 x} + c_2 e^{m_2 x}$$

$$y_p = e^{m_1 x} \int e^{(m_2 - m_1)x} \int e^{-m_2 x} f(x) \, (dx)^2$$

Example.

$$\frac{d^2y}{dx^2} - 5\frac{dy}{dx} + 6y = e^{2x}$$

From our previous calculations we have

$$y_c = c_1e^{2x} + c_2e^{3x}$$

$$y_p = -xe^{2x}$$

$$\therefore \quad y = c_1e^{2x} + c_2e^{3x} - xe^{2x}$$

Problems

Solve the following linear second order differential equations.

1. $\dfrac{d^2y}{dx^2} - 4\dfrac{dy}{dx} - 5y = 0.$

2. $\dfrac{d^2y}{dx^2} - 6\dfrac{dy}{dx} + 8y = 0.$

3. $\dfrac{d^2y}{dx^2} - 6\dfrac{dy}{dx} + 9y = 0.$

4. $\dfrac{d^2y}{dx^2} + 3\dfrac{dy}{dx} + 3y = 0.$

5. $\dfrac{d^2y}{dx^2} - 5\dfrac{dy}{dx} + 7y = 0.$

8.9 Domar's capital expansion model

In Section 6.10 *Domar's capital expansion model* was solved by use of integration. Let us now approach it via differential equations. We obtained the relation

$$I\sigma = \frac{dI}{dt} \cdot \frac{1}{\alpha}$$

where I is investment, σ is investment productivity, and α is marginal propensity to consume. This is a linear first-order differential equation. The dependent variable is I. From Section 8.7 we know the solution is

$$I = ce^{-\int P\,dx}$$

where c is an arbitrary constant to be determined by initial conditions and P is

$$P = -\sigma\alpha$$

$$\therefore \quad -\int_0^t \sigma\alpha \, dt = -(t \, \sigma\alpha)\Big|_0^t = -t\sigma\alpha$$

Thus, the solution is

$$I = ce^{t\sigma\alpha}$$

If

$$I(t) = I(0)$$

when $t = 0$, then,

$$I(0) = ce^0 = c$$

Thus,

$$I(t) = I(0)e^{\alpha\sigma t}$$

which is the same result obtained in Section 6.10.

Notes and References

References for proofs, derivations and further studies are Leighton (1952), Sokolnikoff and Sokolnikoff (1941) Chapter 7, and Wylie (1960) Chapters 2–4.

It will probably be more economical and useful if an elementary calculus text like Smail (1949) Chapter 21 is studied in addition to what has been covered in this chapter and then study the following two references: Baumol (1959) Chapters 14, 15, 16; and Allen (1956) Chapter 5. Baumol gives non-technical discussions of the interpretation of differential equations and also explains systems of differential equations. Allen discusses the topic at an advanced level and emphasizes linear differential equations and Laplace transforms.

Both ordinary and partial differential equations are used frequently in economics in connection with equilibrium and stability conditions. In this case, it is generally not necessary to solve these equations. Many illustrations of such use can be found in Mosak (1944), and the appendix of Lange (1944), and of Hicks (1939). It is also used in business cycle theory and in this case solutions are sought, but the equations are generally of the type that are not difficult to solve. An excellent summary is in Allen (1957) Chapter 8, where he discusses the trade cycle models of R. M. Goodwin, M. Kalecki and A. W. Phillips. He also discusses how electric circuit theory involving differential equations has been used in economics.

Differential equations used in connection with general equilibrium theory and stability conditions (e.g. Mosak) usually involve systems of differential equations. Determinants and matrices are frequently used to solve these systems of equations. Thus, it is advisable to first concentrate on covering the mathematics up through Chapter 12 in this text before going to Mosak, Lange, and other economic references. There is also a brief discussion of systems of equations in Chapter 12.

Baumol, W. J., *Economic Dynamics*, 2nd ed. New York: The Macmillan Company, 1959.

Lange, O., *Price Flexibility and Employment*. Bloomington, Ind.: Principia Press, Inc., 1944.

Leighton, W., *An Introduction to the Theory of Differential Equations*. New York: McGraw-Hill Book Co., Inc., 1952.

Mosak, J. L., *General-Equilibrium Theory in International Trade*. Bloomington, Ind.: Principia Press, Inc., 1944.

Wylie, C. R., *Advanced Engineering Mathematics*, 2nd ed. New York: McGraw-Hill Book Co., Inc., 1960.

CHAPTER 9

Difference Equations

Although the differential equations we have discussed had exact solutions, there are many cases where they cannot be obtained. In these cases, approximate numerical solutions are obtained by various methods. The *finite difference method* is one, and a study of this method for solving equations leads to difference equations and there develops a parallel between *difference equations* and differential equations. Because the variable time in various economic data is usually treated discretely, the difference equation frequently expresses economic relationships more adequately than differential equations. We shall first discuss a few elementary concepts concerning finite differences and then take up difference equations without any discussion of the various techniques for numerical solutions.

9.1 Finite differences

Consider a function $y = f(x)$ as in Figure 9-1. The derivative of $f(x)$ was defined as

$$\lim_{\Delta x \to 0} \frac{f(x + \Delta x) - f(x)}{(x + \Delta x) - x} = \lim_{\Delta x \to 0} \frac{\Delta y}{\Delta x}$$

Instead of taking a limiting process we will now let Δx be a finite quantity and write

$$f(x + \Delta x) - f(x) = y(x + \Delta x) - y(x) = \Delta y(x)$$

Δ is a symbol denoting that we are operating on y in the above fashion and is called a *difference operator*. The finite quantity Δx is called the *difference interval*.

Thus, we have a relationship

(1) $$\Delta y(x) = y(x + \Delta x) - y(x)$$

which means that we take a difference interval Δx from the point x and find the difference between the two values of y at the points x and $x + \Delta x$.

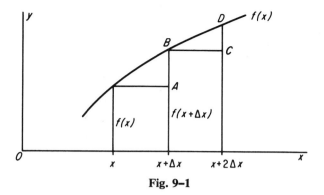

Fig. 9–1

When we were dealing with functions we assumed a domain in which x could take on real values. Any two neighboring points in this domain could be as close as we wished. For example, if an interval on the horizontal axis was the domain, the distance between two neighboring points could be zero.

In the present case when we are dealing with finite differences, the distance between any two successive points in the domain are a finite distance apart. For our subsequent discussion, not only will two successive points be a finite distance apart, but this will also be a constant. Thus, if we have one point x, we can then specify the succeeding points by letting $\Delta x = h$, so that

$$x, \quad x + h, \quad x + 2h, \quad x + 3h, \quad \ldots$$

The points have formed a sequence which will have the characteristics of an arithmetic progression.

Once we have decided that the difference interval $\Delta x = h$ will be a constant, we can simplify matters further by changing the scale of the x-axis so that $h = 1$. Then, successive points starting from x will be

$$x, \quad x + 1, \quad x + 2, \quad x + 3, \quad \ldots$$

Δy of equation (1) is called the first difference. By repeating the process we get

$$\Delta(\Delta y(x)) = \Delta y(x + h) - \Delta y(x)$$

which is called the second difference. This is usually written as

$$\Delta^2 y(x) = \Delta y(x + h) - \Delta y(x)$$

Now,

$$\Delta y(x + h) = y(x + 2h) - y(x + h)$$

Thus,

$$\Delta^2 y(x) = [y(x + 2h) - y(x + h)] - [y(x + h) - y(x)]$$
$$= y(x + 2h) - 2y(x + h) + y(x)$$

If we repeat this process once more, we have

$$\Delta[\Delta^2 y(x)] = \Delta^2 y(x + h) - \Delta^2 y(x)$$
$$= y(x + 3h) - 2y(x + 2h) + y(x + h)$$
$$- [y(x + 2h) - 2y(x + h) + y(x)]$$
$$\therefore \quad \Delta^3 y(x) = y(x + 3h) - 3y(x + 2h) + 3y(x + h) - y(x)$$

By repeating this process we can obtain the general formula

$$(2) \quad \Delta^n y(x) = (-1)^0 \binom{n}{0} y(x + nh) + (-1)^1 \binom{n}{1} y(x + (n - 1)h)$$

$$+ \cdots + (-1)^{n-1} \binom{n}{n-1} y(x + h) + (-1)^n y(x)$$

where

$$\binom{n}{m} = \frac{n!}{m!\,(n - m)!}$$

$$\binom{n}{0} = 1, \qquad 0! = 1$$

Examples. Find the first difference of the following functions.

(a) $y(x) = x^2$ where $x = 2$.

$$\Delta y(x) = y(x + 1) - y(x) = y(3) - y(2) = 3^2 - 2^2 = 5$$

(b) $y(x) = x^2 + x$ where $x = 2$.

$$\Delta y(x) = y(x + 1) - y(x) = y(3) - y(2)$$
$$= 3^2 + 3 - 2^2 - 2 = 6$$

Problems

Find the first difference of the following functions.

1. $y(x) = 3x^2$.

2. $y(x) = 3x^2 + 2x$.

3. $y(x) = x(x - 1)$.

From equation (2) we can write

$$y(x + 1) = y(x) + \Delta y(x)$$
$$y(x + 2) = y(x + 1) + \Delta y(x + 1)$$
$$= [y(x) + \Delta y(x)] + [\Delta y(x) + \Delta^2 y(x)]$$
$$= y(x) + 2\Delta y(x) + \Delta^2 y(x)$$
$$y(x + 3) = y(x) + 3\Delta y(x) + 3\Delta^2 y(x) + \Delta^3 y(x)$$

In general,

(3) $$y(x + n) = y(x) + \binom{n}{1}\Delta y(x) + \binom{n}{2}\Delta^2 y(x)$$

$$\cdots + \binom{n}{n-1}\Delta^{n-1}y(x) + \binom{n}{n}\Delta^n y(x)$$

9.2 Some operators

(i) *The operator* Δ

We have already defined the use of this operator as

$$\Delta y(x) = y(x + 1) - y(x)$$
$$\Delta^2 y(x) = \Delta y(x + 1) - \Delta y(x)$$

and so forth.

(ii) *The operator* E

The operator E is defined as

(1) $$Ey(x) = y(x + h)$$

When we assume $h = 1$, then

$$Ey(x) = y(x + 1)$$
$$E^2 y(x) = E[Ey(x)] = E[y(x + 1)] = y(x + 2)$$

By induction,

(2) $$E^n y(x) = y(x + n), \qquad n = 1, 2, 3, \ldots$$

For completeness the case for $n = 0$ is defined as

$$E^0 y(x) = y(x)$$

(iii) *Relation between* Δ *and* E

$$\Delta y(x) = y(x + 1) - y(x) = Ey(x) - y(x)$$
$$= (E - 1)y(x)$$

From this we can see the relation

(3) $$\Delta = E - 1$$

For the case where

$$\Delta y(x + n) = y(x + n + 1) - y(x + n)$$
$$= Ey(x + n) - y(x + n)$$
$$= (E - 1)y(x + n)$$
$$\Delta = E - 1$$

Thus, the relation between the two operators is, in general,

$$\Delta = E - 1$$

(iv) The relation $E = e^D$

The Taylor series shows

$$f(x + h) = f(x) + hf'(x) + \frac{h^2}{2} f''(x) + \dots$$

or

$$y(x + h) = y(x) + hy'(x) + \frac{h^2}{2} y''(x) + \dots$$

Let

$$\frac{d}{dx} = D, \quad \frac{d^2}{dx^2} = D^2, \dots$$

Then, if we let $h = 1$ we get

$$y(x + 1) = y(x) + Dy(x) + \frac{1}{2!} D^2 y(x) + \frac{1}{3!} D^3 y(x) + \dots$$

$$= \left(1 + D + \frac{1}{2!} D^2 + \frac{1}{3!} D^3 + \dots \right) y(x)$$

$$= e^D y(x)$$

But

$$y(x + 1) = Ey(x)$$
$$\therefore \quad Ey(x) = e^D y(x)$$
$$\therefore \quad E = e^D = 1 + \Delta$$

9.3 Difference equations

Difference equations may be defined in a similar manner to differential equations. An equation that shows the relation between the independent variable x, the dependent variable y and its finite difference is called a difference equation.

The *order* of a difference equation is the maximum difference of the difference intervals of the equation. Thus,

$$y(x + 3) + y(x + 2) - y(x) = x \qquad \text{(order 3)}$$
$$y(x + n) - y(x + 1) = 0 \qquad \text{(order } n - 1)$$

These equations may be presented in a form involving finite differences by the use of equation (9.1.3). For example, the first equation becomes,

$$y(x + 3) = y(x) + 3\Delta y(x) + 3\Delta^2 y(x) + \Delta^3 y(x)$$
$$y(x + 2) = y(x) + 2\Delta y(x) + \Delta^2 y(x)$$
$$\therefore \quad 2y(x) + 5\Delta y(x) + 4\Delta^2 y(x) + \Delta^3 y(x) - y(x) = x$$
$$\therefore \quad y(x) + 5\Delta y(x) + 4\Delta^2 y(x) + \Delta^3 y(x) = x$$

The order of the equation is now shown by the highest difference which is 3.

Change of notation. For convenience we shall now change our notation as follows.

$$y(x + 3) = y_{x+3}$$

$$y(x + n) = y_{x+n}$$

and so forth.

Thus, the equations above can be written

$$y_{x+3} + y_{x+2} - y_x = x$$

$$y_{x+n} - y_{x+1} = 0$$

9.4 Solutions

Consider the following difference equation:

(1) $y_{x+n} - y_x = n, \qquad x = 0, 1, 2, \ldots$

We wish to solve (1). Similar to the discussion of solutions in Chapter 8, let us ask ourselves three questions:

(a) What do we mean by a solution (definition of a solution)?
(b) Is there a solution (existence of a solution)?
(c) How many solutions are there (uniqueness of solutions)?

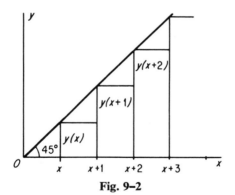

Fig. 9–2

A function y of x is a solution of a difference equation, if every value of y satisfies the difference equation for all values of the independent variable x that are being considered. Let us illustrate. As a solution of (1), try the function

(2) $y_x = x$

This is the equation for a straight line going through the origin at a 45-degree angle (Figure 9–2). For $x + n$, equation (2) becomes

$$y_{x+n} = x + n$$

If this is substituted in the difference equation (1), we get

$$\text{left side} = (x + n) - x = n = \text{right side.}$$

The function (2) will therefore satisfy the difference equation (1) for all values of x ($x = 0, 1, 2, ...$) and the function (2) is a solution of (1).

Consider the function

$$(3) \qquad\qquad y_x = x + k$$

where k is a constant. Substituting this in (1), we find

$$\text{left side} = (x + k + n) - (x + k) = n = \text{right side.}$$

We see that (3) satisfies (1) for all values of x. Thus, (3) is a solution of (1). In fact, (3) is the general solution and (2) is the particular solution where $k = 0$. Graphically, (3) gives us a family of straight lines parallel to the 45-degree line of Figure 9–2.

Now, when we select a point, say $(1, 3)$, is there a solution corresponding to this point; or expressed graphically, is there a straight line going through point $(1, 3)$ that satisfies the requirements of the difference equation (1)? The answer is: yes, there exists *a* solution. Let us approach it as follows:

When the point $(1, 3)$ is given, this means we are given the condition that $y = 3$ when $x = 1$. That is

$$y_{x=1} = 3$$

From the general solution (3), we find

$$y_{x=1} = 1 + k = 3$$

Thus, k becomes $k = 3 - 1 = 2$ and the general solution becomes a particular solution

$$y_x = x + 2$$

As can be seen, for every value of x ($x = 0, 1, 2, ...$) there will be a unique value of y. For example, when $x = 0$, then $y = 2$, or when $x = 1$ then $y = 3$, and so forth. This means once we are given a specific value of y for a given x, i.e., given a point on the graph, all the other y values will be uniquely determined for every x that is being considered. That is, the function y is uniquely determined. Thus, when we are given a point, say $(1, 3)$, not only will there be *a* solution, but it will be *the* solution.

We have shown heuristically that there *exists* a solution, and also that it will be *the* solution.

For a second order linear difference equation we shall consider

$$y_{x+2} - 4y_{x+1} + 4y_x = 2x$$

When we are given two y-values for two consecutive x-values, it can be shown that there is one and only one solution y for every value of x that is being considered.

Let us state as a theorem that: For a linear difference equation of order n, when we are given n y-values for n consecutive x-values, there is one and only one solution y for every value of x that is being considered.

Note two things: First, the theorem is stated for linear difference equations. Secondly, when *a* solution of the difference equation that satisfies the given initial conditions is found, regardless of method, this solution will be *the* solution.

With this much background concerning solutions, we will take up certain types of difference equations and discuss techniques of how to solve these difference equations, and also discuss additional aspects of solutions as they arise.

9.5 Homogeneous linear difference equation with constant coefficients

The general equation of a homogeneous linear difference equation with constant coefficients of order n can be shown as

(1) $$y_{x+n} + A_1 y_{x+n-1} + \ldots + A_{n-1} y_{x+1} + A_n y_x = 0$$

When we had a similar equation in differential equations we found a general solution by first obtaining an auxiliary equation. That was accomplished by setting

$$y = e^{mx}$$

In the case of difference equations we will let

$$y_x = \beta^x$$

where β is a constant. Then (1) becomes

$$(\beta^n + A_1 \beta^{n-1} + \ldots + A_n)\beta^x = 0$$

Thus, we set

$$\beta^n + A_1 \beta^{n-1} + \ldots + A_n = 0$$

and call this the *auxiliary* or *characteristic equation*.

The roots of this equation will be solutions of (1). The general solution is shown as

(2) $$y_x = c_1 \beta_1^x + \ldots + c_n \beta_n^x$$

It will be noted that this is similar to the results we had when discussing differential equations. The proof is omitted but examples are given to demonstrate that it holds true.* (2) will be called the *general solution*.

CASE 1—*Linear homogeneous difference equation with constant coefficients of the first order.*

$$y_{x+1} - A_1 y_x = 0$$

* For proof see Goldberg (1958) Chapter 3.

Let $y_x = \beta^x$, then

$$\beta^{x+1} - A_1\beta^x = 0$$

$$\beta^x(\beta - A_1) = 0$$

$$\therefore \quad \beta = A_1$$

Thus, the solution of the difference equation is

(3)
$$y_x = c_1 A_1^x$$

Check:

$$y_{x+1} = c_1 A_1^{x+1}$$

Thus,

$$\text{the left side} = c_1 A_1^{x+1} - A_1 c_1 A_1^x$$

$$= c_1 A_1^{x+1} - c_1 A_1^{x+1} = 0 = \text{right side}$$

Example.

$$y_{x+1} - 2y_x = 0$$

Let

$$y_x = \beta^x$$

Then, by substitution, we obtain the characteristic equation

$$\beta^{x+1} - 2\beta^x = 0$$

$$\beta^x(\beta - 2) = 0$$

$$\therefore \quad \beta = 2$$

Thus, the solution is

$$y_x = c_1\beta^x = c_1 2^x$$

CASE 2—*Linear homogeneous difference equation with constant coefficients of order 2 or higher.* Take the case of order two. Then,

$$y_{x+2} + A_1 y_{x+1} + A_2 y_x = 0$$

Let $y_x = \beta^x$. Then the auxiliary equation is

$$\beta^2 + A_1\beta + A_2 = 0$$

In this case we have three different situations.

A. When the two roots β_1 and β_2 are real and distinct, the solution is

(4)
$$y_x = c_1\beta_1^x + c_2\beta_2^x$$

Example.

$$y_{x+2} - 6y_{x+1} + 8y_x = 0$$

The auxiliary equation is

$$\beta^2 - 6\beta + 8 = 0$$

$$\beta_1 = 2, \beta_2 = 4$$

Thus the general solution is

$$y_x = c_1 2^x + c_2 4^x$$

Check:

$$y_{x+2} = c_1 2^{x+2} + c_2 4^{x+2} = 4c_1 2^x + 16c_2 4^x$$

$$6y_{x+1} = 6c_1 2^{x+1} + 6c_2 4^{x+1} = 12c_1 2^x + 24c_2 4^x$$

$$8y_x = 8c_1 2^x + 8c_2 4^x$$

$$\text{left side} = 4c_1 2^x + 16c_2 4^x - 12c_1 2^x - 24c_2 4^x$$

$$+ 8c_1 2^x + 8c_2 4^x = 0 = \text{right side.}$$

Problems

Solve and check the following equations.

1. $y_{x+2} - 7y_{x+1} + 12y_x = 0.$

2. $3y_{x+2} - 9y_{x+1} + 6y_x = 0.$

3. $y_{x+3} + 2y_{x+2} - y_{x+1} - 2y_x = 0.$

B. When the two roots are equal, the solution is, where $\beta_1 = \beta_2 = \beta$,

(5) $y_x = c_1 \beta^x + c_2 x \beta^x$

The point to notice is that the second part of the solution is multiplied by x. If we had a third-degree equation with three equal roots, $\beta_1 = \beta_2 = \beta_3 = \beta$, the solution would be

$$y_x = c_1 \beta^x + c_2 x \beta^x + c_3 x^2 \beta^x$$

where the third part of the solution is multiplied by x^2. Solutions for higher-order equations with equal roots are obtained in a similar fashion.

Example.

$$y_{x+2} - 4y_{x+1} + 4y_x = 0$$

$$\beta^2 - 4\beta + 4 = 0$$

$$\beta_1 = \beta_2 = 2$$

$$\therefore \quad y_x = c_1 2^x + c_2 x 2^x$$

Check: Substitute the solution in the difference equation and check.

Problem

Solve and check the following equation.

$$y_{x+2} - 6y_{x+1} + 9y_x = 0$$

When we have an equation of order three and two of the roots are equal, the solution is

$$y_x = c_1\beta_1^x + c_2\beta_1^x + c_3x\beta_3^x$$

Example.

$$y_{x+3} - 5y_{x+2} + 8y_{x+1} - 4y_x = 0$$

$$\beta^3 - 5\beta^2 + 8\beta - 4 = 0$$

$$(\beta - 2)^2(\beta - 1) = 0$$

$$\therefore \quad \beta_1 = 1, \qquad \beta_2 = \beta_3 = 2$$

Thus, the solution is

$$y_x = c_1 + c_2 2^x + c_3 x 2^x$$

Problems

1. Check the above solution.

2. Solve and check the following equation.

$$y_{x+3} - 5y_{x+2} + 7y_{x+1} - 3y_x = 0$$

C. When the roots are conjugate complex numbers, let the roots be

$$\beta_1 = a + ib = \rho(\cos\theta + i\sin\theta)$$

$$\beta_2 = a - ib = \rho(\cos\theta - i\sin\theta)$$

where

$$\rho = \sqrt{a^2 + b^2}, \qquad \theta = \tan^{-1}\frac{b}{a}$$

The solution is

(6) $$\qquad\qquad y_x = d_1\beta_1^x + d_2\beta_2^x$$

where y_x needs to be a real number. But if β_1 and β_2 are complex numbers while d_1 and d_2 are not, y_x may be a complex number. To avoid this, we shall assume d_1 and d_2 are complex conjugates. We can do this because d_1 and d_2 are arbitrary. Thus, let us set

$$d_1 = m + in, \qquad d_2 = m - in$$

To avoid complex numbers, let us show our solution in terms of polar coordinates. We have

$$d_1\beta_1^x = d_1\rho^x(\cos\theta + i\sin\theta)^x$$

$$= d_1\rho^x(\cos\theta\, x + i\sin\theta\, x)$$

$$d_2\beta_2^x = d_2\rho^x(\cos\theta\, x - i\sin\theta\, x)$$

because of de Moivres' Theorem. Thus,

$$y_x = \rho^x[(d_1 + d_2)\cos\theta\, x + i(d_1 - d_2)\sin\theta\, x]$$

(6') $$\qquad \therefore \quad y_x = \rho^x[c_1\cos\theta\, x + c_2\sin\theta\, x]$$

where

$$c_1 = d_1 + d_2 = (m + in) + (m - in) = 2m$$

$$c_2 = i(d_1 - d_2) = i(2in) = -2n$$

Thus, c_1 and c_2 are real numbers and the y_x we have obtained is a real number.
    The solution is sometimes shown in the following form which is easier to interpret when discussing business cycles or economic growth. Let

$$d_1 = m + in = k(\cos B + i \sin B)$$

$$d_2 = m - in = k(\cos B - i \sin B)$$

where

$$k = \sqrt{m^2 + n^2}, \qquad B = \tan^{-1} \frac{m}{n}$$

Then,

$$c_1 = d_1 + d_2 = 2k \cos B$$

$$c_2 = i(d_1 - d_2) = -2k \sin B$$

Substituting these into our solution, we find

$$y_x = \rho^x [2k \cos B \cos \theta \, x - 2k \sin B \sin \theta \, x]$$

which becomes (see Section 7.7)

(7) $$y_x = A\rho^x \cos (\theta \, x + B)$$

where $A = 2k$. Then, for example, if y_x is income, ρ^x shows the amplitude and $\theta \, x$ shows the period of oscillations of y_x.

Example.

$$y_{x+2} - 2y_{x+1} + 2y_x = 0$$

$$\beta^2 - 2\beta + 2 = 0$$

$$\beta_1 = 1 + i, \qquad \beta_2 = 1 - i,$$

i.e., $a = 1, b = 1$. Thus, $\rho = \sqrt{2}, \theta = \pi/4$ and the solution is

$$y_x = 2^{x/2}\left(c_1 \cos \frac{\pi x}{4} + c_2 \sin \frac{\pi x}{4}\right)$$

Problems

Solve and check the following:

1. $y_{x+2} - 3y_{x+1} + 5y_x = 0$

2. $y_{x+2} + 2y_{x+1} + 4y_x = 0$

9.6 Geometric interpretation of solutions

The solution when $\beta_1 \neq \beta_2$ and real was

$$y_x = c_1 \beta_1^x + c_2 \beta_2^x$$

Since c_1 and c_2 are constants, the main influence on y_x when $x \rightarrow \infty$ will be the values of β_1 and β_2. When $\beta_1 \neq \beta_2$, the larger one will eventually determine the behavior of y_x. Let us call the larger root in absolute terms the dominant root and assume for the moment it is β_1. We shall illustrate several cases assuming certain values for c_1 and β_1. Letting $x = 0, 1, 2, \ldots$, we have the following cases:

(i) When $c_1 > 0$, $\beta_1 > 1$: $y_x = c_1 \beta_1^x$ would appear graphically as in Figure 9–3.

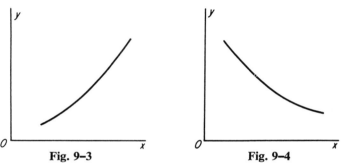

Fig. 9–3   Fig. 9–4

(ii) When $c_1 > 0$, $1 > \beta_1 > 0$, then we have the curve shown in Figure 9–4.

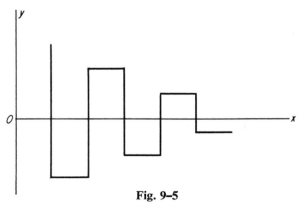

Fig. 9–5

(iii) When $c_1 > 0$, $0 > \beta > -1$, then we have the curve shown in Figure 9–5.

(iv) When $c_1 > 0$, $-1 > \beta$, then we have the curve shown in Figure 9–6.

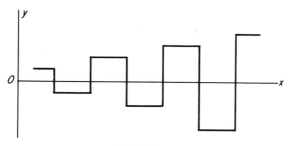

Fig. 9–6

Since $y_x = c_1 \beta^x + c_2 \beta^x$, this will be a combination of any of the above situations.

The complex number case is

$$y_x = \rho^x(c_1 \cos \theta\, x + c_2 \sin \theta\, x) = A\rho^x \cos (\theta\, x + B)$$

ρ^x will give the magnitude of the oscillation while $\theta\, x$ will determine the periodicity.

(v) When $\rho > 1$, we get explosive oscillations (Figure 9–7).

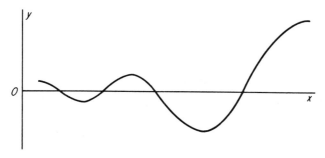

Fig. 9–7

(vi) When $\rho = 1$, we get a simple harmonic motion (Figure 9–8).
(vii) When $\rho < 1$ we get damped oscillations (Figure 9–9).

These will be discussed again when applications are considered.

9.7 Particular solutions of non-homogeneous linear equations

The general expression of a non-homogeneous difference equation can be shown as

(1) $y_{x+n} + A_1 y_{x+n-1} + \dots A_{n-1} y_{x-1} + A_n y_x = g_x$

where g_x is an arbitrary function of x, or it may be a constant.

Fig. 9–8

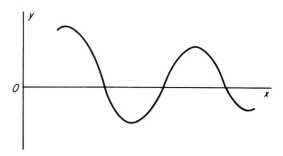

Fig. 9–9

When dealing with differential equations, the method of iteration to find the particular integral was used. There were other methods, such as the method of undetermined coefficients, and the method of partial fractions, which we did not discuss. We shall mainly study the method of undetermined coefficients to obtain the particular solution for difference equations. As in the differential equation case, the solution is expressed as

general solution = (homogeneous solution) + (particular solution)

We will consider (1) linear first-order difference equations with constant coefficients, and (2) linear second-order difference equations with constant coefficients. The higher orders can be solved in a similar manner to the second-order equation.

9.8 Linear first-order difference equations

Let us assume we have adjusted the equation so it is in the form

(1) $$y_{x+1} = Ay_x + B$$

where A and B are constants and the coefficient of y_{x+1} is unity. Then the homogeneous solution can be obtained by letting $B = 0$. Thus,

$$y_{x+1} = Ay_x$$

In the case of differential equations we had set $y = e^x$ to obtain a solution. For difference equations of the present kind let us set

$$y_x = \beta^x$$

Substituting this into our equation we obtain

$$\beta^{x+1} = A\beta^x$$

$$\therefore \quad \beta = A$$

Thus, the homogeneous solution will be

$$y_x = CA^x$$

where C is a constant. The particular solution in this case is

$$y_x = \begin{cases} B\dfrac{1 - A^x}{1 - A} & \text{when } A \neq 1 \\[2ex] Bx & \text{when } A = 1 \end{cases}$$

Thus, the general solution will be

$$y_x = \begin{cases} CA^x + B\dfrac{1 - A^x}{1 - A} & A \neq 1 \\[2ex] C + Bx & A = 1 \end{cases}$$

where $x = 0, 1, 2, 3, \ldots$.

In this simple case we can show how this solution is obtained as follows. Let y_0 be a given initial value. Then,

$$y_1 = Ay_0 + B$$

$$y_2 = Ay_1 + B = A^2 y_0 + AB + B$$

$$y_3 = Ay_2 + B = A^3 y_0 + A^2 B + AB + B$$

For $x = n$ we will have, by repeating this process,

$$y_n = A^n y_0 + (A^{n-1} + A^{n-2} + \ldots + A + 1)B$$

$$= A^n y_0 + B \sum_{i=0}^{n-1} A^i$$

$$\therefore \quad y_x = A^x y_0 + B \sum_{i=0}^{x-1} A^i = A^x y_0 + B\frac{1 - A^x}{1 - A} \qquad (A \neq 1)$$

Example.

$$3y_{x+1} = 6y_x + 9 \qquad x = 0, 1, 2, 3, \ldots$$

First change this to the form of (1).

$$y_{x+1} = 2y_x + 3$$

Thus since the coefficient $A = 2 \neq 1$, from (2) we obtain as a solution

$$y_x = C2^x + 3\frac{1 - 2^x}{1 - 2}$$

If the initial value of y_x is given as $y_0 = 7$, we can determine the C. By substituting in this value we get

$$7 = C \cdot 2^0 + 3\frac{1 - 2^0}{1 - 2}$$

$$\therefore \quad C = 7$$

Thus, the general solution becomes

$$y_x = 7 \cdot 2^x + 3\frac{1 - 2^x}{1 - 2} = 10 \cdot 2^x - 3$$

Problems

1. Substitute the solution of the above example in the original equation and check the answer.

   Solve and check the following equations.

   2. $y_{x+1} = 4y_x + 4$ $y_0 = 2$

   3. $2y_{x+1} = 6y_x - 4$ $y_0 = 2$

   4. $y_{x+1} = y_x + 3$ $y_0 = 2$

   5. $y_{x+1} = -y_x + 3$ $y_0 = 2$

9.9 Linear second-order difference equations with constant coefficients

Let the equation be

(1) $$y_{x+2} + A_1 y_{x+1} + A_2 y_x = g_x$$

Here the function g_x may be a constant as in Section 9.8, or a function of x. The method of undetermined coefficients will be used to find the particular solution and it is suitable when g_x assumes certain functional forms. Several cases of particular interest are considered.

CASE 1

$$g_x = A^x$$

When the form of g_x is A^x where A is a constant, we try as a particular solution

(2) $$y_x = CA^x$$

Example 1.

$$y_{x+2} - 4y_{x+1} + 3y_x = 5^x$$

From the homogeneous equation we find $\beta_1 = 1$, $\beta_2 = 3$. Thus, the homogeneous solution is

$$y_x = C_1 1^x + C_2 3^x = C_1 + C_2 3^x$$

For the particular solution, let $y_x = C5^x$. Substitute this into the equation. Thus, we have, after the necessary calculations,

$$C5^{x+2} - 4C5^{x+1} + 3C5^x = 5^x$$

$$8C5^x = 5^x$$

Equating coefficients we get

$$8C = 1$$

$$C = \tfrac{1}{8}$$

Thus the particular solution is $y_x = \tfrac{1}{8}5^x$ and the general solution is

$$y_x = C_1 + C_2 3^x + \tfrac{1}{8} \cdot 5^x$$

Problems

1. Substitute the particular solution of the above example into the equation and check.

Solve and check the following equations.

2. $y_{x+2} - 5y_{x+1} + 6y_x = 4^x$

3. $y_{x+2} + 5y_{x+1} - 6y_x = 2^x$

Example 2.

$$y_{x+2} - 4y_{x+1} + 3y_x = 3^x$$

The homogeneous solution is the same as above, viz.,

$$y_x = C_1 + C_2 3^x$$

Note in this case part of the homogeneous solution is the same as the function g_x; i.e., 3^x. In such a case where the homogeneous solution includes a term similar to the function g_x, we multiply the particular solution we are about to try by x. Thus, we try

(3) $$y_x = Cx3^x$$

Substituting this into the original equation we get

$$C(x + 2)3^{x+2} - 4C(x + 1)3^{x+1} + 3Cx3^x = 3^x$$

$$6C3^x = 3^x$$

Equating coefficients, we get

$$6C = 1 \quad \text{or} \quad C = \tfrac{1}{6}$$

and the particular solution becomes

$$y_x = \tfrac{1}{6}x3^x$$

Thus, the general solution is

$$y_x = C_1 + C_2 3^x + \tfrac{1}{6} \cdot x \cdot 3^x$$

Problems

1. Substitute the particular solution of the above example into the equation and check.

Solve and check the following equations.

2. $y_{x+2} - 5y_{x+1} + 6y_x = 2^x$.

3. $y_{x+2} - 5y_{x+1} - 6y_x = -6^x$.

4. $y_{x+2} - 5y_{x+1} - 6y_x = 6^x$.

Example 3.

$$y_{x+2} - 6y_{x+1} + 9y_x = 3^x$$

In this case, $\beta_1 = \beta_2 = 3$ and the homogeneous solution is

$$y_x = C_1 3^x + C_2 x 3^x$$

To find the particular solution we try $y_x = C3^x$. But, since the terms in the homogeneous solution include 3^x, we multiply by x and set $y_x = Cx3^x$ as we did in example 2. There is still a term in the homogeneous solution which is the same as the particular solution we propose to try, viz., $C_2 x 3^x$, so we multiply by x once more and obtain

$$y_x = Cx^2 3^x$$

Now, there is no term in the homogeneous solution similar to this. Thus, substituting this in, we have, after the necessary calculations

$$18C3^x = 3^x$$

Equating coefficients we get as a result

$$C = \tfrac{1}{18}$$

and the particular solution is

$$y_x = \frac{x^2}{18} 3^x$$

Thus, the general solution is

$$y_x = C_1 3^x + C_2 x 3^x + \frac{x^2}{18} 3^x$$

Problems

1. Check the above particular solution.

Solve and check the following equations.

2. $y_{x+2} - 4y_{x+1} + 4y_x = 2^x$.

3. $y_{x+2} - 2y_{x+1} + y_x = 1$.

CASE 2

$$g_x = x^n$$

When the form of the function g_x is x^n, we try, as a particular solution

(4) $$y_x = A_0 + A_1 x + A_2 x^2 + \dots + A_n x^n$$

The procedure is similar to Case 1. We first find the homogeneous solution, say,

$$y_x = C_1 \beta_1^x + C_2 \beta_2^x$$

if it is a second-order equation. Then we check to find if the particular solution has any terms similar to the terms in the homogeneous solution. If it has, we multiply with x just as in Case 1. This procedure will be illustrated by examples.

Example 1.

$$y_{x+2} - 4y_{x+1} + 3y_x = x^2$$

The homogeneous solution is, since $\beta_1 = 1$, $\beta_2 = 3$

$$y_x = C_1 + C_2 3^x$$

The particular solution we assume is

$$y_x = A_0 + A_1 x + A_2 x^2$$

This has a constant A_0. The homogeneous solution also has a constant C_1. Thus, we multiply by x and get

$$y_x = A_0 x + A_1 x^2 + A_2 x^3$$

Now there are no similar terms in the homogeneous and particular solution. We substitute this in the equation and, after the necessary calculations, get

$$-6A_2 x^2 + (-4A_1)x + (-2A_0 + 4A_2) = x^2$$

Equating coefficients we get

$$-6A_2 = 1$$

$$-4A_1 = 0$$

$$-2A_0 + 4A_2 = 0$$

Solving these equations we find

$$A_0 = -\tfrac{1}{3}, \qquad A_1 = 0, \qquad A_2 = -\tfrac{1}{6}$$

Then the particular solution is

$$y_x = -\tfrac{1}{3}x - \tfrac{1}{6}x^3$$

Thus the general solution is

$$y_x = C_1 + C_2 3^x - \tfrac{1}{3}x - \tfrac{1}{6}x^3$$

Problems

1. Work out the details of the above example. Also substitute in the particular solution and check.

Solve and check the following equations.

2. $y_{x+2} - 4y_{x+1} + 4y_x = x^2$.
(Hint: $A_0 = 8, A_1 = 4, A_2 = 1$)

3. $y_{x+2} - 3y_{x+1} + 2y_x = 1$.

CASE 3

$$g_x = A^x + B x^n$$

In this case, the previous Case 1 and Case 2 are used simultaneously. We will illustrate with an example.

Example 1.

$$y_{x+2} - 4y_{x+1} + 3y_x = 5^x + 2x$$

The homogeneous solution is

$$y_x = C_1 + C_2 3^x$$

The particular solution for $g_x = 5^x$ is

$$y_x = C5^x$$

The particular solution for $g_x = 2x$ is

$$y_x = A_0 + A_1 x$$

We note we have a constant term A_0 and also a constant term in the homogeneous solution, viz., C_1. We multiply by x and get

$$y_x = A_0 x + A_1 x^2$$

Thus, the combined particular solution is

$$y_x = A_0 x + A_1 x^2 + C5^x$$

Substituting this in, and, after the necessary calculations, we get

$$-2A_0 - 4A_1 x + 8C5^x = 5^x + 2x$$

Equating coefficients we get

$$-2A_0 = 0 \quad \text{thus} \quad A_0 = 0$$
$$-4A_1 = 2 \qquad\qquad A_1 = -\tfrac{1}{2}$$
$$8C = 1 \qquad\qquad C = \tfrac{1}{8}$$

Thus, the particular solution is

$$y_x = -\tfrac{1}{2}x^2 + \tfrac{1}{8} \cdot 5^x$$

and the general solution is

$$y_x = C_1 + C_2 3^x - \tfrac{1}{2}x^2 + \tfrac{1}{8}5^x$$

Problems

1. Work out the details of the above problems and check the particular solution.

Solve and check the following equation.

2. $y_{x+2} - 4y_{x+1} + 3y_x = 4^x + 2x$.

CASE 4

$$g_x = A^x B x^n$$

The particular solution is given as

$$y_x = A^x(A_0 + A_1 x + \dots + A_n x^n)$$

The method of solution is similar to the above cases and will be omitted.

Problem

Solve and check the following equation.

$$y_{x+2} - 4y_{x+1} + 3y_x = 5^x \cdot 2x.$$

9.10 Interaction between the multiplier and acceleration principle

Economic illustrations of the use of difference equations are abundant but we shall only present one in this text. This will be the well-known article, "Interactions between the Multiplier Analysis and the Principle of Acceleration" by P. Samuelson in the *Review of Economic Statistics* (1939). We shall present only the mathematical aspect. It serves as a good illustration because it requires use of the various mathematical techniques we have studied. Let

(1) $$Y_t = G_t + C_t + I_t$$

where Y_t is national income, G_t is government expenditures, C_t is consumption expenditure, and I_t is induced private investment, all at time t.

We assume the following relations:

(2) $$C_t = \alpha Y_{t-1}$$

(3) $$I_t = \beta [C_t - C_{t-1}] = \alpha\beta Y_{t-1} - \alpha\beta Y_{t-2}$$

(4) $$G_t = 1$$

Equation (2) is the consumption function, and α is the marginal propensity to consume. β is called the relation. We have assumed for simplicity that $G_t = 1$. Substituting these relations into (1) we get

$$Y_t = 1 + \alpha(1 + \beta) Y_{t-1} - \alpha\beta Y_{t-2}$$

or

(5) $$Y_t - \alpha(1 + \beta) Y_{t-1} + \alpha\beta Y_{t-2} = 1$$

We wish to solve this second-order linear difference equation and find how Y_t is functionally related to α and β. We first find the homogeneous solution, then the particular solution, combining the two to get the general solution.

(i) *Homogeneous solution*

(6) $$Y_t - \alpha(1 + \beta) Y_{t-1} + \alpha\beta Y_{t-2} = 0$$

Let $Y_t = \lambda^t$. Then the characteristic equation becomes

(7) $$\lambda^2 - \alpha(1 + \beta)\lambda + \alpha\beta = 0$$

Let the two roots be λ_1, λ_2. Assuming $\lambda_1 > \lambda_2$, we find

(8)
$$\lambda_1 = \tfrac{1}{2}[\alpha(1 + \beta) + \sqrt{\alpha^2(1 + \beta)^2 - 4\alpha\beta}]$$
$$\lambda_2 = \tfrac{1}{2}[\alpha(1 + \beta) - \sqrt{\alpha^2(1 + \beta)^2 - 4\alpha\beta}]$$

Then, the homogeneous solution will be

$$Y_t = C_1\lambda_1^t + C_2\lambda_2^t$$

where C_1 and C_2 are constants to be determined from initial conditions. **But,** before that let us find the particular solution.

(ii) *Particular solution*

The constant term in (5) is 1. Thus, we set

$$Y_t = C_3 1^t = C_3$$

Substitute this particular solution in (5),

$$C_3 - \alpha(1 + \beta)C_3 + \alpha\beta C_3 = 1$$

$$\therefore \quad C_3 = \frac{1}{1 - \alpha} \qquad (0 < \alpha < 1)$$

Thus, the particular solution becomes

$$Y_t = C_3 1^t = \frac{1}{1 - \alpha}$$

and the general solution is

(9)
$$Y_t = C_1 \lambda_1^t + C_2 \lambda_2^t + \frac{1}{1 - \alpha}$$

Let us now find C_1 and C_2.

(*iii*) C_1, C_2

For initial conditions let us assume that when $t = 0$, then $Y_t = 0$, and when $t = 1$, then $Y_t = 1$. From (9) we find

$$Y_0 = C_1 + C_2 + \frac{1}{1 - \alpha} = 0$$

$$Y_1 = C_1 \lambda_1 + C_2 \lambda_2 + \frac{1}{1 - \alpha} = 1$$

Solving for C_1 and C_2, we find

(10)
$$C_1 = \frac{\lambda_2 - \alpha}{(1 - \alpha)(\lambda_1 - \lambda_2)}$$

$$C_2 = \frac{\alpha - \lambda_1}{(1 - \alpha)(\lambda_1 - \lambda_2)}$$

Let us illustrate its use. Assume $\alpha = 0.5$, $\beta = 0$. Then from (8) we find λ_1 and λ_2 as follows

$$\lambda_1 = 0.5, \qquad \lambda_2 = 0$$

Thus,

$$C_1 = -2, \qquad C_2 = 0$$

and the general solution is

$$Y_t = (-2)(0.5)^t + 2$$

The results of letting $t = 0, 1, 2, \ldots 9$ are given by Samuelson in his article (Samuelson's Table 2). Let us reproduce several values for this case and also for $\alpha = 0.5$, $\beta = 2$.

Table 1

Period	$\alpha = 0.5$ $\beta = 0$	$\alpha = 0.5$ $\beta = 2$
1	1.00	1.00
2	1.50	2.50
3	1.75	3.75
4	1.875	4.125

(iv) When λ_1, λ_2 are real

As we saw in (ii) above,

$$Y_t = C_1\lambda_1^t + C_1\lambda_2^t + \frac{1}{1-\alpha}$$

Thus, the behavior of Y_t will depend on the values of C_1, λ_1, C_2, and λ_2. We will first consider the case where λ_1 and λ_2 are real and find the values of C_1, C_2, and then the case where λ_1 and λ_2 are conjugate complex numbers.

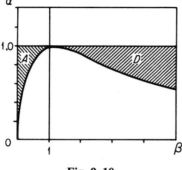

Fig. 9–10

The condition for λ_1, λ_2 to be real is that

(11) $\qquad \alpha^2(1 + \beta)^2 - 4\alpha\beta \geq 0$

This can be shown as

$$\alpha \geq \frac{4\beta}{(1+\beta)^2}$$

Let us graph this as in Figure 9–10. We see that when $\beta = 0$, then $\alpha = 0$; as $\alpha \to 1$, then $\beta \to 1$; when $\alpha = 1$, then $\beta = 1$; when $1 > \beta \to \infty$, then $\alpha \to 0$ again. The shaded region A is where $1 \geq \alpha \geq 0$, $1 \geq \beta \geq 0$, and where (11) holds. The shaded region D is where $1 \geq \alpha \geq 0$, $\infty > \beta \geq 1$, and (11) holds. Let us first investigate the behavior of Y_t when the α and β values are in the A-region.

A-REGION CASE. $1 > \beta \geq 0$. From (10) we can see that the sign of C_1 and C_2 will depend on $\lambda_2 - \alpha$ and $\alpha - \lambda_1$. So let us check these values first.

$$\lambda_2 - \alpha = \tfrac{1}{2}[\alpha(\beta - 1) - \sqrt{\alpha^2(1 + \beta)^2 - 4\alpha\beta}] < 0$$

This implies that $C_1 < 0$. Furthermore, since $1 \geq \alpha \geq 0$, we find that $1 > \alpha > \lambda_2$. Next,

$$\alpha - \lambda_1 = \tfrac{1}{2}[\alpha(1 - \beta) - \sqrt{\alpha^2(1 + \beta)^2 - 4\alpha\beta}]$$

But since $1 \geq \beta \geq 0$, we have $\alpha(1 - \beta) \geq 0$. The square root element is also positive and we can square both elements to check the sign. We find

$$\alpha^2(1 - \beta)^2 - \alpha^2(1 + \beta)^2 + 4\alpha\beta = 4\alpha\beta(1 - \alpha) > 0$$

Thus, $\alpha - \lambda_1 \geq 0$. This implies that $C_2 > 0$ and $1 \geq \alpha > \lambda_1 \geq 0$.

Using these results let us check the behavior of Y_t. For $t = 0$,

$$Y_t = C_1\lambda_1^0 + C_2\lambda_2^0 + \frac{1}{1-\alpha}$$

$$= C_1 + C_2 + \frac{1}{1-\alpha} = -\frac{1}{1-\alpha} + \frac{1}{1-\alpha} = 0$$

For $t \geq 1$, since we have $\alpha > \lambda_1 > \lambda_2 \geq 0$, then,

$$|\lambda_2 - \alpha| > |\alpha - \lambda_1|$$

which in turn implies that $|C_1| > |C_2|$. Thus,

$$|C_1 \lambda_1^t| > |C_2 \lambda_2^t|$$

But we know that $C_1 \lambda_1^t < 0$, $C_2 \lambda_2^t \leq 0$. Thus,

$$C_1 \lambda_1^t + C_2 \lambda_2^t < 0$$

When we let $t \to \infty$, we find that

$$\lim_{t \to \infty} Y_t = \lim \left(C_1 \lambda_1^t + C_2 \lambda_2^t + \frac{1}{1 - \alpha} \right) = \frac{1}{1 - \alpha}$$

since $1 > \lambda_1 > \lambda_2$, and $1/(1 - \alpha)$ will be approached from below. This is illustrated in column one of Table 1 where $\alpha = 0.5$, $\beta = 0$. Graphically, it is as in Figure 9–11.

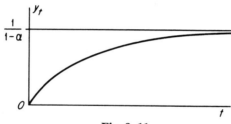

Fig. 9–11

$\beta = 1$ CASE. When $\beta = 1$, then

$$\alpha \geq \frac{4\beta}{(1 + \beta)^2} = 1$$

But we assume that $1 \geq \alpha \geq 0$. Thus, $\alpha = 1$ in this case. Then, from (5).

$$Y_t - 2Y_{t-1} + Y_{t-2} = 1$$

This can be written as

(12)　　　　　　　$$Y_t - 2Y_{t-1} + Y_{t-2} = 1^t$$

Let us now first find the homogeneous solution, then the particular solution, and determine the C_1 and C_2. The homogeneous solution is

$$Y_t = C_1 \lambda_1^t + C_2 t \lambda_2^t$$
$$= C_1 + C_2 t$$

because $\lambda_1 = \lambda_2 = 1$.

For the particular solution, we note that we have 1^t as the constant which is the same as the roots of the homogeneous solution. Thus, we set

$$Y_t = C_3 t^2 1^t = C_3 t^2$$

Substituting this into (12) we find that

$$C_3 t^2 - 2C_3(t-1)^2 + C_3(t-2)^2 = 1^t$$

$$C_3 = \tfrac{1}{2}$$

$$\therefore \quad Y_t = \tfrac{1}{2}t^2$$

Thus, the general solution is

$$Y_t = C_1 \lambda_1^t + C_2 t \lambda_2^t + \tfrac{1}{2}t^2$$

$$Y_t = C_1 + C_2 t + \tfrac{1}{2}t^2$$

The initial conditions were

$$Y_0 = C_1 + 0 + 0 = 0$$

$$Y_1 = C_1 + C_2 + \tfrac{1}{2} = 1$$

$$\therefore \quad C_1 = 0, \qquad C_2 = \tfrac{1}{2}$$

Thus, the general solution is

(13) $$Y_t = \tfrac{1}{2}t + \tfrac{1}{2}t^2$$

As can be seen, when $t \to \infty$, then $Y_t \to \infty$. Thus, when $\alpha = 1$, $\beta = 1$, we have a steadily explosive situation.

D-REGION CASE. $\beta > 1$. Let us start by checking the signs of C_1 and C_2.

Sign of C_1.

$$\lambda_2 - \alpha = \tfrac{1}{2}[\alpha(\beta - 1) - \sqrt{\alpha^2(1 + \beta)^2 - 4\alpha\beta}]$$

$\alpha(\beta - 1) > 0$. Thus, we can square the factors in the brackets to test the magnitude.

$$\alpha^2(\beta - 1)^2 - \alpha^2(1 + \beta)^2 + 4\alpha\beta = 4\alpha\beta(1 - \alpha) > 0$$

so that $\lambda_2 - \alpha > 0$ and write

$$C_1 > 0, \qquad \lambda_2 > \alpha$$

Sign of C_2.

$$\alpha - \lambda_1 = \tfrac{1}{2}[\alpha(1 - \beta) - \sqrt{\alpha^2(1 + \beta)^2 - 4\alpha\beta}] < 0$$

$$\therefore \quad \alpha - \lambda_1 < 0$$

$$\therefore \quad C_2 < 0, \qquad \lambda_1 > \alpha$$

Next let us check the magnitude of λ_1. We know that

$$\lambda_1 = \tfrac{1}{2}[\alpha(1 + \beta) + \sqrt{\alpha^2(1 + \beta)^2 - 4\alpha\beta}]$$

$$\therefore \quad \lambda_1 > \tfrac{1}{2}\alpha(1 + \beta)$$

Since

$$\alpha \geq \frac{4\beta}{(1 + \beta)^2}$$

we have

$$\lambda_1 > \tfrac{1}{2}\alpha(1 + \beta) \geq \tfrac{1}{2}\frac{4\beta}{(1 + \beta)^2} \cdot (1 + \beta) = \frac{2\beta}{1 + \beta}$$

Since $\beta > 1$, we have

$$\lambda_1 > \frac{2\beta}{1 + \beta} = \frac{2}{\dfrac{1}{\beta} + 1} > 1$$

Furthermore, we know that $\lambda_1 > \lambda_2$. That is, λ_1 is the dominant root. Thus,

$$Y_t = C_1 \lambda_1^t + C_2 \lambda_2^t + \frac{1}{1 - \alpha}$$

Fig. 9–12

will increase toward infinity as $t \to \infty$. It can easily be checked if $Y_0 = 0$, $Y_{t=1} = 1$. Graphically we have as in Figure 9–12.

(v) *When λ_1, λ_2 are conjugate complex roots*

This is when

$$\alpha^2(1 + \beta)^2 - 4\alpha\beta < 0.$$

Then we have

$$\lambda_1 = \tfrac{1}{2}[\alpha(1 + \beta) + i\sqrt{4\alpha\beta - \alpha^2(1 + \beta)^2}] = a + ib$$

$$\lambda_2 = \tfrac{1}{2}[\alpha(1 + \beta) - i\sqrt{4\alpha\beta - \alpha^2(1 + \beta)^2}] = a - ib$$

where

$$a = \tfrac{1}{2}\alpha(1 + \beta), \qquad b = \tfrac{1}{2}\sqrt{4\alpha\beta - \alpha^2(1 + \beta)^2}$$

It will be easier to find the behavior of Y_t if we change the λ's into polar coordinates. So let us set

$$a = \rho \cos \theta, \quad b = \rho \sin \theta$$

Then,

$$a \pm ib = \rho(\cos \theta \pm i \sin \theta)$$

$$\rho = \sqrt{a^2 + b^2}$$

$$\tan \theta = \frac{b}{a}$$

Recall that the Euler's formulas were

$$\cos \theta + i \sin \theta = e^{i\theta}$$

$$\cos \theta - i \sin \theta = e^{-i\theta}$$

Thus,

$$\lambda_1 = a + ib = \rho\, e^{i\theta}$$

$$\lambda_2 = a - ib = \rho\, e^{-i\theta}$$

$$\therefore \quad \lambda_1 \lambda_2 = \rho^2$$

$$\rho^2 = \lambda_1 \cdot \lambda_2 = \tfrac{1}{4}(4\alpha\beta) = \alpha\beta$$

$$\therefore \quad \rho = \sqrt{\alpha\beta}$$

$$
\begin{aligned}
Y_t &= C_1\lambda_1^t + C_2\lambda_2^t = C_1(\rho e^{i\theta})^t + C_2(\rho e^{-i\theta})^t \\
&= \rho^t[C_1 e^{i\theta t} + C_2 e^{-i\theta t}] \\
&= \rho^t[C_1(\cos\theta t + i\sin\theta t) + C_2(\cos\theta t - i\sin\theta t)] \\
&= \rho^t[(C_1 + C_2)\cos\theta t + i(C_1 - C_2)\sin\theta t]
\end{aligned}
$$

We know that

$$C_1 = \frac{\lambda_2 - \alpha}{(1 - \alpha)(\lambda_1 - \lambda_2)} \equiv Q(\lambda_2 - \alpha)$$

$$C_2 = \frac{\alpha - \lambda_1}{(1 - \alpha)(\lambda_1 - \lambda_2)} \equiv Q(\alpha - \lambda_1)$$

$$\therefore \quad C_1 + C_2 = Q[\lambda_2 - \alpha + \alpha - \lambda_1] = Q(\lambda_2 - \lambda_1)$$

$$= \frac{-1}{1 - \alpha}$$

$$
\begin{aligned}
C_1 - C_2 &= Q[\lambda_2 + \lambda_1 - 2\alpha] \\
&= Q[a - ib + a + ib - 2\alpha] = 2Q[a - \alpha]
\end{aligned}
$$

$$Q^{-1} = (1 - \alpha)(\lambda_1 - \lambda_2) = 2ib(1 - \alpha)$$

$$\therefore \quad C_1 - C_2 = \frac{2(a - \alpha)}{2ib(1 - \alpha)} = \frac{a - \alpha}{ib(1 - \alpha)}$$

$$\therefore \quad i(C_1 - C_2) = \frac{a - \alpha}{b(1 - \alpha)}$$

Let us set

$$C_1 + C_2 = A_1, \qquad i(C_1 - C_2) = A_2$$

where A_1 and A_2 are real numbers, as we saw above. Thus, Y_t becomes

$$Y_t = \rho^t[A_1 \cos\theta t + A_2 \sin\theta t]$$

We shall now perform one more trick to change Y_t into a more suitable form for investigation. Let us set

$$A_1 = A \cos\epsilon, \qquad A_2 = A \sin\epsilon$$

where

$$A^2 = A_1^2 + A_2^2, \qquad \tan \epsilon = \frac{A_2}{A_1}$$

Then, Y_t becomes

$$Y_t = \rho^t [A \cos \epsilon \cos \theta t + A \sin \epsilon \sin \theta t]$$
$$= A \rho^t \cos (\theta t - \epsilon)$$

This is the homogeneous solution we seek.

The general solution, then, is

$$Y_t = A \rho^t \cos (\theta t - \epsilon) + \frac{1}{1 - \alpha}$$

Let us now check the behavior of Y_t. As can be seen, Y_t is affected by two elements, ρ^t and $\cos (\theta t - \epsilon)$. ρ^t gives the amplitude of the fluctuations and $\cos (\theta t - \epsilon)$ gives the period of the fluctuations.

We have seen that

$$\rho^2 = \alpha\beta$$

Thus, when $\rho < 1$, then $\alpha\beta < 1$; when $\rho = 1$, then $\alpha\beta = 1$; and when $\rho > 1$, then $\alpha\beta > 1$. These three cases can be shown diagrammatically as in

Fig. 9–13

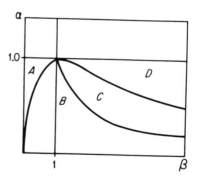

Fig. 9–14

Figure 9–13. Let us superimpose Figure 9–13 and 9–10. Then, we obtain Figure 9–14. The region C is where the conditions

$$\alpha^2(1 + \beta)^2 < 4\alpha\beta, \qquad \alpha\beta > 1$$

hold, and the region B is where

$$\alpha^2(1 + \beta)^2 < 4\alpha\beta, \qquad \alpha\beta < 1$$

hold. Let us discuss region B first.

B-REGION CASE.

$$\rho^2 = \alpha\beta < 1$$

It can easily be checked that when $t = 0$, then $Y_0 = 0$; $t = 1$, then $Y_1 = 1$. Since $\rho < 1$, we have

$$\lim_{t \to \infty} Y_t = \lim_{t \to \infty} \left[A\rho^t \cos(\theta t - \epsilon) + \frac{1}{1 - \alpha} \right]$$

$$= \frac{1}{1 - \alpha}$$

The period of fluctuation is $t = 2\pi/\theta$. Graphically, we have damped-oscillations that converge to $1/(1 - \alpha)$ as in Figure 9–15.

Fig. 9–15

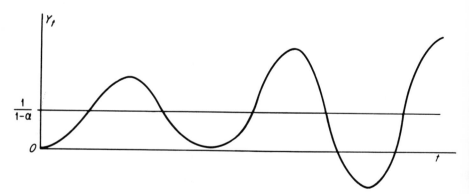

Fig. 9–16

C-REGION CASE. $\rho^2 = \alpha\beta > 1$. In this case,

$$\lim_{t \to \infty} Y_t \to \infty$$

Thus, we have explosive oscillations where the amplitude of the oscillations become larger as $t \to \infty$. This is shown in Figure 9–16. When $\rho^2 = \alpha\beta = 1$, we have simple harmonic oscillations.

Notes and References

For various proofs and derivations that have not been covered, the reader is referred to an excellent book by Goldberg (1958). This book should be sufficient for all practical mathematical needs of an economist. Also see Appendix B of Samuelson (1947), but note that it is very difficult.

For economic applications, see Baumol (1959) Chapters 9–13, 15, and 16; and Allen (1956) Chapter 6. Illustrations of its use can be found in various sections of Allen (1956). Chapters 15, 16 of Baumol (1956) require a knowledge of matrix algebra. We shall discuss briefly systems of difference equations in Chapter 12.

Difference equations are widely used in economics but in many cases only state economic relations without actually solving them. And when they are solved, a qualitative rather than a quantitative solution is usually sought. That is, the economist is interested in the behavior of the dependent variable given certain conditions concerning the independent variable. Samuelson's article discussed in Section 9.10 is an illustration. After studying 9.10 the reader is recommended Allen (1956) Chapter 3, "The Acceleration Principle."

Goldberg, S., *Introduction to Difference Equations*. New York: John Wiley & Sons, Inc., 1958.

Samuelson, P. A., "Interactions between the Multiplier Analysis and the Principle of Acceleration," *R.E.S.*, pp. 75–78, 1939. Reprinted in American Economic Association, *Readings in Business Cycle Theory*, pp. 261–269. New York: Blakiston Division, McGraw-Hill Book Co., Inc., 1951.

CHAPTER 10

Vectors and Matrices (Part 1)

Two main topics, *calculus* and *difference equations,* have been covered. A third topic of importance is *vectors and matrices,* which we will discuss in the next three chapters. Our object will be to learn how to manipulate groups of numbers so that we will be able to solve equations and systems of equations.

10.1 Vectors

(*i*) *Field*

Let us consider a set of numbers $S = \{1, 2, 3, ...\}$; i.e., a set of positive integers. We notice that when we *add* any two of these numbers we will get a positive number that will be a member of this set. The same holds true when we *multiply.* But when we *subtract,* we might get, for example,

$$4 - 6 = -2$$

-2 is not a member of the set S. Similarly, when *dividing,* we might get $10/3 = 3.333 ...$, which again is not a member of the set S.

Addition, subtraction, multiplication, and division (except by 0) will be called *operations.* The question is, is there a set of numbers which, when subjected to these operations, will produce a result that will still be in the same *set* of numbers that the original numbers were taken from to perform the operations? We may answer, "yes," and lead from this idea into the concept of a *field.* The two fields that we are familiar with are the *real field* which is composed of all real numbers and the *rational field* which is composed of all numbers that can be written in the form p/q where p and q are integers.

A field will be defined as a set of numbers which contain the sum, difference, product, and quotient (except by 0) of every two numbers in the set. Furthermore: (1) the numbers must be *commutative* and *associative* with respect to addition and multiplication, and (2) the numbers must be *distributive* with respect to multiplication.

By commutative we mean

$$a + b = b + a \quad \text{or} \quad ab = ba$$

By associative we mean

$$a + (b + c) = (a + b) + c \quad \text{or} \quad (ab)c = a(bc)$$

By distributive we mean

$$a(b + c) = ab + ac$$

In subsequent discussion we shall be assuming a field of real numbers.

(ii) Vectors

Let F be a field, and let a_1, a_2, ... be numbers of F. We shall call an ordered set of numbers

$$v' = \{a_1, a_2, ..., a_n\}$$

a *vector of order n*. a_1, a_2, ..., a_n are called the *components* of the vector v. The numbers a_i are also called *scalars* when we consider them only as numbers rather than components taken from F. When the components are written in a row this is called a *row vector* and it is denoted by v'. When the components are written in a column, it is called a *column vector* and written v.

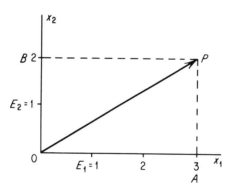

Fig. 10-1

Let us first consider a vector of order 2, say

$$v' = \{a_1, a_2\}$$

Note that this is an ordered pair of numbers and thus can be shown geometrically as follows: Let us draw a two-dimensional space with coordinates X_1 and X_2, and define our unit points E_1 and E_2. If

$$v' = \{3, 2\}$$

we find a point on X_1 that will be three units away from 0 and designate it 3. We likewise find a point on X_2 that will be two units from 0 and designate it 2. Then, a point $(3, 2) = P$ will be determined in the plane. The directed segment **OP** is the *vector*

$$v' = \{a_1, a_2\} = \{3, 2\}$$

It will also be noted that $v_1' = \{3, 0\}$ is the vector **OA** and $v_2' = \{0, 2\}$ is the vector **OB**. Also $v_3' = \{0, 0\} = 0$ is called the *zero vector* or *null vector*, and in terms of our graph, it will be the origin 0.

Furthermore, $\mathbf{OE}_1$, and $\mathbf{OE}_2$ can be shown as

$$\mathbf{OE}_1 = \{1, 0\}$$

$$\mathbf{OE}_2 = \{0, 1\}$$

These will be called *unit vectors*. They are sometimes denoted by ϵ_1, ϵ_2. When we have a three-dimensional space, we have

$$\epsilon_1 = \{1, 0, 0\}$$

$$\epsilon_2 = \{0, 1, 0\}$$

$$\epsilon_3 = \{0, 0, 1\}$$

And so forth for higher-dimension cases.

We have interpreted the vector $v' = \{3, 2\}$ as **OP**. But we can also understand $v' = \{3, 2\}$ to mean the point P. In subsequent discussion, a vector will also be interpreted as a point in the given space, and called a *vector point*.

Two vectors $v_1' = \{a_1, a_2\}$, $v_2' = \{b_1, b_2\}$ of the same order are *equal* if and only if $a_1 = b_1$, $a_2 = b_2$. The same is true for higher-order vectors.

The *sum* of two vectors is defined as

$$v_1' + v_2' = \{a_1 + b_1, a_2 + b_2\}$$

Thus,

$$v_1' + v_2' = \{3, 0\} + \{0, 2\} = \{3 \dot{+} 0, 0 + 2\} = \{3, 2\}$$

The *product* of a vector with a scalar is defined as

$$kv_1' = \{ka_1, ka_2\}$$

Thus, if $k = 2$, $v' = \{3, 2\}$, then,

$$kv' = \{6, 4\}$$

The product of two vectors is defined as

$$v_1'v_2 = \{a_1, a_2\}\begin{bmatrix} b_1 \\ b_2 \end{bmatrix} = a_1b_1 + a_2b_2$$

This is called the *inner product* of two vectors and it is a number. The meaning and use of this will be taken up later. For the present we are interested with the operation. Also note that

$$v_1' v_2 = v_2' v_1 = a_1 b_1 + a_2 b_2$$

and that

$$v_1' v_1 = \{a_1, a_2\} \begin{bmatrix} a_1 \\ a_2 \end{bmatrix} = a_1^2 + a_2^2$$

We also arrive at the relationship

$$(v_1 + v_2)' = v_1' + v_2'$$

which is shown by

$$(v_1 + v_2)' = \left[\begin{bmatrix} a_1 \\ a_2 \end{bmatrix} + \begin{bmatrix} b_1 \\ b_2 \end{bmatrix} \right]' = \begin{bmatrix} a_1 + b_1 \\ a_2 + b_2 \end{bmatrix}'$$

$$= (a_1 + b_1, a_2 + b_2)$$

$$= (a_1, a_2) + (b_1, b_2) = v_1' + v_2'$$

This leads to

$$(v_1 + v_2)' v_1 = (v_1' + v_2') v_1 = v_1' v_1 + v_2' v_1$$

Also

$$(v_1 + v_2)'(v_1 + v_2) = (v_1' + v_2')(v_1 + v_2)$$

$$= v_1' v_1 + v_2' v_1 + v_1' v_2 + v_2' v_2$$

Problem

Put in the a's and b's and check the last two formulas.

Although we have distinguished between a row vector and a column vector,

$$v = \begin{bmatrix} 3 \\ 2 \end{bmatrix}, \qquad v' = \{3 \quad 2\}$$

the meaning will be the same; viz., both will represent the point $(3, 2)$ in a two-dimensional space.

Problems

1. Given: $v_1' = (3, 5, 8)$, $v_2' = (15, 22, 19)$,
  (a) Find: $v_1 + v_2$.
  (b) Find: $2v_1 + v_2$.

2. Given: $v_1' = (2, 3)$, $v_2' = (4, 5)$,
  (a) Plot v_1 and v_2 on diagram.
  (b) Plot $v_1 + v_2$.
  (c) Plot $2v_1$.
  (d) Plot $v_2 - v_1$.

3. Find a_1, a_2, a_3 of the following:

$$\begin{bmatrix} 1 \\ 3 \\ 2 \end{bmatrix} + \begin{bmatrix} a_1 \\ a_2 \\ a_3 \end{bmatrix} = \begin{bmatrix} 4 \\ 5 \\ 6 \end{bmatrix}$$

4. (a) Let us have 6 apples at 5¢ each, 8 oranges at 7¢ each, 9 pears at 9¢ each. Then, calculate the total cost,

$$\alpha\beta = [6, 8, 9] \begin{bmatrix} 5 \\ 7 \\ 9 \end{bmatrix} = \text{total cost}$$

(b) What if we let

$$[5, 7, 9] \begin{bmatrix} 6 \\ 8 \\ 9 \end{bmatrix} = ?$$

Is $\alpha\beta = \beta\alpha$?

5. Given $v_1' = (3, 5, 10)$, $v_2' = (10, 2, 4)$,
    (a) Find $(v_1 + v_2)'$.
    (b) Find $v_1' + v_2'$.
    (c) Find $(v_1 + v_2)'v_1$.
    (d) Find $v_1'v_1 + v_2'v_1$.
    (e) Find $(v_1 + v_2)'(v_1 + v_2)$.
    (f) Find $v_1'v_1 + v_2'v_1 + v_1'v_2 + v_2'v_2$.

(iii) Geometric interpretation

Let us show some of these relationships geometrically by letting

$$v_1 = \begin{bmatrix} 1 \\ 2 \end{bmatrix}, \quad v_2 = \begin{bmatrix} 2 \\ 1 \end{bmatrix}, \quad k = 2$$

The relation

$$kv_1 = 2\begin{bmatrix} 1 \\ 2 \end{bmatrix} = \begin{bmatrix} 2 \\ 4 \end{bmatrix}$$

is shown in Figure 10–2. As is seen, v_1 has been extended to twice its length. For,

$$-kv_1 = \begin{bmatrix} -2 \\ -4 \end{bmatrix}$$

the vector v_1 has been extended in the opposite direction. The minus sign has reversed the direction of the vector. Note the direction of the arrow sign.
    The relation

$$v_1 + v_2 = \begin{bmatrix} 1 \\ 2 \end{bmatrix} + \begin{bmatrix} 2 \\ 1 \end{bmatrix} = \begin{bmatrix} 3 \\ 3 \end{bmatrix}$$

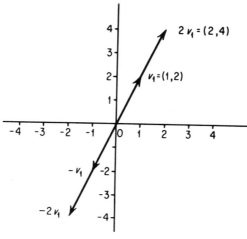

Fig. 10–2

is shown in Figure 10–3. Note that $v_1 + v_2$ is the diagonal of the parallelogram made up of v_1 and v_2. For $v_1 - v_2$, we can show this as

$$v_1 - v_2 = v_1 + (-v_2) = \begin{bmatrix} 1 \\ 2 \end{bmatrix} + \begin{bmatrix} -2 \\ -1 \end{bmatrix} = \begin{bmatrix} -1 \\ 1 \end{bmatrix}$$

This is shown in Figure 10–4. By changing $v_1 - v_2$ to $v_1 + (-v_2)$, we have the sum of two vectors and the result $v_1 - v_2$ becomes the diagonal of the

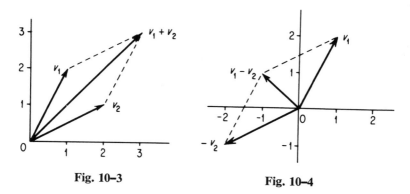

Fig. 10–3   Fig. 10–4

parallelogram as we saw in our previous example. Let us now consider a vector $v_1' = \{x_1, x_2\}$ as in Figure 10–5. We know from elementary geometry that the length of the vector v_1 which we write as $\|v_1\|$ is

$$\|v_1\| = \sqrt{x_1^2 + x_2^2} = (x_1^2 + x_2^2)^{1/2}$$

But note that the inner product of v_1 with itself is

$$v_1'v_1 = \{x_1, x_2\}\begin{bmatrix} x_1 \\ x_2 \end{bmatrix} = x_1^2 + x_2^2$$

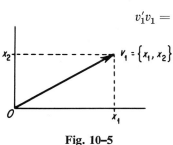

Thus, $\|v_1\|$ can be shown as

$$\|v_1\| = (v_1'v_1)^{1/2}$$

Let us summarize this into a theorem.

Theorem: Let v_1 be a vector. Then the length of the vector which we denote by $\|v_1\|$ will be

$$\|v_1\| = (v_1'v_1)^{1/2}$$

Fig. 10–5

Instead of the term length, we also use the term *norm*.

(*iv*) *Geometrical interpretation* (*Continued*)

The vectors $v_1 = \begin{bmatrix} 2 \\ 6 \end{bmatrix}$, $v_2 = \begin{bmatrix} 4 \\ 3 \end{bmatrix}$ and $v_1 + v_2$ are shown in Figure 10–6. Let us now remove the vectors from the coordinate system and show it as in Figure 10–6(a). The vector $v_1 + v_2$ is obtained by attaching v_2 on v_1 as in

  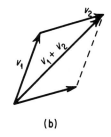

(a)   (b)

Fig. 10–6

Figure 10–6(b). Often in subsequent discussion, the addition of vectors will be shown geometrically as in Figure 10–6(b). We are not adhering to the conventional geometry we studied in high school but have here an abstract mathematical structure following a set of axioms that are consistent with the vector algebra we will use. That is, it will be the vector algebra that is of principal concern and the geometric interpretation will be incidental. It will be helpful, however, in developing an intuitive understanding of the algebra we are doing.

This method can be extended for v_1, v_2, v_3 as in Figure 10–7.

Now let us consider the case for $v_1 - v_2$. The geometric presentation is as shown in Figure 10–8. Let us now take the vectors out of the coordinate system and show it as in Figure 10–9(a). Instead of taking $v_1 - v_2$ as the

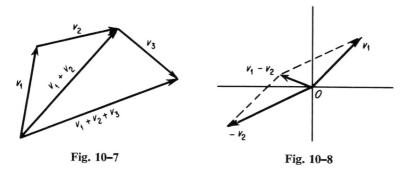

Fig. 10–7　　　　　　　　　　　　Fig. 10–8

diagonal of the parallelogram made by v_1 and $-v_2$ as in Figure 10–9(a), we can show it as in Figure 10–9(b).

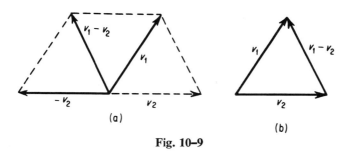

(a)　　　　　　　　　　　　　(b)

Fig. 10–9

What if we have $v_2 - v_1$? Then, we reverse the direction of $v_1 - v_2$. As shown in Figure 10–10,

$$v_2 - v_1 = -(v_1 - v_2)$$

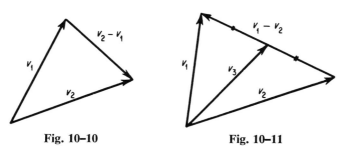

Fig. 10–10　　　　　　　　　Fig. 10–11

Let us give one more illustration. Let v_3 be a vector that goes to the mid point of $v_1 - v_2$ as in Figure 10–11. Then,

$$v_3 + \tfrac{1}{2}(v_1 - v_2) = v_1$$
$$v_2 + \tfrac{1}{2}(v_1 - v_2) = v_3$$

From these two equations we get

$$v_1 = v_3 + \tfrac{1}{2}(v_1 - v_2)$$
$$= [v_2 + \tfrac{1}{2}(v_1 - v_2)] + \tfrac{1}{2}(v_1 - v_2)$$
$$= v_1$$

and we have a consistent relationship.

(v) Geometrical interpretation (Continued)

Let us now see how our ideas of analytical geometry fit in with the ideas we just developed. First we find the distance between two points A and B, in Figure 10–12(a). We know from geometry that

$$AB = \sqrt{(a_1 - a_2)^2 + (b_1 - b_2)^2}$$

 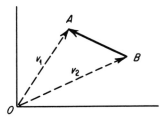

Fig. 10–12

In terms of vectors, points A and B can be shown as

$$v_1 = \begin{bmatrix} a_1 \\ b_1 \end{bmatrix}, \qquad v_2 = \begin{bmatrix} a_2 \\ b_2 \end{bmatrix}$$

Then, the line AB will be shown as the vector

$$\mathbf{AB} = v_1 - v_2$$

Recall that the norm (length) of a vector was given as

$$\|v\| = (v'v)^{1/2}$$

Let us apply this to $(v_1 - v_2)$. Then,

$$\|(v_1 - v_2)\| = [(v_1 - v_2)'(v_1 - v_2)]^{1/2}$$

Now we have

$$v_1 - v_2 = \begin{bmatrix} a_1 \\ b_1 \end{bmatrix} - \begin{bmatrix} a_2 \\ b_2 \end{bmatrix} = \begin{bmatrix} a_1 - a_2 \\ b_1 - b_2 \end{bmatrix}$$

Thus, we get

$$(v_1 - v_2)'(v_1 - v_2) = (a_1 - a_2)^2 + (b_1 - b_2)^2$$

and the norm of $\|v_1 - v_2\|$ becomes

$$\|v_1 - v_2\| = [(a_1 - a_2)^2 + (b_1 - b_2)^2]^{1/2}$$
$$= \sqrt{(a_1 - a_2)^2 + (b_1 - b_2)^2} = AB$$

Thus, we find that $AB = \|v_1 - v_2\|$. Let us summarize this into a theorem.

Theorem: If we have two vectors v_1 and v_2, the distance between the two vector points v_1 and v_2 is given by

$$\|v_1 - v_2\| = [(v_1 - v_2)'(v_1 - v_2)]^{1/2}$$

Next, let θ be the angle between two vectors v_1 and v_2 as in Figure 10–13. The direction of rotation will be, for our subsequent discussion, in a counter-clockwise direction. We say that sense of rotation is *positive*. Recall that the law of cosines is

Fig. 10–13

$$c^2 = a^2 + b^2 - 2ab \cos \theta$$

In vector notation, it will be

$$\|v_1 - v_2\|^2 = \|v_1\|^2 + \|v_2\|^2 - 2 \|v_1\| \|v_2\| \cos \theta$$

We know that

$$\|v_1 - v_2\|^2 = (v_1 - v_2)'(v_1 - v_2) = v_1'v_1 - v_2'v_1 - v_1'v_2 + v_2'v_2$$

$$\|v_1\|^2 = v_1'v_1$$

$$\|v_2\|^2 = v_2'v_2$$

When we substitute these results in we get, noting that $v_1'v_2 = v_2'v_1$,

$$\cos \theta = \frac{v_1'v_2}{\|v_1\| \|v_2\|}$$

To summarize, we have the following theorem.

Theorem: When given two vectors v_1 and v_2, and the angle θ between them, then,

$$\cos \theta = \frac{v_1'v_2}{\|v_1\| \|v_2\|}$$

Let us check this with a simple example as given in Figure 10–14. In this case, we have

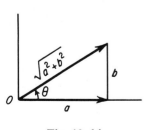

Fig. 10–14

$$v_1 = \begin{bmatrix} a \\ 0 \end{bmatrix} \qquad v_2 = \begin{bmatrix} a \\ b \end{bmatrix}$$

Thus,

$$v_1'v_2 = \begin{bmatrix} a & 0 \end{bmatrix} \begin{bmatrix} a \\ b \end{bmatrix} = a^2$$

$$\|v_1\| = (v_1'v_1)^{1/2} = a$$

$$\|v_2\| = (v_2'v_2)^{1/2} = \sqrt{a^2 + b^2}$$

Thus,

$$\cos \theta = \frac{v_1'v_2}{\|v_1\| \, \|v_2\|} = \frac{a^2}{a\sqrt{a^2 + b^2}} = \frac{a}{\sqrt{a^2 + b^2}}$$

We have used a two-dimensional space and a vector of order-2 to illustrate the relationships, but this can easily be extended to three and higher dimensions and orders.

Problems

Given the following vectors, show the various relationships geometrically.

$$v_1' = [1, 3], \qquad v_2' = [3, 1]$$

1. kv_1 for the case where $k = 2$ and $k = -2$.

2. $v_1 + v_2$.

3. $v_1 - v_2$.

4. Find $\|v_1\|$ and $\|v_2\|$.

5. Find the distance between the two vectors v_1 and v_2.

6. Find the angle θ between v_1 and v_2. Let $v_1' = [1, 0]$, $v_2' = [1, 3]$ for this case.

10.2 Vector spaces

A field was a set of numbers $\{a_1, a_2, ...\}$, and the characteristic of this set of numbers was that the sum, difference, product, or quotient of these numbers were in this set. Instead of numbers let us use vectors to see if we can define something similar for a set of vectors.

First, we recall that a vector was an ordered n-tuple of numbers taken from a field F. We then had a vector of order n, say

$$v' = \{a_1, a_2, ..., a_n\}$$

where the numbers a were called components of the vector.

Now, we say a *vector space* is a set of vectors $\{v_1, v_2, ...\}$ which we denote by R. The characteristic of this set R is such that the sum of every two vectors and the product of kv for every vector v in the set with a scalar k taken from the field of components F, is in the set.

When we say the sum of every two vectors is in the set R, this implies that the sum of n vectors will also be in the space (or set) R. For example, assume we have v_1, v_2, v_3. Then,

$$v_1 + v_2 = v_4$$

is in the space R. But now

$$v_4 + v_3 = v_5$$

is also in R. Clearly,

$$v_5 = v_4 + v_3 = v_1 + v_2 + v_3$$

and we may repeat this procedure for n vectors and show that the sum of n vectors is in R.

Furthermore, if k_1v_1 and k_2v_2 are in the space R,

$$k_1v_1 + k_1v_1$$

is also in R. This is called a linear combination of the vectors v_1 and v_2. In general, if we have v_1, v_2, v_3, ... v_m, then,

$$k_1v_1 + k_2v_2 + \ldots + k_mv_m$$

is also a vector in the vector space R.

Let us interpret this geometrically. Assume a two-dimensional space R_2 (Figure 10–15), and a typical vector

$$v' = \{a_1, a_2\}$$

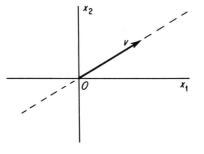

When v' is multiplied by a scalar k, the vector v' will extend in both directions according to the value of k, as shown in the diagram. This straight line can be considered as a one-dimensional vector space generated by v', and the points on it are obtained by kv' and written

$$kv' = \{ka_1, ka_2\}$$

Fig. 10–15

We shall say, the vector space R_1 has been *generated* by the given vector v. Or we may say, R_1 is *spanned* by the given vector v.

Let us now consider a three-dimensional vector space R_3. Let v_1, v_2 be two vectors in R_3. Then k_1v_1 and k_2v_2 will extend the vectors v_1 and v_2 in both directions according to the values of k_1 and k_2. Furthermore, k_1v_1 and k_2v_2 will define a plane in R_3. Let this plane be R_2. Then this R_2 is a vector space *generated* by (or spanned by) the set of given vectors v_1 and v_2. Since R_2 has v_1 and v_2 in it, it will also contain $kv_1 + kv_2$.

We can do the same thing for an n-dimensional space R_n. Just as we did above, we can pick two vectors v_1 and v_2 and determine a plane. This will be a two-dimensional vector space R_2 spanned by the two vectors v_1 and v_2 (which are vectors of order n).

10.3 Linear dependence

Assume we have a n-dimensional space R_n. Let us pick out p vectors $v_1, v_2, ..., v_p$ each of order n. The vector

$$\alpha = k_1 v_1 + k_2 v_2 + ... + k_p v_p$$

is called a *linear combination* of the given vectors, where the k's are scalars.

The vectors $v_1, v_2, ..., v_p$ are said to be *linearly dependent* if there is a set of p scalars $k_1, k_2, ... k_p$, not all zero, such that

$$k_1 v_1 + k_2 v_2 + ... + k_p v_p = 0$$

where 0 is a zero vector.

If there is no such set of p scalars, then $v_1, v_2, ... v_p$ are said to be *linearly independent*. In this case $\alpha = 0$ only if

$$k_1 = k_2 = ... = k_p = 0$$

For example, the three vectors

$$\{1, 4, 3\}, \qquad \{2, 3, 1\}, \qquad \{-1, 1, 2\}$$

are linearly dependent because there is a set of k_1, k_2, k_3 such that

$$k_1\{1, 4, 3\} + k_2\{2, 3, 1\} + k_3\{-1, 1, 2\} = 0$$

To find the values of the k's, we first find the scalar product and then sum the vectors, as follows

$$\{k_1 + 2k_2 - k_3, 4k_1 + 3k_2 + k_3, 3k_1 + k_2 + 2k_3\} = \{0, 0, 0\}$$

Thus, when we equate the components of the vectors on both sides of the equation, we get

$$k_1 + 2k_2 - k_3 = 0$$

$$4k_1 + 3k_2 + k_3 = 0$$

$$3k_1 + k_2 + 2k_3 = 0$$

Solving in terms of k_1 we get

$$k_1, k_2 = -k_1, k_3 = -k_1$$

Thus, if we let $k_1 = 1$, one set of values we seek will be $\{1, -1, -1\}$.

On the other hand, $\{1, 0\}$, $\{0, 1\}$ are linearly independent because

$$k_1\{1, 0\} + k_2\{0, 1\} = 0$$

implies that $k_1 = k_2 = 0$. This can be shown as follows: Take the scalar product and then sum the vectors, obtaining

$$\{k_1, k_2\} = 0 = \{0, 0\}$$

Thus,

$$k_1 = k_2 = 0$$

This result also holds true for higher-order unit vectors and we can say that unit vectors are linearly independent.

10.4 Basis

Using the ideas of vector space and linear independence we may now define a *basis* for a vector space. Let us assume that we have a set of two linearly independent vectors v_1, v_2 each of order 2.

$$v_1' = [2, 3], \qquad v_2' = [3, 1]$$

Construct as in Figure 10–16 a vector space with v_1 and v_2. Then, any vector (point) in this vector space is shown as a linear combination of v_1 and v_2. For example, take $v_3 = [2, 2]$. We wish to find k_1 and k_2 such that

$$k_1 v_1 + k_2 v_2 = v_3$$

For this, we have

$$k_1 \begin{bmatrix} 2 \\ 3 \end{bmatrix} + k_2 \begin{bmatrix} 3 \\ 1 \end{bmatrix} = \begin{bmatrix} 2 \\ 2 \end{bmatrix}$$

$$\begin{bmatrix} 2k_1 + 3k_2 \\ 3k_1 + k_2 \end{bmatrix} = \begin{bmatrix} 2 \\ 2 \end{bmatrix}$$

$$2k_1 + 3k_2 = 2$$

$$3k_1 + k_2 = 2$$

Fig. 10–16

Solving this set of equations we get $k_1 = \frac{4}{7}$, $k_2 = \frac{2}{7}$. Thus, the linear combination will become

$$\tfrac{4}{7} v_1 + \tfrac{2}{7} v_2 = v_3$$

This means that when we have three vectors v_1, v_2, v_3, we can always reduce this to v_1, v_2, and $\frac{4}{7}v_1 + \frac{2}{7}v_2$. That is, the three vectors v_1, v_2, and v_3 can be represented by the two vectors v_1 and v_2. Likewise, if v_2 and v_3 are linearly independent, then v_1 can be represented by v_2 and v_3.

We also see that

$$\tfrac{4}{7}v_1 + \tfrac{2}{7}v_2 - v_3 = 0$$

Thus, there is a set of scalars $\{\frac{4}{7}, \frac{2}{7}, -1\}$ that makes the linear combination of v_1, v_2 and v_3 equal to 0 and v_1, v_2, v_3 are thus linearly dependent.

The *basis* in (or for) a vector space R is the set $\{v_1, v_2\}$ of linearly independent vectors spanning the vector space R. From our definition of vector space we see that every vector in R is a linear combination of v_1, v_2.

We define the *dimension* of the vector space R as the maximum number of linearly independent vectors in R. In our present case, the maximum number is 2. Thus, we have a two-dimensional vector space.

In general, if we select p linearly independent vectors we can form a p-dimensional vector space R_p, and the p vectors that were selected will be a basis for R_p.

From a geometrical standpoint, what we are doing is selecting a coordinate system. If the basis is finite, we have a finite-dimensional vector space.

It should be noted in passing, that a space may be spanned by infinitely many vectors. For example, a three-dimensional vector space could be spanned by infinitely many vectors, but only three of them are linearly independent, and all the other vectors spanning the vector space can be shown as a linear combination of the three linearly independent vectors.

10.5 A matrix

An ordered set of numbers $\{a_1, a_2, \ldots, a_n\}$ from a field F was called a vector of order n. What if we now have an ordered set of vectors? This leads us to the concept of a matrix.

Let us have an ordered set of three vectors of order 3.

$$v_1' = \{a_{11}, a_{12}, a_{13}\}$$

$$v_2' = \{a_{21}, a_{22}, a_{23}\}$$

$$v_3' = \{a_{31}, a_{32}, a_{33}\}$$

Then, we define a matrix A as

$$A = \begin{bmatrix} v_1' \\ v_2' \\ v_3' \end{bmatrix} = \begin{bmatrix} a_{11} & a_{12} & a_{13} \\ a_{21} & a_{22} & a_{23} \\ a_{31} & a_{32} & a_{33} \end{bmatrix}$$

Each row of the matrix is a vector. We may also define a matrix independently as a square array of numbers, but shall define it in connection with the idea of vectors.

We will now tie the idea of a matrix in with a vector space and also with an Euclidean space. The concept of a matrix does not confine itself to an Euclidean space but, for our purposes, it will be sufficient to limit ourselves to this special case.

Consider a three-dimensional Euclidean space as in Figure 10–17. Let E_1, E_2, E_3 be the unit points on the three axes. Then the three unit vectors OE_1, OE_2, OE_3 are shown as

$$OE_1 = v_1' = \{1, 0, 0\}$$
$$OE_2 = v_2' = \{0, 1, 0\}$$
$$OE_3 = v_3' = \{0, 0, 1\}$$

and the vector OP, for example, would be

$$OP = v_1' + v_2' + v_3' = \{1, 1, 1\}$$

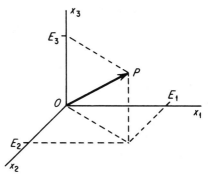

This three-dimensional Euclidean space is a vector space spanned by v_1, v_2, v_3 and the three vectors form a basis for this vector space because they are linearly independent.

Fig. 10–17

It should also be noted that, for example, kv_1, v_2, v_3, where k is a number from the field F, is also a basis because the three vectors are linearly independent. It will also turn out later that all these various bases can be reduced to one unique basis.

Thus, the three-unit vectors we have picked are the simplest ones we can find in the vector space. Furthermore, we also know that all vectors in this vector space are a linear combination of these three vectors.

We now write the above vector space in matrix notation as

$$A = \begin{bmatrix} v_1' \\ v_2' \\ v_3' \end{bmatrix} = \begin{bmatrix} 1 & 0 & 0 \\ 0 & 1 & 0 \\ 0 & 0 & 1 \end{bmatrix}$$

Then, when we are confining our attention to Euclidean space, we can interpret A as indicating the coordinate system in its simplest form.

Let us now reverse the process and see what happens. If we have a matrix B, so that

$$B = \begin{bmatrix} a_{11} & a_{12} & a_{13} \\ a_{21} & a_{22} & a_{23} \\ a_{31} & a_{32} & a_{33} \end{bmatrix}$$

we would like to see if we can do the following:

1. Reduce B by some kind of an operation to a form similar to the matrix A.
2. Then, we would have a set of ordered vectors that are linearly independent in its simplest form.

3. Then, we could interpret the resulting simplified matrix as giving us a set of vectors that span a vector space and that are also the basis of that vector space. The number of linearly independent vectors would give us the dimension of the space which is also the order of the basis.

It turns out that we can do this. Let us now take up the operations for this process.

10.6 Elementary operations

By elementary operations on rows of a matrix we will mean the following:

1. The interchange of two rows in a matrix,
2. The multiplication of any row by a non-zero number from F (i.e., a scalar),
3. The addition to one row of k times another row, where k is in F.

For example, assume a matrix A where we have three linearly independent row vectors as follows

$$A = \begin{bmatrix} 1 & 4 & 3 \\ 3 & -3 & 1 \\ -1 & 1 & 2 \end{bmatrix}$$

Let us perform elementary row operations on this matrix and see if it can be reduced to the simple form where we have 1's in the diagonal and zero elsewhere. Let us first interchange row 2 and row 3. Thus,

$$A_1 = \begin{bmatrix} 1 & 4 & 3 \\ -1 & 1 & 2 \\ 3 & -3 & 1 \end{bmatrix}$$

Next, let us multiply the third row by 3 and subtract from the first, then multiply third row by 2 and subtract from the second. Then,

$$A_2 = \begin{bmatrix} -8 & 13 & 0 \\ -7 & 7 & 0 \\ 3 & -3 & 1 \end{bmatrix}$$

Divide the second row by 7 and then perform operations so that all elements in the second column will become zero except the diagonal element in row two which will be 1. Then, do similar operations for the first row. The result will be

$$A' = \begin{bmatrix} 1 & 0 & 0 \\ 0 & 1 & 0 \\ 0 & 0 & 1 \end{bmatrix}$$

On the other hand, assume a matrix of three row vectors that are not linearly independent as follows

$$A = \begin{bmatrix} 1 & 4 & 3 \\ 2 & 3 & 1 \\ -1 & 1 & 2 \end{bmatrix}$$

Then, when we perform the elementary operations we get

$$A' = \begin{bmatrix} 0 & 0 & 0 \\ 1 & 1 & 0 \\ -1 & 0 & 1 \end{bmatrix}$$

In general, given a *square matrix* (i.e., a matrix where the number of rows and columns are equal), we can reduce it to the following form:

1. Every element above the main diagonal that runs from the upper left hand corner to the lower right hand corner is zero.
2. Every element in the main diagonal is zero or 1.
3. If the diagonal element is zero, the entire row is zero.
4. If the diagonal element is 1, every element below it is zero.

When a matrix is reduced to such a form, it is called the *Hermite canonical form* or simply the *Hermite form*. The above two matrices have been reduced to their Hermite form.

What does this tell us? Looking at the second matrix reduced to its Hermite form, we see that the first row is all zeros. In terms of a vector space or a coordinate system, this matrix shows that instead of a three-dimensional coordinate system, we have a two-dimensional one. The second and third rows are linearly independent and give the dimension of this vector spaces. In terms of basis, we have a basis of order 2.

From the first matrix reduced to its Hermite form, we see that we have a three-dimensional coordinate system, or we can say three linearly independent vectors, or a basis of order 3.

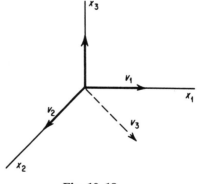

The *rank* of a matrix is defined as the number of non-zero vectors in its Hermite form; i.e., the number of linearly independent row vectors in the matrix. Thus, the rank of a matrix shows the dimension of the coordinate system, or the order of the basis for the vector space.

Consider the following three-dimensional figure (Figure 10–18) to better understand these ideas.

Fig. 10–18

A matrix was a collection of vectors. Let there be three vectors v_1, v_2, v_3

as in Figure 10–18. If, for example, v_3 should be on the (X_1, X_2) plane as shown by the dotted line, instead of on the X_3-axis, then the three vectors would not be linearly independent, but linearly dependent, and in this case v_3 could be shown as a linear combination of v_1 and v_2.

$$k_1 v_1 + k_2 v_2 = v_3$$

Then, the basis is of order 2. In terms of the Hermite form, one of the rows would be all zero. In terms of our graph, we can find k_1 and k_2 where $k_1 k_2 \neq 0$ such that $v_3 = 0$, and the vector space would be a two-dimensional plane. The rank of the matrix is 2.

A question naturally arises: When we have a matrix A and by elementary operations reduce it to its Hermite form B, will A and B have the same rank? The answer is yes, elementary operations do not change the rank of a matrix.* Furthermore it can be shown that the Hermite form is unique.† This means that there is only one basis and implies that if we have a vector space or coordinate system spanned by a set of vectors, we can put this set of vectors in matrix form and then reduce it to its Hermite form. The set of vectors in this Hermite form span the vector space and are linearly independent and all other vectors in the vector space can be found as a linear combination of these linearly independent vectors.

To put it another way, a matrix will have just one Hermite form, but many matrices may have this Hermite form.

So far, by elementary operations, we have meant operations on rows. Can we perform elementary operations on columns? If so, what will the results be? We can perform column operations and shall obtain the Hermite form due to the column operations. This Hermite form will be the transpose (see 10.7) of the Hermite form obtained from row operations. By replacing the word *row* in the rules for elementary operations we get elementary column operations. Let us illustrate with our previous example.

$$A = \begin{bmatrix} 1 & 4 & 3 \\ 3 & -3 & 1 \\ -1 & 1 & 2 \end{bmatrix}$$

Multiply the first column by 4 and subtract it from the second column, and then multiply the first column by 3 and subtract it from the third column. We get

$$A_1 = \begin{bmatrix} 1 & 0 & 0 \\ 3 & -15 & -8 \\ -1 & 5 & 5 \end{bmatrix}$$

---

* For proof, see MacDuffee (1949), pp. 31–32.
† See MacDuffee (1949), pp. 37–38.

Continuing in this manner, we shall finally get

$$A' = \begin{bmatrix} 1 & 0 & 0 \\ 0 & 1 & 0 \\ 0 & 0 & 1 \end{bmatrix}$$

In this case the Hermite form obtained from elementary row operations and elementary column operations are the same.

Elementary operations in subsequent discussions will mean row operations.

Problems

1. Given

$$v_1 = (3, \tfrac{1}{2}, -1), \qquad v_2 = (\tfrac{3}{2}, 1, 0), \qquad v_3 = (1, 0, 0)$$

(a) Find $v_1 + v_2$.
(b) Find $3v_1 + 2v_2$.
(c) Show that v_1, v_2, v_3 are linearly independent.
(d) Find k_1, k_2, k_3 so that

$$k_1 v_1 + k_2 v_2 + k_3 v_3 = (\tfrac{13}{2}, -\tfrac{3}{2}, -2)$$

2. Let F be a rational field. Find a basis for the vector space spanned by

$$v_1 = (3, \tfrac{1}{2}, 2, 5), \quad v_2 = (-1, \tfrac{3}{2}, -2, 3), \quad v_3 = (2, 2, 0, 8), \quad v_4 = (5, \tfrac{5}{2}, 2, 13)$$

3. Determine the rank of the vector space spanned by

$$v_1 = (1, -3, 3, 4), \qquad v_2 = (0, 2, 1, -3)$$
$$v_3 = (1, 1, 4, 1), \qquad v_4 = (3, -5, 8, 9)$$

4. Show that, by means of elementary operations, A can be carried into A_1

$$A = \begin{bmatrix} 3 & 1 & -4 \\ 2 & -1 & 3 \\ 1 & 0 & 1 \end{bmatrix}, \quad A_1 = \begin{bmatrix} 1 & 0 & 0 \\ 0 & 1 & 0 \\ 0 & 0 & 1 \end{bmatrix}$$

5. Show that A and A_1 have the same row vector space.

$$A = \begin{bmatrix} 10 & -13 & 1 & 7 \\ 2 & 3 & 1 & -1 \\ 2 & -4 & 0 & 2 \end{bmatrix}, \quad A_1 = \begin{bmatrix} 0 & 0 & 0 & 0 \\ 3 & 1 & 1 & 0 \\ 1 & -2 & 0 & 1 \end{bmatrix}$$

10.7 Matrix algebra

In high school we learned various rules for manipulating numbers, solving equations, and so forth, and called it algebra. What we wish to do now is to set up a system of rules that can be applied to matrices. We shall call this, non-rigorously, matrix algebra. To be mathematically rigorous it would be necessary to begin with a system called a ring. But, for our purposes, we shall skip such a discussion and simply illustrate the workings of the various operations.*

(*i*) *Part A*

1. Addition. Let

$$A = \begin{bmatrix} a_{11} & a_{12} \\ a_{21} & a_{22} \end{bmatrix} = \begin{bmatrix} \alpha_1 \\ \alpha_2 \end{bmatrix}, \qquad B = \begin{bmatrix} b_{11} & b_{12} \\ b_{21} & b_{22} \end{bmatrix} = \begin{bmatrix} \beta_1 \\ \beta_2 \end{bmatrix}$$

Then, we define,

$$A + B = \begin{bmatrix} \alpha_1 + \beta_1 \\ \alpha_2 + \beta_2 \end{bmatrix} = \begin{bmatrix} a_{11} + b_{11} & a_{12} + b_{12} \\ a_{21} + b_{21} & a_{22} + b_{22} \end{bmatrix}$$

Also,

$$A + B = B + A$$

2. Scalar multiplication.

$$kA = \begin{bmatrix} k\alpha_1 \\ k\alpha_2 \end{bmatrix} = \begin{bmatrix} ka_{11} & ka_{12} \\ ka_{21} & ka_{22} \end{bmatrix}$$

Also,

$$kA = Ak$$

3. Product. The rule concerning the product of two matrices is different from that of ordinary algebra. We need to distinguish between pre-multiplying and post-multiplying as shown below. Pre-multiplying vector B by matrix A, or post-multiplying matrix A by vector B is

$$AB = \begin{bmatrix} a_{11} & a_{12} \\ a_{21} & a_{22} \end{bmatrix} \begin{bmatrix} b_1 \\ b_2 \end{bmatrix} = \begin{bmatrix} a_{11} b_1 + a_{12} b_2 \\ a_{21} b_1 + a_{22} b_2 \end{bmatrix}$$

Post-multiplying vector B by matrix A or pre-multiplying matrix A by vector B is

$$B'A = [b_1 \ b_2] \begin{bmatrix} a_{11} & a_{12} \\ a_{21} & a_{22} \end{bmatrix}$$

$$= [b_1 a_{11} + b_2 a_{21} \quad b_1 a_{12} + b_2 a_{22}]$$

Note that $AB \neq B'A$. The product of two matrices A and B is

$$AB = \begin{bmatrix} a_{11} & a_{12} \\ a_{21} & a_{22} \end{bmatrix} \begin{bmatrix} b_{11} & b_{12} \\ b_{21} & b_{22} \end{bmatrix} = \begin{bmatrix} a_{11} b_{11} + a_{12} b_{21} & a_{11} b_{12} + a_{12} b_{22} \\ a_{21} b_{11} + a_{22} b_{21} & a_{21} b_{12} + a_{22} b_{22} \end{bmatrix}$$

$$= \begin{bmatrix} \sum_{i=1}^{2} a_{ri} b_{is} \end{bmatrix}$$

* See Birkoff and MacLane (1953), for discussion of rings and groups.

where
$$r = \text{row} = 1, 2$$
$$s = \text{column} = 1, 2$$

Also note that $AB \neq BA$.

$$BA = \begin{bmatrix} b_{11} & b_{12} \\ b_{21} & b_{22} \end{bmatrix} \begin{bmatrix} a_{11} & a_{12} \\ a_{21} & a_{22} \end{bmatrix}$$

$$= \begin{bmatrix} a_{11}\, b_{11} + a_{21}\, b_{12} & a_{12}\, b_{11} + a_{22}\, b_{12} \\ a_{11}\, b_{21} + a_{21}\, b_{22} & a_{12}\, b_{21} + a_{22}\, b_{22} \end{bmatrix}$$

$$= \begin{bmatrix} \sum_{i=1}^{2} a_{is}\, b_{ri} \end{bmatrix}$$

where
$$r = 1, 2$$
$$s = 1, 2$$

Example.

$$AB = \begin{bmatrix} 2 & 3 \\ 1 & 2 \end{bmatrix} \begin{bmatrix} 1 & -2 \\ 3 & 0 \end{bmatrix}$$

$$= \begin{bmatrix} 2+9 & -4+0 \\ 1+6 & -2+0 \end{bmatrix} = \begin{bmatrix} 11 & -4 \\ 7 & -2 \end{bmatrix}$$

$$BA = \begin{bmatrix} 1 & -2 \\ 3 & 0 \end{bmatrix} \begin{bmatrix} 2 & 3 \\ 1 & 2 \end{bmatrix}$$

$$= \begin{bmatrix} 2-2 & 3-4 \\ 6+0 & 9+0 \end{bmatrix} = \begin{bmatrix} 0 & -1 \\ 6 & 9 \end{bmatrix}$$

$$AB \neq BA$$

A condition necessary to be able to multiply two matrices is that the number of columns in the first matrix must be equal to the number of rows in the second matrix. For example, if

$$A \text{ is } 4 \times 3, \qquad \text{i.e., 4 rows, 3 columns}$$

$$B \text{ is } 3 \times 2, \qquad \text{i.e., 3 rows, 2 columns}$$

A and B can be multiplied, with the result that

$$A \cdot B \text{ is } 4 \times 2$$

i.e., 4 rows and 2 columns. In general, when matrix A is $m \times n$, B is $n \times p$, and then $A \cdot B$ is $m \times p$.

4. Zero matrix.

$$0 = \begin{bmatrix} 0 & 0 \\ 0 & 0 \end{bmatrix}$$

Thus we have

$$A + 0 = A \qquad \text{and} \qquad 0 + A = A$$
$$0A = 0 \qquad \text{and} \qquad A0 = 0$$

The zero matrix does not need to be square. It is also called the *null matrix*.

Examples.

(1)
$$V_1 + 0 = \begin{bmatrix} 2 \\ 1 \end{bmatrix} + \begin{bmatrix} 0 \\ 0 \end{bmatrix} = \begin{bmatrix} 2 \\ 1 \end{bmatrix}$$

(2)
$$V_1 0 = \begin{bmatrix} 2 \\ 1 \end{bmatrix} \begin{bmatrix} 0 & 0 \end{bmatrix} = \begin{bmatrix} 2 \cdot 0 & 2 \cdot 0 \\ 1 \cdot 0 & 1 \cdot 0 \end{bmatrix} = \begin{bmatrix} 0 & 0 \\ 0 & 0 \end{bmatrix} = 0$$

5. *Identity (unit) matrix* ... I_n.

$$I_n = \begin{bmatrix} \epsilon_1 \\ \vdots \\ \epsilon_n \end{bmatrix} = \begin{bmatrix} 1 & 0 & \cdots & 0 \\ 0 & 1 & \cdots & 0 \\ \cdots & & \cdots & \\ 0 & 0 & & 1 \end{bmatrix}, \qquad n \text{ rows and columns}$$

This is also expressed as

$$I_n = (\delta_{rs}) \qquad \begin{array}{l} \delta_{rs} = 1 \quad \text{for} \quad r = s \\ \delta_{rs} = 0 \quad \text{for} \quad r \neq s \end{array}$$

where δ_{rs} is called *Kronecker's delta*. The ϵ_i are the unit vectors and I_n shows the coordinate system, i.e., the vector space in its simplest form. Then, we have

$$IA = A \qquad \text{and} \qquad AI = A$$

6. *Scalar matrix.* The square matrix

$$S = \lambda \begin{bmatrix} 1 & 0 \\ 0 & 1 \end{bmatrix} = \begin{bmatrix} \lambda & 0 \\ 0 & \lambda \end{bmatrix} = \lambda I$$

is called a scalar matrix.

Examples.

(1)
$$5I = \begin{bmatrix} 5 & 0 & 0 \\ 0 & 5 & 0 \\ 0 & 0 & 5 \end{bmatrix} = 5 \begin{bmatrix} 1 & 0 & 0 \\ 0 & 1 & 0 \\ 0 & 0 & 1 \end{bmatrix}$$

(2)
$$aI = \begin{bmatrix} a & 0 \\ 0 & a \end{bmatrix} = a \begin{bmatrix} 1 & 0 \\ 0 & 1 \end{bmatrix}$$

(3)
$$\lambda_1 I \lambda_2 I = (\lambda_1 \lambda_2) I$$

$$(2I)(3I) = \begin{bmatrix} 2 & 0 \\ 0 & 2 \end{bmatrix} \begin{bmatrix} 3 & 0 \\ 0 & 3 \end{bmatrix} = \begin{bmatrix} 6 & 0 \\ 0 & 6 \end{bmatrix} = 6 \begin{bmatrix} 1 & 0 \\ 0 & 1 \end{bmatrix} = 6I$$

(4)
$$\lambda_1 I + \lambda_2 I = (\lambda_1 + \lambda_2) I$$

$$2I + 3I = 5I$$

Using Kronecker's delta defined above, we have

(5) $$\lambda I = (\lambda \delta_{ij})$$

7. *Diagonal matrix.* A square matrix with scalars in the diagonal and zero elsewhere

$$D = \begin{bmatrix} 1 & 0 & 0 \\ 0 & 2 & 0 \\ 0 & 0 & 5 \end{bmatrix}$$

is called a diagonal matrix. In general,

$$D = \begin{bmatrix} \lambda_1 & 0 & 0 \\ 0 & \lambda_2 & 0 \\ 0 & 0 & \lambda_3 \end{bmatrix}$$

By using Kronecker's delta, this becomes

$$D = (\lambda_i \delta_{ij})$$

8. *Transpose.*

$$A^T = \begin{bmatrix} a_{11} & a_{21} \\ a_{12} & a_{22} \end{bmatrix}$$

i.e., row and columns have been interchanged. The A^T is the transpose of A. We also have

$$(A + B)^T = A^T + B^T$$

$$(AB)^T = B^T A^T$$

$$(ABC)^T = C^T B^T A^T \qquad \text{etc.}$$

Instead of a superscript T, a prime is sometimes used to indicate the transpose of A, i.e., A'.

9. *Multiplication is associative.*

$$A(BC) = (AB)C$$

10. *Inverse matrix.* When $A^{-1}A = I$, A^{-1} is called the inverse of A. Also,

$$(AB)^{-1} = B^{-1}A^{-1}$$

We shall discuss inverse matrices again in Section 11.

Problems

1. Compute the indicated operation.

(a) $\begin{bmatrix} 2 & 3 \\ 4 & 5 \end{bmatrix} + \begin{bmatrix} 6 & 4 \\ 2 & -3 \end{bmatrix}$ (b) $\begin{bmatrix} 2 & 0 \\ 0 & -2 \end{bmatrix} + \begin{bmatrix} -1 & 0 \\ 0 & 1 \end{bmatrix}$

(c) $3 \begin{bmatrix} 2 & 3 \\ 4 & 5 \end{bmatrix}$

(d) $\begin{bmatrix} 2 & 3 \\ 4 & 5 \end{bmatrix} \begin{bmatrix} 6 \\ 2 \end{bmatrix}$

$[2 \quad 3] \begin{bmatrix} 6 & 4 \\ 2 & -3 \end{bmatrix}$

(e) $\begin{bmatrix} 2 & 3 \\ 4 & 5 \end{bmatrix} \begin{bmatrix} 6 & 4 \\ 2 & -3 \end{bmatrix}$

(f) $\begin{bmatrix} 6 & 4 \\ 2 & -3 \end{bmatrix} \begin{bmatrix} 2 & 3 \\ 4 & 5 \end{bmatrix}$

(g) $\begin{bmatrix} 2 & 3 & 4 \\ 5 & 6 & 7 \\ 6 & 7 & 8 \end{bmatrix} \begin{bmatrix} 6 & 7 & 8 \\ 2 & 3 & 4 \\ 1 & 2 & 3 \end{bmatrix}$

(h) $\begin{bmatrix} 3 & 4 & 2 \\ 6 & 5 & 7 \end{bmatrix} \begin{bmatrix} 6 & 7 & 8 \\ 2 & 3 & 4 \\ 1 & 2 & 3 \end{bmatrix}$

(i) $[3 \quad 4 \quad 2] \begin{bmatrix} 6 & 7 & 8 \\ 2 & 3 & 4 \\ 1 & 2 & 3 \end{bmatrix}$

(j) $\begin{bmatrix} 2 & 3 & 4 \\ 4 & 5 & 6 \\ 6 & 7 & 8 \end{bmatrix} \begin{bmatrix} 1 & 0 & 0 \\ 0 & 1 & 0 \\ 0 & 0 & 1 \end{bmatrix}$

$\begin{bmatrix} 1 & 0 & 0 \\ 0 & 1 & 0 \\ 0 & 0 & 1 \end{bmatrix} \begin{bmatrix} 2 & 3 & 4 \\ 4 & 5 & 6 \\ 6 & 7 & 8 \end{bmatrix}$

(k) $[a \quad b \quad c] \begin{bmatrix} d \\ e \\ f \end{bmatrix}$

(l) $[2 \quad 1 \quad 3] \begin{bmatrix} 4 \\ 3 \\ 1 \end{bmatrix}$

(m) $\begin{bmatrix} 1 & 2 & 3 \\ 4 & 5 & 6 \\ 7 & 8 & 9 \end{bmatrix} \begin{bmatrix} 1 \\ 0 \\ 0 \end{bmatrix}$

(n) $\begin{bmatrix} 1 & 2 & 3 \\ 4 & 5 & 6 \\ 7 & 8 & 9 \end{bmatrix} \begin{bmatrix} 0 \\ 1 \\ 0 \end{bmatrix}$

(o) $\begin{bmatrix} 1 & 2 & 3 \\ 4 & 5 & 6 \\ 7 & 8 & 9 \end{bmatrix} \begin{bmatrix} 0 \\ 0 \\ 1 \end{bmatrix}$

(p) $[1 \quad 0 \quad 0] \begin{bmatrix} 1 & 2 & 3 \\ 4 & 5 & 6 \\ 7 & 8 & 9 \end{bmatrix}$

(q) $[0 \quad 1 \quad 0] \begin{bmatrix} 1 & 2 & 3 \\ 4 & 5 & 6 \\ 7 & 8 & 9 \end{bmatrix}$

2. $A = \begin{bmatrix} 2 & 3 \\ 4 & 5 \end{bmatrix} \qquad B = \begin{bmatrix} 3 & 1 \\ 2 & 5 \end{bmatrix}$

Find

(a) A^T.

(b) B^T.

(c) $(A + B)^T$.

(d) $A^T + B^T$.

(e) $(AB)^T$.

(f) $B^T A^T$.

3. $A = \begin{bmatrix} 1 & 2 \\ 2 & 3 \end{bmatrix} \qquad B = \begin{bmatrix} 2 & 5 \\ 3 & 1 \end{bmatrix} \qquad C = \begin{bmatrix} 4 & 3 \\ 4 & 1 \end{bmatrix}$

Find

(a) $A(BC)$.

(b) $(AB)C$.

4. Prove

$$(ABC)^T = C^T B^T A^T$$

(Hint: $(ABC)^T = \{A(BC)\}^T$.)

Using the matrices in Problem 3, check your proof numerically.

5. $\begin{bmatrix} 2 & 6 & 24 \\ 6 & 12 & 36 \\ 24 & 36 & 48 \end{bmatrix} \begin{bmatrix} -\frac{5}{2} & 2 & -\frac{1}{4} \\ 2 & -\frac{5}{3} & \frac{1}{4} \\ -\frac{1}{4} & \frac{1}{2} & -\frac{1}{24} \end{bmatrix} = ?$

(ii) Part B. Multiplication of matrices using vectors

(1)
$$A = \begin{bmatrix} a_{11} & a_{12} \\ a_{21} & a_{22} \end{bmatrix} = [A_1 \quad A_2]$$

$$A_1 = \begin{bmatrix} a_{11} \\ a_{21} \end{bmatrix} \qquad A_2 = \begin{bmatrix} a_{12} \\ a_{22} \end{bmatrix}$$

$$B = \begin{bmatrix} b_{11} & b_{12} \\ b_{21} & b_{22} \end{bmatrix} = [B_1 \quad B_2]$$

$$AB = \begin{bmatrix} a_{11} & a_{12} \\ a_{21} & a_{22} \end{bmatrix} \begin{bmatrix} b_{11} & b_{12} \\ b_{21} & b_{22} \end{bmatrix} = \begin{bmatrix} a_{11}b_{11} + a_{12}b_{21} & a_{11}b_{12} + a_{11}b_{22} \\ a_{21}b_{11} + a_{22}b_{21} & a_{21}b_{12} + a_{22}b_{22} \end{bmatrix}$$

$$AB_1 = \begin{bmatrix} a_{11} & a_{12} \\ a_{21} & a_{22} \end{bmatrix} \begin{bmatrix} b_{11} \\ b_{21} \end{bmatrix} = \begin{bmatrix} a_{11}b_{11} + a_{12}b_{21} \\ a_{21}b_{11} + a_{22}b_{21} \end{bmatrix}$$

$$AB_2 = \begin{bmatrix} a_{11} & a_{12} \\ a_{21} & a_{22} \end{bmatrix} \begin{bmatrix} b_{12} \\ b_{22} \end{bmatrix} = \begin{bmatrix} a_{11}b_{12} + a_{12}b_{22} \\ a_{21}b_{12} + a_{22}b_{22} \end{bmatrix}$$

$$\therefore \ [AB_1 \quad AB_2] = \begin{bmatrix} a_{11}b_{11} + a_{12}b_{21} & a_{11}b_{12} + a_{12}b_{22} \\ a_{21}b_{11} + a_{22}b_{21} & a_{21}b_{12} + a_{22}b_{22} \end{bmatrix}$$

$$\therefore \ AB = [AB_1 \quad AB_2]$$

(2)
$$A = \begin{bmatrix} a_{11} & a_{12} \\ a_{21} & a_{22} \end{bmatrix} = \begin{bmatrix} A_1 \\ A_2 \end{bmatrix}$$

$$A_1 = (a_{11} \quad a_{12}), \qquad A_2 = (a_{21} \quad a_{22})$$

$$B = \begin{bmatrix} b_{11} & b_{12} \\ b_{21} & b_{22} \end{bmatrix} = [B_1 \quad B_2]$$

$$AB = \begin{bmatrix} A_1 \\ A_2 \end{bmatrix} [B_1 \quad B_2] = \begin{bmatrix} A_1B_1 & A_1B_2 \\ A_2B_1 & A_2B_2 \end{bmatrix}$$

$$A_1B_1 = [a_{11} \quad a_{12}] \begin{bmatrix} b_{11} \\ b_{21} \end{bmatrix} = [a_{11}b_{11} + a_{12}b_{21}]$$

In similar manner, find A_1B_1, A_2B_1, and A_2B_2. Then

$$AB = \begin{bmatrix} A_1 \\ A_2 \end{bmatrix} [B_1 \quad B_2] = \begin{bmatrix} A_1B_1 & A_1B_2 \\ A_2B_1 & A_2B_2 \end{bmatrix} = \begin{bmatrix} a_{11}b_{11} + a_{12}b_{21} & a_{11}b_{12} + a_{12}b_{22} \\ a_{21}b_{11} + a_{22}b_{21} & a_{21}b_{12} + a_{22}b_{22} \end{bmatrix}$$

(3)
$$AB = \begin{bmatrix} A_1 \\ A_2 \end{bmatrix} B = \begin{bmatrix} A_1 B \\ A_2 B \end{bmatrix}$$

As an exercise, find $A_1 B$ and $A_2 B$ and check this relation.

(4)
$$Ae_j = A_j$$

$$Ae_2 = [A_1 \ A_2] \begin{bmatrix} 0 \\ 1 \end{bmatrix} = A_2$$

Check

$$Ae_2 = \begin{bmatrix} a_{11} & a_{12} \\ a_{21} & a_{22} \end{bmatrix} \begin{bmatrix} 0 \\ 1 \end{bmatrix} = \begin{bmatrix} a_{12} \\ a_{22} \end{bmatrix} = A_2$$

This shows that, when A is multiplied by e_j, we obtain the *j*th column vector. As an exercise, show that, when we have $e_j A$, we shall obtain the *j*th row vector.

(5) We may express the identity matrix in terms of the e_i vectors.

$$I = \begin{bmatrix} 1 & 0 & 0 \\ 0 & 1 & 0 \\ 0 & 0 & 1 \end{bmatrix} = [e_1 \ e_2 \ e_3]$$

(6)
$$\lambda I = [\lambda e_1 \ \lambda e_2 \ \lambda e_3] = \begin{bmatrix} \lambda & 0 & 0 \\ 0 & \lambda & 0 \\ 0 & 0 & \lambda \end{bmatrix}$$

(7)
$$D = \begin{bmatrix} \lambda_1 & 0 & 0 \\ 0 & \lambda_2 & 0 \\ 0 & 0 & \lambda_3 \end{bmatrix} = [\lambda_1 e \ \lambda_2 e \ \lambda_3 e]$$

Problems

1. Given the following matrices.

$$A = \begin{bmatrix} 1 & 3 \\ 2 & 1 \end{bmatrix} = [A_1 \ A_2], \qquad B = \begin{bmatrix} 4 & 1 \\ 2 & 3 \end{bmatrix} = [B_1 \ B_2]$$

(a) Calculate AB.
(b) Calculate AB_1, AB_2 and check that

$$AB = [AB_1 \ AB_2]$$

(c) Calculate $A_1 B_1$, $A_1 B_2$, $A_2 B_1$, and $A_2 B_2$, and check that

$$AB = \begin{bmatrix} A_1 B_1 & A_1 B_2 \\ A_2 B_1 & A_2 B_2 \end{bmatrix}$$

(d) Calculate $A_1 B$, $A_2 B$, and check that

$$AB = \begin{bmatrix} A_1 \\ A_2 \end{bmatrix} B = \begin{bmatrix} A_1 B \\ A_2 B \end{bmatrix}$$

(e) Calculate Ae_1, and check that

$$Ae_1 = A_1$$

2. Given the following matrices, perform the five operations of Problem 1.

$$A = \begin{bmatrix} 3 & 2 \\ 1 & 1 \end{bmatrix} \qquad B = \begin{bmatrix} 1 & 2 \\ 3 & 1 \end{bmatrix}$$

3. Given the following matrices, perform the five operations of Problem 1.

$$A = \begin{bmatrix} 1 & 0 & 2 \\ 0 & 1 & 3 \\ 3 & 1 & 0 \end{bmatrix} \qquad B = \begin{bmatrix} 1 & 1 & 0 \\ 2 & 5 & 0 \\ 0 & 1 & 4 \end{bmatrix}$$

4. Given $\lambda_1 = 2$, $\lambda_2 = 1$, $\lambda_3 = 4$, express

$$[\lambda_1 e_1 \quad \lambda_2 e_2 \quad \lambda_3 e_3]$$

as a diagonal matrix.

5. Given

$$A = \begin{bmatrix} a_{11} & a_{12} \\ a_{21} & a_{22} \end{bmatrix} \qquad D = [\lambda_1 e_1 \quad \lambda_2 e_2]$$

We have

$$AD = A[\lambda_1 e_1 \quad \lambda_2 e_2] = [A\lambda_1 e_1 \quad A\lambda_2 e_2]$$
$$= [\lambda_1 Ae_1 \quad \lambda_2 Ae_2] = [\lambda_1 A_1 \quad \lambda_2 A_2]$$

Compute $[\lambda_1 A_1 \quad \lambda_2 A_2]$, and then check results by computing AD directly.

6. Given

$$A = \begin{bmatrix} 1 & 3 \\ 2 & 1 \end{bmatrix} \qquad \lambda_1 = 4, \qquad \lambda_2 = 2$$

(a) Compute AD by $[\lambda_1 A_1 \quad \lambda_2 A_2]$.
(b) Check results by computing AD directly.

10.8 Equivalence

A matrix obtained from an identity matrix I by elementary operations is called an *elementary* (elementary transformation) *matrix*. The first elementary row operation was the interchange of two rows. Let

$$I = \begin{bmatrix} 1 & 0 \\ 0 & 1 \end{bmatrix}$$

Interchange rows 1 and 2. Then,

$$E_1 = \begin{bmatrix} 0 & 1 \\ 1 & 0 \end{bmatrix}$$

This is an elementary matrix. Now consider a matrix A

$$A = \begin{bmatrix} 3 & 2 \\ 1 & 4 \end{bmatrix}$$

Then $E_1 A$ is the same as applying the elementary operation of interchanging the first and second rows of A

$$E_1 A = \begin{bmatrix} 0 & 1 \\ 1 & 0 \end{bmatrix} \begin{bmatrix} 3 & 2 \\ 1 & 4 \end{bmatrix} = \begin{bmatrix} 1 & 4 \\ 3 & 2 \end{bmatrix}$$

Note that we pre-multiply A by E_1. If we post-multiply A by E_1, i.e., AE_1, this will give us the elementary operation of interchanging the first and second *columns* of A.

$$AE_1 = \begin{bmatrix} 3 & 2 \\ 1 & 4 \end{bmatrix} \begin{bmatrix} 0 & 1 \\ 1 & 0 \end{bmatrix} = \begin{bmatrix} 2 & 3 \\ 4 & 1 \end{bmatrix}$$

The second elementary row operation was multiplication of a row by a scalar k. Thus, multiply the first row of I by k. Then the elementary matrix will be

$$E_2 = \begin{bmatrix} k & 0 \\ 0 & 1 \end{bmatrix}$$

Then,

$$E_2 A = \begin{bmatrix} k & 0 \\ 0 & 1 \end{bmatrix} \begin{bmatrix} 3 & 2 \\ 1 & 4 \end{bmatrix} = \begin{bmatrix} 3k & 2k \\ 1 & 4 \end{bmatrix}$$

That is, $E_2 A$ gives us the elementary row operation of multiplying the first row of A by k. If we post-multiply, that will give us the elementary *column* operation.

$$AE_2 = \begin{bmatrix} 3 & 2 \\ 1 & 4 \end{bmatrix} \begin{bmatrix} k & 0 \\ 0 & 1 \end{bmatrix} = \begin{bmatrix} 3k & 2 \\ k & 4 \end{bmatrix}$$

The third elementary row operation was the addition to one row of k times another row. Let us multiply the second row of I by k and add it to the first row. Then, the elementary matrix will be

$$E_3 = \begin{bmatrix} 1 & k \\ 0 & 1 \end{bmatrix}$$

Then,

$$E_3 A = \begin{bmatrix} 1 & k \\ 0 & 1 \end{bmatrix} \begin{bmatrix} 3 & 2 \\ 1 & 4 \end{bmatrix} = \begin{bmatrix} 3+k & 2+4k \\ 1 & 4 \end{bmatrix}$$

Thus, we have performed the third elementary row operation on A. If we pre-multiply, i.e., AE_3, then it will become an elementary column operation.

$$AE_3 = \begin{bmatrix} 3 & 2 \\ 1 & 4 \end{bmatrix} \begin{bmatrix} 1 & k \\ 0 & 1 \end{bmatrix} = \begin{bmatrix} 3 & 3k+2 \\ 1 & k+4 \end{bmatrix}$$

Thus, we shall conclude that elementary operations can be shown by elementary matrices.

But recall that the Hermite form H of a matrix A was obtained by applying elementary operations. Thus, we can state: If A is a matrix and H is its Hermite form, there are a finite number of elementary matrices such that

$$E_n E_{n-1} \ldots E_2 E_1 A = H$$

Furthermore, let us set

$$E_n E_{n-1} \ldots E_2 E_1 = B$$

Then we can say that there exists a (non-singular) matrix B such that

$$BA = H$$

Let us define one more term. Two matrices A and B are said to be *equivalent* if B can be obtained from A by applying elementary matrices. Thus, if P and Q are products of elementary matrices and

$$PAQ = B$$

then A and B are equivalent. For the moment, we shall confine ourselves to square matrices.

This idea of equivalence and elementary matrices will be used later.

Problem

From the illustration in Section 10.6, we know that A was reduced to I

$$A = \begin{bmatrix} 1 & 4 & 3 \\ 3 & -3 & 1 \\ -1 & 1 & 2 \end{bmatrix} \rightarrow I = \begin{bmatrix} 1 & 0 & 0 \\ 0 & 1 & 0 \\ 0 & 0 & 1 \end{bmatrix}$$

by elementary row operations. Write out all these elementary operations in terms of elementary matrices, and show that

$$E_k \cdot E_{k-1} \ldots E_2 \cdot E_1 \cdot A = I$$

10.9 Determinants (I)

We interrupt our discussion of vectors and matrices to introduce the concept of a *determinant*. A determinant is a *number* associated with a *square* matrix. For example,

matrix	determinant
$\begin{bmatrix} 2 & 3 \\ 4 & 5 \end{bmatrix}$	$\begin{vmatrix} 2 & 3 \\ 4 & 5 \end{vmatrix} = 2 \cdot 5 - 3 \cdot 4 = -2$
$\begin{bmatrix} 3 & 2 \\ 5 & 5 \end{bmatrix}$	$\begin{vmatrix} 3 & 2 \\ 5 & 5 \end{vmatrix} = 3 \cdot 5 - 2 \cdot 5 = 5$

and so forth. Determinants will be denoted by straight lines, and matrices by brackets, as we have used in the examples above. As can be seen, a determinant is always square.

Let us now investigate some of the properties of a determinant.

(*i*) *Definition*

Consider a 2 × 2 matrix *A*

$$A = \begin{bmatrix} a_{11} & a_{12} \\ a_{21} & a_{22} \end{bmatrix}$$

The determinant associated with *A* is

$$\begin{vmatrix} a_{11} & a_{12} \\ a_{21} & a_{22} \end{vmatrix} = a_{11}a_{22} - a_{12}a_{21}$$

which was obtained by the cross-multiplication of the elements. We note that this can also be expressed as

$$\begin{vmatrix} a_{11} & a_{12} \\ a_{21} & a_{22} \end{vmatrix} = a_{1\alpha}a_{2\beta} = a_{1\beta}a_{2\alpha} = \sum \pm a_{1\alpha}a_{2\beta}$$

where α and β are the numbers 1 and 2, and the sum is over all possible permutations of 1 and 2. There are $2! = 2 \times 1 = 2$ permutations of 1 and 2. That is,

$$(\alpha = 1, \beta = 2) \qquad \text{and} \qquad (\beta = 2, \alpha = 1)$$

If we have a 3 × 3 determinant, then,

$$\begin{vmatrix} a_{11} & a_{12} & a_{13} \\ a_{21} & a_{22} & a_{23} \\ a_{31} & a_{32} & a_{33} \end{vmatrix} = \sum \pm a_{1\alpha}a_{2\beta}a_{3\gamma}$$

The number of possible permutations of α, β, and γ are $3! = 6$. They are

$$\alpha \begin{cases} \beta - \gamma & \dots & \alpha \beta \gamma = 1\ 2\ 3 \\ \gamma - \beta & \dots & \alpha \gamma \beta = 1\ 3\ 2 \end{cases}$$

$$\beta \begin{cases} \gamma - \alpha & \dots & \beta \gamma \alpha = 2\ 3\ 1 \\ \alpha - \gamma & \dots & \beta \alpha \gamma = 2\ 1\ 3 \end{cases}$$

$$\gamma \begin{cases} \alpha - \beta & \dots & \gamma \alpha \beta = 3\ 1\ 2 \\ \beta - \alpha & \dots & \gamma \beta \alpha = 3\ 2\ 1 \end{cases}$$

Thus, the determinant, when written out, will be the six terms

$$a_{11}a_{22}a_{33} - a_{11}a_{23}a_{32} + a_{12}a_{23}a_{31}$$

$$- a_{12}a_{21}a_{33} + a_{13}a_{21}a_{32} - a_{13}a_{22}a_{31}$$

An $n \times n$ determinant will then be

$$\begin{vmatrix} a_{11} & a_{12} & \cdots & a_{1n} \\ a_{21} & a_{22} & \cdots & a_{2n} \\ \vdots & \cdots & \cdots & \cdots \\ a_{n1} & a_{n2} & \cdots & a_{nn} \end{vmatrix} = \sum \pm a_{1\alpha} a_{2\beta} \cdots a_{nv}$$

where the sum is extended over the $n!$ possible permutations of the n terms $(\alpha, \beta, ..., v)$.

Now let us investigate how the $+$ and $-$ are attached to the $n!$ terms. For this we need to discuss odd and even permutations. Consider the numbers $(1, 2, 3, 4)$ in their natural order. When we interchange 2 and 4, we have

$$(1, 4, 3, 2)$$

An interchange of two numbers such as above without changing the rest of the numbers, is called a *transposition*. Thus, we have *transposed* 2 and 4.

But now several of the numbers after transposition are not in their natural order. They are $(4, 3)$, $(4, 2)$, and $(3, 2)$. These are called *inversions*. Hence, we have three inversions.

If we transpose 1 and 4 of the original numbers we have $(4, 2, 3, 1)$. Thus, we have $(4, 2)$, $(4, 3)$, $(4, 1)$, $(2, 1)$, $(3, 1)$ as inversions. There are five inversions.

When there are an even number of inversions, we have *even permutations*, and, when there are an odd number, we have *odd permutations*. A systematic way of calculating the number of inversions is as follows: Consider $(1, 2, 3, 4, 5, 6)$. Let us transpose 2 and 6. Then,

$$(1, 6, 3, 4, 5, 2)$$

Let $\lambda_1, \lambda_2, ..., \lambda_k$ be the number of inversions with respect to $1, 2, ..., 6$. Then,

$\lambda_1 = 0$ There are no inversions.
$\lambda_2 = 0$ There are no inversions.
$\lambda_3 = 1$ The 3 and 2 are inverted.
$\lambda_4 = 1$ The 4 and 2 are inverted.
$\lambda_5 = 1$ The 5 and 2 are inverted.
$\lambda_6 = 4$ The 6 and 3, 4, 5, 2 are inverted.

Thus, the total number of inversions are

$$\lambda = \lambda_1 + \lambda_2 + \lambda_3 + \lambda_4 + \lambda_5 + \lambda_6$$
$$= 0 + 0 + 1 + 1 + 1 + 4 = 7$$

so we have an odd permutation.

Using this notion of odd and even permutations, we can complete our definition of a determinant as follows: An $n \times n$ determinant is defined as

$$\sum \pm a_{1\alpha} a_{2\beta} \dots a_{n\nu}$$

where the sum is taken over all possible $n!$ permutations of $(\alpha, \beta, \dots, \nu)$ and, when we have an odd permutation, the term will have a negative sign and, when we have an even permutation, the term will have a positive sign.

Let us now check this with the examples we have already given. For a 2×2 determinant we have

$$\begin{vmatrix} a_{11} & a_{12} \\ a_{21} & a_{22} \end{vmatrix} = \sum \pm a_{1\alpha} a_{2\beta}$$

$$= a_{1\alpha} a_{2\beta} - a_{1\beta} a_{2\alpha}$$

$$= a_{11} a_{22} - a_{12} a_{21}$$

For the first term we have $(\alpha, \beta) = (1, 2)$, and thus we have no inversions. For the second term we have $(\beta, \alpha) = (2, 1)$ and thus one inversion and a negative sign.

For the 3×3 case we have

$$\begin{vmatrix} a_{11} & a_{12} & a_{13} \\ a_{21} & a_{22} & a_{23} \\ a_{31} & a_{32} & a_{33} \end{vmatrix} = \sum \pm a_{1\alpha} a_{2\beta} a_{3\gamma}$$

$$= a_{11} a_{22} a_{33} - a_{11} a_{23} a_{32} + a_{12} a_{23} a_{31}$$
$$- a_{12} a_{21} a_{33} + a_{13} a_{21} a_{32} - a_{13} a_{22} a_{31}$$

1st term	$(\alpha, \beta, \gamma) = (1, 2, 3),$	$\lambda = 0 \quad +$
2nd term	$(\alpha, \gamma, \beta) = (1, 3, 2),$	$\lambda = 1 \quad -$
3rd term	$(\beta, \gamma, \alpha) = (2, 3, 1),$	$\lambda = 2 \quad +$

Check the other terms and note that the signs correspond to the rule.

(ii) Evaluation of a determinant

A 2×2 determinant can be evaluated by cross-multiplying because the result we obtain by this cross-multiplication satisfies our definition. Thus,

$$\begin{vmatrix} 2 & 3 \\ 5 & 4 \end{vmatrix} = 2 \cdot 4 - 3 \cdot 5 = -7$$

For higher-order determinants, we can expand the 2×2 determinant by using *minors* and *cofactors*, which we shall discuss next. But before discussing these ideas, let us present a convenient cross-multiplication scheme for a 3×3 determinant. This cross-multiplication scheme does not hold for higher-order determinants.

We can find the 3×3 determinant as follows

$$\begin{vmatrix} a_1 & a_2 & a_3 \\ b_1 & b_2 & b_3 \\ c_1 & c_2 & c_3 \end{vmatrix} = \begin{aligned} & a_1 b_2 c_3 + b_1 c_2 a_3 + c_1 b_3 a_2 \\ & -a_3 b_2 c_1 - b_3 c_2 a_1 - c_3 b_1 a_2 \end{aligned}$$

Schematically we have

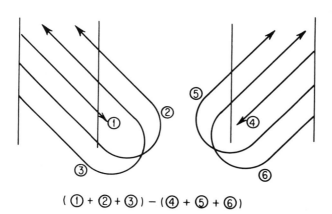

$$(\textcircled{1} + \textcircled{2} + \textcircled{3}) - (\textcircled{4} + \textcircled{5} + \textcircled{6})$$

Example.

$$\begin{vmatrix} 1 & 2 & 3 \\ 2 & 3 & 3 \\ 4 & 6 & 5 \end{vmatrix} = \begin{aligned} & 1 \cdot 3 \cdot 5 + 2 \cdot 6 \cdot 3 + 4 \cdot 3 \cdot 2 \\ & -3 \cdot 3 \cdot 4 - 3 \cdot 6 \cdot 1 - 5 \cdot 2 \cdot 2 = 1 \end{aligned}$$

(iii) Minors and cofactors

Consider a 3×3 determinant

$$\begin{vmatrix} a_{11} & a_{12} & a_{13} \\ a_{21} & a_{22} & a_{23} \\ a_{31} & a_{32} & a_{33} \end{vmatrix}$$

Then, the *minor* of a_{11} is the determinant obtained by deleting the row and column in which we find a_{11}. Thus,

$$\text{minor of } a_{11} = \begin{vmatrix} a_{22} & a_{23} \\ a_{32} & a_{33} \end{vmatrix} = |A_{11}|$$

$$\text{minor of } a_{22} = \begin{vmatrix} a_{11} & a_{13} \\ a_{31} & a_{33} \end{vmatrix} = |A_{22}|$$

$$\text{minor of } a_{23} = \begin{vmatrix} a_{11} & a_{12} \\ a_{31} & a_{32} \end{vmatrix} = |A_{23}|$$

When the minor is given a sign ($+$ or $-$) depending on a rule, it is called a *signed minor* or *cofactor*. The rule is

$$\text{cofactor of } a_{rs} = (-1)^{r+s}|A_{rs}| \equiv A_{rs}$$

where $|A_{rs}| = $ minor of a_{rs}. Thus, the cofactor of a_{11} is

$$A_{11} = (-1)^{1+1} |A_{11}| = \begin{vmatrix} a_{22} & a_{23} \\ a_{32} & a_{33} \end{vmatrix}$$

Example.

$$|A| = \begin{vmatrix} 1 & 2 & 3 \\ 2 & 3 & 3 \\ 4 & 6 & 5 \end{vmatrix}$$

$$|A_{11}| = \begin{vmatrix} 3 & 3 \\ 6 & 5 \end{vmatrix} = 15 - 18 = -3 \qquad \text{(minor of } a_{11})$$

$$A_{11} = (-1)^{1+1} |A_{11}| = (-1)^{1+1} \begin{vmatrix} 3 & 3 \\ 6 & 5 \end{vmatrix} = -3 \qquad \text{(cofactor of } a_{11})$$

$$|A_{12}| = \begin{vmatrix} 2 & 3 \\ 4 & 5 \end{vmatrix} = 10 - 12 = -2 \qquad \text{(minor of } a_{12})$$

$$A_{12} = (-1)^{1+2} |A_{12}| = -\begin{vmatrix} 2 & 3 \\ 4 & 5 \end{vmatrix} = -(10 - 12) = 2 \qquad \text{(cofactor of } a_{12})$$

Problem

Given

$$|A| = \begin{vmatrix} 1 & 2 & 3 \\ 2 & 3 & 3 \\ 4 & 6 & 5 \end{vmatrix}$$

Find cofactors and minors of a_{13}, a_{32}.

(iv) *Expansion of a determinant (I)*

The determinant was defined as

$$\begin{vmatrix} a_{11} & a_{12} & a_{13} \\ a_{21} & a_{22} & a_{23} \\ a_{31} & a_{32} & a_{33} \end{vmatrix} = \sum \pm a_{1\alpha} a_{2\beta} a_{3\gamma}$$

For a 2×2 or a 3×3 determinant there was a simple cross-multiplication scheme that gave us all the terms in $\sum \pm a_{1\alpha} a_{2\beta} a_{3\gamma}$. But, when we have a 4×4 determinant or higher, these simple cross-multiplication schemes will not work. The problem is to find some kind of a computational scheme that will allow us to expand the higher-order determinants to lower-order ones, i.e., a 2×2, or a 3×3, so that they can be computed easily. It turns out that this can be done by use of signed minors (cofactors).

Let us investigate a 2×2 determinant. We find

$$|A| = \begin{vmatrix} a_{11} & a_{12} \\ a_{21} & a_{22} \end{vmatrix} = a_{11}a_{22} - a_{12}a_{21} = a_{11}A_{11} + a_{12}A_{12}$$

where $A_{11} = |a_{22}|$ is the cofactor of a_{11}, and $A_{12} = -|a_{21}|$ is the cofactor of a_{12}. Thus, the determinant $|A|$ has been expanded by multiplying the elements of a row by its cofactor and summing the results. A check will show we can use any row or any column and expand A in the above manner. That is,

$$\begin{aligned} |A| &= a_{11}A_{11} + a_{12}A_{12} \\ &= a_{21}A_{21} + a_{22}A_{22} \\ &= a_{11}A_{11} + a_{21}A_{21} \\ &= a_{12}A_{12} + a_{22}A_{22} \end{aligned}$$

where the A_{ij} are cofactors.

Let us apply this to a 3×3 determinant. Then, by letting the A_{ij} be cofactors

$$\begin{aligned} |A| &= \begin{vmatrix} a_{11} & a_{12} & a_{13} \\ a_{21} & a_{22} & a_{23} \\ a_{31} & a_{32} & a_{33} \end{vmatrix} \\ &= a_{11}A_{11} + a_{12}A_{12} + a_{13}A_{13} \\ &= a_{11}(-1)^{1+1}|A_{11}| + a_{12}(-1)^{1+2}|A_{12}| + a_{13}(-1)^{1+3}|A_{13}| \\ &= a_{11}\begin{vmatrix} a_{22} & a_{23} \\ a_{32} & a_{33} \end{vmatrix} - a_{12}\begin{vmatrix} a_{21} & a_{23} \\ a_{31} & a_{33} \end{vmatrix} + a_{13}\begin{vmatrix} a_{21} & a_{22} \\ a_{31} & a_{32} \end{vmatrix} \\ &= \sum \pm a_{1\alpha}a_{2\beta}a_{3\gamma} \end{aligned}$$

Thus, this procedure is valid for a 3×3 determinant. Note that each cofactor is a 2×2 determinant and is thus made up of two terms. There are three elements in a row so that there are altogether $3 \times 2 = 6$ terms in the sum. We know that $(\alpha\beta\gamma)$ can be permuted in $3! = 6$ different ways.

A check will show that $|A|$ can be expanded by using any row or column and its corresponding cofactors.

Furthermore, this procedure is applicable to higher-order determinants. For a 4×4 determinant, we expand it by cofactors that are 3×3, and these can in turn be expanded by 2×2 cofactors. By repetition of this process, higher-order determinants can be reduced to sums of lower-order determinants.

Also note that for the 4×4 determinant we first find four 3×3 cofactors. Each of these cofactors expands to three 2×2 cofactors, and each 2×2 cofactor expands to two 1×1 cofactors, and we have $4 \times 3 \times 2 \times 1 = 4!$ terms, which is the same as the number of terms obtained by permuting the four numbers $(\alpha, \beta, \gamma, \delta)$.

Example.

$$\begin{vmatrix} 1 & 2 & 4 \\ 4 & 5 & 6 \\ 7 & 8 & 9 \end{vmatrix} = a_{11}A_{11} + a_{12}A_{12} + a_{13}A_{13}$$

$$= 1(-1)^{1+1}\begin{vmatrix} 5 & 6 \\ 8 & 9 \end{vmatrix} + 2(-1)^{1+2}\begin{vmatrix} 4 & 6 \\ 7 & 9 \end{vmatrix} + 4(-1)^{1+3}\begin{vmatrix} 4 & 5 \\ 7 & 8 \end{vmatrix}$$

$$= (45 - 48) - 2(36 - 42) + 4(32 - 35) = -3$$

Problems

1. Expand the above determinant using row 2.

2. Expand it by using row 3.

3. Expand it by using column 1.

4. Find the value of the determinant using the cross-multiplication scheme.

(v) Expansion of a determinant (II)

We have so far stated the rule for the expansion of a determinant by cofactors and have familiarized ourselves with the computational procedures. Let us now give a non-rigorous proof of this procedure.

The first step is to show that a single interchange of two elements will either introduce or remove an inversion. Suppose we have

(1)   1, 2, 3, 4, 5

Interchange 3 and 4.

(2)   1, 2, 4, 3, 5

As is seen, we have introduced one inversion. If we interchange 4 and 3 of (2), we remove one inversion.

Now interchange 1 and 4 of (1). Let us do this in two steps. Move 4 in front of 1.

(3)   4, 1, 2, 3, 5
                                       $m = 3$

We may think of this as interchanging 4 with 3, then with 2, then with 1. In each case we either add or remove an inversion (in this case add inversions). There are $m = 3$ inversions added in this case.

Next, move 1 to the position before 5.

(4)   4, 2, 3, 1, 5
                                       $m - 1 = 2$

In this case, we interchange 1 with 2, then 1 with 3, and there are $m - 1 = 3 - 1 = 2$ inversions.

Combining the two operations shown in (3) and (4), we find there are a total of

$$m + m - 1 = 2m - 1 = 6 - 1 = 5 \text{ inversions}$$

As is seen, this m may be expressed as follows. When moving 4 in front of 1, we move over $m = j - i = 4 - 1 = 3$ places. When moving 1 to 4's place, we move over $m - 1 = j - i - 1 = 4 - 1 - 1 = 2$ places. Hence we move over

$$(j - i) + (j - i - 1) = 2(j - i) - 1$$

places. This clearly is an odd number. Hence, there is a change in the sign of the permutation when there is an interchange of two elements.

Applying this to the definition of a determinant, say,

$$\sum \pm a_{1\alpha} a_{2\beta} a_{3\gamma} a_{4\delta}$$

an interchange of any two adjacent columns will mean an addition or removal of one inversion and hence the sign will change.

When we move a column over two columns, for example, move the third column to the first column,

$$3, 1, 2, 4$$

there will be $j - i = 3 - 1 = 2$ inversions and the sign will be $(-1)^2$; i.e., no change, and so forth.

It can be shown that this operation will also hold for rows.

Using this result, let us now investigate the sign of a cofactor. Let

$$A = \begin{bmatrix} a_{11} & a_{12} & a_{13} \\ a_{21} & a_{22} & a_{23} \\ a_{31} & a_{32} & a_{33} \end{bmatrix}$$

For the purpose of investigation, let us put the second row and third column in the first row and first column, respectively. Then

$$B = \begin{bmatrix} a_{23} & a_{21} & a_{22} \\ a_{13} & a_{11} & a_{12} \\ a_{33} & a_{31} & a_{32} \end{bmatrix} = \begin{bmatrix} b_{11} & b_{12} & b_{13} \\ b_{21} & b_{22} & b_{23} \\ b_{31} & b_{32} & b_{33} \end{bmatrix}$$

As is seen, the minor $|A_{23}|$ of $|A|$ corresponds to the minor $|B_{11}|$ of B.

Let us now compare the determinants $|B|$ and $|A|$. The $|B|$ has been obtained by shifting the rows in $|A|$ by $i - 1 = 2 - 1$, and the columns by $j - 1 = 3 - 1 = 2$. Thus the number of inversions that have been added or removed will be

$$(i - 1) + (j - 1) = (i + j) - 2$$

Thus $|B|$ is equal to

$$|B| = (-1)^{i+j-2} |A|$$
$$= (-1)^{i+j} |A|$$

But this is equal to

$$|A| = (-1)^{i+j} |B|$$

Let us now expand $|B|$. We have

$$|B| = \sum \pm b_{1\alpha} b_{2\beta} b_{3\gamma}$$
$$= b_{11} b_{22} b_{33} - b_{11} b_{23} b_{32}$$
$$+ b_{12} b_{21} b_{33} - b_{12} b_{23} b_{31}$$
$$+ b_{13} b_{21} b_{32} - b_{13} b_{22} b_{31}$$

Hence when each of these 6 terms is multiplied by $(-1)^{i+j}$ we get $|A|$. Let us regroup these 6 terms as follows.

$$|B| = b_{11}(b_{22} b_{33} - b_{23} b_{32})$$
$$+ b_{12}(b_{21} b_{33} - b_{23} b_{31})$$
$$+ b_{13}(b_{21} b_{32} - b_{22} b_{31})$$
$$= b_{11} |B_{11}| + b_{12} |B_{12}| + b_{13} |B_{13}|$$

and when we multiply each of these terms by $(-1)^{i+j}$, we obtain $|A|$. Hence we may write

$$|A| = (-1)^{i+j} b_{11} |B_{11}| + (-1)^{i+j} b_{12} |B_{12}| + (-1)^{i+j} b_{13} |B_{13}|$$

But we can easily see that

$$(-1)^{i+j} b_{11} |B_{11}| = (-1)^{i+j} a_{23} |A_{23}|$$
$$= (-1)^{i+j} a_{ij} |A_{ij}|$$

Hence the cofactor of a_{ij} is the minor $|A_{ij}|$ multiplied by $(-1)^{i+j}$.

Since we may repeat this derivation for each a_{ij} in A, we obtain the general result that the cofactor A_{ij} is equal to

$$A_{ij} = (-1)^{i+j} |A_{ij}|$$

(vi) Properties of a determinant

We shall next list several important properties.
1. The interchange of rows and columns leaves the value of the determinant unchanged.

$$\begin{vmatrix} a_1 & a_2 & a_3 \\ b_1 & b_2 & b_3 \\ c_1 & c_2 & c_3 \end{vmatrix} = \begin{vmatrix} a_1 & b_1 & c_1 \\ a_2 & b_2 & c_2 \\ a_3 & b_3 & c_3 \end{vmatrix}$$

2. The interchange of two adjacent rows or columns in a determinant multiplies the value of the determinant by -1.

$$\begin{vmatrix} a_1 & a_2 & a_3 \\ b_1 & b_2 & b_3 \\ c_1 & c_2 & c_3 \end{vmatrix} = - \begin{vmatrix} b_1 & b_2 & b_3 \\ a_1 & a_2 & a_3 \\ c_1 & c_2 & c_3 \end{vmatrix} = \begin{vmatrix} b_1 & b_2 & b_3 \\ c_1 & c_2 & c_3 \\ a_1 & a_2 & a_3 \end{vmatrix}.$$

3. If each element in a row or column is multiplied by a factor λ, the value of the determinant is also multiplied by λ.

$$\lambda \begin{vmatrix} a_1 & a_2 & a_3 \\ b_1 & b_2 & b_3 \\ c_1 & c_2 & c_3 \end{vmatrix} = \begin{vmatrix} a_1\lambda & a_2\lambda & a_3\lambda \\ b_1 & b_2 & b_3 \\ c_1 & c_2 & c_3 \end{vmatrix} = \begin{vmatrix} a_1\lambda & a_2 & a_3 \\ b_1\lambda & b_2 & b_3 \\ c_1\lambda & c_2 & c_3 \end{vmatrix}$$

4. If a determinant has two columns or two rows that are identical or are multiples of each other, its value is zero.

$$\begin{vmatrix} a_1 & a_2 & a_3 \\ b_1 & b_2 & b_3 \\ a_1 & a_2 & a_3 \end{vmatrix} = 0, \qquad \begin{vmatrix} a_1 & a_2 & a_3 \\ b_1 & b_2 & b_3 \\ a_1\lambda & a_2\lambda & a_3\lambda \end{vmatrix} = 0$$

5. The following holds.

$$\begin{vmatrix} a_1 & b_1 & c_1 \\ a_2 & b_2 & c_2 \\ a_3 & b_3 & c_3 \end{vmatrix} = \begin{vmatrix} a_1 + \lambda b_1 & b_1 & c_1 \\ a_2 + \lambda b_2 & b_2 & c_2 \\ a_3 + \lambda b_3 & b_3 & c_3 \end{vmatrix}$$

6. The following holds.

$$\begin{vmatrix} a_1 & b_1 & c_1 \\ a_2 & b_2 & c_2 \\ a_3 & b_3 & c_3 \end{vmatrix} = \begin{vmatrix} a_1' & b_1 & c_1 \\ a_2' & b_2 & c_2 \\ a_3' & b_3 & c_3 \end{vmatrix} + \begin{vmatrix} a_1 - a_1' & b_1 & c_1 \\ a_2 - a_2' & b_2 & c_2 \\ a_3 - a_3' & b_3 & c_3 \end{vmatrix}$$

Using the results of property (4) above and our discussion of signed minors, we find the following result: Let Δ be a 3×3 determinant and expand it by its first row

$$\Delta = \begin{vmatrix} a_{11} & a_{12} & a_{13} \\ a_{21} & a_{22} & a_{23} \\ a_{31} & a_{32} & a_{33} \end{vmatrix} = a_{11}A_{11} + a_{12}A_{12} + a_{13}A_{13}$$

Let us now replace the first row by a row identical with the second row and expand the determinant by cofactors. Then we have

$$\Delta_1 = \begin{vmatrix} a_{21} & a_{22} & a_{23} \\ a_{21} & a_{22} & a_{23} \\ a_{31} & a_{32} & a_{33} \end{vmatrix} = a_{21}A_{11} + a_{22}A_{12} + a_{23}A_{13}$$

But, from property (4) above, $\Delta_1 = 0$. Thus,

$$\Delta_1 = a_{21}A_{11} + a_{22}A_{12} + a_{23}A_{13} = 0$$

This can be generalized as follows: Let A be an $n \times n$ determinant. Then,

$$\Delta = a_{i1}A_{j1} + a_{i2}A_{j2} + a_{i3}A_{j3} + \ldots + a_{in}A_{jn}$$

where A_{jk} are the cofactors. If $i = j$, then Δ has been expanded by the ith row and its cofactors. If $i \neq j$, then the expansion is equal to zero, i.e.,

$$a_{i1}A_{j1} + a_{i2}A_{j2} + \ldots + a_{in}A_{jn} = 0$$

Example.

$$\Delta = \begin{vmatrix} 1 & 2 & 4 \\ 4 & 5 & 6 \\ 7 & 8 & 9 \end{vmatrix}$$

$$\Delta = a_{11}A_{11} + a_{12}A_{12} + a_{13}A_{13}$$

$$= 1(-1)^{1+1}\begin{vmatrix} 5 & 6 \\ 8 & 9 \end{vmatrix} + 2(-1)^{1+2}\begin{vmatrix} 4 & 6 \\ 7 & 9 \end{vmatrix} + 4(-1)^{1+3}\begin{vmatrix} 4 & 5 \\ 7 & 8 \end{vmatrix}$$

$$= (45 - 48) - 2(36 - 42) + 4(32 - 35) = -3$$

$$\Delta_1 = a_{21}A_{11} + a_{22}A_{12} + a_{23}A_{13}$$

$$= 4(-1)^{1+1}\begin{vmatrix} 5 & 6 \\ 8 & 9 \end{vmatrix} + 5(-1)^{1+2}\begin{vmatrix} 4 & 6 \\ 7 & 9 \end{vmatrix} + 6(-1)^{1+3}\begin{vmatrix} 4 & 5 \\ 7 & 8 \end{vmatrix}$$

$$= 4(45 - 48) - 5(36 - 42) + 6(32 - 35)$$

$$= -12 + 30 - 18 = 0$$

(*vii*) *Multiplication relation between matrices and determinants*

Suppose we have

$$D = AB$$

where A, B, and D are $n \times n$ square matrices. Then

$$|D| = |AB| = |A|\,|B|$$

Example 1.

$$D = \begin{bmatrix} 1 & 2 \\ 3 & 1 \end{bmatrix}\begin{bmatrix} 1 & 0 \\ 2 & 1 \end{bmatrix} = \begin{bmatrix} 5 & 2 \\ 5 & 1 \end{bmatrix}$$

$$|A|\,|B| = \begin{vmatrix} 1 & 2 \\ 3 & 1 \end{vmatrix}\begin{vmatrix} 1 & 0 \\ 2 & 1 \end{vmatrix} = (1 - 6)(1 - 0) = -5$$

$$|AB| = \begin{vmatrix} 5 & 2 \\ 5 & 1 \end{vmatrix} = (5 - 10) = -5$$

We can extend this result as follows.

$$D = ABC = (AB)C$$
$$|D| = |AB|\,|C| = |A|\,|B|\,|C|$$
$$|ABC| = |A|\,|B|\,|C|$$

These are useful results we shall be using in subsequent discussion.

Two additional properties concerning matrices and determinants are: If A is an $n \times n$ square matrix, then

$$|A| = |A^T|$$

$$|\lambda A| = \lambda^n |A|$$

Examples.

(1)

$$A = \begin{bmatrix} 1 & 2 \\ 3 & 1 \end{bmatrix} \qquad A^T = \begin{bmatrix} 1 & 3 \\ 2 & 1 \end{bmatrix}$$

$$|A| = \begin{vmatrix} 1 & 2 \\ 3 & 1 \end{vmatrix} = 1 - 6 = -5$$

$$|A^T| = \begin{vmatrix} 1 & 3 \\ 2 & 1 \end{vmatrix} = 1 - 6 = -5$$

(2) Let $\lambda = 2$. Then,

$$2A = 2 \begin{bmatrix} 1 & 2 \\ 3 & 1 \end{bmatrix} = \begin{bmatrix} 2 & 4 \\ 6 & 2 \end{bmatrix}$$

$$|2A| = \begin{vmatrix} 2 & 4 \\ 6 & 2 \end{vmatrix} = 4 - 24 = 20$$

$$|2A| = 2^2 |A| = 4 \begin{vmatrix} 1 & 2 \\ 3 & 1 \end{vmatrix} = 4(-5) = -20$$

$$\therefore \quad |2A| = 2^2 |A|$$

Problems

1. Evaluate the following determinant first by expanding it and reducing it to 2×2 determinants. Then evaluate it by using the cross-multiplication scheme.

$$\begin{vmatrix} 2 & 3 & 5 \\ 6 & 5 & 1 \\ 4 & 7 & 8 \end{vmatrix}$$

2. Expand, and find the value of the determinant.

$$\begin{vmatrix} 1 & 2 & 3 & 4 \\ 2 & 2 & 3 & 5 \\ 3 & 4 & 4 & 5 \\ 4 & 5 & 6 & 6 \end{vmatrix}$$

3. Evaluate the following determinants first by expanding it by cofactors. Then evaluate it by using the cross-multiplication scheme.

(a) $\begin{vmatrix} 2 & 3 & 4 \\ 6 & 5 & 1 \\ 4 & 7 & 8 \end{vmatrix}$, $\quad \begin{vmatrix} 2 & 6 & 4 \\ 3 & 5 & 7 \\ 4 & 1 & 8 \end{vmatrix}$

(b) $\begin{vmatrix} 6 & 5 & 1 \\ 2 & 3 & 5 \\ 4 & 7 & 8 \end{vmatrix}$, $\quad \begin{vmatrix} 6 & 5 & 1 \\ 4 & 7 & 8 \\ 2 & 3 & 5 \end{vmatrix}$

(c) $\begin{vmatrix} 2\lambda & 3\lambda & 5\lambda \\ 6 & 5 & 1 \\ 4 & 7 & 8 \end{vmatrix}$, $\quad \lambda\begin{vmatrix} 2 & 3 & 5 \\ 6 & 5 & 1 \\ 4 & 7 & 8 \end{vmatrix}$, $\quad \begin{vmatrix} 2\lambda & 3 & 5 \\ 6\lambda & 5 & 1 \\ 4\lambda & 7 & 8 \end{vmatrix}$

(d) $\begin{vmatrix} 1 & 2 & 3 \\ 1 & 2 & 3 \\ 4 & 4 & 6 \end{vmatrix}$, $\quad \begin{vmatrix} 1 & 2 & 3 \\ 2 & 4 & 6 \\ 4 & 4 & 6 \end{vmatrix}$

(e) $\begin{vmatrix} 2 & 3 & 5 \\ 6 & 5 & 1 \\ 4 & 7 & 8 \end{vmatrix}$, $\quad \begin{vmatrix} 2+5 & 3 & 5 \\ 6+1 & 5 & 1 \\ 4+8 & 7 & 8 \end{vmatrix}$

4.

$$\Delta = \begin{vmatrix} 1 & 3 & 5 \\ 2 & 1 & 4 \\ 5 & 0 & 2 \end{vmatrix}$$

(a) Expand the determinant Δ by cofactors A_{11}, A_{12}, A_{13}, using different rows, and check the cases where the expansion becomes zero.

(b) Expand the determinant Δ by cofactors A_{11}, A_{21}, A_{31}, using different columns, and check the cases where the expansion becomes zero.

5. Given the following square matrices, check the relations.

$$|AB| = |A|\,|B|, \qquad |ABC| = |A|\,|B|\,|C|$$

(a) $A = \begin{bmatrix} 1 & 0 \\ 3 & 1 \end{bmatrix}$ $\qquad B = \begin{bmatrix} 4 & 1 \\ 0 & 2 \end{bmatrix}$ $\qquad C = \begin{bmatrix} 1 & 2 \\ 2 & 1 \end{bmatrix}$

(b) $A = \begin{bmatrix} 1 & 0 & 1 \\ 2 & 3 & 0 \\ 0 & 4 & 1 \end{bmatrix}$ $\quad B = \begin{bmatrix} 0 & 1 & 4 \\ 1 & 2 & 1 \\ 0 & 1 & 3 \end{bmatrix}$ $\quad C = \begin{bmatrix} 1 & 1 & 0 \\ 3 & 1 & 0 \\ 1 & 2 & 3 \end{bmatrix}$

6. Given the following square matrices, check the relations.

$$|A| = |A^T|, \qquad |\lambda A| = \lambda^n\,|A|$$

(a) $A = \begin{bmatrix} 1 & 0 \\ 3 & 1 \end{bmatrix}$ $\qquad \lambda = 3$

(b) $A = 2\begin{bmatrix} 1 & 0 & 1 \\ 2 & 3 & 0 \\ 0 & 4 & 1 \end{bmatrix}$ $\quad \lambda = 2$

7. Check the following relations.

$$A = \begin{vmatrix} 0 & f_1 & f_2 \\ f_1 & f_{11} & f_{12} \\ f_2 & f_{21} & f_{22} \end{vmatrix}$$

$$A = \left(\frac{1}{\lambda}\right) \begin{vmatrix} 0 & \lambda f_1 & \lambda f_2 \\ f_1 & f_{11} & f_{12} \\ f_2 & f_{21} & f_{22} \end{vmatrix}$$

$$A = \left(\frac{1}{\lambda}\right)^2 \begin{vmatrix} 0 & \lambda f_1 & \lambda f_2 \\ \lambda f_1 & f_{11} & f_{12} \\ \lambda f_2 & f_{21} & f_{22} \end{vmatrix}$$

8. Check the following relations.

$$\begin{vmatrix} 0 & f_1 & f_2 \\ f_1 & f_{11} & f_{12} \\ f_2 & f_{21} & f_{22} \end{vmatrix} = \begin{vmatrix} f_{11} & f_{12} & f_1 \\ f_{21} & f_{22} & f_2 \\ f_1 & f_2 & 0 \end{vmatrix}$$

where $f_{ij} = f_{ji}$

9. Check the following relations.

$$\begin{vmatrix} 0 & \dfrac{-F'f_1}{\lambda} & \dfrac{-F'f_2}{\lambda} \\ \dfrac{-F'f_1}{\lambda} & F'f_{11} + F'f_1^2 & F'f_{12} + F'f_1f_2 \\ \dfrac{-F'f_2}{\lambda} & F'f_{21} + F'f_1f_2 & F'f_{22} + F'f_2^2 \end{vmatrix} = \dfrac{(F')^3}{\lambda^2} \begin{vmatrix} 0 & f_1 & f_2 \\ f_1 & f_{11} & f_{12} \\ f_2 & f_{21} & f_{22} \end{vmatrix}$$

10.10 Determinants (II)

(This section may be omitted on the first reading without loss of continuity.)

In this section we shall explain Jacobi's theorem, which is used in economics when deriving second-order stability conditions for maximum utility and other similar maximizing or minimizing problems. We shall start with a discussion of the properties of determinants and then give an explanation and illustration of Jacobi's theorem.

(i) A property of a determinant

$$\begin{vmatrix} a_{11} & a_{12} \\ a_{21} & a_{22} \end{vmatrix} = \begin{vmatrix} a_{11} & a_{12} & 0 \\ a_{21} & a_{22} & 0 \\ 0 & 0 & 1 \end{vmatrix}$$

$$= \begin{vmatrix} a_{11} & a_{12} & 0 \\ a_{21} & a_{22} & 0 \\ x & y & 1 \end{vmatrix} = \begin{vmatrix} 1 & x & y \\ 0 & a_{11} & a_{12} \\ 0 & a_{21} & a_{22} \end{vmatrix} = \begin{vmatrix} a_{11} & a_{21} \\ a_{12} & a_{22} \end{vmatrix}$$

(ii) *Adjugate of a determinant*

$$D = \begin{vmatrix} a_{11} & a_{12} & a_{13} \\ a_{21} & a_{22} & a_{23} \\ a_{31} & a_{32} & a_{33} \end{vmatrix}$$

Let A_{ij} be the cofactor of a_{ij}. Then the adjugate (or adjoint) of D is defined as

$$D^* = \begin{vmatrix} A_{11} & A_{12} & A_{13} \\ A_{21} & A_{22} & A_{23} \\ A_{31} & A_{32} & A_{33} \end{vmatrix} = \begin{vmatrix} A_{11} & A_{21} & A_{31} \\ A_{12} & A_{22} & A_{32} \\ A_{13} & A_{23} & A_{33} \end{vmatrix}$$

(iii) *Theorem on adjugates (I)*

Let D be an $n \times n$ determinant. Then

$$D^* = D^{n-1}$$

To explain this result, let D be a 3×3 determinant. Then

$$DD^* = \begin{vmatrix} a_{11} & a_{12} & a_{13} \\ a_{21} & a_{22} & a_{23} \\ a_{31} & a_{32} & a_{33} \end{vmatrix} \begin{vmatrix} A_{11} & A_{12} & A_{13} \\ A_{21} & A_{22} & A_{23} \\ A_{31} & A_{32} & A_{33} \end{vmatrix}$$

$$= \begin{vmatrix} a_{11} & a_{12} & a_{13} \\ a_{21} & a_{22} & a_{23} \\ a_{31} & a_{32} & a_{33} \end{vmatrix} \begin{vmatrix} A_{11} & A_{21} & A_{31} \\ A_{12} & A_{22} & A_{32} \\ A_{13} & A_{23} & A_{33} \end{vmatrix}$$

$$= \begin{vmatrix} D & 0 & 0 \\ 0 & D & 0 \\ 0 & 0 & D \end{vmatrix} = D^3$$

$$D^* = D^{3-1}$$

and this may be generalized to an $n \times n$ determinant.

(iv) *Theorem on adjugates (II)*

The cofactor of A_{11} in D^* is equal to

$$a_{11}D^{n-2}$$

To explain this result, let D be a 3×3 determinant. Then

$$D^* = \begin{vmatrix} A_{11} & A_{12} & A_{13} \\ A_{21} & A_{22} & A_{23} \\ A_{31} & A_{32} & A_{33} \end{vmatrix}$$

Then the cofactor of A_{11} is

$$\text{cofactor } A_{11} = \begin{vmatrix} A_{22} & A_{23} \\ A_{32} & A_{33} \end{vmatrix} = \begin{vmatrix} 1 & 0 & 0 \\ A_{21} & A_{22} & A_{23} \\ A_{31} & A_{32} & A_{33} \end{vmatrix}$$

Then

$$(\text{cofactor } A_{11})D = \begin{vmatrix} 1 & 0 & 0 \\ A_{21} & A_{22} & A_{23} \\ A_{31} & A_{32} & A_{33} \end{vmatrix} \begin{vmatrix} a_{11} & a_{12} & a_{13} \\ a_{21} & a_{22} & a_{23} \\ a_{31} & a_{32} & a_{33} \end{vmatrix}$$

$$= \begin{vmatrix} 1 & 0 & 0 \\ A_{21} & A_{22} & A_{23} \\ A_{31} & A_{32} & A_{33} \end{vmatrix} \begin{vmatrix} a_{11} & a_{21} & a_{31} \\ a_{12} & a_{22} & a_{32} \\ a_{13} & a_{23} & a_{33} \end{vmatrix}$$

$$= \begin{vmatrix} a_{11} & a_{21} & a_{31} \\ 0 & D & 0 \\ 0 & 0 & D \end{vmatrix} = a_{11}D^2 = a_{11}D^{3-1}$$

$$(\text{cofactor } A_{11})D = a_{11}D^{3-1}$$
$$\text{cofactor } A_{11} = a_{11}D^{3-2}$$

We may extend this to an $n \times n$ determinant, and find

$$\text{cofactor } A_{11} = a_{11}D^{n-2}$$

(v) *Minors and cofactors*

Let $|A|$ be a 4×4 determinant

$$|A| = \begin{vmatrix} a_{11} & a_{12} & a_{13} & a_{14} \\ a_{21} & a_{22} & a_{23} & a_{24} \\ a_{31} & a_{32} & a_{33} & a_{34} \\ a_{41} & a_{42} & a_{43} & a_{44} \end{vmatrix}$$

Then the minor of a_{11}, for example, was defined as the determinant obtained by deleting the 1st row and 1st column

$$|A_{11}| = \begin{vmatrix} a_{22} & a_{23} & a_{24} \\ a_{32} & a_{33} & a_{34} \\ a_{42} & a_{43} & a_{44} \end{vmatrix}$$

Since it has 3 rows and 3 columns, it is also called a *minor of order* $k = 3$. More fully, we should say a third-order minor of the determinant $|A|$. We shall denote this by $M_r = M_3$.

Let us now delete 2 rows and 2 columns from $|A|$. Suppose we delete the 1st and 2nd rows and the 2nd and 3rd columns. Then the determinant of the remaining elements is

$$|M_2| = \begin{vmatrix} a_{31} & a_{34} \\ a_{41} & a_{44} \end{vmatrix}$$

and this is called a *2nd order minor of the determinant* $|A|$.

If we delete rows 1, 2, and 3 and columns 1, 3, and 4 of $|A|$, we obtain

$$|M_1| = |a_{42}|$$

and this is a 1st order minor of $|A|$.

To summarize, we may generalize the definition of a minor and state: Given an $n \times n$ determinant $|A|$, the kth-order minor of the determinant $|A|$ is the determinant obtained from $|A|$ by deleting $n - k$ rows and $n - k$ columns.

In the above examples, the first was a minor of order $k = 3$ obtained by deleting $n - k = 4 - 3 = 1$ row and column from $|A|$. To show explicitly the remaining rows and columns, we may write

$$D(2, 3, 4 \,|\, 2, 3, 4) = \begin{vmatrix} a_{22} & a_{23} & a_{24} \\ a_{32} & a_{33} & a_{34} \\ a_{42} & a_{43} & a_{44} \end{vmatrix}$$
$$\quad\quad\quad\quad\quad \uparrow \quad\quad\quad \uparrow$$

rows columns

$$D(3, 4 \,|\, 1, 4) = \begin{vmatrix} a_{31} & a_{34} \\ a_{41} & a_{44} \end{vmatrix}$$

$$D(4 \,|\, 2) = |a_{42}|$$

In our previous discussion, the cofactors of the minors were defined as

$$\text{cofactors } a_{ij} = (-1)^{i+j} |A_{ij}| \equiv A_{ij}$$

and were obtained by adding the sign $(-1)^{i+j}$. When the definition is extended to include the deletion of more than one row and column, the cofactor is defined as follows: Given an $n \times n$ determinant and a minor $D(r_1, r_2, \ldots, r_k \,|\, s_1, s_2, \ldots, s_k)$, the cofactor of the minor is

$$\bar{D}(r_1, \ldots, r_k \,|\, s_1, \ldots, s_k) = (-1)^{r_1+\ldots+r_k+s_1+\ldots+s_k} D(r_{k+1}, \ldots, r_n \,|\, s_{k+1}, \ldots, s_n)$$

Using the above examples, we find

$$\bar{D}(2, 3, 4 \,|\, 2, 3, 4) = (-1)^{2+3+4+2+3+4} D(1 \,|\, 1)$$
$$= |a_{11}|$$
$$\bar{D}(3, 4 \,|\, 1, 4) = (-1)^{3+4+1+4} D(1, 2 \,|\, 2, 3)$$

$$= \begin{vmatrix} a_{12} & a_{13} \\ a_{22} & a_{23} \end{vmatrix}$$
$$\bar{D}(4 \,|\, 2) = (-1)^{4+2} D(1, 2, 3 \,|\, 1, 3, 4)$$

$$= \begin{vmatrix} a_{11} & a_{13} & a_{14} \\ a_{21} & a_{23} & a_{24} \\ a_{31} & a_{33} & a_{34} \end{vmatrix}$$

As is seen from the examples, the third illustration is the definition that we used in the previous section. That is, our previous definition of a cofactor is a special case of this general definition.

There is an alternative way of defining minors in terms of matrices. Let us explain this next.

Given an $m \times n$ matrix A, the kth-order minor of A is the determinant obtained from A by deleting $m - k$ rows and $n - k$ columns. Note that we are expressing terms by matrices and not determinants. As an example, suppose we have a 3×4 matrix A

$$A = \begin{bmatrix} a_{11} & a_{12} & a_{13} & a_{14} \\ a_{21} & a_{22} & a_{23} & a_{24} \\ a_{31} & a_{32} & a_{33} & a_{34} \end{bmatrix}$$

Let us delete the 1st row and 3rd and 4th columns. Then we get

$$|M_2| = \begin{vmatrix} a_{21} & a_{22} \\ a_{31} & a_{32} \end{vmatrix} = D(2, 3 \,|\, 1, 2)$$

which is a 2nd order minor of A. As is seen, the matrix A does not need to be square, but the minor is a determinant and has to be square.

By the definition, a 2nd order minor is obtained by deleting $3 - 2 = 1$ row and $4 - 2 = 2$ columns. A 1st order minor is obtained by deleting $3 - 1 = 2$ rows and $4 - 1 = 3$ columns.

(vi) Complementary minor

If the kth-order minor of matrix A is obtained by the $i_1, i_2, \ldots, i_k$ rows and $j_1, j_2, \ldots, j_k$ columns of A, the complementary minor is the determinant of elements obtained after deleting these $i_1, i_2, \ldots, i_k$ rows and $j_1, j_2, \ldots, j_k$ columns from matrix A.

For example, let A be a 4×4 square matrix

$$A = \begin{bmatrix} a_{11} & a_{12} & a_{13} & a_{14} \\ a_{21} & a_{22} & a_{23} & a_{24} \\ a_{31} & a_{32} & a_{33} & a_{34} \\ a_{41} & a_{42} & a_{43} & a_{44} \end{bmatrix}$$

Let us obtain a $k = $ 2nd order minor M_2 by the $i_1, i_2 = $ 1st and 3rd rows and $j_1, j_2 = $ 1st and 2nd columns.

$$M_2 = \begin{vmatrix} a_{11} & a_{12} \\ a_{31} & a_{32} \end{vmatrix} = D(1, 3 \,|\, 1, 2)$$

The complementary minor of $M_2 = D(1, 3 \,|\, 1, 2)$ is obtained after deleting $i_1, i_2 = $ 1st and 3rd rows and $j_1, j_2 = $ 1st and 2nd columns. Thus

$$\bar{M}_{4-2} = \begin{vmatrix} a_{23} & a_{24} \\ a_{43} & a_{44} \end{vmatrix}$$

Example. Find the $k = $ 3rd order minor by letting $i_1, i_2, i_3 = 1, 3, 4$ and $j_1, j_2, j_3 = 1, 2, 4$.

$$M_3 = \begin{vmatrix} a_{11} & a_{12} & a_{14} \\ a_{31} & a_{32} & a_{34} \\ a_{41} & a_{42} & a_{44} \end{vmatrix} = D(1, 3, 4 \mid 1, 2, 4)$$

The complementary minor is

$$\bar{M}_{4-1} = M_1 = |a_{23}| = D(2 \mid 3)$$

(vii) Jacobi's theorem

Jacobi's theorem is used frequently in economics when proving second-order conditions in maximum and minimum problems. We shall merely state and illustrate the theorem.

Let D be a 4×4 determinant

$$D = \begin{vmatrix} a_{11} & a_{12} & a_{13} & a_{14} \\ a_{21} & a_{22} & a_{23} & a_{24} \\ a_{31} & a_{32} & a_{33} & a_{34} \\ a_{41} & a_{42} & a_{43} & a_{44} \end{vmatrix}$$

Then the adjugate of D is defined as

$$D^* = \begin{vmatrix} A_{11} & A_{12} & A_{13} & A_{14} \\ A_{21} & A_{22} & A_{23} & A_{24} \\ A_{31} & A_{32} & A_{33} & A_{34} \\ A_{41} & A_{42} & A_{43} & A_{44} \end{vmatrix}$$

Let M_r^* be a minor of order r of D^*. For example, let $i_1, i_2 = 1, 3$ and $j_1, j_2 = 1, 3$. Then

$$M_2^* = \begin{vmatrix} A_{11} & A_{13} \\ A_{31} & A_{33} \end{vmatrix}$$

Let $\bar{M}_{n-r}$ be the complementary minor of the corresponding minor M_r of D. Hence

$$\bar{M}_{n-r} = \bar{M}_{4-2} = \begin{vmatrix} a_{22} & a_{24} \\ a_{42} & a_{44} \end{vmatrix}$$

Then we have the following relation:

$$\begin{vmatrix} A_{11} & A_{13} \\ A_{31} & A_{33} \end{vmatrix} = \begin{vmatrix} a_{22} & a_{24} \\ a_{42} & a_{44} \end{vmatrix} D^{2-1}$$

which may be expressed as

$$M_2^* = \bar{M}_{4-2} D^{2-1}$$

or, in general,

$$M_r^* = \bar{M}_{n-r} D^{r-1}$$

This result is called *Jacobi's theorem*. Let us illustrate this theorem with a numerical example.

Example 1.

$$D = \begin{vmatrix} 1 & 0 & 2 & 4 \\ 3 & 2 & 0 & 2 \\ 1 & 3 & 0 & 2 \\ 2 & 0 & 1 & 1 \end{vmatrix} = -20$$

Let M_2^* be obtained by letting $i_1, i_2 = 1, 2$ and $j_1, j_2 = 1, 2$:

$$M_2^* = \begin{vmatrix} A_{11} & A_{12} \\ A_{21} & A_{22} \end{vmatrix} = \begin{vmatrix} 2 & -4 \\ 6 & 8 \end{vmatrix} = 40$$

Then

$$\bar{M}_{4-2} = \begin{vmatrix} a_{33} & a_{34} \\ a_{43} & a_{44} \end{vmatrix} = \begin{vmatrix} 0 & 2 \\ 1 & 1 \end{vmatrix} = -2$$

Hence

$$M_2^* = \bar{M}_{4-2} D^{2-1}$$

$$40 = (-2)(-20)^{2-1}$$

Example 2. Let us try Example 1 by letting $i_1, i_2 = 1, 3$ and $j_1, j_2 = 1, 3$

$$M_2^* = \begin{vmatrix} A_{11} & A_{13} \\ A_{31} & A_{33} \end{vmatrix} = \begin{vmatrix} 2 & 3 \\ 4 & -14 \end{vmatrix} = -40$$

$$\bar{M}_{4-2} = \begin{vmatrix} 2 & 2 \\ 0 & 1 \end{vmatrix} = 2$$

$$D = -20$$

Hence

$$M_2^* = \bar{M}_{4-} D_2{}^{2-1}$$

$$-40 = (2)(-20)^{2-1}$$

Problems

1. Work out the calculation details of Examples 1 and 2.

2. Using the data of Example 1, obtain M_r^* by letting $i_1, i_2 = 1, 2$ and $j_1, j_2 = 2, 4$, and check the relation $M_r^* = \bar{M}_{n-r} D^{r-1}$.

3. Using the data of Example 1, find M_r^* by letting $i_1 = 1$ and $j_1 = 1$, and check the relation $M_r^* = \bar{M}_{n-r} D^{r-1}$. Note that in this case $M_r^* = \bar{M}_{n-r}$.

10.11 Inverse matrix

We now return to our discussion of matrices.

(i) Inverse matrix

Let

$$A = \begin{bmatrix} a_{11} & a_{12} \\ a_{21} & a_{22} \end{bmatrix}$$

We wish to find a matrix B such that

$$AB = I$$

This matrix B is called the *inverse* of A and is written A^{-1}. Thus,

$$AA^{-1} = I$$

It is also called the *reciprocal* matrix. The analogy in algebra is

$$a \times \frac{1}{a} = a \times a^{-1} = 1$$

Let us set

$$B = \begin{bmatrix} x & y \\ z & w \end{bmatrix}$$

Then, if B is the inverse matrix of A, we have

$$\begin{bmatrix} a_{11} & a_{12} \\ a_{21} & a_{22} \end{bmatrix} \begin{bmatrix} x & y \\ z & w \end{bmatrix} = \begin{bmatrix} 1 & 0 \\ 0 & 1 \end{bmatrix}$$

$$\begin{bmatrix} a_{11}x + a_{12}z & a_{11}y + a_{12}w \\ a_{21}x + a_{22}z & a_{21}y + a_{22}w \end{bmatrix} = \begin{bmatrix} 1 & 0 \\ 0 & 1 \end{bmatrix}$$

Thus, we obtain the following simultaneous equations

$$\begin{cases} a_{11}x + a_{12}z = 1, \\ a_{21}x + a_{22}z = 0 \end{cases} \quad \begin{cases} a_{11}y + a_{12}w = 0, \\ a_{21}y + a_{22}w = 1 \end{cases}$$

Using Cramers' rule (see Section 12.4), we find

$$\begin{cases} x = \dfrac{a_{22}}{D} \\ z = -\dfrac{a_{21}}{D} \end{cases} \quad \begin{cases} y = -\dfrac{a_{12}}{D} \\ w = \dfrac{a_{11}}{D} \end{cases} \quad D = \begin{vmatrix} a_{11} & a_{12} \\ a_{21} & a_{22} \end{vmatrix} \neq 0$$

Substituting these values back into B, we find

$$B = \frac{1}{D} \begin{bmatrix} a_{22} & -a_{12} \\ -a_{21} & a_{11} \end{bmatrix} = \frac{1}{D} \begin{bmatrix} A_{11} & A_{21} \\ A_{12} & A_{22} \end{bmatrix}$$

where the A_{ij} are cofactors. Note that the rows and columns in the last matrix are transposed. Let us now check to see whether $AB = I$.

$$AB = \begin{bmatrix} a_{11} & a_{12} \\ a_{21} & a_{22} \end{bmatrix} \cdot \frac{1}{D} \begin{bmatrix} A_{11} & A_{21} \\ A_{12} & A_{22} \end{bmatrix}$$

$$= \frac{1}{D} \begin{bmatrix} a_{11}A_{11} + a_{12}A_{12} & a_{11}A_{21} + a_{12}A_{22} \\ a_{21}a_{11} + a_{22}A_{12} & a_{21}A_{21} + a_{22}A_{22} \end{bmatrix}$$

But recall that the determinant D can be expanded by its cofactors and that when we replace a row by another row and expand, the sum will be zero. Thus, we find

$$AB = \frac{1}{D} \begin{bmatrix} D & 0 \\ 0 & D \end{bmatrix} = \begin{bmatrix} 1 & 0 \\ 0 & 1 \end{bmatrix}$$

and B is the inverse matrix of A.

Note two things: First, that $D \neq 0$ is a necessary condition for B to be an inverse. Second, the order of the cofactors in B were transposed.

Keeping these in mind, let us apply them to a 3×3 determinant. We find that

$$A = \begin{bmatrix} a_{11} & a_{12} & a_{13} \\ a_{21} & a_{22} & a_{23} \\ a_{31} & a_{32} & a_{33} \end{bmatrix}$$

and according to our results from above,

$$B = \frac{1}{D} \begin{bmatrix} A_{11} & A_{21} & A_{31} \\ A_{12} & A_{22} & A_{32} \\ A_{13} & A_{23} & A_{33} \end{bmatrix}, \quad D \neq 0$$

where the A_{ij} are the cofactors. Thus, when A and B are multiplied, we find

$$AB = \frac{1}{D} \begin{bmatrix} D & 0 & 0 \\ 0 & D & 0 \\ 0 & 0 & D \end{bmatrix} = \begin{bmatrix} 1 & 0 & 0 \\ 0 & 1 & 0 \\ 0 & 0 & 1 \end{bmatrix} = I$$

A check will show that the results we have obtained are *general*. So let us summarize our results as follows: Let $|A| = \Delta$ be the determinant of A. Assume $\Delta \neq 0$. Then the matrix A is said to be non-singular (when $\Delta = 0$, it is said to be singular). Let A_{ij} be the cofactor of element a_{ij}. Furthermore, let us denote an element of A^{-1} as a^{ij}. Then, the elements of A^{-1} are

$$a^{ij} = \frac{A_{ji}}{\Delta}$$

Noting that $[A_{ji}]$ is obtained by transposing $[A_{ij},]$ we can write the inverse matrix as

$$[a^{ij}] = \frac{1}{\Delta} \begin{bmatrix} A_{11} & A_{21} & A_{31} \\ A_{12} & A_{22} & A_{32} \\ A_{13} & A_{23} & A_{33} \end{bmatrix}$$

Let us illustrate.

$$A = \begin{bmatrix} 1 & 2 & 3 \\ 5 & 7 & 4 \\ 2 & 1 & 3 \end{bmatrix}$$

$$|A| = \Delta = 1 \times 7 \times 3 + 5 \times 1 \times 3 + 2 \times 4 \times 2 - 3 \times 7 \times 2$$

$$- 4 \times 1 \times 1 - 3 \times 5 \times 2 = -24$$

The cofactors A_{ij} are, for example,

$$A_{11} = (-1)^{1+1} \begin{vmatrix} 7 & 4 \\ 1 & 3 \end{vmatrix} = 21 - 4 = 17$$

$$A_{12} = (-1)^{1+2} \begin{vmatrix} 5 & 4 \\ 2 & 3 \end{vmatrix} = -(15 - 8) = -7$$

and so forth. Thus, we obtain the matrix of the cofactors

$$[A_{ij}] = \begin{bmatrix} A_{11} & A_{12} & A_{13} \\ A_{21} & A_{22} & A_{23} \\ A_{31} & A_{32} & A_{33} \end{bmatrix} = \begin{bmatrix} 17 & -7 & -9 \\ -3 & -3 & 3 \\ -13 & 11 & -3 \end{bmatrix}$$

and the transpose matrix of the cofactors becomes

$$[A_{ji}] = \begin{bmatrix} 17 & -3 & -13 \\ -7 & -3 & 11 \\ -9 & 3 & -3 \end{bmatrix}$$

The inverse matrix will be

$$A^{-1} = \frac{1}{\Delta} [A_{ji}] = \frac{1}{-24} \begin{bmatrix} 17 & -3 & -13 \\ -7 & -3 & 11 \\ -9 & 3 & -3 \end{bmatrix}$$

We check this by $AA^{-1} = I$. Thus,

$$\begin{bmatrix} 1 & 2 & 3 \\ 5 & 7 & 4 \\ 2 & 1 & 3 \end{bmatrix} \cdot \left(\frac{1}{-24} \right) \begin{bmatrix} 17 & -3 & -13 \\ -7 & -3 & 11 \\ -9 & 3 & -3 \end{bmatrix}$$

$$= \frac{1}{-24} \begin{bmatrix} -24 & 0 & 0 \\ 0 & -24 & 0 \\ 0 & 0 & -24 \end{bmatrix} = \begin{bmatrix} 1 & 0 & 0 \\ 0 & 1 & 0 \\ 0 & 0 & 1 \end{bmatrix}$$

Problem

Work out the above multiplication. Also work out the case for

$$A^{-1}A = I$$

(*ii*) *Properties of inverse matrices*

(a)
$$AA^{-1} = A^{-1}A = I$$

Let $A*A = I$. Then, since $AA^{-1} = I$,

$$(A*A)A^{-1} = A^{-1}$$
$$A*(AA^{-1}) = A^{-1}$$
$$\therefore \quad A* = A^{-1}$$

(b)
$$(AB)^{-1} = B^{-1}A^{-1}$$

Because

$$(B^{-1}A^{-1})AB = B^{-1}(A^{-1}A)B = B^{-1}B = I$$

(c)
$$(A^T)^{-1} = (A^{-1})^T$$
$$\because \quad (A^{-1}A)^T = A^T(A^{-1})^T$$

But

$$(A^{-1}A)^T = (I)^T = I$$
$$\therefore \quad A^T(A^{-1})^T = I$$
$$\therefore \quad (A^{-1})^T = (A^T)^{-1}$$

(*iii*) *Gauss elimination method*

Another method of finding the inverse of a matrix which is sometimes called the *Gauss elimination method* or *pivotal method* will be presented. An identity matrix is placed along side a matrix A that is to be inverted. Then, the same elementary row operations are performed on *both* matrices until A has been reduced to an identity matrix. The identity matrix upon which the elementary row operations have been performed will then become the inverse matrix we seek. Let us show this process by an example.

$$\begin{bmatrix} 2 & 3 \\ 4 & 2 \end{bmatrix}\begin{bmatrix} 1 & 0 \\ 0 & 1 \end{bmatrix}$$

Change the $a_{11} = 2$ to 1 by dividing the first row by 2 and then perform the necessary elementary operations so that all the elements below it will become zero.

$$\begin{bmatrix} 1 & \frac{3}{2} \\ 4 & 2 \end{bmatrix}\begin{bmatrix} \frac{1}{2} & 0 \\ 0 & 1 \end{bmatrix}$$

$$\begin{bmatrix} 1 & \frac{3}{2} \\ 0 & -4 \end{bmatrix}\begin{bmatrix} \frac{1}{2} & 0 \\ -2 & 1 \end{bmatrix}$$

Next let $a_{22} = -4$ become 1 and everything above (and below) it become zero. Thus,

$$\begin{bmatrix} 1 & \frac{3}{2} \\ 0 & 1 \end{bmatrix}\begin{bmatrix} \frac{1}{2} & 0 \\ \frac{1}{2} & -\frac{1}{4} \end{bmatrix}$$

$$\begin{bmatrix} 1 & 0 \\ 0 & 1 \end{bmatrix}\begin{bmatrix} -\frac{1}{4} & \frac{3}{8} \\ \frac{1}{2} & -\frac{1}{4} \end{bmatrix}$$

The inverse is

$$A^{-1} = \begin{bmatrix} -\frac{1}{4} & \frac{3}{8} \\ \frac{1}{2} & -\frac{1}{4} \end{bmatrix}$$

Various commutational steps were carried out to show what was being done. But when we have two rows (n rows), we can show the process schematically in two steps (n steps);

$$\begin{bmatrix} 2 & 3 \\ 4 & 2 \end{bmatrix}\begin{bmatrix} 1 & 0 \\ 0 & 1 \end{bmatrix}$$

Step 1. $a_{11} = 1$ and all elements below it are zero,

$$\begin{bmatrix} 1 & \frac{3}{2} \\ 0 & -4 \end{bmatrix}\begin{bmatrix} \frac{1}{2} & 0 \\ -2 & 1 \end{bmatrix}$$

Step 2. $a_{22} = 1$ and all elements above (and below) it are zero.

$$\begin{bmatrix} 1 & 0 \\ 0 & 1 \end{bmatrix}\begin{bmatrix} -\frac{1}{4} & \frac{3}{8} \\ \frac{1}{2} & -\frac{1}{4} \end{bmatrix}$$

Check:

$$AA^{-1} = \begin{bmatrix} 2 & 3 \\ 4 & 2 \end{bmatrix}\begin{bmatrix} -\frac{1}{4} & \frac{3}{8} \\ \frac{1}{2} & -\frac{1}{4} \end{bmatrix} = \begin{bmatrix} 1 & 0 \\ 0 & 1 \end{bmatrix}$$

Recall our discussion of equivalence and elementary matrices and notice that the Gauss elimination method is an application of these ideas. Let us illustrate this using our example.

$$E_1: \begin{bmatrix} 1 & 0 \\ 0 & 1 \end{bmatrix}\begin{bmatrix} 2 & 3 \\ 4 & 2 \end{bmatrix}$$

$$E_2: \begin{bmatrix} \frac{1}{2} & 0 \\ 0 & 1 \end{bmatrix}\begin{bmatrix} 2 & 3 \\ 4 & 2 \end{bmatrix} = \begin{bmatrix} 1 & \frac{3}{2} \\ 4 & 2 \end{bmatrix}$$

$$E_3: \begin{bmatrix} 1 & 0 \\ -4 & 1 \end{bmatrix}\begin{bmatrix} 1 & \frac{3}{2} \\ 4 & 2 \end{bmatrix} = \begin{bmatrix} 1 & \frac{3}{2} \\ 0 & -4 \end{bmatrix}$$

$$E_4: \begin{bmatrix} 1 & 0 \\ 0 & -\frac{1}{4} \end{bmatrix}\begin{bmatrix} 1 & \frac{3}{2} \\ 0 & -4 \end{bmatrix} = \begin{bmatrix} 1 & \frac{3}{2} \\ 0 & 1 \end{bmatrix}$$

$$E_5: \begin{bmatrix} 1 & -\frac{3}{2} \\ 0 & 1 \end{bmatrix}\begin{bmatrix} 1 & \frac{3}{2} \\ 0 & 1 \end{bmatrix} = \begin{bmatrix} 1 & 0 \\ 0 & 1 \end{bmatrix}$$

Thus,

$$E_5 \cdot E_4 \cdot E_3 \cdot E_2 \cdot E_1 \cdot A$$

$$= \begin{bmatrix} 1 & -\frac{3}{2} \\ 0 & 1 \end{bmatrix} \begin{bmatrix} 1 & 0 \\ 0 & -\frac{1}{4} \end{bmatrix} \begin{bmatrix} 1 & 0 \\ -4 & 1 \end{bmatrix} \begin{bmatrix} \frac{1}{2} & 0 \\ 0 & 1 \end{bmatrix} \begin{bmatrix} 1 & 0 \\ 0 & 1 \end{bmatrix} \begin{bmatrix} 2 & 3 \\ 4 & 2 \end{bmatrix}$$

$$= \begin{bmatrix} 1 & 0 \\ 0 & 1 \end{bmatrix} = I$$

$$E_5 \cdot E_4 \cdot E_3 \cdot E_2 \cdot E_1 = A^{-1} = \begin{bmatrix} -\frac{1}{4} & \frac{3}{8} \\ \frac{1}{2} & -\frac{1}{4} \end{bmatrix} = \frac{1}{8} \begin{bmatrix} -2 & 3 \\ 4 & -2 \end{bmatrix}$$

In terms of the scheme we set up, step 1 is a combination of $E_3 \cdot E_2 \cdot E_1$ and step 2 is a combination of $(E_5 \cdot E_4)(E_3 \cdot E_2 \cdot E_1)$

$$E_3 \cdot E_2 \cdot E_1 = \begin{bmatrix} 1 & 0 \\ -4 & 1 \end{bmatrix} \begin{bmatrix} \frac{1}{2} & 0 \\ 0 & 1 \end{bmatrix} \begin{bmatrix} 1 & 0 \\ 0 & 1 \end{bmatrix} = \begin{bmatrix} \frac{1}{2} & 0 \\ -2 & 1 \end{bmatrix}$$

$$(E_5 \cdot E_4)(E_3 \cdot E_2 \cdot E_1) = \begin{bmatrix} 1 & -\frac{3}{2} \\ 0 & 1 \end{bmatrix} \begin{bmatrix} 1 & 0 \\ 0 & -\frac{1}{4} \end{bmatrix} \begin{bmatrix} \frac{1}{2} & 0 \\ -2 & 1 \end{bmatrix}$$

$$= \begin{bmatrix} -\frac{1}{4} & \frac{3}{8} \\ \frac{1}{2} & -\frac{1}{4} \end{bmatrix} = A^{-1}$$

(iv) Inverse of elementary matrices

The first elementary matrix in Section 10.9 was the interchange of rows.

$$E_1 = \begin{bmatrix} 0 & 1 \\ 1 & 0 \end{bmatrix}$$

But

$$E_1 E_1 = \begin{bmatrix} 0 & 1 \\ 1 & 0 \end{bmatrix} \begin{bmatrix} 0 & 1 \\ 1 & 0 \end{bmatrix} = \begin{bmatrix} 1 & 0 \\ 0 & 1 \end{bmatrix}$$

That is, the inverse of E_1 is E_1 itself.

The second elementary matrix was the multiplication of a row by a scalar k.

$$E_2 = \begin{bmatrix} k & 0 \\ 0 & 1 \end{bmatrix}$$

But

$$\begin{bmatrix} k & 0 \\ 0 & 1 \end{bmatrix} \begin{bmatrix} \dfrac{1}{k} & 0 \\ 0 & 1 \end{bmatrix} = \begin{bmatrix} 1 & 0 \\ 0 & 1 \end{bmatrix}$$

That is, the inverse of E_2 is obtained by replacing k by $1/k$.

The third elementary matrix was the addition to a row of k times another row.

$$E_3 = \begin{bmatrix} 1 & k \\ 0 & 1 \end{bmatrix}$$

But

$$\begin{bmatrix} 1 & k \\ 0 & 1 \end{bmatrix}\begin{bmatrix} 1 & -k \\ 0 & 1 \end{bmatrix} = \begin{bmatrix} 1 & 0 \\ 0 & 1 \end{bmatrix}$$

Thus, the inverse is obtained by replacing k by $-k$.

We have seen that a matrix A can be reduced to I by elementary matrices. For example,

$$E_3 \cdot E_2 \cdot E_1 \cdot A = I$$

Then,

$$A = E_1^{-1} \cdot E_2^{-1} \cdot E_3^{-1} \cdot I$$

But E_1^{-1}, E_2^{-1}, E_3^{-1} as we saw are also elementary matrices and we may conclude that a matrix A can be factored into elementary matrices.

Problems

1. Find the inverse of the following matrices. Use the cofactor method, and the Gauss elimination method. Check that it is non-singular.

(a)
$$A = \begin{bmatrix} 3 & 1 & 1 \\ 2 & 0 & 2 \\ 5 & 1 & 2 \end{bmatrix}$$

(b)
$$A = \begin{bmatrix} 2 & -2 & 3 \\ 1 & 0 & -3 \\ 3 & 4 & 0 \end{bmatrix}$$

(c)
$$A = \begin{bmatrix} 5 & 1 & 1 \\ 0 & 2 & 2 \\ 3 & 1 & 4 \end{bmatrix}$$

2. Factor the following matrices into elementary matrices.

(a)
$$A = \begin{bmatrix} 5 & 2 \\ 6 & 1 \end{bmatrix}$$

(b)
$$A = \begin{bmatrix} 1 & 3 \\ 5 & 4 \end{bmatrix}$$

3. Using the results of Problem 2, find the inverse of the elementary matrices, and then find the inverse of A.

10.12 Linear and quadratic forms

Before getting into the topic of linear transformations let us define a few terms. An expression

$$\sum_j a_{ij}x_j = a_{i1}x_1 + a_{i2}x_2 + \ldots + a_{in}x_n, \qquad i = 1, 2, \ldots m$$

is called a *linear form* in the variable x.

Example.

$$2x_1 + 5x_2 - x_3$$

An expression

$$\sum_i^m \sum_j^n a_{ij} x_i y_j$$

$$= \sum_i (a_{i1} x_i y_1 + a_{i2} x_i y_2 + \ldots + a_{in} x_i y_n)$$

$$= a_{11} x_1 y_1 + a_{12} x_1 y_2 + \ldots + a_{1n} x_1 y_n$$

$$+ a_{21} x_2 y_1 + a_{22} x_2 y_2 + \ldots + a_{2n} x_2 y_n$$

$$+ \ldots$$

$$+ a_{m1} x_m y_1 + a_{m2} x_m y_2 + \ldots + a_{mn} x_m y_n$$

is called a *bilinear form* in x_i and y_j.

Example.

$$2x_1 y_1 + 3x_1 y_2 + 5x_2 y_1 - 3x_2 y_2 + x_3 y_2$$

$$= 2x_1 y_1 + 3x_1 y_2 + 0x_1 y_3$$

$$+ 5x_2 y_1 - 3x_2 y_2 + 0x_2 y_3$$

$$+ 0 + x_3 y_2 + 0$$

A special case of the bilinear form where

$$y_j = x_j \quad \text{and} \quad a_{ij} = a_{ji}$$

is called a *quadratic form* in x_i and is expressed as (for $n = 3$)

$$\sum_i^n \sum_j^n a_{ij} \cdot x_i x_j = a_{11} x_1^2 + a_{12} x_1 x_2 + a_{13} x_1 x_3$$

$$+ a_{21} x_2 x_1 + a_{22} x_2^2 + a_{23} x_2 x_3$$

$$+ a_{31} x_3 x_1 + a_{32} x_3 x_2 + a_{33} x_3^2$$

$$= a_{11} x_1^2 + a_{22} x_2^2 + a_{33} x_3^2 + 2a_{12} x_1 x_2 + 2a_{13} x_1 x_3 + 2a_{23} x_2 x_3$$

$$(a_{12} = a_{21}, a_{13} = a_{31}, a_{23} = a_{32})$$

Examples.

(1)

$$a_{11} x_1 y_1 + a_{12} x_1 y_1$$

$$+ a_{21} x_2 y_1 + a_{22} a x_2 y_2$$

Let

$$a_{11} = a, \qquad a_{12} = a_{21} = b, \qquad a_{22} = c,$$

$$x_1 = y_1 = x, \qquad x_2 = y_2 = y$$

Then the expression becomes

$$axx + bxy + bxy + cyy = ax^2 + 2bxy + cy^2$$

which is a quadratic form.

(2)
$$2x^2 + 4xy + 3y^2$$
$$= 2xx + 2xy$$
$$+ 2xy + 3yy$$
$$= a_{11}x_1y_1 + a_{12}x_1y_2$$
$$+ a_{21}x_2y_1 + a_{22}x_2y_2$$

where

$$a_{11} = 2, \qquad a_{12} = a_{21} = 2, \qquad a_{22} = 3$$
$$x_1 = y_1 = x, \qquad x_2 = y_2 = y$$

If we use matrix notation and let

$$A = \begin{bmatrix} a_{11} & a_{12} & \cdots & a_{1n} \\ \cdots & & & \\ a_{n1} & a_{n2} & \cdots & a_{nn} \end{bmatrix}$$

and

$$X = \begin{bmatrix} x_1 \\ \cdot \\ \cdot \\ \cdot \\ x_n \end{bmatrix} \qquad Y = \begin{bmatrix} y_1 \\ \cdot \\ \cdot \\ \cdot \\ y_n \end{bmatrix}$$

then,

linear form AX

bilinear form X^TAY

quadratic form X^TAX

$$AX = \begin{bmatrix} a_{11} & a_{12} \end{bmatrix} \begin{bmatrix} x_1 \\ x_2 \end{bmatrix} = a_{11}x_1 + a_{12}x_2$$

$$X^TAY = \begin{bmatrix} x_1 & x_2 \end{bmatrix} \begin{bmatrix} a_{11} & a_{12} \\ a_{21} & a_{22} \end{bmatrix} \begin{bmatrix} y_1 \\ y_2 \end{bmatrix}$$
$$= a_{11}x_1y_1 + a_{21}x_2y_1 + a_{12}x_1y_2 + a_{22}x_2y_2$$
$$= a_{11}x_1y_1 + a_{12}x_1y_2$$
$$+ a_{21}x_2y_1 + a_{22}x_2y_2$$

$$X^TAX = \begin{bmatrix} x_1 & x_2 \end{bmatrix} \begin{bmatrix} a_{11} & a_{12} \\ a_{21} & a_{22} \end{bmatrix} \begin{bmatrix} x_1 \\ x_2 \end{bmatrix}$$
$$= a_{11}x_1x_1 + a_{12}x_1x_2$$

$$+ a_{21}x_2x_1 + a_{22}x_2x_2$$
$$= a_{11}x_1^2 + 2a_{12}x_1x_2 + a_{22}x_2^2$$

where $a_{12} = a_{21}$.

Examples.

(1)
$$AX = \begin{bmatrix} 2 & 5 & -1 \end{bmatrix} \begin{bmatrix} x_1 \\ x_2 \\ x_3 \end{bmatrix} = 2x_1 + 5x_2 - x_3$$

(2)
$$X^T AY = \begin{bmatrix} x_1 & x_2 \end{bmatrix} \begin{bmatrix} 1 & 2 \\ 3 & 1 \end{bmatrix} \begin{bmatrix} y_1 \\ y_2 \end{bmatrix}$$
$$= x_1y_1 + 3x_2y_1 + 2x_1y_2 + x_2y_2$$
$$= x_1y_1 + 2x_1y_2$$
$$+ 3x_2y_1 + x_2y_2$$

(3)
$$X^T AX = \begin{bmatrix} x_1 & x_2 \end{bmatrix} \begin{bmatrix} 1 & 3 \\ 3 & 2 \end{bmatrix} \begin{bmatrix} x_1 \\ x_2 \end{bmatrix}$$
$$= x_1^2 + 3x_1x_2 + 3x_1x_2 + 2x_2^2$$
$$= x_1^2 + 6x_1x_2 + 2x_2^2$$

Note that $a_{12} = a_{21} = 3$.

Problems

1. Given A, find the bilinear form $X^T A Y$.
$$A = \begin{bmatrix} 4 & 2 \\ -1 & 3 \end{bmatrix}$$

2. Given A, find $X^T A Y$.
$$A = \begin{bmatrix} 2 & 0 & 4 \\ -1 & 2 & -1 \\ 3 & -2 & 0 \end{bmatrix}$$

3. Find the quadratic form $X^T A X$.
$$A = \begin{bmatrix} 3 & 4 \\ 4 & -2 \end{bmatrix}$$

4. Find the quadratic form $X^T A X$.
$$A = \begin{bmatrix} 3 & 4 & 6 \\ 4 & -2 & 0 \\ 6 & 0 & 1 \end{bmatrix}$$

5. Given the bilinear expression
$$3x_1y_1 + 2x_1y_2 - 4x_1y_3 + x_2y_2 + 2x_2y_3 - x_3y_1 + 5x_3y_3$$
find A of $X^T A Y$

6. Given the quadratic
$$3x^2 - 6xy + y^2$$
find the matrix A of $X^T A X$.

7. Given the quadratic
$$x^2 + 2y^2 + 3z^2 + 4xy - 2yz + 6zx$$
find A of $X^T A X$.

8. Let $A = I$ in the quadratic form. Work out the case where
$$m = n = 3 \quad \text{for} \quad X^T I X$$

10.13 Linear transformations

(i) Mapping

In our previous discussion of mapping, we used a simple illustration (Figure 10–19)

$$f: \quad S_1 \to S_2$$

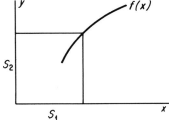

where S_1 and S_2 were given sets. The points in S_1 were called pre-image and those in S_2 were called the image points. In the conventional functional form, this was

$$y = f(x)$$

and the function f showed a *rule* of mapping.

Fig. 10–19

Let us generalize this idea in the following way: Assume S_1 is a two-dimensional space and S_2 a one-dimensional space. We shall show this

Fig. 10–20

graphically in Figure 10–20. A point in S_1 is shown as (x_1, x_2) which, in our newly acquired terminology, can be called a *vector point*. We wish to map this vector point $X = (x_1, x_2)$ into S_2. Let us now denote this mapping by T

instead of f. Thus,

$$T: \quad S_1 \to S_2$$

or we may express this as

$$T(X) = Y$$

where Y is the vector point in S_2 to which the vector point X has been mapped by T.

Let us illustrate by a simple example. Assume S_1 is a space made up of points that are combinations of the numbers of two dice. There will be $6 \times 6 = 36$ points in S_1.

Fig. 10–21

Let us pick a vector point, say, $X = (3, 4)$. We wish to map this point X from S_1 into S_2 where the vector points Y in S_2 will be defined as the sum of two elements in X. This is the *rule of mapping*. Since the smallest number on a die is 1 and the largest is 6, we can see that the points in S_2 will be 2, 3, ... 11, 12. We have 11 points.

Now that we have set up the *rule* that Y will be the sum of the elements of X, how are we going to show this in the form of $T(X) = Y$? This is an easy case and we can see that when

$$T = (1, 1)$$

then,

$$T(X)^T = [1, 1] \begin{bmatrix} x_1 \\ x_2 \end{bmatrix} = x_1 + x_2 = y = Y$$

i.e.,

$$T(X)^T = Y$$

What if we set up the rule that Y is to be the arithmetic mean of the x's?

What would T be then? We can see that it will be

$$T(X)^T = [\tfrac{1}{2}, \tfrac{1}{2}]\begin{bmatrix} x_1 \\ x_2 \end{bmatrix} = \tfrac{1}{2}(x_1 + x_2) = \bar{y} = Y$$

Suppose we toss n dice. Then S_1 will be a n-dimensional (vector) space and

$$X = (x_1, x_2, \dots x_n)$$

$$T(X)^T = \begin{bmatrix} \dfrac{1}{n}, \dfrac{1}{n}, \dots \dfrac{1}{n} \end{bmatrix}\begin{bmatrix} x_1 \\ x_2 \\ \cdot \\ \cdot \\ \cdot \\ x_n \end{bmatrix} = \frac{1}{n}\sum x_i = \bar{y} = Y$$

Thus, we have mapped the vector points X of the n-dimensional space S_1 into a one-dimensional vector space S_2, and this mapping can be shown in general as

$$T(X)^T = Y$$

Let us now let S_1 be three-dimensional, and S_2 be two-dimensional. Graphically we have Figure 10–22. In this case, using the ordinary functional notation, the mapping is

$$y_1 = f_1(x_1, x_2, x_3)$$

$$y_2 = f_2(x_1, x_2, x_3)$$

f gives the rule of mapping. Let us assume that the rule is, "y_i is the sum of x_1, x_2, x_3." Thus,

$$x_1 + x_2 + x_3 = y_1$$

$$x_1 + x_2 + x_3 = y_2$$

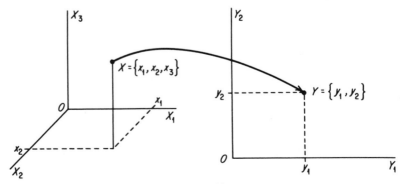

Fig. 10–22

Using matrix notation, we write this mapping as

$$\begin{bmatrix} 1 & 1 & 1 \\ 1 & 1 & 1 \end{bmatrix} \begin{bmatrix} x_1 \\ x_2 \\ x_3 \end{bmatrix} = \begin{bmatrix} x_1 + x_2 + x_3 \\ x_1 + x_2 + x_3 \end{bmatrix} = \begin{bmatrix} y_1 \\ y_2 \end{bmatrix}$$

Thus,

$$T = \begin{bmatrix} 1 & 1 & 1 \\ 1 & 1 & 1 \end{bmatrix}$$

If we set up the rule that

$$a_{11}x_1 + a_{12}x_2 + a_{13}x_3 = y_1$$

$$a_{21}x_1 + a_{22}x_2 + a_{23}x_3 = y_2$$

then, in matrix notation, we write this mapping as

$$\begin{bmatrix} a_{11} & a_{12} & a_{13} \\ a_{21} & a_{22} & a_{23} \end{bmatrix} \begin{bmatrix} x_1 \\ x_2 \\ x_3 \end{bmatrix} = \begin{bmatrix} y_1 \\ y_2 \end{bmatrix}$$

and

$$T = \begin{bmatrix} a_{11} & a_{12} & a_{13} \\ a_{21} & a_{22} & a_{23} \end{bmatrix}$$

This is easily generalized to n-dimensions. When S_1 is n-dimensions and S_2 is m-dimensions, then $T(X)^T = Y$ is written

$$\begin{bmatrix} a_{11} & a_{12} & \cdots & a_{1n} \\ a_{21} & a_{22} & \cdots & a_{2n} \\ \cdot & & & \\ \cdot & & & \\ \cdot & & & \\ a_{m1} & a_{m2} & \cdots & a_{mn} \end{bmatrix} \begin{bmatrix} x_1 \\ x_2 \\ \cdot \\ \cdot \\ \cdot \\ x_n \end{bmatrix} = \begin{bmatrix} y_1 \\ y_2 \\ \cdot \\ \cdot \\ \cdot \\ y_m \end{bmatrix}$$

Note that when mapping from S_1 (n-dimensions) to S_2 (m-dimensions), the T will be an $m \times n$ matrix.

Thus, we see that T is a matrix, and, conversely, that a matrix can be interpreted as a mapping. But also note that for $T(X)^T$ we get a *linear form* in the variable x_i. Let us discuss this point a little further.

Problems

1. For the case where

$$T = \begin{bmatrix} 1 & 1 & 1 \\ 1 & 1 & 1 \end{bmatrix}$$

what will the graph of S_2 look like?

2. What would S_2 look like when

$$T = \begin{bmatrix} 1 & 1 & 1 \\ 1 & 1 & 1 \\ 1 & 1 & 1 \end{bmatrix}$$

3. Given the transformation

$$x_1 + x_2 + x_3 = y_1$$

$$2x_1 + 2x_2 + 2x_3 = y_2$$

write this out in matrix notation showing all the elements. Draw a graph showing what is being done. What will the graph of Y look like in S_2?

(ii) Linear transformations

Consider S_1 (two-dimensions) and S_2 (two-dimensions) and map the points of S_1 into S_2 by some *rule*. (Figure 10–23). Let the rule (transformation) be as follows:

$$T(X)^T = Y$$

where

$$T = \begin{bmatrix} a_{11} & a_{12} \\ a_{21} & a_{22} \end{bmatrix}$$

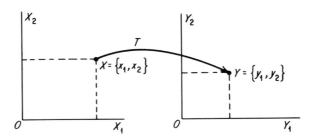

Fig. 10–23

Thus, when we write it out, we have

$$\begin{bmatrix} a_{11} & a_{12} \\ a_{21} & a_{22} \end{bmatrix} \begin{bmatrix} x_1 \\ x_2 \end{bmatrix} = \begin{bmatrix} y_1 \\ y_2 \end{bmatrix}$$

or

$$\begin{bmatrix} a_{11}x_1 + a_{12}x_2 \\ a_{21}x_2 + a_{22}x_2 \end{bmatrix} = \begin{bmatrix} y_1 \\ y_2 \end{bmatrix}$$

or, in conventional simultaneous equation form,

$$\begin{cases} a_{11}x_1 + a_{12}x_2 = y_1 \\ a_{21}x_1 + a_{22}x_2 = y_2 \end{cases}$$

Note three things. First, S_1 and S_2 are of the same dimensions. Thus, instead of saying we are mapping from S_1 into S_2, we could also say we are mapping S_1 into itself. Second, the equations are of a *linear form*. Third, we are assuming that the rows of T are linearly independent. Or we may say that the row rank of T is 2. The implication is that the simultaneous equations have a unique solution. This in turn means that for each value of X there is only one unique image vector Y.

Now let us juggle the above mapping and find more of its characteristics. First, let us multiply X by a scalar λ and map λX into S_2 by T. Then,

$$T(\lambda X)^T = \begin{bmatrix} a_{11} & a_{12} \\ a_{21} & a_{22} \end{bmatrix} \cdot \begin{bmatrix} \lambda x_1 \\ \lambda x_2 \end{bmatrix}$$

$$= \begin{bmatrix} \lambda a_{11} x_1 + \lambda a_{12} x_2 \\ \lambda a_{21} x_1 + \lambda a_{22} x_2 \end{bmatrix}$$

$$= \lambda \begin{bmatrix} a_{11} x_1 + a_{12} x_2 \\ a_{21} x_1 + a_{22} x_2 \end{bmatrix} = \lambda T(X)^T = \lambda Y$$

In general, we may state

$$T(\lambda X)^T = \lambda T(X)^T = \lambda Y$$

i.e., if Y is the image of X then λY is the image of λX under the transformation T. Second, let us try

$$T(X + X')^T$$

i.e., map $X + X'$ from S_1 into S_2. Then,

$$T(X + X')^T = \begin{bmatrix} a_{11} & a_{12} \\ a_{21} & a_{22} \end{bmatrix} \begin{bmatrix} x_1 + x_1' \\ x_2 + x_2' \end{bmatrix}$$

$$= \begin{bmatrix} a_{11}(x_1 + x_1') + a_{12}(x_2 + x_2') \\ a_{21}(x_1 + x_1') + a_{22}(x_2 + x_2') \end{bmatrix}$$

$$= \begin{bmatrix} (a_{11} x_1 + a_{12} x_2) + (a_{11} x_1' + a_{12} x_2') \\ (a_{21} x_1 + a_{22} x_2) + (a_{21} x_1' + a_{22} x_2') \end{bmatrix}$$

$$= \begin{bmatrix} a_{11} x_1 + a_{12} x_2 \\ a_{21} x_1 + a_{22} x_2 \end{bmatrix} + \begin{bmatrix} a_{11} x_1' + a_{12} x_2') \\ a_{21} x_1' + a_{22} x_2') \end{bmatrix}$$

$$= T(X)^T + T(X')^T = Y + Y'$$

Thus, we say that if Y and Y' are images of X and X' under the transformation T, then $Y + Y'$ will be the image of $X + X'$ under the transformation T. Graphically, this can be shown as Figure 10–24.

A transformation that has the above two characteristics will be called a *linear transformation*. We can show the characteristics compactly by

$$T(\lambda X)^T = \lambda T(X)^T = \lambda Y$$

$$T(X + X')^T = T(X)^T + T(X')^T = Y + Y'$$

Thus, we have shown that a square matrix can be interpreted as a linear transformation.

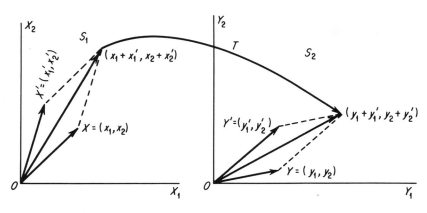

Fig. 10–24

(iii) Other properties of transformations

We have seen that a linear transformation T is a square matrix. Instead of using T, we can use a square matrix A in our subsequent discussion. Recalling some of the properties of matrix algebra, we now interpret those in connection with linear transformations.

Singular and non-singular transformations.

$$A = \begin{bmatrix} a_{11} & a_{12} & \cdots & a_{1n} \\ a_{21} & a_{22} & \cdots & a_{2n} \\ \cdot & & & \\ \cdot & & & \\ \cdot & & & \\ a_{n1} & a_{n2} & \cdots & a_{nn} \end{bmatrix}$$

When the n-row vectors were linearly independent, we said that the rank of A was n. This meant in graphic terms that we had an n-dimensional vector space.

When only $n-1$-row vectors were linearly independent, this meant that one of the row vectors could be shown as a linear combination of the other $n-1$-vectors, that we had an $n-1$-dimensional vector space, and that the matrix A was made up of n vectors in this $n-1$-dimensional vector space. We can also interpret this as a case where we have an n-dimensional space but one of the coordinates is zero.

Now what will happen when we apply this transformation matrix A to an n-dimensional vector? We can explain the result heuristically as follows: The n-dimensional vector (point) will be defined by n-coordinates. When the transformation A is applied, one of the coordinates will be mapped into a null (zero) vector.

Or we could say that the n-coordinates (each which can be considered as a vector) are linearly dependent, and only $n-1$ of them are linearly independent. We can find whether or not the row vectors of a matrix are linearly independent by applying elementary operations to the matrix and reducing it to Hermite form to find if any of the rows are zero.

Recalling our discussion of determinants, we saw that a determinant would be zero if any of the rows were zero or if any row was a linear combination of the other rows. This implies that the rows of the matrix are not linearly independent. When the determinant $|A| = 0$, we say we have a *singular transformation*. On the other hand, when the row vectors of a matrix are linearly independent, then $|A| \neq 0$. In this case we say that the transformation matrix (or linear transformation) is *non-singular*.

(iv) Other examples of transformations

We have discussed linear transformations in terms of a square matrix. But, as the following examples show, depending on the dimensions of S_1 and S_2, the transformation matrices need not be square. The transformation matrix will have m rows if S_2 is an m-dimensional space and n columns if S_1 is an n-dimensional space. Let us now examine several examples of the transformation process.

Example 1. Given the transformation

$$T = \begin{bmatrix} 2 & 3 \\ 4 & 5 \end{bmatrix}$$

find the point $X = \{x_1, x_2\}$ that maps into $Y = \{5, 9\}$. For this we set

$$TX^T = Y$$

$$\begin{bmatrix} 2 & 3 \\ 4 & 5 \end{bmatrix} \begin{bmatrix} x_1 \\ x_2 \end{bmatrix} = \begin{bmatrix} 5 \\ 9 \end{bmatrix}$$

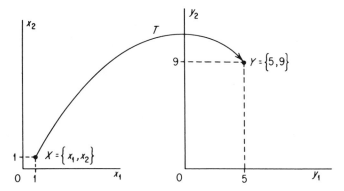

Fig. 10–25

In terms of equations this becomes

$$2x_1 + 3x_2 = 5$$
$$4x_1 + 5x_2 = 9$$

Solving this we get

$$x_1 = 1, \; x_2 = 1.$$

Thus the point we seek is $X = \{1, 1\}$.

Example 2. Given the transformation

$$T = [2, 3]$$

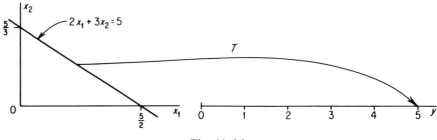

Fig. 10–26

find the point $X = \{x_1, x_2\}$ that maps into $Y = \{y_1\} = \{5\}$. For this we set

$$TX^T = Y$$

$$[2 \quad 3]\begin{bmatrix} x_1 \\ x_2 \end{bmatrix} = 5$$

Thus,

$$2x_1 + 3x_2 = 5$$

and the solution to this equation will be

$$x_1 = \tfrac{1}{2}(5 - 3m), \quad x_2 = m$$

where we have set $x_2 = m$, which is an arbitrary constant. The point we are seeking can thus be shown as

$$X = \{\tfrac{1}{2}(5 - 3m), \; m\}$$

For example, when $m = 1$, $X = \{1, 1\}$; when $m = 2$, $X = \{-\tfrac{1}{2}, 2\}$, and so forth. We have an infinite set of points in S_1 that will map into $y = 5$ in S_2, and these points are given by the straight line $2x_1 + 3x_2 = 5$ as shown in Figure 10–26.

Example 3. Map the point $X = \{x_1, x_2, x_3\}$ into $y = 5$, given the following T:

$$T = \{2, 2, 1\}$$

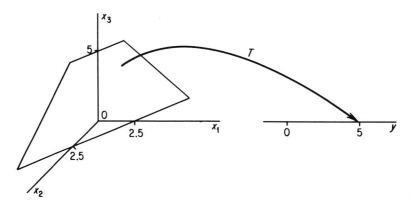

Fig. 10–27

This gives us

$$TX^T = y$$

$$[2 \quad 2 \quad 1] \begin{bmatrix} x_1 \\ x_2 \\ x_3 \end{bmatrix} = 5$$

$$2x_1 + 2x_2 + x_3 = 5$$

Let us set $x_1 = m$, $x_2 = n$ where m and n are arbitrary constants. Then,

$$x_3 = 5 - 2m - 2n$$

$m = 1$, and $n = 1$, for example, gives us

$$x_1 = 1, \qquad x_2 = 1, \qquad x_3 = 1$$

Thus, a point in S_1 that maps into $y = 5$ of S_2 will be $X = \{1, 1, 1\}$. And we can find an infinite number of points X that will satisfy our transformation and map into $y = 5$. As can be seen, these solution points will be the hyperplane* given by

$$2x_1 + 2x_2 + x_3 = 5$$

---

* A hypersurface is the locus of a point in n-dimensional space. When the point is restricted by a linear function as in our present case, we have a hyperplane.

Example 4. Map $X = \{x_1, x_2, x_3\}$ into $Y = \{y_1, y_2\}$ by the transformation,

$$T = \begin{bmatrix} 2 & 3 & 4 \\ 1 & 3 & 1 \end{bmatrix}$$

Fig. 10–28

Let us assume $Y = \{18 \quad 10\}$. Then we have

$$2x_1 + 3x_2 + 4x_3 = 18$$

$$x_1 + 3x_2 + x_3 = 10$$

Solving this we find

$$x_1 = 8 - 3x_3$$

$$x_2 = \tfrac{1}{3}[2 + 2x_3]$$

$$x_3 = m$$

where m is an arbitrary constant. When $m = 2$, then $x_2 = 2$, $x_1 = 2$. Therefore $X = \{2, 2, 2\}$ is one of the points that maps into Y. The points in S_1 that map into S_2 are the points of the intersection of the two hyperplanes given by the two equations.

Problems

1. Given the following set of equations

$$x_1 + 3x_2 = 7$$

$$4x_1 - x_2 = 2$$

(a) Rewrite this in matrix form $TX^T = Y$.
(b) Find the vector point X that maps into Y by the transformation T.
(c) Draw a graph of this mapping.

2. (a) Using the results of Problem 1, find λX where λ is an arbitrary constant. Let $\lambda = 1, 2, 3$, and plot these points on the graph and show what λX will be.

   (b) Then map λX into Y where $\lambda = 2$. Explain graphically what happens as λ takes on various values.

   (c) Let

$$X_1 = [1, 5], \qquad X_2 = [5, 2]$$

$$T = \begin{bmatrix} 1, & 3 \\ 4, & -1 \end{bmatrix}$$

   (1) Map X_1 into Y_1,
   (2) Map X_2 into Y_2,
   (3) Find $X_1 + X_2$,
   (4) Map $X_1 + X_2$ into the Y-space.
   (5) Find $Y_1 + Y_2$ and show that $TX_1^T + TX_2^T = Y_1 + Y_2$.

3. Given

$$3x_1 + 4x_2 = 12$$

   (a) Rewrite this in matrix form $TX^T = Y$,
   (b) Find the vector point X that maps into Y,
   (c) Draw a graph.

4. Find the points $X = \{x_1, x_2, x_3\}$ that map into $Y = \{y\} = \{6\}$, given the following T:

$$T = [2, 3, -6]$$

   Draw a rough graph schematically and show what has been done.

5. Find the points $X = \{x_1, x_2, x_3\}$ that map into $Y = \{y_1, y_2\} = \{27, 19\}$ given T.

$$T = \begin{bmatrix} 1 & 3 & 4 \\ 4 & 1 & 2 \end{bmatrix}$$

   Draw a rough graph and visualize the process.
   (Hint: $x_1 = \frac{1}{11} [30 - 2x_3]$, $x_2 = \frac{1}{11} [89 - 14x_3]$.)

10.14 Orthogonal transformations

Orthogonal transformations will be discussed again in the next chapter. At this point only a few definitions will be presented.

(i) Orthogonal vectors

When the inner product of two vectors is zero, the two vectors are said to be *orthogonal*. For example, let α and β be two vectors of the same order. When $\alpha\beta = 0$, then α and β are orthogonal. We know that

$$\cos \theta = \frac{\alpha \beta}{\|\alpha\| \, \|\beta\|}$$

Thus, when $\alpha \beta = 0$, then $\cos \theta = 0$. Thus, $\theta = 90°$, and so α and β are perpendicular. Furthermore, if $\|\alpha\| = 1$ and $\|\beta\| = 1$, then $\cos \theta = \alpha \beta$.

Example.

$$\alpha = \left(\frac{1}{\sqrt{2}}, \frac{1}{3\sqrt{2}}, \frac{2}{3} \right) \qquad \beta = \left(\frac{-1}{\sqrt{2}}, \frac{1}{3\sqrt{2}}, \frac{2}{3} \right)$$

$$\|\alpha\|^2 = (\alpha' \alpha) = \left(\frac{1}{\sqrt{2}}, \frac{1}{3\sqrt{2}}, \frac{2}{3} \right) \begin{bmatrix} \dfrac{1}{\sqrt{2}} \\ \dfrac{1}{3\sqrt{2}} \\ \dfrac{2}{3} \end{bmatrix} = \frac{1}{2} + \frac{1}{9 \times 2} + \frac{4}{9} = 1$$

Likewise for β. Thus, $\cos \theta = \alpha \beta$. Furthermore,

$$\cos \theta = \alpha \beta = \left(\frac{1}{\sqrt{2}}, \frac{1}{3\sqrt{2}}, \frac{2}{3} \right) \begin{bmatrix} \dfrac{-1}{\sqrt{2}} \\ \dfrac{1}{3\sqrt{2}} \\ \dfrac{2}{3} \end{bmatrix} = -\frac{1}{2} + \frac{1}{9 \times 2} + \frac{4}{9} = 0$$

Thus, $\theta = 90°$, i.e., α and β are orthogonal.

(ii) Orthogonal matrix

When

$$AA^T = I$$

where A is a square matrix, it is called an *orthogonal matrix*. Having defined an orthogonal matrix, let us investigate some of its properties. Let

$$A = \begin{bmatrix} a_{11} & a_{12} & a_{13} \\ a_{21} & a_{22} & a_{23} \\ a_{31} & a_{32} & a_{33} \end{bmatrix} = \begin{bmatrix} v_1 \\ v_2 \\ v_3 \end{bmatrix}$$

$$A^T = \begin{bmatrix} v_1 & v_2 & v_3 \end{bmatrix}$$

$$AA^T = \begin{bmatrix} a_{11} & a_{12} & a_{13} \\ a_{21} & a_{22} & a_{23} \\ a_{31} & a_{32} & a_{33} \end{bmatrix} \begin{bmatrix} a_{11} & a_{21} & a_{31} \\ a_{12} & a_{22} & a_{32} \\ a_{13} & a_{23} & a_{33} \end{bmatrix}$$

$$= \begin{bmatrix} v_1 v_1 & v_1 v_2 & v_1 v_3 \\ v_2 v_1 & v_2 v_2 & v_2 v_3 \\ v_3 v_1 & v_3 v_2 & v_3 v_3 \end{bmatrix} = \begin{bmatrix} 1 & 0 & 0 \\ 0 & 1 & 0 \\ 0 & 0 & 1 \end{bmatrix}$$

Thus, the implication of the definition is that

$$v_i v_j = 1 \quad \text{when} \quad i = j$$

$$v_i v_j = 0 \quad \text{when} \quad i \neq j$$

But, when two vectors $v_i v_j = 0$, $(i \neq j)$, it meant that they were perpendicular to each other. Also v_i^2 gave us the length of vector v_i. Thus, the definition implies we have a set of coordinates that are perpendicular to each other and we have 1 as the unit length of the vector. Since $AA^T = I$, we can multiply by A^{-1}. Then,

$$A^{-1}AA^T = A^{-1}$$

$$\therefore \quad A^T = A^{-1}$$

(iii) Orthogonal transformations

Let $X = AY$ be a linear transformation. If A is an orthogonal matrix, then this is called an orthogonal transformation.

We shall discuss these ideas again in more detail in the next chapter.

10.15 Rank of a matrix

In Section 10.6 the rank of a matrix was defined as the number of linearly independent row vectors in a matrix. This concept of a rank will become very important in subsequent discussion, but discussion of it was postponed until a certain amount of matrix algebra was covered. We may now consider the concept of rank and its implications in more detail. The main problem in this section will be: When given a matrix, how do we determine its rank. Let us start our discussion with a geometrical interpretation of a basis of a vector space.

(i) Basis

A *basis* in a vector space is a set of linearly independent vectors spanning the vector space, such that every vector of the space is a linear combination of vectors of this set. For example, let

$$v_1 = (2 \quad 1) \qquad v_2 = (1 \quad 2)$$

be the 2 vectors in Figure 10–29. Then, when we set

(1) $$k_1 v_1 + k_2 v_2 = 0$$

we find this holds only when $k_1 = k_2 = 0$ and hence v_1 and v_2 are linearly independent.

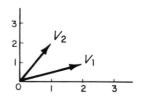

Fig. 10–29

Let us now find a vector $v_3 \neq 0$ such that

(2) $$v_3 = \alpha_1 v_1 + \alpha_2 v_2$$

Then, for example, are v_1 and v_3 linearly independent? The answer is: If $\alpha_2 \neq 0$, we may replace v_2 with v_3 and the 2 vectors v_1 and v_3 will be linearly independent.

To show that v_1 and v_3 are linearly independent, let us set

(3) $$\beta_1 v_1 + \beta_3 v_3 = 0$$

and check whether $\beta_1 = \beta_3 = 0$. If so, v_1 and v_3 will be linearly independent. For this we substitute (2) in (3)

(4) $$\beta_1 v_1 + \beta_3 [\alpha_1 v_1 + \alpha_2 v_2] = 0$$
$$[\beta_1 + \beta_3 \alpha_1] v_1 + \beta_3 \alpha_2 v_2 = 0$$

Since v_1 and v_2 are linearly independent, we must have

(5) $$\beta_1 + \beta_3 \alpha_1 = 0$$

(6) $$\beta_3 \alpha_2 = 0$$

But we have assumed $\alpha_2 \neq 0$. Thus $\beta_3 = 0$. Then (5) becomes

$$\beta_1 + 0\alpha_1 = 0$$
$$\beta_1 = 0$$

Hence, $\beta_1 = 0$ and $\beta_3 = 0$, and from (3) we conclude that v_1 and v_3 are linearly independent.

Let us now interpret (2) geometrically. For simplicity, let $\alpha_1 = 1$ and $\alpha_2 = 2$. Then v_3 may be shown geometrically, as in Figure 10–30.

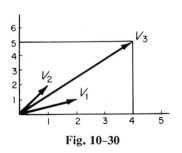

Fig. 10–30

$$v_3 = v_1 + 2v_2 = \begin{bmatrix} 2 \\ 1 \end{bmatrix} + 2 \begin{bmatrix} 1 \\ 2 \end{bmatrix} = \begin{bmatrix} 4 \\ 5 \end{bmatrix}$$

Then, as we have seen, v_1 and v_3 are linearly independent. Also, since we have set $\alpha_1 = 1 \neq 0$, v_2 and v_3 are linearly independent.

Equation (2) may be interpreted as elementary row operations. For example, the 2 vectors v_1 and v_2 may be shown in matrix form as

$$A = \begin{bmatrix} v_1 \\ v_2 \end{bmatrix} = \begin{bmatrix} 2 & 1 \\ 1 & 2 \end{bmatrix}$$

Then (2) is the operation

$$\begin{bmatrix} v_1 \\ \alpha_1 v_1 + \alpha_2 v_2 \end{bmatrix} = \begin{bmatrix} v_1 \\ v_1 + 2v_2 \end{bmatrix} = \begin{bmatrix} v_1 \\ v_3 \end{bmatrix} = \begin{bmatrix} 2 & 1 \\ 4 & 5 \end{bmatrix}$$

where we have replaced v_2 with v_3.

We may also express matrix A as a set of column vectors, and it is easily seen that equation (2) may also be interpreted as elementary column operations.

Hence, we may summarize our discussion as follows: Given a 2×2 matrix A which has 2 linearly independent row vectors, the elementary row operations may be interpreted geometrically as constructing new vectors v_3 as linear combinations of these 2 vectors, and, when $\alpha_2 \neq 0$ in (2), we may replace v_2 with v_3 and v_1 and v_3 will be linearly independent.

There are several more questions we should like to investigate. One is: Are v_1 and v_3 a basis for this 2-dimensional space? A second is: Are v_1, v_2, and v_3 linearly independent? That is, can there be more than 2 linearly independent vectors in this 2-dimensional space? If it turns out that v_1 and v_3 are a basis and that there are only 2 linearly independent vectors in the 2-dimensional space, the implication is that we may perform elementary row operations on a matrix A and construct as many new vectors, such as v_3, as we wish, but the 2 row vectors that finally remain in A (such as v_1 and v_3) will be linearly independent. That is, elementary row operations will not change the number of linearly independent vectors in a matrix. This is the important conclusion we seek. Let us first check whether v_1 and v_3 are a basis.

(ii) Vectors v_1 and v_3 are a basis

Suppose we construct a vector v_4 as

(7) $$v_4 = \lambda_1 v_1 + \lambda_2 v_2$$

We have from (2), since we have assumed $\alpha_2 \neq 0$,

(8) $$v_2 = \frac{\alpha_1}{\alpha_2} v_1 - \frac{1}{\alpha_2} v_3$$

Substituting (8) in (7) gives us

$$v_4 = \lambda_1 v_1 + \lambda_2 \left[\frac{\alpha_1}{\alpha_2} v_1 - \frac{1}{\alpha_2} v_3 \right]$$

$$= \left[\lambda_1 + \lambda_2 \frac{\alpha_1}{\alpha_2} \right] v_1 - \frac{\lambda_2}{\alpha_2} v_3$$

$$= \delta_1 v_1 + \delta_2 v_2$$

where

$$\delta_1 = \lambda_1 + \lambda_2 \frac{\alpha_1}{\alpha_2}$$

$$\delta_2 = - \frac{\lambda_2}{\alpha_2}$$

We have shown that v_4 can be expressed as a linear combination of v_1 and v_3, which we know are linearly independent. Hence v_1 and v_3 are a basis.

(iii) The basis is unique

Let us next show that every basis of the 2-dimensional space has exactly 2 linearly independent vectors. To show this, suppose we have two sets

$$v_1, v_2$$
$$q_1, q_2, q_3$$

of vectors where each is a basis. Since v_1 and v_2 are a basis, we may write

$$q_1 = m_1 v_1 + m_2 v_2$$

Assuming $m_2 \neq 0$, we know that v_1 and q_1 are a basis.

Using v_1 and q_1, we now may write

$$q_2 = n_1 v_1 + n_2 q_1$$

Assuming $n_1 \neq 0$, then q_1 and q_2 will be a basis.

But, if q_1 and q_2 are linearly independent and form a bais, q_3 can be expressed as a linear combination of q_1 and q_2. That is, q_1, q_2, and q_3 become linearly dependent. But this result contradicts the assumption we started with, namely, that q_1, q_2, and q_3 are a basis. To avoid this contradiction, there must be at least 3 vectors v_1, v_2, and v_3.

On the other hand, since q_1, q_2, and q_3 are a basis, we may write

$$v_1 = \mu_1 q_1 + \mu_2 q_2 + \mu_3 q_3$$

Assume $\mu_3 \neq 0$. Then we know that q_1, q_2, and v_1 will form a basis. Next let

$$v_2 = \nu_1 q_1 + \nu_2 q_2 + \nu_3 v_1$$

Let $\nu_2 \neq 0$. Then q_1, v_1, and v_2 are linearly independent and form a basis. But, since we have assumed v_1 and v_2 to be a basis, q_1, v_1, and v_2 must be linearly dependent. But this is a contradiction and has arisen from the assumption that q_1, q_2, and q_3 are linearly independent. Hence, for this assumption to be consistent, at most only 2 of q_1, q_2, and q_3 can be linearly independent.

Therefore, we cannot have (v_1, v_2) and (q_1, q_2, q_3). We must choose

$$(v_1, v_2, v_3) \quad \text{and} \quad (q_1, q_2, q_3)$$

or

$$(v_1, v_2) \quad \text{and} \quad (q_1, q_2)$$

Which is it?

Since we have a 2-dimensional space, it has 2 unit vectors e_1 and e_2 and we know that this set (e_1, e_2) forms a basis of the 2-dimensional space. Hence it must be (v_1, v_2) and (q_1, q_2).

Our conclusion is that, given E_2, every basis for E_2 consists of exactly 2 linearly independent vectors. That is, the basis is unique, and the number of vectors in the basis is equal to the dimensions of the vector space.

(iv) Elementary row operations do not change the row rank of a matrix

We have explained in Section (*i*) above that, given a 2×2 matrix A with 2 linearly independent row vectors, elementary row operations do not change the number of independent vectors. Let us now investigate this problem a little further. Let the matrix be

$$A = \begin{bmatrix} 2 & 1 \\ 1 & 2 \end{bmatrix} = \begin{bmatrix} v_1 \\ v_2 \end{bmatrix}$$

as before. Figure 10–29 is reproduced here as Figure 10–31 for convenience.

Let us now perform elementary row operations and reduce A to its Hermite form.

Fig. 10–31

$$\begin{array}{ccc} E_1 & A & B \end{array}$$
$$\begin{bmatrix} \frac{1}{2} & 0 \\ 0 & 1 \end{bmatrix} \begin{bmatrix} 2 & 1 \\ 1 & 2 \end{bmatrix} = \begin{bmatrix} 1 & \frac{1}{2} \\ 1 & 2 \end{bmatrix}$$

$$\begin{array}{ccc} E_2 & B & C \end{array}$$
$$\begin{bmatrix} 1 & 0 \\ -1 & 1 \end{bmatrix} \begin{bmatrix} 1 & \frac{1}{2} \\ 1 & 2 \end{bmatrix} = \begin{bmatrix} 1 & \frac{1}{2} \\ -1+1 & -\frac{1}{2}+2 \end{bmatrix} = \begin{bmatrix} 1 & \frac{1}{2} \\ 0 & \frac{3}{2} \end{bmatrix}$$

$$\begin{array}{ccc} E_3 & C & D \end{array}$$
$$\begin{bmatrix} 1 & 0 \\ 0 & \frac{2}{3} \end{bmatrix} \begin{bmatrix} 1 & \frac{1}{2} \\ 0 & \frac{3}{2} \end{bmatrix} = \begin{bmatrix} 1 & \frac{1}{2} \\ 0 & 1 \end{bmatrix}$$

$$\begin{array}{ccc} E_4 & D \end{array}$$
$$\begin{bmatrix} 1 & -\frac{1}{2} \\ 0 & 1 \end{bmatrix} \begin{bmatrix} 1 & \frac{1}{2} \\ 0 & 1 \end{bmatrix} = \begin{bmatrix} 1 & \frac{1}{2}-\frac{1}{2} \\ 0 & 1 \end{bmatrix} = \begin{bmatrix} 1 & 0 \\ 0 & 1 \end{bmatrix}$$

$$\therefore \quad \overset{E_4}{\begin{bmatrix} 1 & -\frac{1}{2} \\ 0 & 1 \end{bmatrix}} \overset{E_3}{\begin{bmatrix} 1 & 0 \\ 0 & \frac{2}{3} \end{bmatrix}} \overset{E_2}{\begin{bmatrix} 1 & 0 \\ -1 & 1 \end{bmatrix}} \overset{E_1}{\begin{bmatrix} \frac{1}{2} & 0 \\ 0 & 1 \end{bmatrix}} \overset{A}{\begin{bmatrix} 2 & 1 \\ 1 & 2 \end{bmatrix}} = \begin{bmatrix} 1 & 0 \\ 0 & 1 \end{bmatrix}$$

For example, E_1 is the operation of multiplying v_1 by $\frac{1}{2}$. Diagrammatically, the length of v has been reduced to $\frac{1}{2}$.

In terms of linear combinations, we have

$$v_3 = k_1 v_1 + k_2 v_2 = \tfrac{1}{2} v_1 + 0 v_2$$

Since $k_1 = \frac{1}{2} \neq 0$, we may replace v_1 with v_3, and hence

$$v_3 = (1, \tfrac{1}{2}), \quad \text{and} \quad v_1 = (2, 1)$$

are the 2 linearly independent vectors.

The E_2, E_3, and E_4 may be interpreted in similar manner. And in each case we get a new set of 2 linearly independent vectors which are a basis of the 2-dimensional space.

Let us now combine E_1, E_2, E_3, and E_4.

$$P = E_4 E_3 E_2 E_1 = \begin{bmatrix} 1 & -\frac{1}{2} \\ 0 & 1 \end{bmatrix} \begin{bmatrix} 1 & 0 \\ 0 & \frac{2}{3} \end{bmatrix} \begin{bmatrix} 1 & 0 \\ -1 & 1 \end{bmatrix} \begin{bmatrix} \frac{1}{2} & 0 \\ 0 & 1 \end{bmatrix}$$

$$= \begin{bmatrix} \frac{4}{6} & -\frac{1}{3} \\ -\frac{1}{3} & \frac{2}{3} \end{bmatrix}$$

Then,

$$PA = \begin{bmatrix} \frac{4}{6} & -\frac{1}{3} \\ -\frac{1}{3} & \frac{2}{3} \end{bmatrix} \begin{bmatrix} 2 & 1 \\ 1 & 2 \end{bmatrix} = \begin{bmatrix} 1 & 0 \\ 0 & 1 \end{bmatrix}$$

We shall denote $PA = H$ to show it is in Hermite form. This matrix P has performed all 4 steps in 1 step. And, according to our discussion above, this matrix PA should have 2 linearly independent vectors.

Let us now check to see whether PA has 2 linearly independent row vectors. In our present case, PA has turned out to be an identity matrix, and we can easily determine by observation that there are 2 linearly independent row vectors.

But, in general, the Hermite form will be

$$H = \begin{bmatrix} 1 & a_{12} & a_{13} & a_{14} \\ 0 & 1 & a_{23} & a_{24} \\ 0 & 0 & 1 & a_{34} \\ 0 & 0 & 0 & 0 \end{bmatrix} = \begin{bmatrix} v_1 \\ v_2 \\ v_3 \\ v_4 \end{bmatrix}$$

and it will turn out that the number of non-zero row vectors will be the number of linearly independent row vectors. Let us check this statement.

Let k_1, k_2, k_3, and k_4 be scalars. Set

(8) $$k_1 v_1 + k_2 v_2 + k_3 v_3 + k_4 v_4 = 0$$

This becomes

$$(k_1 \quad k_1 a_{12} \quad k_1 a_{13} \quad k_1 a_{14})$$
$$+ \ (0 \quad k_2 \quad k_2 a_{23} \quad k_2 a_{24})$$
$$+ \ (0 \quad 0 \quad k_3 \quad k_3 a_{34})$$
$$+ \ (0 \quad 0 \quad 0 \quad k_4 0) = (0 \quad 0 \quad 0 \quad 0)$$

This may be written as

$$k_1 + 0 + 0 + 0 = 0$$
$$k_1 a_{12} + k_2 + 0 + 0 = 0$$
$$k_1 a_{13} + k_2 a_{23} + k_3 + 0 = 0$$
$$k_1 a_{14} + k_2 a_{24} + k_3 a_{34} + k_4 0 = 0$$
$$\therefore \quad k_1 = 0, \qquad k_2 = 0, \qquad k_3 = 0$$

But from the last equation we see that k_4 may be an arbitrary constant and hence $k_4 \neq 0$. Hence we have a set of scalars k_1, k_2, k_3, and k_4 not all zero that satisfies (8), which means the vectors v_1, v_2, v_3, and v_4 are linearly dependent.

If we repeat this process for v_1, v_2, and v_3 and set

$$l_1 v_1 + l_2 v_2 + l_3 v_3 = 0$$

we can easily see that $l_1 = l_1 = l_3 = 0$ and the three vectors will be linearly independent.

Hence we may conclude that the number of non-zero row vectors will give us the number of linearly independent row vectors in a Hermite form.

Let us now summarize our results. Given a matrix A, we may perform elementary row operations and reduce it to its Hermite form. Let this be expressed by

$$PA = H$$

The elementary row operations do not change the number of linearly independent row vectors in A.

The rank of a matrix A is defined as the number of linearly independent row vectors. Let this be denoted by $r(A)$. Then we may state that

$$r(PA) = r(A)$$

and also, since $PA = H$,

$$r(A) = r(H)$$

The rank of H is determined by counting the number of non-zero rows.

This result $r(A) = r(H)$ gives us a means of finding the rank of A very easily. It is easy to see that, when given a matrix A, it will be a difficult task to find $r(A)$ from A directly. However, by reducing A to H, the rank is determined by merely counting the number of non-zero row vectors of H.

(v) $r(AP) = r(A)$

Up to now we have explained things in terms of row operations. But we can also reduce A to its Hermite form by elementary column operations. Let this be shown by

$$AP = H$$

That is, the column operations are shown by post-multiplying A by P. Like row operations, the column operations do not change the rank of the matrix. Hence,

$$r(AP) = r(A) = r(H)$$

(*vi*) *PAQ*

It is clear from Sections (*iv*) and (*v*) above that we may perform elementary row and column operations on A and the rank of A will remain unchanged. Let us express the row and column operations on A by PAQ. Also let $r(A) = R = 3$. Then

$$r(PAQ) = r(A) = R = 3$$

But, when row and column operations are performed, A will be reduced to a very simple form such as

$$N = \begin{bmatrix} 1 & 0 & 0 & 0 \\ 0 & 1 & 0 & 0 \\ 0 & 0 & 1 & 0 \\ 0 & 0 & 0 & 0 \\ 0 & 0 & 0 & 0 \end{bmatrix} = \begin{bmatrix} I_3 & 0 \\ 0 & 0 \end{bmatrix}$$

where we can immediately see that $r(N) = R = 3$. The reason for this is that the PA operation will reduce A to its Hermite form H, and, when column operations are performed on H, it will be further reduced to a form such as shown by N above. We may express this by

(9) $$PAQ = N$$

and

$$r(PAQ) = r(A) = r(N) = R = 3$$

Let us illustrate this as follows.

$$P: \quad p \times p = 5 \times 5$$
$$A: \quad p \times p = 5 \times 4$$
$$Q: \quad q \times q = 4 \times 4$$
$$N: \quad (p \times p) \times (p \times q) \times (q \times q) = p \times q = 5 \times 4$$

From (9) we find, since P and Q are non-singular square matrices,

(10) $$A = P^{-1}NQ^{-1}$$

Now let B be a $q \times n = 4 \times 6$ matrix. Then

(11) $AB = P^{-1}NQ^{-1}B$

Since P is non-singular, we know that

(12) $r(PAB) = r(AB)$

But

(13) $PAB = P(P^{-1}NQ^{-1}B)$
$$= NQ^{-1}B$$

Therefore, from (12) and (13),

$$r(AB) = r(PAQ) = r(NQ^{-1}B)$$

Let us check the matrix $NQ^{-1}B$.

$$
\begin{array}{cc}
5 \times 4 & 4 \times 4 \quad 4 \times 6
\end{array}
$$

$$NQ^{-1}B = \begin{bmatrix} I_R & 0 \\ 0 & 0 \end{bmatrix} \times [Q] \times [B]$$

$$= \begin{bmatrix} 1 & 0 & 0 & 0 \\ 0 & 1 & 0 & 0 \\ 0 & 0 & 1 & 0 \\ 0 & 0 & 0 & 0 \\ 0 & 0 & 0 & 0 \end{bmatrix} \begin{bmatrix} (QB)_{11} & (QB)_{12} & (QB)_{13} & \cdots & (QB)_{15} & (QB)_{16} \\ (QB)_{21} & \cdots & & & & \\ \cdots & & & & & \\ (QB)_{41} & \cdots & & & & (QB)_{46} \end{bmatrix}$$

$$= \begin{bmatrix} (QB)_{11} & \cdots & (QB)_{16} \\ (QB)_{21} & \cdots & (QB)_{26} \\ (QB)_{31} & \cdots & (QB)_{36} \\ 0 & \cdots & 0 \\ 0 & \cdots & 0 \end{bmatrix}$$

Hence, $NQ^{-1}B$ is a 5×6 matrix. Furthermore its first $R = 3$ rows will be the first $R = 3$ rows of $Q^{-1}B$, and the remaining $p - R = 5 - 3 = 2$ rows will be zeros.

The rank of $NQ^{-1}B$ will be $R = 3$ or less, since the other rows are zeros. We do not know whether the $R = 3$ rows are linearly independent. If they are, then the rank of $NQ^{-1}B$ will be 3; otherwise it will be less. Thus we may write

$$r(NQ^{-1}B) \leq R = 3$$

Since $r(NQ^{-1}B) = r(AB)$, we can now say that

$$r(AB) \leq R = 3$$

But we have assumed that $r(A) = R = 3$. Therefore, we conclude that

$r(AB) \leq r(A) = R = 3$. In a similar manner we can find that

$$r(AB) \leq r(B)$$

These two results may be combined and expressed by

$$r(AB) \leq \min \{r(A), r(B)\}$$

(vii) Row rank = column rank

We have stated that elementary row and column operations do not change the rank of a matrix. We have also seen that

$$PAQ = \begin{bmatrix} I_R & 0 \\ 0 & 0 \end{bmatrix}$$

Quite clearly, the row rank and column rank of PAQ are both $r(PAQ) = R$. But $r(PAQ) = r(A)$. Thus the row and column rank of A are equal.

Notes and References

Matrix algebra is a broad topic, and as economists we have selected certain parts of it that are of special interest. The topics we have discussed are also mentioned under similar headings in the following references, so specific page references have been omitted. The most useful reference for finding proofs and further study for economic and business students is Hadley (1961). In addition, the student will find that three useful and not too difficult references for finding proofs and derivations are Ferrar (1941), Murdoch (1957), and Mirsky (1957). Also recommended is Chapter 4, "Linear Algebra," of Kemeny (1958), which discusses mainly vectors and linear transformations. Since matrix algebra is a broad topic, it is probably advisable to read Chapters 10 and 11 of this book first. Then read Allen (1956), Chapters 12, 13, and 14; Chapter 12 of this book and Chapter 12 of Baumol (1959), which deals with systems of equations. Then, Chapter 3 of Johnston (1963); and Chapter 2 of Goldberger (1964). This should provide an adequate background for economists who do not plan to become mathematical economists or econometricians.

For economic illustrations see Allen (1956), Chapter 10, "General Economic Equilibrium," and Chapter 11, "Inter-Industry Relations," which discuss input-output analysis. An excellent book on an advanced level dealing with topics of interest to economists, programmers, or statisticians is Bellman (1960).

Aitken, A. C., *Determinants and Matrices*, 9th ed. London: Oliver & Boyd, Ltd., 1958.

Bellman, R., *Introduction to Matrix Analysis*. New York: McGraw-Hill Book Company, 1960.

Birkhoff, G. and MacLane, S., *A Survey of Modern Algebra*. New York: The Macmillan Company, 1953.

Ferrar, W. C., *Algebra*. New York: Oxford University Press, 1941.

Frazer, R. A., Duncan, W. J., and Collar, A. R., *Elementary Matrices*. New York: Cambridge University Press, 1957.

Gantmacher, F. R., *The Theory of Matrices*, Vol. I, transl. by K. A. Hirsch. New York: Chelsea Publishing Co., 1959.

Goldberger, A. S., *Econometric Theory*. New York: John Wiley & Sons, Inc., 1964.

Hadley, G., *Linear Algebra*. Reading, Mass.: Addison-Wesley Publishing Co., Inc., 1961.

Johnston, J., *Econometric Methods*. New York: McGraw-Hill Book Company, 1963.

MacDuffee, C. C., *Vectors and Matrices*, revd. ed. La Salle, Ill.: Open Court Publishing Co., 1949.

Mirsky, L., *An Introduction to Linear Algebra*. New York: Oxford University Press, 1955.

Murdoch, D. C., *Linear Algebra for Undergraduates*. New York: John Wiley & Sons, Inc., 1957.

Perlis, S., *Theory of Matrices*. Reading, Mass.: Addison-Wesley Publishing Co., Inc., 1952.

Schreier, O., and Sperner, E., *Introduction to Modern Algebra and Matrix Theory*, transl. by M. Davis and M. Hausner. New York: Chelsea Publishing Co., 1955.

Wade, T. L., *The Algebra of Vectors and Matrices*. Reading, Mass.: Addison-Wesley Publishing Co., Inc., 1951.

CHAPTER 11

Vectors and Matrices (Part II)

Using the basic ideas of vectors and matrices discussed in Chapter 10, we shall now develop additional ideas which will enable us to investigate properties of equations and systems of equations. We shall find ways of transforming a complicated equation into a simple form and, using this simple form, find conditions that will qualify the behavior of the equations or systems of equations. These techniques are used frequently in mathematical economics when discussing general equilibrium analysis, input-output analysis, matrix multipliers, sector analysis, and linear programming. They are also used in statistics when discussing analysis of variance and multivariate analysis. In the natural sciences they are used in stability problems.

11.1 Characteristic equation of a square matrix

Let A be a square matrix that is non-singular.

$$A = \begin{bmatrix} 2 & 3 \\ 3 & 2 \end{bmatrix}$$

Let us construct a matrix $[A - \lambda I]$, where λ is a scalar variable and I is the unit matrix. Then,

$$A - \lambda I = \begin{bmatrix} 2 & 3 \\ 3 & 2 \end{bmatrix} - \lambda \begin{bmatrix} 1 & 0 \\ 0 & 1 \end{bmatrix} = \begin{bmatrix} 2 - \lambda & 3 \\ 3 & 2 - \lambda \end{bmatrix}$$

The $[A - \lambda I]$ is called the *characteristic matrix* of A. The determinant $|A - \lambda I|$ is called the *characteristic determinant* of A. We can expand the determinant as

$$|A - \lambda I| = (2 - \lambda)(2 - \lambda) - 3 \cdot 3 = \lambda^2 - 4\lambda - 5$$

This scalar polynomial

$$f(\lambda) = |A - \lambda I| = \lambda^2 - 4\lambda - 5$$

is called the *characteristic function (polynomial)* of the matrix A. As seen, we have a polynomial of degree two in the scalar variable λ. If we had an order-n matrix A, the function will be of order n.

Next, set

$$f(\lambda) = \lambda^2 - 4\lambda - 5 = 0$$

This is called the *characteristic equation* of matrix A. Let us solve this. We find

$$f(\lambda) = (\lambda + 1)(\lambda - 5) = 0$$

Thus, $\lambda_1 = -1$, $\lambda_2 = 5$, satisfies this characteristic equation. These two roots are called the *characteristic roots* of the matrix A.

The Hamilton-Cayley theorem* tells us that every matrix satisfies its characteristic equation. Using our example, this means

$$f(A) = (A + 1I)(A - 5I) = 0$$

Let us check this.

$$f(A) = (A + I)(A - 5I)$$

$$= \begin{bmatrix} 3 & 3 \\ 3 & 3 \end{bmatrix} \begin{bmatrix} -3 & 3 \\ 3 & -3 \end{bmatrix} = \begin{bmatrix} 0 & 0 \\ 0 & 0 \end{bmatrix}$$

Note that the order of the matrix factors is immaterial. That is,

$$f(A) = (A + I)(A - 5I) = (A - 5I)(A + I) = 0$$

We can also express this equation $f(A) = 0$ as

$$f(A) = -5I - 4A + A^2 = 0$$

Let us check this.

$$f(A) = -5I - 4A + A^2$$

$$= \begin{bmatrix} -5 & 0 \\ 0 & -5 \end{bmatrix} - 4\begin{bmatrix} 2 & 3 \\ 3 & 2 \end{bmatrix} + \begin{bmatrix} 2 & 3 \\ 3 & 2 \end{bmatrix}\begin{bmatrix} 2 & 3 \\ 3 & 2 \end{bmatrix}$$

$$= \begin{bmatrix} -5 & -8 + 13 & 0 - 12 + 12 \\ 0 - 12 + 12 & -5 & -8 + 13 \end{bmatrix} = \begin{bmatrix} 0 & 0 \\ 0 & 0 \end{bmatrix}$$

In general, if we have a square matrix A, then,

$$f(\lambda) = |A - \lambda I| = a_0 + a_1\lambda + a_2\lambda^2 + \ldots + a_n\lambda^n = 0$$

is its characteristic equation and $f(\lambda)$ is satisfied by A, i.e., $f(A) = 0$, where this is a matrix polynomial.

Problems

Find the characteristic roots of the following matrices.

1. $A = \begin{bmatrix} 1 & 4 \\ 1 & 1 \end{bmatrix}$ Ans. $-1, 3$.

* See MacDuffee, *Vectors and Matrices* (1943), p. 76.

2. $A = \begin{bmatrix} 2 & 1 \\ 1 & 2 \end{bmatrix}$

Ans. 1, 3.

3. $A = \begin{bmatrix} 3 & 0 & 4 \\ 1 & 1 & 2 \\ 1 & -2 & 2 \end{bmatrix}$

Ans. 1, 2, 3.

4. Substitute the matrix A in the characteristic equation, and check that $f(A) = 0$, for Problems 1, 2, and 3 above.

11.2 Similar matrices

We have previously stated that two matrices A and B are equivalent if two non-singular matrices P and Q exist such that $B = PAQ$. This means that by applying elementary operations on A we can transform it into B.

Now let us define as follows: If we have two square matrices A and B and if there exists a non-singular matrix P such that

$$B = P^{-1}AP$$

then A and B are said to be *similar*.

Let us now present some properties related to similar matrices and give content to this idea. First, if A and B are similar and B and C are similar, then A and C are similar. This can easily be seen by

$$A, \quad B = P^{-1}AP, \quad B, \quad C = Q^{-1}BQ$$

Thus,

$$C = Q^{-1}BQ = Q^{-1}(P^{-1}AP)Q = (PQ)^{-1}A(PQ)$$

i.e., A and C are similar.

Second, if A and B are similar, they have the same characteristic function. We know that $B = P^{-1}AP$. Thus,

$$B - \lambda I = P^{-1}AP - \lambda I = P^{-1}(A - \lambda I)P$$

Thus, the characteristic function of B becomes

$$|B - \lambda I| = |P^{-1}| \, |A - \lambda I| \, |P|$$
$$= |P^{-1}| \, |P| \, |A - \lambda I| = |A - \lambda I|$$

since $P^{-1}P = I$. Thus A and B have the same characteristic function.

It can also be shown that, when A and B are similar, they have the same determinant and the same rank.

Problems

1. Given

$$A = \begin{bmatrix} 1 & 4 \\ 1 & 1 \end{bmatrix}, \quad P = \begin{bmatrix} 1 & 2 \\ 0 & 1 \end{bmatrix}$$

Find
(a) P^{-1}. Note P is an elementary matrix.
(b) $B = P^{-1}AP$.
(c) $|B - \lambda I|$. Note that this is equal to $|A - \lambda I|$, which we have calculated in problems of the previous section.
(d) $|A|, |B|$.
(e) Reduce A and B to Hermite form.

2. Given

$$A = \begin{bmatrix} 1 & 0 & 0 \\ 1 & 3 & 2 \\ 1 & 0 & 2 \end{bmatrix}, \qquad P = \begin{bmatrix} 1 & 2 & 0 \\ 0 & 1 & 0 \\ 0 & 0 & 1 \end{bmatrix}$$

Find
(a) P^{-1}. Note P is an elementary matrix.
(b) $B = P^{-1}AP$.
(c) $|B - \lambda I|$. Note that this is equal to $|A - \lambda I|$ of the previous section.
(d) $|A|, |B|$.
(e) Reduce A and B to Hermite form.

11.3 Characteristic vector

Let

$$A = \begin{bmatrix} 2 & 0 & 1 \\ 1 & 1 & 1 \\ 1 & -1 & 3 \end{bmatrix}$$

Then the characteristic equation will be

$$|A - \lambda I| = (1 - \lambda)(2 - \lambda)(3 - \lambda) = 0$$

Thus, the characteristic roots are

$$\lambda_1 = 1, \qquad \lambda_2 = 2, \qquad \lambda_3 = 3$$

Using $\lambda_1 = 1$, for example, we know that

$$\Delta = |A - \lambda_1 I| = \begin{vmatrix} 1 & 0 & 1 \\ 1 & 0 & 1 \\ 1 & -1 & 2 \end{vmatrix} = 0$$

Using the elements of Δ, let us construct a set of linear homogeneous equations

$$x + z = 0$$
$$x + z = 0$$
$$x - y + 2z = 0$$

A theorem (Section 12.6) tells us that the necessary and sufficient condition for this system to have a non-trivial solution is that $\Delta = 0$. But we know that $\Delta = 0$. Thus, it has a non-trivial solution, and it is

$$x = -m, \quad y = m, \quad z = m$$

where m is an arbitrary constant. We can show this as

$$v_1' = (x, y, z) = m(-1, 1, 1)$$

and call it the *characteristic vector* when the characteristic root is $\lambda_1 = 1$. In similar manner we can find v_2 and v_3 that correspond to λ_2 and λ_3. This will turn out to be

$$\lambda_1: \quad v_1' = (-1, 1, 1)$$
$$\lambda_2: \quad v_2' = (1, 1, 0)$$
$$\lambda_3: \quad v_3' = (1, 1, 1)$$

where we have set $m = 1$.

Next let us show the system in matrix form.

(1) $$[A - \lambda_i I]v_i = 0 \qquad i = 1, 2, 3$$

where $v_i = (x, y, z)$. If we find a characteristic root and the corresponding characteristic vector, then the characteristic matrix times the characteristic vector is zero. That is, for v_1, for example,

$$\begin{bmatrix} 1 & 0 & 1 \\ 1 & 0 & 1 \\ 1 & -1 & 2 \end{bmatrix} \begin{bmatrix} -m \\ m \\ m \end{bmatrix} = \begin{bmatrix} 0 \\ 0 \\ 0 \end{bmatrix}$$

Transposing the $\lambda_i I v_i$ to the right-hand side of equation (1), we have

$$A v_i = \lambda_i v_i$$

and using this we can define the characteristic vector as a non-zero column vector that satisfies this relation where λ_i is a scalar. But, since this becomes, reversing the procedure,

$$[A - \lambda_i I]v_i = 0$$

and v_i is non-zero, then $[A - \lambda_i I] = 0$ and thus λ_i must be a characteristic root.

To summarize: If we have a square matrix A of order n with n distinct characteristic roots, we can obtain a characteristic vector v_i corresponding to a root λ_i. Then,

$$[A - \lambda_i I]v_i = 0$$

Using this result, we may easily show that, if λ_i is a characteristic root of A, then λ_i^2 is a characteristic root of A^2. This is shown as follows. From our result we have

$$A v_i = \lambda v_i$$

Multiply the left-hand side by A. Then

$$A^2 v_i = A(Av_i) = A(\lambda_i v_i)$$
$$= \lambda_i Av_i = \lambda_i(\lambda_i v_i)$$
$$= \lambda_i^2 v$$

Hence, λ_i^2 is a characteristic root of A^2. In general, if p is a positive integer, then λ_i^p is a characteristic root of A^p.

If $|A| \neq 0$, then λ_i^{-1} is a characteristic root of A^{-1}. For this we set

$$\lambda_i^{-1} A^{-1} AX = \lambda_i^{-1} A^{-1} \lambda_i v_i$$
$$\lambda_i^{-1} X = A^{-1} v_i$$

and λ_i^{-1} is a characteristic root of A^{-1}. In general, λ_i^{-p} is a characteristic root of A^{-p}.

Problems

Given the matrix A, find the characteristic vectors.

1. $A = \begin{bmatrix} 1 & 4 \\ 1 & 1 \end{bmatrix}$

2. $A = \begin{bmatrix} 2 & 1 \\ 1 & 2 \end{bmatrix}$

3. $A = \begin{bmatrix} 0 & -1 & 1 \\ -1 & 0 & 1 \\ 1 & 1 & 1 \end{bmatrix}$

4. $A = \begin{bmatrix} 3 & 0 & 4 \\ 1 & 1 & 2 \\ 1 & -2 & 2 \end{bmatrix}$

5. Find A^2 where

$$A = \begin{bmatrix} 1 & 4 \\ 1 & 1 \end{bmatrix}$$

and check that λ_i^2 is the characteristic root of A^2.

6. Do the same as Problem 5 for the following matrix.

$$A = \begin{bmatrix} 2 & 1 \\ 1 & 2 \end{bmatrix}$$

7. Do the same as Problem 5 for the following matrix.

$$A = \begin{bmatrix} 3 & 0 & 4 \\ 1 & 1 & 2 \\ 1 & -2 & 2 \end{bmatrix}$$

11.4 Diagonalization of a square matrix

We now wish to show that we can find a matrix P such that

$$P^{-1}AP = D = \begin{bmatrix} \lambda_1 & & & \\ & \lambda_2 & & \\ & & \ddots & \\ & & & \lambda_n \end{bmatrix}$$

where D is a diagonal matrix that has the n characteristic roots in its diagonal. Note that A and D are similar. For this we first find the modal matrix of A.

(i) Modal matrix of A

We found the three characteristic vectors v_1, v_2, and v_3 of A. Using these, let us construct a matrix P such that

$$P = [v_1, v_2, v_3] = \begin{bmatrix} -1 & 1 & 1 \\ 1 & 1 & 1 \\ 1 & 0 & 1 \end{bmatrix}$$

where each column is a characteristic vector of A. We shall call this the *modal matrix of A*, and this will be the matrix that transforms A into the desired diagonal matrix D.

(ii) Diagonalization of a square matrix

We now have the modal matrix $P = [v_1, v_2, v_3]$. We also know that

$$[A - \lambda_1 I]v_1 = 0$$

where λ_1 is the characteristic root and v_1 is the corresponding characteristic vector. From this we have $Av_1 = \lambda_1 v_1$. Likewise for v_2 and v_3 we have

$$Av_2 = \lambda_2 v_2, \qquad Av_3 = \lambda_3 v_3$$

Since D is the diagonal matrix, we may write

$$D = [\lambda_1 e_1 \quad \lambda_2 e_2 \quad \lambda_3 e_3]$$

Then

$$PD = (\lambda_1 P e_1 \quad \lambda_2 P e_2 \quad \lambda_3 P e_3)$$

But, for example,

$$Pe_1 = [v_1 \quad v_2 \quad v_3]\begin{bmatrix} 1 \\ 0 \\ 0 \end{bmatrix} = v_1$$

Hence

(1) $$PD = (\lambda_1 v_1 \quad \lambda_2 v_2 \quad \lambda_3 v_3)$$

Let us now consider the product AP. We have

$$AP = A[v_1 \quad v_2 \quad v_3] = [Av_1 \quad Av_2 \quad Av_3]$$

But, since we have $Av_i = \lambda_i v_i$, this AP becomes

(2) $AP = [\lambda_1 v_1 \quad \lambda_2 v_2 \quad \lambda_3 v_3]$

Therefore, from (1) and (2) we may conclude that

$$AP = PD$$

Since the v_i are non-zero, we have, upon pre-multiplying by P^{-1},

$$P^{-1}AP = D$$

Thus, the modal matrix P transforms A into a diagonal matrix which has the characteristic roots in its diagonal.

Let us illustrate this. We have P. We need to find P^{-1}, and this can be obtained by the Gauss elimination method. It will be

$$P^{-1} = \begin{bmatrix} -\frac{1}{2} & \frac{1}{2} & 0 \\ 0 & 1 & -1 \\ \frac{1}{2} & -\frac{1}{2} & 1 \end{bmatrix}$$

Thus,

$$D = P^{-1}AP = \begin{bmatrix} -\frac{1}{2} & \frac{1}{2} & 0 \\ 0 & 1 & -1 \\ \frac{1}{2} & -\frac{1}{2} & 1 \end{bmatrix} \begin{bmatrix} 2 & 0 & 1 \\ 1 & 1 & 1 \\ 1 & -1 & 3 \end{bmatrix} \begin{bmatrix} -1 & 1 & 1 \\ 1 & 1 & 1 \\ 1 & 0 & 1 \end{bmatrix}$$

$$= \begin{bmatrix} 1 & 0 & 0 \\ 0 & 2 & 0 \\ 0 & 0 & 3 \end{bmatrix} = \begin{bmatrix} \lambda_1 & 0 & 0 \\ 0 & \lambda_2 & 0 \\ 0 & 0 & \lambda_3 \end{bmatrix}$$

Note that D and A are similar matrices.

It will be convenient for us to summarize this result as a theorem.

Theorem. If we have a square matrix A that has n distinct characteristic roots, we can find n characteristic vectors v_i. Let P be the modal matrix with the v_i as the column vectors. Then $P^{-1}AP$ is a diagonal matrix D similar to A that has the n characteristic roots in the main diagonal.

Several comments have to be made. First, we are assuming a square matrix with n *distinct* characteristic roots. The case where some of the roots may be equal will not be discussed.*

Secondly, as our illustration shows, the characteristic vector was

$$v_1' = (-m, m, m)$$

where m was an arbitrary constant. For illustrative purposes, we let $m = 1$, although m can take on any real value (except zero). And, in this sense the modal matrix is not unique. There will be many modal matrices, depending on the value of m.

* See Wade (1951), Chap. 8.

Problems

Given the following matrices, perform the following three operations.

(a) Find the modal matrix P.
(b) Find P^{-1}.
(c) Find $D = P^{-1}AP$.

1.
$$A = \begin{bmatrix} 1 & 4 \\ 1 & 1 \end{bmatrix}$$

2.
$$A = \begin{bmatrix} 2 & 1 \\ 1 & 2 \end{bmatrix}$$

3.
$$A = \begin{bmatrix} 0 & -1 & 1 \\ -1 & 0 & 1 \\ 1 & 1 & 1 \end{bmatrix}$$

4.
$$A = \begin{bmatrix} 3 & 0 & 4 \\ 1 & 1 & 2 \\ 1 & -2 & 2 \end{bmatrix}$$

11.5 Orthogonal transformations

Given a matrix A, a modal matrix P was obtained and used to diagonalize the matrix A. When A is a *symmetric matrix*, P becomes an orthogonal matrix as well as a modal matrix. In this section we shall discuss orthogonal matrices and, in the next, use them to diagonalize symmetric matrices. Symmetric matrices are important because they are the matrices associated with quadratic forms.

(i) An orthogonal transformation

Consider a vector α in the (X_1, X_2) plane. Let ϵ_1, ϵ_2 be the unit vectors

$$\epsilon_1 = (1, 0), \qquad \epsilon_2 = (0, 1)$$

Then we can show α as the sum of two vectors

(1)
$$\alpha = x_1 \epsilon_1 + x_2 \epsilon_2$$

where x_1 and x_2 are scalars (Figure 11–1). Or we can say in terms of coordinates that the vector point α is (x_1, x_2).

Now let us rotate the axes by θ, leaving α as it is, and call this new coordinate system (Y_1, Y_2). Let the vector point α be shown by (y_1, y_2) in relation to this new coordinate system. Then in terms of vectors, we have

(2)
$$\alpha = y_1 \epsilon_1' + y_2 \epsilon_2'$$

where ϵ_1', ϵ_2' are the unit vectors for the (Y_1, Y_2) coordinate system. Multiply (1)

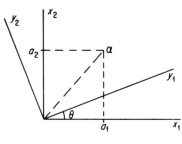

Fig. 11–1

by ϵ_1' and ϵ_2'. Thus,

$$\epsilon_1'\alpha = x_1\epsilon_1'\epsilon_1 + x_2\epsilon_1'\epsilon_2$$

$$\epsilon_2'\alpha = x_1\epsilon_2'\epsilon_1 + x_2\epsilon_2'\epsilon_2$$

But $\epsilon_1'\alpha$ will give us the first coordinate relative to the (Y_1, Y_2) coordinate system and, also for $\epsilon_2'\alpha$. Thus,

(3)
$$y_1 = x_1\epsilon_1'\epsilon_1 + x_2\epsilon_1'\epsilon_2$$

$$y_2 = x_1\epsilon_2'\epsilon_1 + x_2\epsilon_2'\epsilon_2$$

$\epsilon_1'\epsilon_1$ is the product of two vectors. But, as we have seen, the inner product of two vectors gives us

$$\cos\theta = \frac{\epsilon_1'\epsilon_1}{\|\epsilon_1'\|\,\|\epsilon_1\|}$$

Since ϵ_1' and ϵ_1 are unit vectors, we have

$$\epsilon_1'\epsilon_1 = \cos\theta$$

For $\epsilon_1'\epsilon_2$ we see that the angle is $90 - \theta$ with similar relations for the other pairs of unit vectors. Thus,

$$\epsilon_1'\epsilon_2 = \cos(90 - \theta) = \sin\theta$$

$$\epsilon_2'\epsilon_1 = \cos(90 + \theta) = -\sin\theta$$

$$\epsilon_2'\epsilon_2 = \cos\theta$$

Thus,

(4)
$$y_1 = x_1\cos\theta + x_2\sin\theta$$

$$y_2 = x_1(-\sin\theta) + x_2\cos\theta$$

Let us assume we have rotated the axis by $45°$. Then,

$$\cos\theta = \cos 45 = \frac{1}{\sqrt{2}}, \qquad \sin\theta = \frac{1}{\sqrt{2}}$$

Thus,

(5)
$$y_1 = \frac{1}{\sqrt{2}}x_1 + \frac{1}{\sqrt{2}}x_2$$

$$y_2 = -\frac{1}{\sqrt{2}}x_1 + \frac{1}{\sqrt{2}}x_2$$

or

(6)
$$\begin{bmatrix} y_1 \\ y_2 \end{bmatrix} = \begin{bmatrix} \dfrac{1}{\sqrt{2}} & \dfrac{1}{\sqrt{2}} \\ \dfrac{-1}{\sqrt{2}} & \dfrac{1}{\sqrt{2}} \end{bmatrix} \begin{bmatrix} x_1 \\ x_2 \end{bmatrix}$$

By using (4), this would be

(7)
$$\begin{bmatrix} y_1 \\ y_2 \end{bmatrix} = \begin{bmatrix} \cos\theta & \sin\theta \\ -\sin\theta & \cos\theta \end{bmatrix} \begin{bmatrix} x_1 \\ x_2 \end{bmatrix}$$

Looking at (7), we note two things in the transformation matrix. First, the lengths of the row vectors are 1.

$$(\cos\theta)^2 + (\sin\theta)^2 = 1$$
$$(-\sin\theta)^2 + (\cos\theta)^2 = 1$$

Second, the inner product of the two row vectors is 0. That is,

$$[\cos\theta \quad \sin\theta]\begin{bmatrix} -\sin\theta \\ \cos\theta \end{bmatrix} = 0$$

This is so because the two axes are perpendicular. We conclude that the transformation matrix is an orthogonal matrix, and we have an orthogonal transformation. That is, (5) gives us an orthogonal transformation.

We have showed it for two dimensions. In general, if we have a linear transformation

$$y = Ax$$

where

$$A = \begin{bmatrix} a_{11} & a_{12} & \cdots & a_{1n} \\ \vdots & & & \\ a_{n1} & a_{n2} & \cdots & a_{nn} \end{bmatrix}$$

and

$$a_{i1}^2 + a_{i2}^2 + \ldots + a_{in}^2 = 1$$
$$a_{i1}a_{j1} + \ldots + a_{in}a_{jn} = 0 \qquad (i \neq j)$$

then it is an orthogonal transformation. It can be interpreted geometrically as a rotation of axes, and the distance of the point from the origin is invariant.

(ii) Properties of an orthogonal matrix

Let A be an orthogonal matrix

$$A = \begin{bmatrix} a_{11} & a_{12} \\ a_{21} & a_{22} \end{bmatrix}$$

Then the transpose A^T will be

$$A^T = \begin{bmatrix} a_{11} & a_{21} \\ a_{12} & a_{22} \end{bmatrix}$$

Recalling that the length of row (or column) vectors is 1 and the inner product of two row (or column) vectors is zero, we find

$$AA^T = \begin{bmatrix} a_{11} & a_{12} \\ a_{21} & a_{22} \end{bmatrix} \begin{bmatrix} a_{11} & a_{21} \\ a_{12} & a_{22} \end{bmatrix}$$

$$= \begin{bmatrix} a_{11}^2 + a_{12}^2 & a_{11}a_{21} + a_{12}a_{22} \\ a_{21}a_{11} + a_{22}a_{12} & a_{21}^2 + a_{22}^2 \end{bmatrix} = \begin{bmatrix} 1 & 0 \\ 0 & 1 \end{bmatrix} = I$$

Thus, the first property is

$$AA^T = I$$

The second property is obtained from this by

$$A^{-1}AA^T = A^{-1}I$$

$$\therefore \quad A^T = A^{-1}$$

The third property is obtained by

$$AA^{-1} = A^{-1}A = I$$

$$\therefore \quad AA^T = A^TA = I$$

An example of an orthogonal matrix is

$$A = \begin{bmatrix} \dfrac{1}{\sqrt{2}} & \dfrac{1}{3\sqrt{2}} & \dfrac{2}{3} \\ \dfrac{-1}{\sqrt{2}} & \dfrac{1}{3\sqrt{2}} & \dfrac{2}{3} \\ 0 & \dfrac{4}{3\sqrt{2}} & -\dfrac{1}{3} \end{bmatrix}$$

Thus,

$$A^TA = \begin{bmatrix} \dfrac{1}{\sqrt{2}} & \dfrac{-1}{\sqrt{2}} & 0 \\ \dfrac{1}{3\sqrt{2}} & \dfrac{1}{3\sqrt{2}} & \dfrac{4}{3\sqrt{2}} \\ \dfrac{2}{3} & \dfrac{2}{3} & -\dfrac{1}{3} \end{bmatrix} \begin{bmatrix} \dfrac{1}{\sqrt{2}} & \dfrac{1}{3\sqrt{2}} & \dfrac{2}{3} \\ \dfrac{-1}{\sqrt{2}} & \dfrac{1}{3\sqrt{2}} & \dfrac{2}{3} \\ 0 & \dfrac{4}{3\sqrt{2}} & -\dfrac{1}{3} \end{bmatrix}$$

$$= \begin{bmatrix} 1 & 0 & 0 \\ 0 & 1 & 0 \\ 0 & 0 & 1 \end{bmatrix}$$

Also $AA^T = I$, and the inner product of the vectors is zero and the length of the row (or column) vectors is 1.

(*iii*) *Normalization of vectors*

A vector $v = (a_1, a_2, a_3)$ is said to be normalized if

$$a_1^2 + a_2^2 + a_3^2 = 1$$

Assume $v = (1, 2, 3)$. Then,

$$1^2 + 2^2 + 3^2 = 14$$

We can normalize this vector by finding

$$k = \frac{1}{\sqrt{1^2 + 2^2 + 3^2}} = \frac{1}{\sqrt{14}}$$

Then,

$$kv = (k, 2k, 3k)$$

and

$$(k)^2 + (2k)^2 + (3k)^2 = \tfrac{1}{14} + \tfrac{4}{14} + \tfrac{9}{14} = 1$$

In general, if $v = (a_1, a_2, a_3)$ is not normalized and $v \neq 0$, then, the vector kv will be normalized when

$$k = \frac{1}{\sqrt{a_1^2 + a_2^2 + a_3^2}}$$

This k is called a *normalizing factor*.

The vectors in an orthogonal matrix are normalized. Let us illustrate. Let

$$P = \begin{bmatrix} -1 & 1 \\ 1 & 1 \end{bmatrix}$$

We can see that the inner product of the row (or column) vectors is zero.

$$\begin{bmatrix} -1 & 1 \end{bmatrix} \begin{bmatrix} 1 \\ 1 \end{bmatrix} = -1 + 1 = 0$$

But the length of the vectors is not 1.

$$v_1: \quad (-1)^2 + (1)^2 = 2$$
$$v_2: \quad (1)^2 + (1)^2 = 2$$

and we see that

$$PP^T = \begin{bmatrix} -1 & 1 \\ 1 & 1 \end{bmatrix} \begin{bmatrix} -1 & 1 \\ 1 & 1 \end{bmatrix} = \begin{bmatrix} 2 & 0 \\ 0 & 2 \end{bmatrix} \neq I$$

Also $P^T P \neq I$.

Let us normalize these vectors. First, find the normalizing factor

$$k_1 = \frac{1}{\sqrt{(-1)^2 + (1)^2}} = \frac{1}{\sqrt{2}}$$

$$k_2 = \frac{1}{\sqrt{(1)^2 + (1)^2}} = \frac{1}{\sqrt{2}}$$

Thus,

$$P = \begin{bmatrix} \dfrac{-1}{\sqrt{2}} & \dfrac{1}{\sqrt{2}} \\ \dfrac{1}{\sqrt{2}} & \dfrac{1}{\sqrt{2}} \end{bmatrix}$$

Now we have

$$PP^T = \begin{bmatrix} \dfrac{-1}{\sqrt{2}} & \dfrac{1}{\sqrt{2}} \\ \dfrac{1}{\sqrt{2}} & \dfrac{1}{\sqrt{2}} \end{bmatrix}\begin{bmatrix} \dfrac{-1}{\sqrt{2}} & \dfrac{1}{\sqrt{2}} \\ \dfrac{1}{\sqrt{2}} & \dfrac{1}{\sqrt{2}} \end{bmatrix} = \begin{bmatrix} 1 & 0 \\ 0 & 1 \end{bmatrix}$$

and also $P^T P = I$.

Problems

1. Using the matrix

$$A = \begin{bmatrix} \dfrac{1}{\sqrt{2}} & \dfrac{1}{\sqrt{2}} \\ \dfrac{-1}{\sqrt{2}} & \dfrac{1}{\sqrt{2}} \end{bmatrix}$$

of equation (6), check its orthogonality, i.e.,
(a) The inner product of the row vectors is equal to zero.
(b) The length of the row vectors is unity.
(c) $AA^T = A^T A = I$.

2. Let $\theta = 30°$, and find A from (7) and check the properties of A as in Problem 1. Draw a graph, and show what has been done.

11.6 Diagonalization of real, symmetric matrices

We have seen how a square matrix A was transformed into a diagonal matrix by use of the modal matrix P of A. Now, instead of merely a square matrix, we have a symmetric matrix. In this case, it turns out that the modal matrix P will become an orthogonal matrix. Let us start with a few new definitions and then develop the discussion.

(i) Definitions

When we had two square matrices A and B, B was said to be similar to A when $B = P^{-1}AP$. Now let P be an orthogonal matrix. Then we say B is *orthogonally similar* to A.

Next, let us set

$$A = \begin{bmatrix} a_{11} & a_{12} & a_{13} \\ a_{21} & a_{22} & a_{23} \\ a_{31} & a_{32} & a_{33} \end{bmatrix}$$

Then,

$$A^T = \begin{bmatrix} a_{11} & a_{21} & a_{31} \\ a_{12} & a_{22} & a_{32} \\ a_{13} & a_{23} & a_{33} \end{bmatrix}$$

If $A = A^T$, then the matrix A is said to be *symmetric*. In general, $A = (a_{ij})$ is symmetric if $a_{ij} = a_{ji}$. For example,

$$A = \begin{bmatrix} 2 & 3 & 4 \\ 3 & 5 & 6 \\ 4 & 6 & 7 \end{bmatrix}$$

The identity matrix I is also an example.

(ii) Orthogonal modal matrix

We wish to show that when A is real and symmetric, the modal matrix P will be, after normalization, an orthogonal matrix. We know that, when P is the modal matrix of A, we get $P^{-1}AP = D$, where D is the diagonal matrix with characteristic roots in the diagonal. This becomes $AP = PD$. Let v_1 be one of the characteristic vectors of P. Then, by letting λ_1 be a characteristic root,

$$Av_1 = \lambda_1 v_1$$

Next, multiply both sides by v_2^T (this will be a row vector). Thus,

$$(1) \qquad v_2^T A v_1 = v_2^T \lambda_1 v_1 = \lambda_1 v_2^T v_1$$

Let us now juggle $v_2^T A v_1$ as follows, remembering that $(AB)^T = B^T A^T$ and using the assumption that A is symmetric, i.e., $A = A^T$. We get

$$v_2^T A v_1 = v_2^T A^T v_1 = (Av_2)^T v_1$$

But we know that

$$Av_2 = \lambda_2 v_2$$

Substituting this in the preceding expression, we get

$$(2) \qquad v_2^T A v_1 = (\lambda_2 v_2)^T v_1 = \lambda_2 v_2^T v_1$$

since λ_1 is a scalar. Putting (1) and (2) together, we get

$$\lambda_2 v_2^T v_1 = \lambda_1 v_2^T v_1$$

Thus,

$$(\lambda_1 - \lambda_2) v_2^T v_1 = 0$$

But A is an $n \times n$ real, symmetric matrix. A theorem (which we shall not prove) tells us that the characteristic roots of a real symmetric matrix are *all* real. We shall furthermore assume that the rank of A is n. Then, all the real n roots will be *distinct*.* Thus, $\lambda_1 \neq \lambda_2$ and $v_2^T v_1 = 0$ so that v_1 and v_2 are orthogonal, and the same is true for the other vectors. We conclude that the vectors in the modal matrix P are mutually orthogonal when A is real and symmetric, and of rank n. If we normalize the vectors, then P will be an orthogonal matrix.

(iii) Diagonalization of a real, symmetric matrix

Quadratic forms have real symmetric matrices associated with them. Therefore, by using the above results, we can state as follows: Let A be the real symmetric matrix associated with the quadratic form Q. Then we can find an orthogonal modal matrix P such that $P^{-1}AP = D$, where D is a diagonal matrix with the characteristic roots in the diagonal.

Let us illustrate this by letting

$$Q(x_1, x_2, x_3) = 2x_1^2 + x_2^2 + x_3^2 + 2x_1x_2 + 2x_1x_3$$

$$= [x_1, x_2, x_3] \begin{bmatrix} 2 & 1 & 1 \\ 1 & 1 & 0 \\ 1 & 0 & 1 \end{bmatrix} \begin{bmatrix} x_1 \\ x_2 \\ x_3 \end{bmatrix} = x'Ax$$

The characteristic equation is

$$|A - \lambda I| = \lambda(1 - \lambda)(\lambda - 3) = 0$$

Thus, the characteristic roots are

$$\lambda_1 = 1, \qquad \lambda_2 = 3, \qquad \lambda_3 = 0$$

The characteristic vector was found by letting

$$[A - \lambda I]v_i = 0$$

Solving these sets of linear homogeneous equations, we find

$$\lambda_1 = 1: \qquad v_1' = \quad (0, -1, 1)$$

$$\lambda_2 = 3: \qquad v_2' = \quad (2, \quad 1, 1)$$

$$\lambda_3 = 0: \qquad v_3' = (-1, \quad 1, 1)$$

From this we can find the modal matrix P

$$P = [v_1, v_2, v_3] = \begin{bmatrix} 0 & 2 & -1 \\ -1 & 1 & 1 \\ 1 & 1 & 1 \end{bmatrix}$$

* See MacDuffee (1943), Chap. 8.

The vectors of P are mutually orthogonal, i.e., $v_i v_j = 0$ $(i \neq j)$. For example,

$$v_1' v_2 = [0 \quad -1 \quad 1] \begin{bmatrix} 2 \\ 1 \\ 1 \end{bmatrix} = 0 - 1 + 1 = 0$$

Next, let us normalize these vectors. They will be

$$v_1^0 = \left(0 \quad \frac{-1}{\sqrt{2}} \quad \frac{1}{\sqrt{2}} \right)$$

$$v_2^0 = \left(\frac{2}{\sqrt{6}} \quad \frac{1}{\sqrt{6}} \quad \frac{1}{\sqrt{6}} \right)$$

$$v_3^0 = \left(\frac{-1}{\sqrt{3}} \quad \frac{1}{\sqrt{3}} \quad \frac{1}{\sqrt{3}} \right)$$

Then the desired orthogonal modal matrix will be

$$P_0 = \begin{bmatrix} 0 & \dfrac{2}{\sqrt{6}} & \dfrac{-1}{\sqrt{3}} \\ \dfrac{-1}{\sqrt{2}} & \dfrac{1}{\sqrt{6}} & \dfrac{1}{\sqrt{3}} \\ \dfrac{1}{\sqrt{2}} & \dfrac{1}{\sqrt{6}} & \dfrac{1}{\sqrt{3}} \end{bmatrix}$$

Let us check this. We need

$$\| v_i^0 \| = 1, \qquad v_i^0 v_j^0 = 0, \qquad i \neq j$$

We already know that $\| v_i^o \| = 1$. So let us check $v_i^0 v_j^0 = 0$.

$$v_1^0 v_2^0 = \left[0 \quad \frac{-1}{\sqrt{2}} \quad \frac{1}{\sqrt{2}} \right] \begin{bmatrix} \dfrac{2}{\sqrt{6}} \\ \dfrac{1}{\sqrt{6}} \\ \dfrac{1}{\sqrt{6}} \end{bmatrix} = 0 - \frac{1}{\sqrt{12}} + \frac{1}{\sqrt{12}} = 0$$

and likewise for the rest of $v_i v_j = 0$ where $i \neq j$. Using P_0 we can find the diagonal matrix D which, after calculations, will be

$$D = P_0^T A P_0 = \begin{bmatrix} 1 & & \\ & 3 & \\ & & 0 \end{bmatrix} = \begin{bmatrix} \lambda_1 & & \\ & \lambda_2 & \\ & & \lambda_3 \end{bmatrix}$$

Note that $P_0^T = P_0^{-1}$. Thus, if we denote the transformation by

$$P_0 y = x$$

where $y = (y_1, y_2, y_3)$ and $x = (x_1, x_2, x_3)$ are column vectors, we get

$$Q(x_1, x_2, x_3) = x^T A x = (P_0 y)^T A(P_0 y)$$

$$= y^T P_0^T A P_0 y = y^T D y$$

Thus,

$$Q(x_1, x_2, x_3) = [y_1 \quad y_2 \quad y_3]\begin{bmatrix} 1 & & \\ & 3 & \\ & & 0 \end{bmatrix}\begin{bmatrix} y_1 \\ y_2 \\ y_3 \end{bmatrix}$$

$$= y_1^2 + 3y_2^2$$

This means that we have performed a transformation on (x_1, x_2, x_3) by the orthogonal modal matrix P_0 and have mapped it into (y_1, y_2, y_3). Geometrically, we have rotated the axes. Graphically we have Figure 11–2 where, for simplicity, only two of the three axes are shown.

The transformation $P_0 y = x$, when written out in full, is as follows

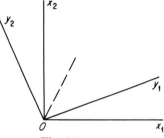

Fig. 11–2

$$\begin{bmatrix} 0 & \dfrac{2}{\sqrt{6}} & \dfrac{-1}{\sqrt{3}} \\ \dfrac{-1}{\sqrt{2}} & \dfrac{1}{\sqrt{6}} & \dfrac{1}{\sqrt{3}} \\ \dfrac{1}{\sqrt{2}} & \dfrac{1}{\sqrt{6}} & \dfrac{1}{\sqrt{3}} \end{bmatrix}\begin{bmatrix} y_1 \\ y_2 \\ y_3 \end{bmatrix} = \begin{bmatrix} x_1 \\ x_2 \\ x_3 \end{bmatrix}$$

In algebraic equation form, this is

$$\frac{2}{\sqrt{6}}y_2 - \frac{1}{\sqrt{3}}y_3 = x_1$$

(1)

$$\frac{-1}{\sqrt{2}}y_1 + \frac{1}{\sqrt{6}}y_2 + \frac{1}{\sqrt{3}}y_3 = x_2$$

$$\frac{1}{\sqrt{2}}y_1 + \frac{1}{\sqrt{6}}y_2 + \frac{1}{\sqrt{3}}y_3 = x_3$$

Let us solve this and use it to check our result

$$Q(x_1, x_2, x_3) = y_1^2 + 3y_2^2$$

As is seen, we need only y_1 and y_2 in our present case. We find from (1)

$$y_1 = \frac{\sqrt{2}}{2}(x_3 - x_2)$$

$$y_2 = \frac{\sqrt{6}}{6}(2x_1 + x_2 + x_3)$$

Substituting this in $Q(x_1, x_2, x_3)$, we find

$$Q(x_1, x_2, x_3) = y_1^2 + 3y_2^2$$
$$= \tfrac{2}{4}(x_3 - x_2)^2 + 3 \cdot \tfrac{6}{36}(2x_1 + x_2 + x_3)^2$$
$$= 2x_1^2 + x_2^2 + x_3^2 + 2x_1x_2 + 2x_1x_3$$

which is the original quadratic form we started with.

Thus, we see that, when we have a quadratic form $Q(x_1, x_2, x_3)$ as given and use the linear transformation (1), the quadratic form becomes

$$Q(x_1, x_2, x_3) = y_1^2 + 3y_2^2$$

where the coefficients 1 and 3 are the characteristic roots of the matrix associated with the quadratic form.

Let us summarize this as a theorem.

Theorem. If we have a real quadratic form $Q(x_1, x_2, \ldots, x_n)$, there is associated a real, symmetric matrix A. Then we can find an orthogonal modal matrix P such that the real quadratic form will become

$$\lambda_1 y_1^2 + \lambda_2 y_2^2 + \ldots + \lambda_n y_n^2$$

where λ_i are the characteristic roots of the symmetric matrix and the y_i are the new set of x_i with respect to the new set of coordinates, obtained from the linear transformation $Py = x$.

Problems

1. Given the quadratic form

$$Q(x_1, x_2, x_3) = 5x_1^2 + x_2^2 + x_3^2 + 4x_1x_2 + 2x_1x_3$$

make the following calculations.

(a) Find the matrix A associated to Q.
(b) Find the characteristic roots of A.

Ans. $\lambda_1 = 1$, $\lambda_2 = 6$, $\lambda_3 = 0$.

(c) Find the orthogonal modal matrix P.
(d) Calculate $P^T A P$, and find the diagonal matrix D.
(e) Let $Py = x$. Then find $x^T A x$ in terms of y.

(f) Write out in full $Py = x$. Check whether $Q(x_1, x_2, x_3) = y^2 + 6y_2^2$ is the same as the original equation by substituting values from $Py = x$.

2. Given the quadratic form

$$Q(x_1, x_2, x_3) = x_1^2 + 2x_2^2 + 4x_3^2 + 2x_1x_2 - 2x_1x_3 - 4x_2x_3$$

perform the calculations in Problem 1.

11.7 Non-negative quadratic forms

It was shown in the previous section that a quadratic form $Q(x_1, x_2, x_3)$ that has cross products such as x_1x_2, x_2x_3, x_3x_1 could be transformed by an orthogonal transformation $Py = x$ into

$$Q(x_1, x_2, x_3) = \lambda_1 y_1^2 + \lambda_2 y_2^2 + \lambda_3 y_3^2$$

where λ_1, λ_2, λ_3 are the characteristic roots of the symmetric matrix associated with $Q(x_1, x_2, x_3)$.

Nothing was said about $Q(x_1, x_2, x_3)$ except that the associated matrix was real and symmetric. Now let us add conditions concerning the sign of Q and show some interesting properties that are useful in problems such as determining the maximum or minimum of functions in economics (which we show later) and also in statistics.

But first we shall explain a few new terms that are related to quadratic forms.

(i) Discriminant and modulus

Let us explain these terms by use of an illustration. Let

$$Q(x_1, x_2) = 2x_1^2 + 6x_1x_2 + 2x_2^2$$

$$= [x_1 \quad x_2] \begin{bmatrix} 2 & 3 \\ 3 & 2 \end{bmatrix} \begin{bmatrix} x_1 \\ x_2 \end{bmatrix}$$

$$= [x_1 \quad x_2] \begin{bmatrix} a_{11} & a_{12} \\ a_{21} & a_{22} \end{bmatrix} \begin{bmatrix} x_1 \\ x_2 \end{bmatrix}$$

$$= \sum_{i=1}^{2} \sum_{j=1}^{2} a_{ij}x_ix_j, \qquad a_{ij} = a_{ji}$$

Let us next apply the linear transformation

$$x_1 = y_1 + 2y_2$$
$$x_2 = 2y_1 + y_2$$

which can be shown as

$$x_i = b_{i1}y_1 + b_{i2}y_2 = \sum_{k=1}^{2} b_{ik}y_k, \qquad i = 1, 2$$

Then, the quadratic form $Q(x_1, x_2)$ becomes, after substitution,

$$Q(x_1, x_2) = 22y_1^2 + 46y_1y_2 + 22y_2^2$$

$$= [y_1 \quad y_2] \begin{bmatrix} 22 & 23 \\ 23 & 22 \end{bmatrix} \begin{bmatrix} y_1 \\ y_2 \end{bmatrix}$$

$$= [y_1 \quad y_2] \begin{bmatrix} c_{11} & c_{12} \\ c_{21} & c_{22} \end{bmatrix} \begin{bmatrix} y_1 \\ y_2 \end{bmatrix}$$

The determinant of the matrix associated with a quadratic form is called the *discriminant* of the quadratic form. Thus, $|a_{ij}|$ and $|c_{ij}|$ are discriminants.

Next, the determinant of the coefficients of a transformation is called the *modulus* of the transformation. Thus,

$$M = \begin{vmatrix} 1 & 2 \\ 2 & 1 \end{vmatrix}$$

is the modulus of our transformation.

Then we have the following relationship

$$|c_{ij}| = M^2 |a_{ij}|$$

In our present case,

$$|c_{ij}| = \begin{vmatrix} 22 & 23 \\ 23 & 22 \end{vmatrix} = -45$$

$$M^2 = \begin{vmatrix} 1 & 2 \\ 2 & 1 \end{vmatrix}^2 = (-3)^2 = 9$$

$$|a_{ij}| = \begin{vmatrix} 2 & 3 \\ 3 & 2 \end{vmatrix} = -5$$

Thus,

$$|c_{ij}| = M^2 |a_{ii}| = -45$$

To summarize, if we have a quadratic form

$$Q(x_1, x_2) = \sum_{i=1}^{2} \sum_{j=1}^{2} a_{ij}x_ix_j, \qquad a_{ij} = a_{ji}$$

and a linear transformation

$$x_i = \sum_{k=1}^{2} b_{ik}y_k, \qquad i = 1, 2$$

we can show this in matrix form as

$$Q = x'Ax$$

$$x = By \qquad |B| \text{ is modulus}$$

Then the result of the linear transformation will be

$$Q = (By)'A(By)$$

$$= y'B'ABy = y'Cy$$

where we have set
$$C = B'AB$$
Hence
$$|C| = |B'|\,|A|\,|B| = |B|^2\,|A|$$
because $|B'| = |B|$. This holds in general for $i = k = 1, 2, \ldots, n$.

Problem

Given the quadratic
$$Q(x_1, x_2) = x_1^2 + 4x_1x_2 + x^2$$

and a linear transformation
$$x = By$$
where
$$B = \begin{bmatrix} 2 & -1 \\ 1 & -2 \end{bmatrix}$$

1. Find the symmetric matrix A associated with $Q(x_1, x_2)$.

2. Find $Q(x_1, x_2)$ in terms of y, using the transformation, i.e., find $y'cy$.

3. Show that $|c| = |B^2\,|A|$.

(ii) Positive definite, negative definite

Let us now discuss the sign of $Q(x_1, x_2)$. Let
$$Q(x_1, x_2) = \sum_{i=1}^{2} \sum_{j=1}^{2} a_{ij}x_ix_j$$
be a quadratic form. When
$$Q(x_1, x_2) \geq 0$$
for all real values of x_1 and x_2, Q is called a *non-negative quadratic form*. If $Q(x_1, x_2) > 0$ for all values of x_1 and x_2, except $x_1 = x_2 = 0$, the Q is called *positive definite*. If $Q < 0$ for all values of x_1 and x_2, except $x_1 = x_2 = 0$, then it is said to be *negative definite*.

For example,

$$3x_1^2 + 4x_2^2 \qquad \text{positive-definite quadratic form}$$
$$-3x_1^2 - 4x_2^2 \qquad \text{negative-definite quadratic form}$$
$$3x_1^2 - 4x_2^2 \qquad \text{neither}$$

When we have
$$(3x_1 - 4x_2)^2 + x_3^2$$
we see that, when $x_1 = 4$, $x_2 = 3$, and $x_3 = 0$, it becomes zero. On the other hand, it is seen that it will never become negative. This is called a

positive semi-definite quadratic form. When we have

$$-(3x_1 - 4x_2)^2 - x_3^2$$

it is called a negative semi-definite quadratic form.

So far we have defined terms concerning $Q(x_1, x_2)$. But similar terms are applied to the matrix associated with $Q(x_1, x_2)$. For example, we had above

$$Q(x_1, x_2) = 3x_1^2 + 4x_2^2$$

$$= [x_1 \quad x_2] \begin{bmatrix} 3 & 0 \\ 0 & 4 \end{bmatrix} \begin{bmatrix} x_1 \\ x_2 \end{bmatrix} = x'Ax$$

As we saw, $Q > 0$ and is positive definite. Let us now define as follows: The symmetric matrix A is called positive definite if the quadratic form that corresponds to A is positive definite. Thus, when

$$A = \begin{bmatrix} 3 & 0 \\ 0 & 4 \end{bmatrix}$$

then $Q = x'Ax > 0$, and therefore A is positive definite. Likewise, A is called positive semi-definite when the corresponding form $Q = x'Ax$ is positive semi-definite and negative definite if the corresponding quadratic form is negative definite.

Note that

$$|A| = \begin{vmatrix} 3 & 0 \\ 0 & 4 \end{vmatrix} = 12 > 0$$

Let us check the matrix for the positive semi-definite quadratic form.

$$(3x_1 - 4x_2)^2 + x_3^2 = 9x_1^2 - 24x_1x_2 + 16x_2^2 + x_3^2$$

$$= [x_1 \quad x_2 \quad x_3] \begin{bmatrix} 9 & -12 & 0 \\ -12 & 16 & 0 \\ 0 & 0 & 1 \end{bmatrix} \begin{bmatrix} x_1 \\ x_2 \\ x_3 \end{bmatrix}$$

$$|A| = \begin{vmatrix} 9 & -12 & 0 \\ -12 & 16 & 0 \\ 0 & 0 & 1 \end{vmatrix} = 9 \cdot 16 \cdot 1 - 12 \cdot 12 = 0$$

and A is singular. A check will show that A is also singular for the negative semi-definite quadratic form. For the negative-definite form, we can only say that A is non-singular.

A more precise definition of these terms, using the singular and non-singular properties of A, would be as follows.

$Q = X'AX > 0$	$\|A\| > 0$	positive definite
$Q = X'AX \geq 0$	$\|A\| = 0$	positive semi-definite
$Q = X'AX < 0$	$\|A\| \neq 0$	negative definite
$Q = X'AX \leq 0$	$\|A\| = 0$	negative semi-definite

(iii) Application of orthogonal transformation

The transformation in Section (i) above from $Q(x_1, x_2)$ to $Q(y_1, y_2)$ gave us a new quadratic form which contained cross products such as $46y_1y_2$. But we have seen that, by use of an orthogonal transformation $x = Pz$, where P is an orthogonal modal matrix, we were able to transform Q as follows

$$Q = x'Ax = (Pz)'A(Pz) = z'P'APz = z'Dz$$

where D is a diagonal matrix with characteristic roots of A in the diagonal. Then,

(1) $$Q = z'Dz = \lambda_1 z_1^2 + \lambda_2 z_2^2$$

where λ_1 and λ_2 are the characteristic roots of A.

The advantage of performing such a transformation is that we can use (1) to discuss the sign of Q. For example, if $\lambda_1 > 0$ and $\lambda_2 > 0$, we may have $z_1 = 0$, $z_2 \neq 0$. Then (1) is $\lambda_2 z_2^2 > 0$. If $z_1 \neq 0$, $z_2 = 0$, then (1) is $\lambda_1 z_1^2 > 0$. Only when $z_1 = z_2 = 0$ will (1) be equal to zero. Thus, when $\lambda_1 > 0$, $\lambda_2 > 0$, then Q is positive definite. Note that, if $\lambda_1 \geq 0$, $\lambda_2 > 0$, we may have $\lambda_1 = 0$, $\lambda_2 > 0$ and $z_1 \neq 0$, $z_2 = 0$, which means that $\lambda_1 z_1^2 + \lambda_2 z_2^2 = 0$ and thus (1) will not be positive definite. It will be positive semi-definite. Likewise, only when $\lambda_1 < 0$, $\lambda_2 < 0$ will (1) be negative definite.

We have seen that the diagonal matrix D obtained from A has the same rank as A with the characteristic roots in the diagonal. Therefore, if A is of rank 2, then, in our present case, $\lambda_1 \neq 0$, $\lambda_2 \neq 0$. Thus, if Q is positive definite and A is of rank two, we must have $\lambda_1 > 0$, $\lambda_2 > 0$.

Conversely, if $\lambda_1 > 0$, $\lambda_2 > 0$, then, Q is positive definite and A is also positive definite and of rank two. To state this another way, we may say that, if A is of rank n and the n characteristic roots of A are all positive, then A is positive definite; and conversely, if A is positive definite, then its n characteristic roots are all positive.

Let us illustrate this with a simple example. Let

$$Q(x_1, x_2) = 4x_1^2 + 4x_1x_2 + 7x_2^2$$

We can show that this is positive definite by

$$Q(x_1, x_2) = (2x_1 + x_2)^2 + 6x_2^2 > 0$$

for all real values of x_1 and x_2 except for $x_1 = x_2 = 0$. In matrix form this becomes

$$Q(x_1, x_2) = (x_1, x_2)\begin{bmatrix} 4 & 2 \\ 2 & 7 \end{bmatrix}\begin{bmatrix} x_1 \\ x_2 \end{bmatrix} = x'Ax$$

Let us apply an orthogonal transformation $Py = x$, where P is the orthogonal modal matrix we wish to find. For this we first find the characteristic vectors

$$|A - \lambda I| = \begin{vmatrix} 4 - \lambda & 2 \\ 2 & 7 - \lambda \end{vmatrix} = \lambda^2 - 11\lambda + 24 = (\lambda - 3)(\lambda - 8) = 0$$

Thus, the characteristic roots are $\lambda_1 = 3$, $\lambda_2 = 8$, and we can anticipate that the diagonal matrix D will be

$$D = \begin{bmatrix} 3 & 0 \\ 0 & 8 \end{bmatrix}$$

The characteristic vectors v_1 and v_2 are

$$[A - \lambda_1 I]v_1 = 0$$
$$[A - \lambda_2 I]v_2 = 0$$

Thus, for v_1

$$\begin{bmatrix} 4 - 3 & 2 \\ 2 & 7 - 3 \end{bmatrix}\begin{bmatrix} x_1 \\ x_2 \end{bmatrix} = 0$$

$$\begin{bmatrix} 1 & 2 \\ 2 & 4 \end{bmatrix}\begin{bmatrix} x_1 \\ x_2 \end{bmatrix} = 0$$

In equation form this can be written as

$$x_1 + 2x_2 = 0$$
$$2x_1 + 4x_2 = 0$$

Solving this simultaneous set of linear homogeneous equations gives us the characteristic vector v_1

$$v_1 = (-2m, m) = m(-2, 1)$$

We can find v_2 in a similar manner. It will turn out to be

$$v_2 = (\tfrac{1}{2}m, m) = m(\tfrac{1}{2}, 1)$$

Thus, the matrix P will be

$$P = [v_1 \quad v_2] = \begin{bmatrix} -2m & \tfrac{1}{2}m \\ m & m \end{bmatrix}$$

Let us check whether $v_1 v_2 = 0$.

$$v_1 v_2 = [-2m \quad m]\begin{bmatrix} \tfrac{1}{2}m \\ m \end{bmatrix} = -m^2 + m^2 = 0$$

One more condition we need is that the vectors be *normalized*. For this, set

$$(-2mk_1)^2 + (mk_1)^2 = 1$$

and

$$(\tfrac{1}{2}mk_2)^2 + (mk_2)^2 = 1$$

Then, the scalars k_i (the normalizing factor) become

$$k_1 = \frac{1}{\sqrt{m^2 + 4m^2}} = \frac{1}{m\sqrt{5}}$$

$$k_2 = \frac{1}{\sqrt{m^2 + m^2/4}} = \frac{2}{m\sqrt{5}}$$

and the orthogonal modal matrix P we are looking for becomes

$$P = \begin{bmatrix} -2mk_1 & \tfrac{1}{2}mk_2 \\ \\ mk_1 & mk_2 \end{bmatrix} = \begin{bmatrix} \dfrac{-2}{\sqrt{5}} & \dfrac{1}{\sqrt{5}} \\ \dfrac{1}{\sqrt{5}} & \dfrac{2}{\sqrt{5}} \end{bmatrix}$$

Checking,

$$v_1 v_2 = \begin{bmatrix} \dfrac{-2}{\sqrt{5}} & \dfrac{1}{\sqrt{5}} \end{bmatrix} \begin{bmatrix} \dfrac{1}{\sqrt{5}} \\ \dfrac{2}{\sqrt{5}} \end{bmatrix} = -\frac{2}{5} + \frac{2}{5} = 0$$

and

$$\left(-\frac{2}{\sqrt{5}}\right)^2 + \left(\frac{1}{\sqrt{5}}\right)^2 = 1$$

$$\left(\frac{1}{\sqrt{5}}\right)^2 + \left(\frac{2}{\sqrt{5}}\right)^2 = 1$$

Also,

$$PP^T = \begin{bmatrix} \dfrac{-2}{\sqrt{5}} & \dfrac{1}{\sqrt{5}} \\ \dfrac{1}{\sqrt{5}} & \dfrac{2}{\sqrt{5}} \end{bmatrix} \begin{bmatrix} \dfrac{-2}{\sqrt{5}} & \dfrac{1}{\sqrt{5}} \\ \dfrac{1}{\sqrt{5}} & \dfrac{2}{\sqrt{5}} \end{bmatrix}$$

$$= \begin{bmatrix} 1 & 0 \\ 0 & 1 \end{bmatrix} = I$$

Now that we have the P, let us perform the orthogonal transformation $Py = x$. Written out in full, this is

$$\begin{bmatrix} \dfrac{-2}{\sqrt{5}} & \dfrac{1}{\sqrt{5}} \\ \dfrac{1}{\sqrt{5}} & \dfrac{2}{\sqrt{5}} \end{bmatrix} \begin{bmatrix} y_1 \\ y_2 \end{bmatrix} = \begin{bmatrix} x_1 \\ x_2 \end{bmatrix}$$

or, in equation form, it is

$$\frac{-2}{\sqrt{5}} y_1 + \frac{1}{\sqrt{5}} y_2 = x_1$$

$$\frac{1}{\sqrt{5}} y_1 + \frac{2}{\sqrt{5}} y_2 = x_2$$

By using this transformation, $Q(x_1, x_2)$ becomes

$$Q(x_1, x_2) = x'Ax = (Py)'A(Py) = y'P'APy = y'Dy$$

where

$$D = P'AP = \begin{bmatrix} \dfrac{-2}{\sqrt{5}} & \dfrac{1}{\sqrt{5}} \\ \dfrac{1}{\sqrt{5}} & \dfrac{2}{\sqrt{5}} \end{bmatrix} \begin{bmatrix} 4 & 2 \\ 2 & 7 \end{bmatrix} \begin{bmatrix} \dfrac{-2}{\sqrt{5}} & \dfrac{1}{\sqrt{5}} \\ \dfrac{1}{\sqrt{5}} & \dfrac{2}{\sqrt{5}} \end{bmatrix}$$

$$= \begin{bmatrix} 3 & 0 \\ 0 & 8 \end{bmatrix}$$

Thus, the quadratic form $Q(x_1, x_2)$ becomes

$$Q(x_1, x_2) = y'Dy = (y_1, y_2) \begin{bmatrix} 3 & 0 \\ 0 & 8 \end{bmatrix} \begin{bmatrix} y_1 \\ y_2 \end{bmatrix}$$

$$= 3y_1^2 + 8y_2^2$$

As we see, the coefficients 3 and 8 are the characteristic roots of A. Furthermore, since both are positive, $Q(x_1, x_2) > 0$ for all real values of x_1 and x_2 (or y_1 and y_2) except for $x_1 = x_2 = 0$ (or $y_1 = y_2 = 0$). That is, Q is positive definite.

In general we can say that, if A (and Q) is positive definite, then the diagonal matrix obtained by an orthogonal transformation will have the characteristic roots of A in its diagonal and they will all be positive.

Problems

1. Given the quadratic form

$$Q(x_1, x_2) = 3x_1^2 + 4x_1x_2 + 6x_2^2$$

investigate the following steps.

a. Show it is positive definite, by grouping into squares.
b. Eliminate the cross products in Q by means of an orthogonal transformation.
c. Write out the transformation in a system of equations.

2. Given the quadratic form

$$Q(x_1, x_2) = -4x_1^2 - 4x_1x_2 - 7x_2^2$$

investigate the following steps.

a. Show it is negative definite, by grouping into squares.
b. Eliminate the cross products in Q by means of an orthogonal transformation.
c. Write out the transformation in a system of equations.

3. Given the quadratic form

$$Q(x_1, x_2) = -3x_1^2 - 4x_1x_2 - 6x_2^2$$

investigate the three steps of Problem 2.

(iv) Positive semi-definite

Next, if we have an $n \times n$ *positive semi-definite* matrix A which is of rank $r (r < n)$, we shall find after an orthogonal transformation that $\lambda_1 \ldots \lambda_r$ are all positive and that $\lambda_{r+1} \ldots \lambda_n$ are all zero. This can be seen by noting that an $n \times n$ positive matrix with rank n was transformed by an orthogonal transformation into a diagonal matrix that had the n characteristic roots in the diagonal, where all the λ_i were positive. We also know that the rank of a diagonal matrix is given by the number of non-zero elements in the diagonal. Thus, if the rank of A should be $n - 1$, then one of the elements in the diagonal needs to be zero, and the remaining $n - 1$ elements will be positive. If the rank of A should be $n - 2$, then two of the elements in the diagonal need to be zero, and the remaining $n - 2$ elements will be positive. In general, if the rank is $r (r < n)$, then the r characteristic roots in the diagonal will be positive and the remaining $n - r$ elements in the diagonal will be zero.

Let us illustrate this by the following simple example

$$Q(x_1, x_2, x_3) = (x_1 - 2x_2)^2 + 3x_3^2 = x'Ax$$

When $x_1 = 2m$, $x_2 = m$, $x_3 = 0$, then $Q = 0$. Thus, Q (and A) is positive semi-definite, and, when we apply an orthogonal transformation, we anticipate that the diagonal matrix will have zeros in the diagonal, depending on the rank of A. In our present case, A is of rank two, and we thus expect one zero in the diagonal, and two positive roots. Let us now work this out. Q can be shown as

$$Q = x_1^2 - 4x_1x_2 + 4x_2^2 + 3x_3^2$$

$$= [x_1 \quad x_2 \quad x_3] \begin{bmatrix} 1 & -2 & 0 \\ -2 & 4 & 0 \\ 0 & 0 & 3 \end{bmatrix} \begin{bmatrix} x_1 \\ x_2 \\ x_3 \end{bmatrix} = x'Ax$$

$$|A - \lambda I| = \begin{vmatrix} 1 - \lambda & -2 & 0 \\ -2 & 4 - \lambda & 0 \\ 0 & 0 & 3 - \lambda \end{vmatrix} = (\lambda - 3)(\lambda - 5)\lambda$$

Thus, the three characteristic roots are $\lambda_1 = 3$, $\lambda_2 = 5$, and $\lambda_3 = 0$, and we anticipate that the diagonal matrix D is

$$D = \begin{bmatrix} 3 & 0 & 0 \\ 0 & 5 & 0 \\ 0 & 0 & 0 \end{bmatrix}$$

The quadratic form Q will become

$$Q(x_1, x_2, x_3) = 3y_1^2 + 5y_2^2$$

To check this, let us find the orthogonal modal matrix P that performs this transformation. For this, we look for the characteristic vectors which we obtained by solving $[A - \lambda_i I]v_i = 0$. For v_1 we find, since $\lambda_1 = 3$,

$$\begin{bmatrix} 1-3 & -2 & 0 \\ -2 & 4-3 & 0 \\ 0 & 0 & 3-3 \end{bmatrix} \begin{bmatrix} x_1 \\ x_2 \\ x_3 \end{bmatrix} = 0$$

In terms of equations we have

$$\begin{aligned} -2x_1 - 2x_2 &= 0 \\ -2x_1 + x_2 &= 0 \\ 0x_3 &= 0 \end{aligned}$$

Thus,

$$v_1 = (0, 0, m)$$

Likewise, we find

$$v_2 = (m, -2m, 0)$$
$$v_3 = (m, \tfrac{1}{2}m, 0)$$

so that the modal matrix we want is

$$P = \begin{bmatrix} 0 & m & m \\ 0 & -2m & \tfrac{1}{2}m \\ m & 0 & 0 \end{bmatrix}$$

We see that the inner products of the vectors are zero. Thus, they are orthogonal. But they are not normal, so let us normalize them. The normalizing factors will be

$$k_1 = \frac{1}{m}$$

$$k_2 = \frac{1}{\sqrt{m^2 + 4m^2}} = \frac{1}{m\sqrt{5}}$$

$$k_3 = \frac{1}{\sqrt{m^2 + \tfrac{1}{4}m^2}} = \frac{2}{m\sqrt{5}}$$

Thus, the orthogonal modal matrix P will be

$$P = \begin{bmatrix} 0 & \dfrac{1}{\sqrt{5}} & \dfrac{2}{\sqrt{5}} \\ 0 & \dfrac{-2}{\sqrt{5}} & \dfrac{1}{\sqrt{5}} \\ 1 & 0 & 0 \end{bmatrix}$$

A check will show that $P^T P = P P^T = I$.

By using this the linear transformation, $Py = x$ will become

$$
\begin{bmatrix}
0 & \dfrac{1}{\sqrt{5}} & \dfrac{2}{\sqrt{5}} \\[2ex]
0 & \dfrac{-2}{\sqrt{5}} & \dfrac{1}{\sqrt{5}} \\[2ex]
1 & 0 & 0
\end{bmatrix}
\begin{bmatrix}
y_1 \\[1ex] y_2 \\[1ex] y_3
\end{bmatrix}
=
\begin{bmatrix}
x_1 \\[1ex] x_2 \\[1ex] x_3
\end{bmatrix}
$$

or, in equation form,

$$
\frac{1}{\sqrt{5}}\, y_2 + \frac{2}{\sqrt{5}}\, y_3 = x_1
$$

$$
-\frac{2}{\sqrt{5}}\, y_2 + \frac{1}{\sqrt{5}}\, y_3 = x_2
$$

$$
y_1 = x_3
$$

Then, by applying this transformation, the quadratic form becomes

$$
Q(x_1, x_2, x_3) = x'Ax = (Py)'A(Py)
$$
$$
= y'P'APy = y'Dy
$$

$$
D = P'AP =
\begin{bmatrix}
0 & 0 & 1 \\[2ex]
\dfrac{1}{\sqrt{5}} & \dfrac{-2}{\sqrt{5}} & 0 \\[2ex]
\dfrac{2}{\sqrt{5}} & \dfrac{1}{\sqrt{5}} & 0
\end{bmatrix}
\begin{bmatrix}
1 & -2 & 0 \\
-2 & 4 & 0 \\
0 & 0 & 3
\end{bmatrix}
\begin{bmatrix}
0 & \dfrac{1}{\sqrt{5}} & \dfrac{2}{\sqrt{5}} \\[2ex]
0 & \dfrac{-2}{\sqrt{5}} & \dfrac{1}{\sqrt{5}} \\[2ex]
1 & 0 & 0
\end{bmatrix}
$$

$$
=
\begin{bmatrix}
3 & 0 & 0 \\
0 & 5 & 0 \\
0 & 0 & 0
\end{bmatrix}
$$

Thus, we get

$$
Q = y'Dy = [y_1 \ \ y_2 \ \ y_3]
\begin{bmatrix}
3 & 0 & 0 \\
0 & 5 & 0 \\
0 & 0 & 0
\end{bmatrix}
\begin{bmatrix}
y_1 \\ y_2 \\ y_3
\end{bmatrix}
$$

$$
= 3y_1^2 + 5y_2^2
$$

which is as we expected.

Problems

Given the quadratic form

$$
Q(x_1, x_2, x_3) = x_1^2 - 6x_1x_2 + 9x_2^2 + 2x_3^2
$$

1. Show this is positive semi-definite.

2. Eliminate the cross products in the quadratic form by an orthogonal transformation.

(v) Submatrices

Next let us apply these properties to the submatrices of A. Let A be

$$A = \begin{bmatrix} a_{11} & a_{12} & a_{13} & a_{14} \\ a_{21} & a_{22} & a_{23} & a_{24} \\ a_{31} & a_{32} & a_{33} & a_{34} \\ a_{41} & a_{42} & a_{43} & a_{44} \end{bmatrix}$$

Let A_{11} be the submatrix obtained by deleting row 1 and column 1, i.e.,

$$A_{11} = \begin{bmatrix} a_{22} & a_{23} & a_{24} \\ a_{32} & a_{33} & a_{34} \\ a_{42} & a_{43} & a_{44} \end{bmatrix}$$

Likewise we can find A_{22}, A_{33}, and A_{44}.

Next, let us delete rows 1 and 3 and columns 1 and 3 and denote this submatrix by $A_{11,33}$.

$$A_{11,33} = \begin{bmatrix} a_{22} & a_{24} \\ a_{42} & a_{44} \end{bmatrix}$$

In general, when we obtain a submatrix by deleting rows and corresponding columns, it will be called a *principal submatrix*. The determinant of a principal submatrix will be called a *principal subdeterminant*, or *principal minor*. The latter term is used more often.

We state that: If A is positive definite, every principal submatrix is positive definite.

This can be explained with an example. Let $Q(x_1, x_2, x_3)$ be positive definite. Then, the submatrix A_{11}, for example, implies that we have set $x_1 = 0$. This is shown as

$$Q(x_1, x_2, x_3) = [x_1 \quad x_2 \quad x_3] \begin{bmatrix} a_{11} & a_{12} & a_{13} \\ a_{21} & a_{22} & a_{23} \\ a_{31} & a_{32} & a_{33} \end{bmatrix} \begin{bmatrix} x_1 \\ x_2 \\ x_3 \end{bmatrix}$$

$$= a_{11}x_1^2 + a_{22}x_2^2 + a_{33}x_3^2 + 2a_{12}x_1x_2$$
$$+ 2a_{23}x_2x_3 + 2a_{31}x_3x_1$$

Let $x_1 = 0$. Then,

$$Q(x_2, x_3) = a_{22}x_2^2 + a_{33}x_3^2 + 2a_{23}x_2x_3$$

$$= [x_2 \quad x_3] \begin{bmatrix} a_{22} & a_{23} \\ a_{32} & a_{33} \end{bmatrix} \begin{bmatrix} x_2 \\ x_3 \end{bmatrix}$$

In other words, deleting row 1 and column 1 means we have set $x_1 = 0$. The value of $Q(x_1, x_2, x_3)$ for all real values of x_1, x_2, and x_3, where $x_1 = 0$, $x_2 \neq 0$, and $x_3 \neq 0$, is equal to $Q(x_2, x_3)$ for all values of $x_2 \neq 0$ and $x_3 \neq$

0. Thus, $Q(x_2, x_3)$ will also be positive definite for $x_2 \neq 0$ and $x_3 \neq 0$, and the submatrix A_{11} will also be positive definite.

In similar fashion we can see that every principal submatrix will be positive definite when the original matrix is positive definite.

A similar explanation can be made for the negative definite case, and we shall find that every principal submatrix will be negative definite when the original matrix is negative definite.

Note carefully that we are stating the conditions in terms of matrices. We shall state the conditions of positive (negative) definite in terms of *determinants* in the next section.

11.8 Determining the sign of a quadratic form

In statistics and economics, we are frequently faced with the problem of finding the sign of $Q(x, y)$. That is, we wish to find whether or not Q is positive or negative definite. Let us approach this problem first via simple algebra and then restate it in terms of matrix algebra.

(*i*) *Two variables case*

Let the quadratic form be

$$Q(x, y) = ax^2 + by^2 + 2hxy$$

This can be transformed as follows

$$Q(x, y) = [x \quad y]\begin{bmatrix} a & h \\ h & b \end{bmatrix}\begin{bmatrix} x \\ y \end{bmatrix}$$

$$= a\left(x + \frac{hy}{a}\right)^2 + \frac{ab - h^2}{a}y^2$$

For $Q(x, y) > 0$, we must have

$$a > 0, \qquad \frac{ab - h^2}{a} > 0$$

But since $a > 0$, the second condition becomes $ab - h^2 > 0$. We can show this in the form of determinants as

$$|a| > 0, \qquad ab - h^2 = \begin{vmatrix} a & h \\ h & b \end{vmatrix} > 0$$

Note that the second determinant is the determinant of the matrix of coefficients of $Q(x, y)$, and $|a|$ will be the minor of the element a_{22} or the determinant of the submatrix A_{22}. For $Q(x, y) < 0$, we need

$$|a| < 0, \qquad \begin{vmatrix} a & h \\ h & b \end{vmatrix} > 0$$

(ii) Three variables case

Now let us try it with three variables.

$$Q(x, y, z) = ax^2 + by^2 + cz^2 + 2hxy + 2fyz + 2gzx$$

$$= [x \quad y \quad z] \begin{bmatrix} a & h & g \\ h & b & f \\ g & f & c \end{bmatrix} \begin{bmatrix} x \\ y \\ z \end{bmatrix}$$

By algebraic manipulation we get

$$Q(x, y, z) = a\left(x + \frac{h}{a}y + \frac{g}{a}z\right)^2 + \frac{ab - h^2}{a}\left(y + \frac{af - gh}{ab - h^2}\right)^2$$

$$+ \frac{abc - af^2 - bg^2 - ch^2 + 2fgh}{ab - h^2}z^2$$

Thus, for $Q(x, y, z)$ to be positive, we need

$$a > 0, \quad ab - h^2 > 0, \quad abc - af^2 - bg^2 - ch^2 + 2fgh > 0$$

But note that this can be shown as

$$|a| > 0, \quad \begin{vmatrix} a & h \\ h & b \end{vmatrix} > 0, \quad \begin{vmatrix} a & h & g \\ h & b & f \\ g & f & c \end{vmatrix} > 0$$

For Q to be negative, we need

$$|a| < 0, \quad \begin{vmatrix} a & h \\ h & b \end{vmatrix} > 0, \quad \begin{vmatrix} a & h & g \\ h & b & f \\ g & f & c \end{vmatrix} < 0$$

(iii) General case

In general the necessary and sufficient conditions for the real quadratic form

$$Q(x_1, x_2, ..., x_n) = \sum_i \sum_j a_{ij} x_i x_j, \quad a_{ij} = a_{ji}$$

to be positive definite are that

$$|a_{11}| > 0, \quad \begin{vmatrix} a_{11} & a_{12} \\ a_{21} & a_{22} \end{vmatrix} > 0, ..., \quad \begin{vmatrix} a_{11} & \cdots & a_{1n} \\ \vdots & & \\ a_{n1} & \cdots & a_{nn} \end{vmatrix} > 0$$

And Q will be negative definite, if and only if the sequence of determinants alternate in sign, i.e.,

$$a_{11} < 0, \quad \begin{vmatrix} a_{11} & a_{12} \\ a_{21} & a_{22} \end{vmatrix} > 0, \quad \begin{vmatrix} a_{11} & a_{12} & a_{13} \\ a_{21} & a_{22} & a_{23} \\ a_{31} & a_{32} & a_{33} \end{vmatrix} < 0, ..., (-1)^n \begin{vmatrix} a_{11} & \cdots & a_{1n} \\ \vdots & & \\ a_{n1} & \cdots & a_{nn} \end{vmatrix}$$

$$> 0$$

(*iv*) *Principal minors*

Positive definite case. We have seen that, if A is a symmetric matrix, there exists an orthogonal modal matrix P such that

$$P'AP = D = \begin{bmatrix} \lambda_1 & & \\ & \lambda_2 & \\ & & \lambda_3 \end{bmatrix}$$

where the λ_i are the characteristic roots of A. We also saw that, when A is positive definite, the $\lambda_i > 0$. Let us now set $D^{1/2}$ as

$$D^{1/2} = \begin{bmatrix} \sqrt{\lambda_1} & & \\ & \sqrt{\lambda_2} & \\ & & \sqrt{\lambda_3} \end{bmatrix}$$

Then,

$$D^{-1/2} = \begin{bmatrix} \dfrac{1}{\sqrt{\lambda_1}} & & \\ & \dfrac{1}{\sqrt{\lambda_2}} & \\ & & \dfrac{1}{\sqrt{\lambda_3}} \end{bmatrix}$$

so that

$$D^{1/2}D^{-1/2} = D^{-1/2}D^{1/2} = \begin{bmatrix} 1 & & \\ & 1 & \\ & & 1 \end{bmatrix} = I$$

Now, instead of using P, let us use $PD^{-1/2}$. Then, noting that $D^{-1/2} = (D^{-1/2})'$ because it is a diagonal matrix (i.e., symmetric), we get

$$(PD^{-1/2})'A(PD^{-1/2}) = (D^{-1/2})'P'APD^{-1/2}$$

$$= (D^{-1/2})'DD^{-1/2}$$

$$= \begin{bmatrix} \dfrac{1}{\sqrt{\lambda_1}} & & \\ & \dfrac{1}{\sqrt{\lambda_2}} & \\ & & \dfrac{1}{\sqrt{\lambda_3}} \end{bmatrix} \begin{bmatrix} \lambda_1 & & \\ & \lambda_2 & \\ & & \lambda_3 \end{bmatrix} \begin{bmatrix} \dfrac{1}{\sqrt{\lambda_1}} & & \\ & \dfrac{1}{\sqrt{\lambda_2}} & \\ & & \dfrac{1}{\sqrt{\lambda_3}} \end{bmatrix}$$

$$= \begin{bmatrix} 1 & & \\ & 1 & \\ & & 1 \end{bmatrix}$$

Thus, there exists a non-singular matrix $PD^{-1/2} = C$ such that

$$C'AC = I$$

Next, let us transfer the C's to the right-hand side. We get

$$A = (C')^{-1}IC^{-1}$$

Now let us take the determinants on both sides. Then

$$|A| = |C'|^{-1}\,|I|\,|C| = |C'|^{-1}\,|C|^{-1}$$

C' is the transpose of C. But the transpose of a determinant is equal to the original determinant. Thus, $|C'| = |C|$ and

$$|A| = |C'|^{-1}\,|C|^{-1} = |C|^{-2} = \frac{1}{|C|^2}$$

Since $|C|$ is a real number, when squared, it will be positive. Thus, $|A| > 0$.

We may summarize this in the following theorem.

Theorem. If A is positive definite, then $|A| > 0$.

We also said that all principal submatrices of a positive-definite matrix A are also positive definite. Then, by applying the above we have the following theorem.

Theorem. If A is positive definite, every principal minor is positive.

Using these theorems, we shall restate in terms of matrix algebra the results previously obtained by algebra.

(1) If Q is a positive definite quadratic form, then the associated matrix A's determinant $|A|$ and its principal minors will all be positive.
(2) Conversely if $|A|$ and the principal minors are positive, we will have a positive definite A.

Negative definite case. We know for example that

$$-A = -\begin{bmatrix} 1 & 2 \\ 3 & 4 \end{bmatrix} = \begin{bmatrix} -1 & -2 \\ -3 & -4 \end{bmatrix}$$

and hence

$$|-A| = \begin{vmatrix} -1 & -2 \\ -3 & -4 \end{vmatrix} = (-1)^2 \begin{vmatrix} 1 & 2 \\ 3 & 4 \end{vmatrix}$$

In general, when A is $n \times n$, then

$$|-A| = (-1)^n |A|$$

We also know that when

$$Q(x_1, x_2, x_3) = x'Ax$$

is positive definite, then

$$|A_{11,22}| > 0, \qquad |A_{11}| > 0, \qquad |A| > 0$$

Suppose

$$Q(x_1, x_2, x_3) = x'Ax$$

is negative definite. Then

$$-Q(x_1, x_2, x_3) = x'(-A)x$$

is positive definite. Hence, the conditions that will make $-Q$ positive definite will be the conditions that make Q negative definite. But the conditions that make $-Q = x'(-A)x$ positive definite are

$$|-A_{11,22}| > 0, \qquad |-A_{11}| > 0 \qquad |-A| > 0$$

which in our present example becomes

$$(-1)' |A_{11,22}| > 0, \qquad (-1)^2 |A_{11}| > 0, \qquad (-1)^3 |A| > 0$$

or

$$|A_{11,22}| < 0, \qquad |A_{11}| > 0, \qquad |A| < 0$$

Hence we may conclude that: The conditions (necessary and sufficient) for Q to be negative definite are that the determinant $|A|$ and its principal minors alternate in sign, the minors with odd numbers of rows and columns being negative.

Since these are very useful theorems in economics, let us present an alternative proof using discriminants and modulus of a transformation as an exercise.

Alternative proof. Let $Q = x'Ax$ and $Py = x$, where P is the orthogonal modal matrix. Then, we know that

$$Q = x'Ax = (Py)'A(Py) = y'Dy$$

where D is the diagonal matrix with the characteristic roots of A in it. We also know from Section 11.7 that

$$|D| = |P|^2 \, |A|$$

where $|D|$ and $|A|$ are the discriminants and $|P|$ is the modulus of the transformation.

In our discussion above we have seen that, when Q is *positive definite*, $|A|$ and the principal minors are positive. Using our relation between discriminants, we can show this as follows: $|P|^2 > 0$. Thus, $|D|$ and $|A|$ must have the same sign. For simplicity, let

$$|A| = \begin{vmatrix} a_{11} & a_{12} & a_{13} \\ a_{21} & a_{22} & a_{23} \\ a_{31} & a_{32} & a_{33} \end{vmatrix}$$

and

$$|D| = \begin{vmatrix} \lambda_1 & & \\ & \lambda_2 & \\ & & \lambda_3 \end{vmatrix} = \lambda_1 \lambda_2 \lambda_3$$

Let us assume that $x_2 = x_3 = 0$. Then, if Q is to be positive definite, $\lambda_1 > 0$. Thus, $|D| = \lambda_1 > 0$. Thus, $|A| = a_{11} > 0$, since $|D|$ and $|A|$ have the same sign.

Now, if $x_1 \neq 0$ and $x_2 \neq 0$, then, $\lambda_1 > 0$ and $\lambda_2 > 0$. Thus,

$$|D| = \lambda_1 \lambda_2 > 0$$

and, since $|D|$ and $|A|$ have the same sign,

$$|A| = \begin{vmatrix} a_{11} & a_{12} \\ a_{21} & a_{22} \end{vmatrix} > 0$$

If $x_1 \neq 0$, $x_2 \neq 0$, and $x_3 \neq 0$, then,

$$|D| = \lambda_1 \lambda_2 \lambda_3 > 0$$

and, therefore,

$$|A| = \begin{vmatrix} a_{11} & a_{12} & a_{13} \\ a_{21} & a_{22} & a_{23} \\ a_{31} & a_{32} & a_{33} \end{vmatrix} > 0$$

and so forth.

For the *negative-definite* case, when $x_2 = x_3 = 0$ and $x_1 \neq 0$, then $\lambda_1 < 0$. Thus, $|D| = \lambda_1 < 0$, which implies that $|A| = a_{11} < 0$.

For $x_1 \neq 0$, $x_2 \neq 0$, and $x_3 = 0$, then, $\lambda_1 < 0$ and $\lambda_2 < 0$. Thus,

$$|D| = \lambda_1 \lambda_2 > 0$$

and

$$|A| = \begin{vmatrix} a_{11} & a_{12} \\ a_{21} & a_{22} \end{vmatrix} > 0$$

For $x_1 \neq 0$, $x_2 \neq 0$, and $x_3 \neq 0$, we have, $\lambda_1 < 0$, $\lambda_2 < 0$, and $\lambda_3 < 0$. Thus,

$$|D| = \lambda_1 \lambda_2 \lambda_3 < 0$$

and, therefore,

$$A = \begin{vmatrix} a_{11} & a_{12} & a_{13} \\ a_{21} & a_{22} & a_{23} \\ a_{31} & a_{32} & a_{33} \end{vmatrix} < 0$$

Thus, for Q (and A) to be negative definite, we need

$$a_{11} < 0, \qquad \begin{vmatrix} a_{11} & a_{12} \\ a_{21} & a_{22} \end{vmatrix} > 0, \qquad \begin{vmatrix} a_{11} & a_{12} & a_{13} \\ a_{21} & a_{22} & a_{23} \\ a_{31} & a_{32} & a_{33} \end{vmatrix} < 0$$

(v) *Linear constraint—two variables case*

Let the quadratic form be

$$Q(x_1, x_2) = a_{11}x_1^2 + a_{22}x_2^2 + 2a_{12}x_1x_2$$

We wish that $Q > 0$, i.e., positive definite, subject to the linear constraint

$$b_1 x_1 + b_2 x_2 = 0$$

From the linear constraint, we have

$$x_2 = -\frac{b_1}{b_2} x_1$$

Substituting this in Q gives us

$$Q(x_1, x_2) = (a_{22}b_1^2 + a_{11}b_2^2 - 2a_{12}b_1b_2) \frac{x_1^2}{b_2^2}$$

Obviously, the sign of Q will depend on the sign of the portion in the parenthesis, which can be shown in determinant form as

$$-\begin{vmatrix} 0 & b_1 & b_2 \\ b_1 & a_{11} & a_{12} \\ b_2 & a_{21} & a_{22} \end{vmatrix} = a_{22}b_1^2 + a_{11}b_2^2 - 2a_{12}b_1b_2$$

where $a_{12} = a_{21}$. Thus, the condition that $Q(x_1, x_2) > 0$ is

$$\begin{vmatrix} 0 & b_1 & b_2 \\ b_1 & a_{11} & a_{12} \\ b_2 & a_{21} & a_{22} \end{vmatrix} < 0$$

As can be seen, this determinant is made up of the determinant of the matrix of coefficients of the quadratic form Q which is *bordered* by the coefficients of the linear relation. This is called a *bordered determinant*.

For $Q(x_1, x_2) < 0$, the necessary condition is that the bordered determinant be positive. But this is when there are only two variables x_1 and x_2.

When we have three or more, the signs of the bordered determinant will alternate, as we shall see next. Note also that

$$\begin{vmatrix} a_{11} & a_{12} & b_1 \\ a_{21} & a_{22} & b_2 \\ b_1 & b_2 & 0 \end{vmatrix} = \begin{vmatrix} 0 & b_1 & b_2 \\ b_1 & a_{11} & a_{12} \\ b_2 & a_{21} & a_{22} \end{vmatrix}$$

(vi) *Linear constraint—three variables case*

Let us try

$$Q(x_1, x_2, x_3) = a_{11}x_1^2 + a_{22}x_2^2 + a_{33}x_3^2 + 2a_{23}x_2x_3$$
$$+ 2a_{31}x_3x_1 + 2a_{12}x_1x_2$$

subject to

$$b_1x_1 + b_2x_2 + b_3x_3 = 0$$

To find the conditions for $Q > 0$, let us set

$$x_1 = -\frac{1}{b_1}(b_2x_2 + b_3x_3)$$

and substitute this in Q. Then,

$$Q(x_1, x_2, x_3) = Ax_2^2 + Bx_3^2 + 2Hx_2x_3$$

where

$$A = \frac{1}{b_1^2}(a_{22}b_1^2 + b_1b_2^2 - 2a_{12}b_1b_2)$$

$$B = \frac{1}{b_1^2}(a_{33}b_1^2 + b_1b_3^2 - 2a_{31}b_1b_3)$$

$$H = \frac{1}{b_1^2}(b_1b_2b_3 - a_{31}b_1b_2 - a_{12}b_1b_3 + a_{23}b_1^2)$$

As seen previously, $Q > 0$ when

$$A > 0, \quad \begin{vmatrix} A & H \\ H & B \end{vmatrix} = AB - H^2 > 0$$

and $Q < 0$ when

$$A < 0, \quad \begin{vmatrix} A & H \\ H & B \end{vmatrix} > 0$$

Furthermore, noting that $a_{12} = a_{21}$, $a_{13} = a_{31}$, and $a_{23} = a_{32}$,

$$A = \frac{1}{b_1^2}(a_{22}b_1^2 + b_1b_2^2 - 2a_{12}b_1b_2)$$

$$= -\frac{1}{b_1^2}\begin{vmatrix} 0 & b_1 & b_2 \\ b_1 & a_{11} & a_{12} \\ b_2 & a_{21} & a_{22} \end{vmatrix}$$

$$AB - H^2 = -\frac{1}{b_1^4}[(a_{22}a_{33} - a_{23}^2)b_1^2 + (a_{11}a_{22} - a_{31}^2)b_2^2$$

$$+ (a_{11}a_{22} - a_{12}^2)b_3^2 - 2(a_{11}a_{23} - a_{31}a_{12})b_2b_3$$

$$- 2(a_{22}a_{31} - a_{23}a_{12})b_1b_3 - 2(a_{33}a_{12} - a_{23}a_{13})b_1b_2]$$

$$= -\frac{1}{b_1^4}\begin{vmatrix} 0 & b_1 & b_2 & b_3 \\ b_1 & a_{11} & a_{12} & a_{13} \\ b_2 & a_{21} & a_{22} & a_{23} \\ b_3 & a_{31} & a_{32} & a_{33} \end{vmatrix}$$

Thus, for $Q > 0$, we need,

$$\Delta_1 = \begin{vmatrix} 0 & b_1 & b_2 \\ b_1 & a_{11} & a_{12} \\ b_2 & a_{21} & a_{22} \end{vmatrix} < 0, \qquad \Delta_2 = \begin{vmatrix} 0 & b_1 & b_2 & b_3 \\ b_1 & a_{11} & a_{12} & a_{13} \\ b_2 & a_{21} & a_{22} & a_{23} \\ b_3 & a_{31} & a_{32} & a_{33} \end{vmatrix} < 0$$

and for $Q < 0$, we need

$$\Delta_1 > 0, \qquad \Delta_2 < 0$$

In general, let the quadratic form be

$$Q(x_1, x_2, \ldots, x_n) = x'Ax$$

$$= [x_1 \quad x_2 \quad \ldots \quad x_n]\begin{bmatrix} a_{11} & \cdots & a_{1n} \\ \vdots & & \vdots \\ a_{n1} & \cdots & a_{nn} \end{bmatrix}\begin{bmatrix} x_1 \\ \vdots \\ x_n \end{bmatrix}$$

subject to the linear constraint

$$B'x = b_1x_1 + b_2x_2 + \ldots + b_nx_n = 0$$

Then Q is positive definite when

$$\begin{vmatrix} 0 & b_1 & b_2 \\ b_1 & a_{11} & a_{12} \\ b_2 & a_{21} & a_{22} \end{vmatrix} < 0, \qquad \ldots, \qquad \begin{vmatrix} 0 & b_1 & \cdots & b_n \\ b_1 & a_{11} & \cdots & a_{1n} \\ \vdots & \vdots & & \vdots \\ b_n & a_{n1} & \cdots & a_{nn} \end{vmatrix} < 0$$

and will be negative definite when the bordered determinants are alternately positive and negative, the first one being positive. These are necessary and sufficient conditions.

Problems

1. Given the following quadratic form

$$Q(x, y, z) = x^2 + 2y^2 + z^2 + 2xy + xz$$

test for the sign of Q by use of determinants and principal minors associated with the matrix $A(Q = x'Ax)$.

2. Given the following quadratic form, check its sign.

$$Q(x, y, z) = -x^2 - y^2 - z^2 - 2xy - 2yz - 2zx$$

3. Given the following quadratic form with a constraint

$$Q = x^2 - 4y^2 - z^2 + 2xy$$
$$2x + y + z = 0$$

test the sign of the quadratic form.

11.9 Maxima and minima of functions

In Chapter 5, we found the first- and second-order conditions for extreme values of functions, using differentials. The second-order condition turned out to be a quadratic, and the problem of determining the sign of the second-order conditions became one of determining the conditions for a quadratic to be positive or negative. We mentioned in Chapter 5 that this problem would be considered in Chapter 11 with the help of matrices and determinants. We are now ready to consider this problem.

(*i*) *Unconstrained case*

Consider a function

$$u = f(x_1, x_2, \ldots, x_n)$$

The first- and second-order conditions for this to have a *maximum* was

$$du = 0, \qquad d^2u < 0$$

First-order condition. From $du = 0$, we have

$$f_1 \, dx_1 + f_2 \, dx_2 + \ldots + f_n \, dx_n = 0$$

and, since $x_1, x_2, \ldots, x_n$ are independent variables, the first-order condition for this equation to be satisfied is

$$f_1 = f_2 = \ldots = f_n = 0$$

Second-order condition. For $d^2u < 0$ we have

$$d^2u = (f_1 \, dx_1 + f_2 \, dx_2 + \ldots + f_n \, dx_n)^2$$

$$= [dx_1 \quad dx_2 \quad \ldots \quad dx_n] \begin{bmatrix} f_{11} & f_{12} & \cdots & f_{1n} \\ f_{21} & & & \\ \vdots & & & \\ f_{n1} & \cdots & & f_{nn} \end{bmatrix} \begin{bmatrix} dx_1 \\ dx_2 \\ \vdots \\ dx_n \end{bmatrix}$$

We have a quadratic form and the associated matrix is a real, symmetric matrix. Thus, $d^2u < 0$ in matrix algebra means that we want the quadratic form to be negative definite. We know that the condition for it to be negative definite is that the principal minors of the matrix alternate in sign, the odd-numbered minors being negative. That is,

$$f_{11} < 0, \quad \begin{vmatrix} f_{11} & f_{12} \\ f_{21} & f_{22} \end{vmatrix} > 0, \quad \ldots, \quad (-1)^n \begin{vmatrix} f_{11} & \cdots & f_{1n} \\ \vdots & & \vdots \\ f_{n1} & \cdots & f_{nn} \end{vmatrix} > 0$$

Since $d^2u < 0$ when the above conditions hold, they are the second-order conditions for a maximum that we seek.

For a *minimum u*, we need $du = 0$ and $d^2u > 0$. The first-order condition $du = 0$ is the same as the maximum case. As for the second-order condition, we know from previous discussion that the quadratic $d^2u > 0$ when the principal minors of the associated matrix of d^2u are all positive. Hence

$$f_{11} > 0, \quad \begin{vmatrix} f_{11} & f_{12} \\ f_{21} & f_{22} \end{vmatrix} > 0, \quad \begin{vmatrix} f_{11} & \cdots & f_{1n} \\ \vdots & & \vdots \\ f_{n1} & \cdots & f_{nn} \end{vmatrix} > 0$$

are the second-order conditions for u to have a minimum.

Example 1. Given the following function, find its extreme value.

$$u = 2x^2 + y^2 - 4x + 8y$$

First-order condition.

$$f_x = 4x - 4 = 0$$

$$f_y = 2y + 8 = 0$$

$$\therefore \quad x = 1, \quad y = -4$$

Second-order condition.

$$f_{xx} = 4 > 0, \quad \begin{vmatrix} f_{xx} & f_{xy} \\ f_{yx} & f_{yy} \end{vmatrix} = \begin{vmatrix} 4 & 0 \\ 0 & 2 \end{vmatrix} = 8 > 0$$

$$\therefore \quad d^2u < 0$$

and hence

$$u = 2(1)^2 + (-4)^2 - 4(1) + 8 = 22$$

is a minimum value.

(ii) Constrained case—two variables

We found in Section 5.6 that, when given a function

$$u = f(x_1, x_2)$$

with a constraint

$$\phi(x_1, x_2) = 0$$

the first- and second-order conditions for an extreme value were:

	maximum	minimum
First-order conditions	$du = 0$	$du = 0$
	$d\phi = 0$	$d\phi = 0$
Second-order conditions	$d^2u < 0$	$d^2u > 0$
	$d\phi = 0$	$d\phi = 0$

Recall also that the algebra involved in the second-order conditions becomes quite involved. We are now in a position to use matrix algebra and state these conditions in a more concise manner. Let us start with the first-order conditions.

First-order conditions. Recall that these were

$$\frac{f_1}{\phi_1} = \frac{f_2}{\phi_2}$$

$$\phi(x_1, x_2) = 0$$

and by solving these two equations we were able to find x_1 and x_2 for the extreme value.

Second-order conditions. When finding d^2u, we need to consider the fact that x_1 and x_2 are not independent. Let us consider x_1 the dependent variable and x_2 the independent variable. Then, we know that

$$d^2u = f_1\, d^2x_1 + f_{11}\, dx_1^2 + f_{22}\, dx_2^2 + 2f_{12}\, dx_1\, dx_2$$
$$d^2\phi = \phi_1\, d^2x_1 + \phi_{11}\, dx_1^2 + \phi_{22}\, dx_2^2 + 2\phi_{12}\, dx_1\, dx_2 = 0$$

To eliminate the term with d^2x_1, we calculate

$$\phi_1\, d^2u - f_1\, d^2\phi = [\phi_1 f_{11} - \phi_{11} f_1]\, dx_1^2 + [\phi_1 f_{11} - \phi_{22} f_1]\, dx_2^2$$
$$+ 2[\phi_1 f_{12} - \phi_{12} f_1]\, dx_1\, dx_2$$

Dividing through by ϕ_1 and noting that $d^2\phi = 0$, we get

$$d^2u = \left[f_{11} - \frac{f_1}{\phi_1}\phi_{11}\right] dx_1^2 + \left[f_{22} - \frac{f_1}{\phi_1}\phi_{22}\right] dx_2^2$$
$$+ 2\left[f_{12} - \frac{f_1}{\phi_1}\phi_{12}\right] dx_1\, dx_2$$

This is a quadratic. Hence, to find the conditions for $d^2u > 0$ or $d^2u < 0$ becomes a problem of finding the conditions for a quadratic to be positive definite or negative definite, subject to the linear constraint

$$d\phi = \phi_1\, dx_1 + \phi_2\, dx_2 = 0$$

Minimum case. We know from Section 11.8 that the condition for $d^2u > 0$ is that the principal minors of the matrix associated with the quadratic bordered by the coefficient of the constraint equation should be all negative. In our present case,

$$\begin{vmatrix} 0 & \phi_1 & \phi_2 \\ \phi_1 & f_{11} - \dfrac{f_1}{\phi_1}\phi_{11} & f_{12} - \dfrac{f_1}{\phi_1}\phi_{12} \\ \phi_2 & f_{21} - \dfrac{f_1}{\phi_1}\phi_{21} & f_{22} - \dfrac{f_1}{\phi_1}\phi_{22} \end{vmatrix} < 0$$

and hence this is the second-order condition for u to be a minimum, which we seek.

Maximum case. For u to be a maximum, the first-order condition is the same as the minimum case. The second-order condition was that $d^2u < 0$ subject to $d\phi = 0$. We know that when the principal minors bordered by the coefficient of the constraint equation alternate in sign, the first one being positive, we have $d^2u < 0$. Hence, this becomes the second-order condition for u to be a maximum that we seek.

(iii) Constrained case—three variables

$$u = f(x_1, x_2, x_3)$$
$$\phi(x_1, x_2, x_3) = 0$$

The same procedure is used when we interpret x_1 as the dependent variable and x_2, x_3 as the independent variables. Then, the first-order conditions for an extreme value are

$$\frac{f_1}{\phi_1} = \frac{f_2}{\phi_2} = \frac{f_3}{\phi_3}$$

$$\phi(x_1, x_2, x_3) = 0$$

These three equations will give us the x_1, x_2, x_3 we seek.

The second-order conditions given $du = 0$ to determine whether we have a maximum or minimum are

$$d\phi = 0$$
$$d^2u > 0 \qquad \text{minimum}$$
$$d^2u < 0 \qquad \text{maximum}$$

We know from Section 11.8 that the conditions for these quadratics to be positive or negative are

$$
\begin{vmatrix}
0 & \phi_1 & \phi_2 \\
\phi_1 & v_{11} & v_{12} \\
\phi_2 & v_{21} & v_{22}
\end{vmatrix},
\qquad
\begin{vmatrix}
0 & \phi_1 & \phi_2 & \phi_3 \\
\phi_1 & v_{11} & v_{12} & v_{13} \\
\phi_2 & v_{21} & v_{22} & v_{23} \\
\phi_3 & v_{31} & v_{32} & v_{33}
\end{vmatrix}
$$

where for $d^2u > 0$ these bordered principal minors need to be all negative, and for $d^2u > 0$ they need to alternate in sign, the first one being positive. Here the v_{ij}'s are

$$
v_{ij} = f_{ij} - \frac{f_1}{\phi_1} \phi_{ij}
$$

Example 2. Given a utility function

$$
u = f(q_1, q_2, q_3)
$$

subject to a budget constraint

$$
p_1 q_1 + p_2 q_2 + p_3 q_3 = M
$$

where p_1, p_2, p_3 are given and M is total income (given), find the first- and second-order conditions for maximum utility. Let

$$
\phi(q_1, q_2, q_3) = p_1 q_1 + p_2 q_2 + p_3 q_3 - M = 0
$$

First-order conditions

$$
\frac{f_1}{p_1} = \frac{f_2}{p_2} = \frac{f_3}{p_3}
$$

because $\phi_i = p_i$. This result is the law of equi-marginal utility.

Second-order conditions

$$
d^2u = f_1\, d^2q_1 + f_{11}\, dq_1^2 + f_{22}\, dq_2^2 + f_{33}\, dq_3^2 + 2f_{12}\, dq_1\, dq_2
$$
$$
+ 2f_{13}\, dq_1\, dq_3 + 2f_{23}\, dq_2\, dq_3
$$

where we have considered q_1 the dependent variable. But

$$
q_1 = \frac{M - p_2 q_2 - p_3 q_3}{p_1}
$$

and is a linear function. Hence we find

$$
d^2q_1 = 0
$$

$$
\therefore \quad d^2u = f_{11}\, dq_1^2 + f_{22}\, dq_2^2 + f_{33}\, dq_3^2 + 2f_{12}\, dq_1\, dq_2
$$
$$
+ 2f_{13}\, dq_1\, dq_3 + 2f_{23}\, dq_2\, dq_3
$$

and is now a quadratic. We also have

$$
d^2\phi = \phi_1\, dq_1 + \phi_2\, dq_2 + \phi_3\, dq_3 = 0
$$

The necessary and sufficient conditions for $d^2u < 0$ subject to $d\phi = 0$ are, recalling that $\phi_i = p_i$,

$$\begin{vmatrix} 0 & p_1 & p_2 \\ p_1 & f_{11} & f_{12} \\ p_2 & f_{21} & f_{22} \end{vmatrix} > 0 \qquad \begin{vmatrix} 0 & p_1 & p_2 & p_3 \\ p_1 & f_{11} & f_{12} & f_{13} \\ p_2 & f_{21} & f_{22} & f_{23} \\ p_3 & f_{31} & f_{32} & f_{33} \end{vmatrix} < 0$$

Example 3. Given a production function

$$q = f(x_1, x_2, x_3)$$

and a cost constraint

$$C = x_1 r_1 + x_2 r_2 + x_3 r_3 + F$$

where q is output; x_1, x_2, x_3 are inputs; r_1, r_2, r_3 are input prices, which are given; C is total cost; and F is fixed cost; find the conditions for maximum output subject to a given cost C. Let,

$$\phi(x_1, x_2, x_3) = x_1 r_1 + x_2 r_2 + x_3 r_3 + F - C = 0$$

First-order condition

$$\frac{f_1}{r_1} = \frac{f_2}{r_2} = \frac{f_3}{r_3}$$

noting that $\phi_i = r_i$. The f_i are marginal physical products. Hence this is the law of equi-marginal productivities.

Second-order conditions

Let x_1 be the dependent variable. Then

$$x_1 = \frac{C - x_2 r_2 - x_3 r_3 - F}{r_1}$$

$$\therefore \quad d^2 x_1 = 0$$

$$\therefore \quad d^2 q = f_{11}\, dx_1^2 + f_{22}\, dx_2^2 + f_{33}\, dx_3^2 + 2f_{12}\, dx_1\, dx_2$$
$$+ 2f_{13}\, dx_1\, dx_3 + 2f_{23}\, dx_2\, dx_3$$

and is a quadratic. For maximum q, we need $d^2q < 0$, subject to $d\phi = 0$. We know the conditions for this are

$$\begin{vmatrix} 0 & r_1 & r_2 \\ r_1 & f_{11} & f_{12} \\ r_2 & f_{21} & f_{22} \end{vmatrix} > 0 \qquad \begin{vmatrix} 0 & r_1 & r_2 & r_3 \\ r_1 & f_{11} & f_{12} & f_{13} \\ r_2 & f_{21} & f_{22} & f_{23} \\ r_3 & f_{31} & f_{32} & f_{33} \end{vmatrix} < 0$$

(iv) The Lagrange multiplier method

In Chapter 5, we found the first-order conditions for extreme values of a function

$$u = f(x_1, x_2)$$

subject to a constraint

$$\phi(x_1, x_2) = 0$$

by the Lagrange multiplier method. We mentioned that the second-order conditions would be postponed until determinants and matrices were discussed. Let us now consider this problem.

In Chapter 5, the first- and second-order conditions were obtained by setting

$$z = f(x_1, x_2) + \lambda\phi(x_1, x_2)$$

and finding

$$\frac{\partial z}{\partial x_1} = f_1 + \lambda\phi_1 = 0$$

$$\frac{\partial z}{\partial x_2} = f_2 + \lambda\phi_2 = 0$$

$$\frac{\partial z}{\partial \lambda} = \phi(x_1, x_2) = 0$$

An alternative way (which is used frequently in economics) of finding the first-order conditions for extreme values is to use differentials. We set

$$dz = d(f + \lambda\phi) = 0$$

This becomes

$$(f_1 + \lambda\phi_1)\, dx_1 + (f_2 + \lambda\phi_2)\, dx_2 = 0$$

Assuming x_1 and x_2 to be the independent variables and λ to be the dependent variable, the necessary condition for $dz = 0$ is

$$f_1 + \lambda\phi_1 = 0$$

$$f_2 + \lambda\phi_2 = 0$$

which as we can see is the same as the first-order conditions we obtained above.

The convenience of this alternative method is that the second-order conditions are easily found. We know from previous discussion that the condition for a maximum is

(1) $$d^2z < 0$$

subject to the constraint

(2) $$\phi_1 \, dx_1 + \phi_2 \, dx_2 = 0$$

Hence our problem is to find the conditions which make (1) hold subject to (2). But d^2z becomes

$$d^2z = (f_{11} + \lambda\phi_{11}) \, dx_1^2 + 2(f_{12} + \lambda\phi_{12}) \, dx_1 \, dx_2 + (f_{22} + \lambda\phi_{22}) \, dx_2^2$$

which is a quadratic. Hence the problem becomes one of finding the conditions for the quadratic d^2z to be negative definite, subject to the constraint (2). We already know that the necessary and sufficient conditions for $d^2z < 0$, subject to (2) is that the bordered principal minors alternate in sign. In our present case where there are an even number of ϕ_1, ϕ_2, we have

$$\begin{vmatrix} 0 & \phi_1 & \phi_2 \\ \phi_1 & f_{11} + \lambda\phi_{11} & f_{12} + \lambda\phi_{12} \\ \phi_2 & f_{21} + \lambda\phi_{21} & f_{22} + \lambda\phi_{22} \end{vmatrix} > 0$$

In general, when the principal minor has an odd number of $\phi_1, \dots, \phi_{11}$, it is negative, and when it has an even number, it is positive.

For a *minimum*, we need $d^2z > 0$ subject to (2). In this case, the necessary and sufficient conditions for the quadratic to be positive definite is that the bordered principal minors be all negative.

Note that $\lambda = -f_1/\phi_1$ and hence the conditions we just found are the same as those found above.

When $\phi(x_1, x_2) = 0$ is a linear function, such as

$$\phi = 2x_1 + 3x_2 = 0$$

the $d^2\phi = 0$. Hence the second-order condition of the results of the Lagrange multiplier method simply becomes

$$d^2z = d^2f + \lambda \, d^2\phi$$

$$= d^2f$$

Hence, the condition for $d^2z = d^2f < 0$ or > 0 is determined by the sign of the principal minor

$$\begin{vmatrix} 0 & \phi_1 & \phi_2 \\ \phi_1 & f_{11} & f_{12} \\ \phi_2 & f_{21} & f_{22} \end{vmatrix}$$

Example 4. Using the data of Example 1, we have

$$u = f(q_1, q_2, q_3)$$

$$p_1 q_1 + p_2 q_2 + p_3 q_3 = M$$

Using the Lagrange multiplier method, we set

$$z = f + \lambda\phi$$

where

$$\phi = \phi(q_1, q_2, q_3) = p_1 q_1 + p_2 q_2 + p_3 q_3 - M = 0$$

For maximum utility we need

$$dz = 0$$

$$d^2z < 0$$

$$d\phi = 0$$

First-order condition

$$dz = d(f + \lambda\phi) = 0$$

$$\therefore \quad f_1 + \lambda\phi_1 = 0$$

$$f_2 + \lambda\phi_2 = 0$$

$$f_3 + \lambda\phi_3 = 0$$

which give us, since $\phi_i = p_i$,

$$\frac{f_1}{p_1} = \frac{f_2}{p_2} = \frac{f_3}{p_3} = -\lambda$$

Second-order condition. We need

$$d^2z < 0$$

$$d\phi = 0$$

This leads to

$$\begin{vmatrix} 0 & \phi_1 & \phi_2 \\ \phi_1 & f_{11} + \lambda\phi_{11} & f_{12} + \lambda\phi_{12} \\ \phi_2 & f_{21} + \lambda\phi_{21} & f_{22} + \lambda\phi_{22} \end{vmatrix} > 0,$$

$$\begin{vmatrix} 0 & \phi_1 & \phi_2 & \phi_3 \\ \phi_1 & f_{11} + \lambda\phi_{11} & f_{12} + \lambda\phi_{12} & f_{13} + \lambda\phi_{13} \\ \phi_2 & f_{21} + \lambda\phi_{21} & f_{22} + \lambda\phi_{22} & f_{23} + \lambda\phi_{23} \\ \phi_3 & f_{31} + \lambda\phi_{31} & f_{32} + \lambda\phi_{32} & f_{33} + \lambda\phi_{33} \end{vmatrix} < 0$$

But we see that $\phi_i = p_i$ and $\phi_{ij} = 0$. Hence the necessary and sufficient conditions for d^2z to be negative definite subject to the constraint are

$$\begin{vmatrix} 0 & p_1 & p_2 \\ p_1 & f_{11} & f_{12} \\ p_2 & f_{21} & f_{22} \end{vmatrix} > 0, \qquad \begin{vmatrix} 0 & p_1 & p_2 & p_3 \\ p_1 & f_{11} & f_{12} & f_{13} \\ p_2 & f_{21} & f_{22} & f_{23} \\ p_3 & f_{31} & f_{32} & f_{33} \end{vmatrix} < 0$$

Problems

1. Examine the functions for maximum or minimum.

(a) $u = 3x^2 + y^3 - 3xy$
(b) $u = 2x^2 + 2y^2 + 9 - 6x - 6y - 2xy$
(c) $u = 4x + 2y - x^2 - y^2$

2. Examine the function u subject to the constraint for maximum or minimum using the method of Sections (ii) and (iii) in the text. Then check the results using the Lagrange multiplier method of Section (iv).

(a) $u = 2x^2 - 6y^2$
$x + 2y = 6$

(b) $u = x^2 + 3xy - 5y^2$

   $2x + 3y = 6$

(c) $u = 6x^2 + y^2$

   $4x - y = 1$

(d) $u = x^2 + xy + y^2 + 3z^2$

   $x + 2y + 4z = 60$

3. Given the utility function

$$u = q_1 q_2^2 + q_2 q_3^2 + q_3 q_1^2$$

   and the budget constraint

$$M = p_1 q_1 + p_2 q_2 + p_3 q_3$$

   find the first- and second-order conditions for maximum utility, given M.

4. Given the production function

$$q = x_1^2 x_2^2 + x_2^2 x_3^2 + x_3^2 x_1^2$$

   and the cost function

$$C = x_1 r_1 + x_2 r_2 + x_3 r_3 + F$$

   find the first- and second-order conditions for maximum output, given C.

5. Given the cost function

$$C = r_1 x_1 + r_2 x_2 + r_3 x_3 + F$$

   where F is fixed cost and the production function is

$$q = f(x_1, x_2, x_3)$$

   find the first- and second-order conditions for minimum cost, given q.

6. Given the profit function

$$\pi = pq - C$$

   where

$$q = f(x_1, x_2, x_3)$$
$$C = x_1 r_1 + x_2 r_2 + x_3 r_3 + F$$

   find the first- and second-order conditions for maximum profits.

7. Find the first- and second-order conditions of Problems 3, 4, 5, and 6 above by the Lagrange multiplier method.

8. Demonstrate that

$$\begin{vmatrix} 0 & r_1 & r_2 & r_3 \\ r_1 & f_{11} & f_{12} & f_{13} \\ r_2 & f_{21} & f_{22} & f_{23} \\ r_3 & f_{31} & f_{32} & f_{33} \end{vmatrix} = \begin{vmatrix} f_{11} & f_{12} & f_{13} & r_1 \\ f_{21} & f_{22} & f_{23} & r_2 \\ f_{31} & f_{32} & f_{33} & r_3 \\ r_1 & r_2 & r_3 & 0 \end{vmatrix}$$

11.10 Partitioned matrices

In the subsequent sections we shall consider several special topics of vectors and matrices that are used in economics. They are partitioned matrices, the derivatives of a matrix, the idempotent matrix, matrix series, and, finally, the theory of non-negative matrices.

Ideas related to partitioned matrices are used in linear economics and statistics. So let us develop a few elementary ideas. Let A be a given matrix

$$A = \begin{bmatrix} a_{11} & a_{12} & a_{13} & a_{14} \\ a_{21} & a_{22} & a_{23} & a_{24} \\ a_{31} & a_{32} & a_{33} & a_{34} \\ a_{41} & a_{42} & a_{43} & a_{44} \end{bmatrix}$$

If we delete rows 3 and 4 and columns 1 and 2, we obtain

$$A(3, 4 \mid 1, 2) = \begin{bmatrix} a_{13} & a_{14} \\ a_{23} & a_{24} \end{bmatrix}$$

The numbers in the parenthesis indicate the rows and columns that have been deleted. A matrix obtained by deleting rows and columns of the original matrix is called a *submatrix* of A. In particular, a_{11} is a submatrix

$$A(2, 3, 4 \mid 2, 3, 4)$$

Thus, we can *partition* the matrix A into submatrices, for example,

$$A = \begin{bmatrix} a_{11} & a_{12} & a_{13} & a_{14} \\ a_{21} & a_{22} & a_{23} & a_{24} \\ a_{31} & a_{32} & a_{33} & a_{34} \\ a_{41} & a_{42} & a_{43} & a_{44} \end{bmatrix} = \begin{bmatrix} A(3, 4 \mid 3, 4) & A(3, 4 \mid 1, 2) \\ A(1, 2 \mid 3, 4) & A(1, 2 \mid 1, 2) \end{bmatrix}$$

Let us now discuss several matrix operations on partitioned matrices.

(i) Simple partition

Let us start with a discussion of matrices partitioned into two submatrices.

Addition. Let A and B be two matrices

$$A = \begin{bmatrix} a_{11} & a_{12} & a_{13} & a_{14} \\ a_{21} & a_{22} & a_{23} & a_{24} \\ a_{31} & a_{32} & a_{33} & a_{34} \\ a_{41} & a_{42} & a_{43} & a_{44} \end{bmatrix} = [A_1 \mid A_2]$$

$$B = \begin{bmatrix} b_{11} & b_{12} & b_{13} & b_{14} \\ b_{21} & b_{22} & b_{23} & b_{24} \\ b_{31} & b_{32} & b_{33} & b_{34} \\ b_{41} & b_{42} & b_{43} & b_{44} \end{bmatrix} = [B_1 \mid B_2]$$

Then

$$A + B = [A_1 + B_1 \mid A_2 + B_2]$$

That is, the sum of two identically partitioned matrices is a matrix with the same partitioning and the submatrices are the sums of the corresponding submatrices of A and B.

Transpose.

$$A = [A_1 \mid A_2]$$

$$A' = [A_1 \mid A_2]' = \begin{bmatrix} A_1' \\ A_2' \end{bmatrix}$$

Product.

$$A = [A_1 \mid A_2] \qquad A_1: \ mn_1, \ A_2: \ mn_2$$

$$B = \begin{bmatrix} B_1 \\ B_2 \end{bmatrix} \qquad B_1: \ n_1 p, \ B_2: \ n_2 p$$

$$C = AB = [A_1 \quad A_2] \begin{bmatrix} B_1 \\ B_2 \end{bmatrix} = [A_1 B_1 + A_2 B_2]$$

Note that the submatrices must have rows and columns such that the usual multiplication rule applies. Proofs will not be given, but the student should carry out the multiplications with an example and verify that the above operations hold.

(ii) Finer partition

Let us now consider a matrix partitioned into 4 submatrices.

Sum.

$$A = \begin{bmatrix} A_{11} & A_{12} \\ A_{21} & A_{22} \end{bmatrix} \qquad B = \begin{bmatrix} B_{11} & B_{12} \\ B_{21} & B_{22} \end{bmatrix}$$

$$A + B = \begin{bmatrix} A_{11} + B_{11} & A_{12} + B_{12} \\ A_{21} + B_{21} & A_{22} + B_{22} \end{bmatrix}$$

Transpose.

$$A = \begin{bmatrix} A_{11} & A_{12} \\ A_{21} & A_{22} \end{bmatrix} \qquad A' = \begin{bmatrix} A_{11}' & A_{21}' \\ A_{12}' & A_{22}' \end{bmatrix}$$

Product.

$$C = AB = \begin{bmatrix} A_{11} & A_{12} \\ A_{21} & A_{22} \end{bmatrix} \begin{bmatrix} B_{11} & B_{12} \\ B_{21} & B_{22} \end{bmatrix}$$

$$= \begin{bmatrix} A_{11}B_{11} + A_{12}B_{21} & A_{11}B_{12} + A_{12}B_{22} \\ A_{21}B_{11} + A_{22}B_{21} & A_{21}B_{12} + A_{22}B_{22} \end{bmatrix}$$

Kronecker (or direct) product. We mention the direct product for the sake of completeness. Let A be an $m \times m$ matrix and B be an $n \times n$ matrix. Then the direct product of A and B is defined as

$$A \otimes B = \begin{bmatrix} a_{11}B & \cdots & a_{1m}B \\ & \cdots & \\ a_{m1}B & \cdots & a_{mm}B \end{bmatrix}$$

Problems

1. Given

$$A = \begin{bmatrix} 1 & 2 & 3 & 4 \\ 2 & 0 & 3 & 1 \\ 0 & 2 & 1 & 5 \\ \hline 3 & 1 & 0 & 2 \end{bmatrix} = \begin{bmatrix} A_{11} & A_{12} \\ A_{21} & A_{22} \end{bmatrix}$$

(a) Find A' using the submatrices.
(b) Find A' by the usual method of interchanging rows and columns, and check the result of (a).

2. Given

$$B = \begin{bmatrix} 1 & 0 & 1 & 1 & 0 \\ 0 & 2 & 1 & 3 & 0 \\ 3 & 0 & 1 & 0 & 1 \\ \hline 2 & 1 & 0 & 1 & 1 \end{bmatrix} = \begin{bmatrix} B_{11} & B_{12} \\ B_{21} & B_{22} \end{bmatrix}$$

(a) Using the A of Problem 1, find AB by the product rule of partitioned matrices.
(b) Find AB by the ordinary method, and check the result of (a).

11.11 Partitioned inverse

We have studied inverse matrices in Section 10.7. There are, however, cases where the matrix shows a natural partition, and, when finding the inverse, it would be desirable if the inverse could be carried out in its partitioned form. Such cases may be found in regression analysis, which is used extensively in econometrics. So let us now discuss the problem of finding an inverse for a partitioned matrix.

Let the two matrices A and B be partitioned as follows.

$$A = \begin{bmatrix} p \times m & p \times n \\ A_{11} & A_{12} \\ q \times m & q \times n \\ A_{21} & A_{22} \end{bmatrix} \qquad B = \begin{bmatrix} m \times r & m \times q \\ B_{11} & B_{12} \\ n \times p & n \times q \\ B_{21} & B_{22} \end{bmatrix}$$

If B is the inverse of A, we have

$$AB = I = BA$$

If we can express the terms B_{ij} in terms of A_{ij} and substitute this into B, we shall have obtained the inverse of A. So let us first express AB and BA in terms of submatrices A_{ij} and B_{ij}. We find

$$AB = \begin{bmatrix} \overset{p \times p}{A_{11}B_{11} + A_{12}B_{21}} & \overset{p \times q}{A_{11}B_{12} + A_{12}B_{22}} \\ \overset{q \times p}{A_{21}B_{11} + A_{22}B_{21}} & \overset{q \times q}{A_{21}B_{12} + A_{22}B_{22}} \end{bmatrix}$$

$$= I = \begin{bmatrix} I_p & 0 \\ 0 & I_q \end{bmatrix}$$

$$BA = \begin{bmatrix} \overset{m \times m}{B_{11}A_{11} + B_{12}A_{21}} & \overset{m \times n}{B_{11}A_{12} + B_{12}A_{22}} \\ \overset{n \times m}{B_{21}A_{11} + B_{22}A_{21}} & \overset{n \times n}{B_{21}A_{12} + B_{22}A_{22}} \end{bmatrix}$$

$$= I = \begin{bmatrix} I_m & 0 \\ 0 & I_n \end{bmatrix}$$

Hence we obtain the following relations.

(1) $A_{11}B_{11} + A_{12}B_{21} = I_p$

(2) $A_{11}B_{12} + A_{12}B_{22} = 0$

(3) $B_{21}A_{11} + B_{22}A_{21} = 0$

(4) $B_{21}A_{12} + B_{22}A_{22} = I_n$

We have 4 unknowns B_{11}, B_{12}, B_{21}, B_{22}, and our problem is to solve for these unknowns in terms of the A_{ij}. Let $B_{22} = D^{-1}$. Then from (2) we find

(5) $B_{12} = -A_{11}^{-1}A_{12}D^{-1}$

From (3) we find

(6) $B_{21} = -D^{-1}A_{21}A_{11}^{-1}$

From (1) we find

(7) $B_{11} = A_{11}^{-1} + A_{11}^{-1}A_{12}D^{-1}A_{21}A_{11}^{-1}$

Finally, from (4) and (5), (6), and (7) we find

(8) $B_{22}^{-1} = D = A_{22} - A_{21}A_{11}^{-1}A_{12}$

Substituting (5), (6), (7), and (8) in B gives us

(9) $B = \begin{bmatrix} A_{11}^{-1} + A_{11}^{-1}A_{12}D^{-1}A_{21}A_{11}^{-1} & -A_{11}^{-1}A_{12}D^{-1} \\ -D^{-1}A_{21}A_{11}^{-1} & D^{-1} \end{bmatrix}$

$$= A^{-1}$$

Example.

$$A = \begin{bmatrix} 1 & 2 & | & 3 \\ 1 & 3 & | & 0 \\ \hline 3 & 0 & | & 28 \end{bmatrix} = \begin{bmatrix} A_{11} & A_{12} \\ A_{21} & A_{22} \end{bmatrix}$$

$$D = A_{22} - A_{21}A_{11}^{-1}A_{12} = 1$$

$$B_{11} = \begin{bmatrix} 84 & -56 \\ -28 & 19 \end{bmatrix}$$

$$B_{12} = \begin{bmatrix} -9 \\ 3 \end{bmatrix} \qquad B_{21} = [-9 \quad 6] \qquad B_{22} = D^{-1} = 1$$

$$\therefore \quad A^{-1} = B = \begin{bmatrix} B_{11} & B_{12} \\ B_{21} & B_{22} \end{bmatrix} = \begin{bmatrix} 84 & -56 & -9 \\ -28 & 19 & 3 \\ -9 & 6 & 1 \end{bmatrix}$$

$$AA^{-1} = I$$

Problems

1. Check that

$$B_{22}^{-1} = D = A_{22} - A_{21}A_{11}^{-1}A_{12}$$

2. Check whether $AB = I$ by multiplying out the partitioned matrices A and B as given by equation (9).

3. Work through the calculations of the example and check whether $AA^{-1} = I$.

11.12 Differentiation of matrices and determinants

As we have seen, matrices and determinants express equations and systems of equations in compact form. An example may be found in regression analysis, which we shall discuss in later chapters. Another example is consideration of systems of equations for stability problems, which are also discussed later.

Frequently we have to differentiate systems of equations. It would be convenient if we could perform the differentiation directly on the matrices and determinants without referring back to the original system of equations. Our problem in this section is to study the procedures of differentiating. determinants and matrices.

(i) Differentiation of a function by a vector

Let the elements of a vector $\mathbf{X} = [x_1 \quad x_2]$ be the variables of a function

$$y = f(x_1, x_2)$$

Then the partial derivative of y with respect to the vector $\mathbf{X}$ is defined as

$$\frac{\partial y}{\partial \mathbf{X}} = \begin{bmatrix} \dfrac{\partial y}{\partial x_1} \\ \dfrac{\partial y}{\partial x_2} \end{bmatrix}$$

Example 1. Let $\mathbf{X} = [x_1 \quad x_2]$ and the function be

$$y = a_1 x_1 + a_2 x_2 = [a_1 \quad a_2]\begin{bmatrix} x_1 \\ x_2 \end{bmatrix} = a'\mathbf{X}$$

Then

$$\frac{\partial y}{\partial \mathbf{X}} = \begin{bmatrix} \dfrac{\partial q}{\partial x_1} \\ \dfrac{\partial y}{\partial x_2} \end{bmatrix} = \begin{bmatrix} a_1 \\ a_2 \end{bmatrix} = a'$$

Hence when $y = a'\mathbf{X}$ is linear, we have

$$\frac{\partial y}{\partial \mathbf{X}} = \frac{\partial}{\partial \mathbf{X}}(a'\mathbf{X}) = a'$$

Example 2. Let $\mathbf{X} = [x_1 \quad x_2]$ and

$$y = a_1 x_1^2 + a_2 x_2^3$$

$$= [a_1 \quad a_2]\begin{bmatrix} x_1^2 \\ x_2^3 \end{bmatrix} = a'\mathbf{X}$$

$$\therefore \quad \frac{\partial y}{\partial \mathbf{X}} = \begin{bmatrix} \dfrac{\partial y}{\partial x_1} \\ \dfrac{\partial y}{\partial x_2} \end{bmatrix} = \begin{bmatrix} 2a_1 x_1 \\ 3a_2 x_2^2 \end{bmatrix} = [a_1 \quad a_2]\begin{bmatrix} 2x_1 \\ 3x_2^2 \end{bmatrix}$$

Example 3. Let $a' = [a_1 \quad a_2]$ and

$$y = a'\mathbf{X} = a_1 x_1^2 + a_2 x_2^3$$

Then

$$\frac{\partial y}{\partial a} = \begin{bmatrix} \dfrac{\partial y}{\partial a_1} \\ \dfrac{\partial y}{\partial a_2} \end{bmatrix} = \begin{bmatrix} x_1^2 \\ x_2^3 \end{bmatrix} = \mathbf{X}$$

Hence, when $y = a'\mathbf{X}$ is linear in a

$$\frac{\partial y}{\partial a} = \frac{\partial}{\partial a}(a'\mathbf{X}) = \mathbf{X}$$

Example 4. Let $b = [b_1 \quad b_2]$ and $y = a'X$. Then

$$\frac{\partial y}{\partial b} = \begin{bmatrix} \dfrac{\partial y}{\partial b_1} \\ \dfrac{\partial y}{\partial b_2} \end{bmatrix} = \begin{bmatrix} 0 \\ 0 \end{bmatrix} = 0$$

Example 5. Let $X = [x_1 \quad x_2]$ and

$$y = X'AX = [x_1 \quad x_2]\begin{bmatrix} a_{11} & a_{12} \\ a_{21} & a_{22} \end{bmatrix}\begin{bmatrix} x_1 \\ x_2 \end{bmatrix}$$

$$= a_{11}x_1^2 + 2a_{12}x_1x_2 + a_{22}x_2^2$$

where $a_{12} = a_{21}$. Then

$$\frac{\partial y}{\partial X} = \begin{bmatrix} \dfrac{\partial y}{\partial x_1} \\ \dfrac{\partial y}{\partial x_2} \end{bmatrix} = \begin{bmatrix} 2a_{11}x_1 + 2a_{12}x_2 \\ 2a_{21}x_1 + 2a_{22}x_2 \end{bmatrix}$$

$$= 2AX = 2X'A$$

We may show this as

$$\frac{\partial y}{\partial X} = \frac{\partial}{\partial X}(X'AX)$$

$$= 2AX = 2X'A$$

(ii) *Differentiation of a vector by a vector*

Let the elements of a vector $X = [x_1 \quad x_2]$ be the variables of a function

$$y = \begin{bmatrix} y_1 \\ y_2 \end{bmatrix} = \begin{bmatrix} f_1(x_1, x_2) \\ f_2(x_1, x_2) \end{bmatrix}$$

Then the derivative of the vector y is

$$\frac{\partial y}{\partial X} = \begin{bmatrix} \dfrac{\partial y_1}{\partial X} & \dfrac{\partial y_2}{\partial X} \end{bmatrix}$$

$$= \begin{bmatrix} \dfrac{\partial y_1}{\partial x_1} & \dfrac{\partial y_2}{\partial x_1} \\ \dfrac{\partial y_1}{\partial x_2} & \dfrac{\partial y_2}{\partial x_2} \end{bmatrix}$$

(iii) *Second derivative*

Let the elements of $X = [x_1 \quad x_2]$ be the variables of

$$y = f(x_1, x_2)$$

Then the second derivative of y with respect to $\mathbf{X}$ is as follows.

$$\frac{\partial y}{\partial \mathbf{X}} = \begin{bmatrix} \dfrac{\partial y}{\partial x_1} \\ \dfrac{\partial y}{\partial x_2} \end{bmatrix}$$

$$\frac{\partial^2 y}{\partial \mathbf{X}^2} = \begin{bmatrix} \dfrac{\partial^2 y}{\partial x_1^2} & \dfrac{\partial^2 y}{\partial x_2 \, \partial x_1} \\ \dfrac{\partial^2 y}{\partial x_1 \, \partial x_2} & \dfrac{\partial^2 y}{\partial x_2^2} \end{bmatrix}$$

Example 1. Given $y = f(x_1, x_2)$ find the first- and second-order conditions for an extreme value.

First-order conditions

$$\frac{\partial y}{\partial \mathbf{X}} = \begin{bmatrix} \dfrac{\partial y}{\partial x_1} \\ \dfrac{\partial y}{\partial x_2} \end{bmatrix} = \begin{bmatrix} 0 \\ 0 \end{bmatrix} = 0$$

Second-order conditions. We know that

$$d^2 y = f_{11} \, dx_1^2 + f_{22} \, dx_2^2 + 2f_{12} \, dx_1 \, dx_2$$

$$= [dx_1 \quad dx_2] \begin{bmatrix} f_{11} & f_{12} \\ f_{21} & f_{22} \end{bmatrix} \begin{bmatrix} dx_1 \\ dx_2 \end{bmatrix}$$

$$\frac{\partial^2 y}{\partial \mathbf{X}^2} = \begin{bmatrix} \dfrac{\partial^2 y}{\partial x_1^2} & \dfrac{\partial^2 y}{\partial x_2 \, \partial x_1} \\ \dfrac{\partial^2 y}{\partial x_1 \, \partial x_2} & \dfrac{\partial^2 y}{\partial x_2^2} \end{bmatrix}$$

$$= \begin{bmatrix} f_{11} & f_{12} \\ f_{21} & f_{22} \end{bmatrix}$$

$$\therefore \quad d^2 y = (d\mathbf{X})' \, \frac{\partial^2 y}{\partial \mathbf{X}^2} (d\mathbf{X}) \quad \begin{matrix} < 0 \\ > 0 \end{matrix} \quad \begin{matrix} \text{maximum} \\ \text{minimum} \end{matrix}$$

11.13 Differentiation of determinants

(i) Differentiation of a determinant

Consider a determinant

$$\Delta = \begin{vmatrix} x & x^3 \\ x^3 & x^4 \end{vmatrix}$$

where the elements are functions of x. Then the derivative of Δ, i.e., $d\Delta/dx$ is

$$\frac{d\Delta}{dx} = \begin{vmatrix} 1 & 3x^2 \\ x^3 & x^4 \end{vmatrix} + \begin{vmatrix} x & x^3 \\ 3x^2 & 4x^3 \end{vmatrix}$$

We have differentiated each row separately and then summed the two determinants. For a determinant of n rows, we differentiate each row separately and then sum the n determinants.

Let us check our result.

$$\Delta = \begin{vmatrix} x & x^3 \\ x^3 & x^4 \end{vmatrix} = x^5 - x^6$$

$$\therefore \quad \frac{d\Delta}{dx} = 5x^4 - 6x^5$$

$$\frac{d\Delta}{dx} = \begin{vmatrix} 1 & 3x^2 \\ x^3 & x^4 \end{vmatrix} + \begin{vmatrix} x & x^3 \\ 3x^2 & 4x^3 \end{vmatrix} = 5x^4 - 6x^5$$

Next, recall that the value of a determinant is unaltered by an interchange of rows and columns. This implies that, instead of differentiating rows, we can differentiate columns. For example,

$$\frac{d\Delta}{dx} = \begin{vmatrix} 1 & x^3 \\ 3x^2 & x^4 \end{vmatrix} + \begin{vmatrix} x & 3x^2 \\ x^3 & 4x^3 \end{vmatrix} = 5x^4 - 6x^5$$

(ii) Jacobians

Consider two continuous functions

$$u = u(x, y) = 2x^2 - 3y^2$$
$$v = v(x, y) = x^2 + 2y^2$$

The partial derivatives are assumed to be continuous. Then the Jacobian of the system of equations is the determinant of the first partial derivatives of u and v. Thus,

$$J = \frac{\partial(u, v)}{\partial(x, y)} = \begin{vmatrix} \dfrac{\partial u}{\partial x} & \dfrac{\partial v}{\partial x} \\ \dfrac{\partial u}{\partial y} & \dfrac{\partial v}{\partial y} \end{vmatrix} = \begin{vmatrix} 4x & 2x \\ -6y & 4y \end{vmatrix}$$

The two main uses of Jacobians in economics are, (1) to show the *existence* of a solution for a set of simultaneous equations, and (2) to perform a transformation from one set of variables to another. An example of the first is proving the existence of a solution of a multimarket competitive economy. An example of the second use is found in statistics where one set of random variables is transformed into another set. This second use will be considered in Chapter 13.

The existence theorem may be stated as follows: Consider a system of simultaneous equations

(1)
$$f_1(x_1, x_2) = y_1$$
$$f_2(x_1, x_2) = y_2$$

The functions f_i are continuous and possess continuous first partial derivatives. For example, y_1, y_2 may be quantity and, x_1, x_2 may be prices. We wish to show x_1 and x_2 in terms of y_1 and y_2. That is, we wish to find the solutions

(2)
$$x_1 = g_1(y_1, y_2)$$
$$x_2 = g_2(y_1, y_2)$$

The necessary and sufficient condition for (1) to have a solution (2) is for the Jacobian of (1) to be non-vanishing in the neighborhood of a point (x_1^0, x_2^0) where

$$f_1(x_1^0, x_2^0) = y_1$$
$$f_2(x_1^0, x_2^0) = y_2$$

The Jacobian is

$$J = \frac{\partial(y_1, y_2)}{\partial(x_1, x_2)} = \begin{vmatrix} \dfrac{\partial y_1}{\partial x_1} & \dfrac{\partial y_1}{\partial x_2} \\ \dfrac{\partial y_2}{\partial x_1} & \dfrac{\partial y_2}{\partial x_2} \end{vmatrix} \neq 0$$

For proof and further discussion of the Jacobian, see the references in Notes and References at the end of the chapter.

(iii) Hessians

Let $U = f(x_1, x_2, x_3)$. Then, the determinant

$$H = \begin{vmatrix} f_{11} & f_{12} & f_{13} \\ f_{21} & f_{22} & f_{23} \\ f_{31} & f_{32} & f_{33} \end{vmatrix}$$

which is made up of the second partial derivatives in the order indicated above, is called the Hessian determinant of U. In Section 11.9 we have been using Hessians and bordered Hessians without mentioning them by name.

Problems

1. Differentiate the following determinant with respect to x.

$$\Delta = \begin{vmatrix} 2x^2 & x \\ 1 & 3x^3 \end{vmatrix}$$

Expand the determinant, and differentiate the expanded form, and check your answer.

2. Given

$$u = 3x^2 - y^2$$
$$v = 2x^2 + 3y^2$$

Find the Jacobian $\dfrac{\partial(u, v)}{\partial(x, y)}$

3. Given the excess demand functions

$$E_1 = E_1(P_1, P_2)$$
$$E_2 = E_2(P_1, P_2)$$

Find the Jacobian $\dfrac{\partial(E_1, E_2)}{\partial(P_1, P_2)}$. What do the elements in the Jacobian mean in economics?

4. Given a utility function

$$u = f(x_1, x_2, x_3) = x_1^2 + 2x_2^2 + 3x_3^2$$

Find the Hessian of u.

11.14 Idempotent matrix

Given a symmetric matrix A. If

$$A' = A \qquad \text{and} \qquad AA = A$$

the matrix A is said to be idempotent. Idempotent matrices play an important role in regression analysis, which will be discussed in Chapter 16. Let us give several illustrations.

Example 1. I is idempotent because $I' = I$ and $II = I$.

Example 2. Suppose we have

$$\begin{cases} b_1 \sum x_1^2 + b_2 \sum x_1 x_2 = \sum x_1 y \\ b_1 \sum x_1 x_2 + b_2 \sum x_2^2 = \sum x_2 y \end{cases}$$

Then

$$\begin{bmatrix} \sum x_1^2 & \sum x_1 x_2 \\ \sum x_1 x_2 & \sum x_2^2 \end{bmatrix} \begin{bmatrix} b_1 \\ b_2 \end{bmatrix} = \begin{bmatrix} \sum x_1 y \\ \sum x_2 y \end{bmatrix}$$

Let

$$X = \begin{bmatrix} \sum x_1^2 & \sum x_1 x_2 \\ \sum x_1 x_2 & \sum x_2^2 \end{bmatrix}$$

Construct a matrix

$$M = I - X(X'X)^{-1}X'$$

Since X is a symmetric matrix, M will also be symmetric and, furthermore, will be idempotent. This is easily seen as follows.

$$
\begin{aligned}
M' &= (I - X(X'X)X')' \\
&= I' - [X(X'X)^{-1}X']' \\
&= I - (X')'[(X'X)^{-1}]'(X)' \\
&= I - X(X'X)X' = M \\
MM &= [I - X(X'X)^{-1}X'][I - X(X'X)^{-1}X'] \\
&= II - X(X'X)^{-1}X'(I) \\
&\quad - IX(X'X)^{-1}X' + X(X'X)^{-1}X' : \ X(X'X)^{-1}X' \\
&= I - X(X'X^{-1}X' - X(X'X)^{-1}X' + X(X'X)^{-1}X' \\
&= I - X(X'X)^{-1}X' = M
\end{aligned}
$$

As we shall see later, the above set of equations comprises the normal equations for the method of least squares.

11.15 Matrix series

Let us present a simple Leontief input-output model,

$$
\begin{aligned}
(1 - a_{11})x_1 - a_{12}x_2 - a_{13}x_3 &= c_1 \\
-a_{21}x_1 + (1 - a_{22})x_2 - a_{23}x_3 &= c_2 \\
-a_{31}x_1 - a_{32}x_2 + (1 - a_{33})x_3 &= c_3
\end{aligned}
$$

where the subscript 1 indicates agriculture, 2 manufacturing, 3 household and x_1 is agricultural output, x_2 manufacturing output, x_3 labor supply and c_i is final goods. Therefore, c_1 would be the amount of x_1 used for final consumption by household. The a_{ij} are the production coefficients. Thus $a_{12}x_2$ shows the amount of x_1 used by industry 2, and likewise for the other $a_{ij}x_j$.

This can be shown in matrix form as

$$
x = Ax + c
$$

where

$$
A = \begin{bmatrix} a_{11} & a_{12} & a_{13} \\ a_{21} & a_{22} & a_{23} \\ a_{31} & a_{32} & a_{33} \end{bmatrix}
$$

Or it may be shown as

$$
(I - A)x = c
$$

This shows that gross outputs x are transformed into final products c by the matrix $(I - A)$. The matrix $(I - A)$, which gives the technical conditions of production, is usually given, and the problem can be set up as follows:

Given final demand c, how much should be produced by the various industries; i.e., what is x? Two problems arise. (1) Is there a solution, and (2) if there is, what is it? If the inverse of $(I - A)$ exists, the solution will be

$$x = (I - A)^{-1}c$$

For this to make economic sense, the elements of x, $(I - A)^{-1}$ and c must be non-negative.

In this section we shall study how $(I - A)^{-1}$ may be found. As can be seen, when the A becomes large, finding $(I - A)^{-1}$ in a straightforward manner will become a complicated computational problem. It will be helpful if some simple computational procedure can be found. It will turn out that this can be accomplished by using matrix power series. To study matrix power series, we shall first discuss a matrix sequence, then a matrix series, and finally a matrix power series.

Other properties of matrices such as A and $(I - A)^{-1}$ will be studied in Section 11.16.

(i) Matrix sequence

Consider a matrix sequence

(1) $$A_1, A_2, A_3, \ldots$$

where the A_i are of the same order. The first question we ask is: How is the convergence of this sequence defined? This will be defined by extending the idea of a limit of a sequence, discussed in Chapter 2, by noting that each element of the matrix A_i forms a sequence. We say the matrix sequence (1) will converge to a limit if and only if each element of the matrix converges to a limit.

For example, suppose we have

$$\begin{bmatrix} a_{11} & a_{12} \\ a_{21} & a_{22} \end{bmatrix}, \quad \begin{bmatrix} a'_{11} & a'_{12} \\ a'_{21} & a'_{22} \end{bmatrix}, \quad \begin{bmatrix} a''_{11} & a''_{12} \\ a''_{21} & a''_{22} \end{bmatrix}, \ldots$$

Then this matrix sequence will converge if

$$a_{ij}, a'_{ij}, a''_{ij}, \ldots \qquad \text{all } i, j$$

converges to a limit α_{ij}. That is,

$$\lim_{n \to \infty} (a_{ij})^{(n)} = \alpha_{ij}$$

for all (i, j). Then, we may write

$$\lim_{n \to \infty} A_n = A$$

and say that the sequence $\{A_n\}$ converges to A.

(*ii*) *Matrix power series*

Our next step is to follow the procedure developed in Chapter 7 and construct a matrix power series. Let A_i be square matrices, and set

$$S_0 = \lambda_0 A^0 = \lambda_0 \quad \text{(where we define } A^0 = I)$$
$$S_1 = \lambda_0 + \lambda_1 A$$
$$S_2 = \lambda_0 + \lambda_1 A + \lambda_2 A^2$$
$$\vdots$$
$$S_k = \lambda_0 + \lambda_1 A + \lambda_2 A^2 + \dots + \lambda_k A^k + \dots$$

Then

$$\lim_{n \to \infty} S_n = \sum_{n=0}^{\infty} \lambda_n A^n$$
$$= \lambda_0 + \lambda_1 A + \lambda_2 A^2 + \dots$$

is called a *matrix power series*. When S_n approaches a limit S, we say the series converges.

To determine whether or not a matrix power series converges, we use the Cauchy test from Chapter 2. That is, it is necessary for us to make

$$|S_n - S_m| < \epsilon$$

for an arbitrarily small $\epsilon > 0$, by making m, n sufficiently large.

Let $n = m + 1$. Then

$$|S_n - S_m| = |\sum_{k}^{n} \lambda_k A^k - \sum_{k}^{m} \lambda_k A^k|$$
$$= |\lambda_n A^n| < \epsilon$$
$$= |\lambda_n A^n - 0| < \epsilon$$

Hence, we may state it is necessary that

$$\lim_{k \to \infty} \lambda_k A^k \to 0$$

for the matrix power series to converge.

With this much background, let us consider the matrix $(I - A)^{-1}$.

(*iii*) $(I - A)^{-1}$

Using the technique developed in Chapter 7, let us construct

$$S_3 = I + A + A^2 + A^3$$
$$AS_3 = A + A^2 + A^3 + A^4$$
$$\therefore \quad (I - A)S_3 = I - A^4$$

If $A^4 \cong 0$, we get

$$(I - A)S_3 = I$$

Assuming $|I - A| \neq 0$, we find

$$(I - A)^{-1} = S_3$$
$$= I + A + A^2 + A^3$$

Hence, the problem is to investigate whether $A^4 \simeq 0$. Let us use a simple example and investigate this problem. Suppose

$$A = \begin{bmatrix} a_{11} & a_{12} \\ a_{21} & a_{22} \end{bmatrix}$$

Then

$$A^2 = \begin{bmatrix} a_{11} & a_{12} \\ a_{21} & a_{22} \end{bmatrix} \begin{bmatrix} a_{11} & a_{12} \\ a_{21} & a_{22} \end{bmatrix}$$

$$= \begin{bmatrix} a_{11}a_{11} + a_{12}a_{21} & a_{11}a_{12} + a_{12}a_{22} \\ a_{21}a_{11} + a_{22}a_{21} & a_{21}a_{12} + a_{22}a_{22} \end{bmatrix}$$

$$= \begin{bmatrix} a_{11}^{(2)} & a_{12}^{(2)} \\ a_{21}^{(2)} & a_{22}^{(2)} \end{bmatrix}$$

where

$$a_{11}^{(2)} = a_{11}a_{11} + a_{12}a_{21} = \sum_{k=1}^{n=2} a_{1k}a_{k1}$$

$$a_{12}^{(2)} = a_{11}a_{12} + a_{12}a_{22} = \sum_{k=1}^{n=2} a_{1k}a_{k2}$$

and, in general,

$$a_{ij}^{(2)} = \sum_{k=1}^{n=2} a_{ik}a_{kj}$$

For A^3, we find

$$A^3 = A^2 A$$

$$= \begin{bmatrix} a_{11}^{(2)} & a_{12}^{(2)} \\ a_{21}^{(2)} & a_{22}^{(2)} \end{bmatrix} \begin{bmatrix} a_{11} & a_{12} \\ a_{21} & a_{22} \end{bmatrix} = \begin{bmatrix} a_{11}^{(3)} & a_{12}^{(3)} \\ a_{21}^{(3)} & a_{22}^{(3)} \end{bmatrix}$$

where

$$a_{ij}^{(3)} = \sum_{k=1}^{n=2} a_{ik}^{(2)} a_{kj}$$

and, as we can see, we may repeat this process for A^4, A^5; and so forth.

In input-output analysis, the A matrix usually shows production coefficients and has the properties that

$$0 \leq a_{ij} < 1 \qquad \text{all } i, j$$

$$\sum_{i}^{n} a_{ij} < 1 \qquad \text{all } j$$

Using these properties we may write

$$0 \leq \sum_{i}^{n} a_{ij} \leq r < 1$$

Hence, for A^2, we find

$$\sum_{i}^{n} a_{ij}^{(2)} = \sum_{i}^{n} \left(\sum_{k}^{n} a_{ik} a_{kj} \right)$$

$$= \sum_{k}^{n} \left(\sum_{i}^{n} a_{ik} \right) a_{kj}$$

$$\leq r \sum_{k}^{n} a_{kj}$$

$$\leq r^2 \qquad \qquad \text{all } j$$

The matrix A^2 is

$$A^2 = \begin{bmatrix} a_{11}^{(2)} & a_{12}^{(2)} \\ a_{21}^{(2)} & a_{22}^{(2)} \end{bmatrix}$$

Hence the above result shows that the sum of each column is less than r^2. Since $0 \leq a_{ij} < 1$, this implies that the terms $a_{ij}^{(2)} \geq 0$. Hence $a_{ij}^{(2)} \leq r^2$.

We may continue the process, and we shall find that for A^m, we get

$$a_{ij}^{(m)} \leq r^m$$

Since $0 \leq r < 1$, as $m \rightarrow \infty$, then $r^m \rightarrow 0$. Hence as $m \rightarrow \infty$, we get $a_{ij}^{(m)} \rightarrow 0$. According to our definition of convergence, this means

$$A^m \rightarrow 0 \qquad \text{as} \qquad m \rightarrow \infty$$

and the series

$$S = I + A + A^2 + A^3 + \dots$$

will converge.

In our hypothetical problem, we assumed $A^4 \simeq 0$. If the a_{ij} are such that A^4 is close to zero, then

$$S = I + A + A^2 + A^3$$

will be a good approximation of the true value of $(I - A)^{-1}$. By extending the series, we can obtain better approximations.

11.16 Non-negative square matrices

In this section we shall study about matrices such as A or $(I - A)^{-1}$ which have elements that are all non-negative. Such matrices occur in input-output analysis, Markov chains, and other economic topics where all the data are usually non-negative. A discussion of *non-negative square matrices* is mathematically advanced and at the level of this book only a heuristic discussion will be given. References are given at the end of the chapter for those interested in pursuing the topic. We start our discussion with some preliminary ideas.

If all the elements a_{ij} of a square matrix A are non-negative, i.e., $a_{ij} \geq 0$, we say A is a *non-negative square matrix* and write $A \geq 0$. If $a_{ij} > 0$, then we say A is a *positive square matrix*.

(*i*) Permutation matrix

A permutation matrix is a square matrix which has 1 in a row or column with all other elements equal to zero. Thus, for a 3×3 permutation matrix we have

$$\begin{bmatrix} 1 & 0 & 0 \\ 0 & 1 & 0 \\ 0 & 0 & 1 \end{bmatrix}, \quad \begin{bmatrix} 1 & 0 & 0 \\ 0 & 0 & 1 \\ 0 & 1 & 0 \end{bmatrix}, \quad \begin{bmatrix} 0 & 1 & 0 \\ 1 & 0 & 0 \\ 0 & 0 & 1 \end{bmatrix}$$

$$\begin{bmatrix} 0 & 1 & 0 \\ 0 & 0 & 1 \\ 1 & 0 & 0 \end{bmatrix}, \quad \begin{bmatrix} 0 & 0 & 1 \\ 0 & 1 & 0 \\ 1 & 0 & 0 \end{bmatrix}, \quad \begin{bmatrix} 0 & 0 & 1 \\ 1 & 0 & 0 \\ 0 & 1 & 0 \end{bmatrix}$$

There are $3! = 6$ matrices and, as can be seen, these permutation matrices have been obtained by interchanging rows. Let us look at the second matrix

$$\pi_2 = \begin{bmatrix} 1 & 0 & 0 \\ 0 & 0 & 1 \\ 0 & 1 & 0 \end{bmatrix}$$

We have interchanged the second and third rows. Note that the inner product of the rows is zero and also that the length of the rows is unity. Thus, π_2 is an orthogonal matrix and we should have $\pi_2 \pi_2^T = I$. Let us check.

$$\pi_2 \pi_2^T = \begin{bmatrix} 1 & 0 & 0 \\ 0 & 0 & 1 \\ 0 & 1 & 0 \end{bmatrix} \begin{bmatrix} 1 & 0 & 0 \\ 0 & 0 & 1 \\ 0 & 1 & 0 \end{bmatrix} = \begin{bmatrix} 1 & 0 & 0 \\ 0 & 1 & 0 \\ 0 & 0 & 1 \end{bmatrix} = I$$

Note that $\pi_1 = I$ is also considered as a permutation matrix.

Next, let us see what happens when we apply these matrices to a matrix A.

$$A = \begin{bmatrix} 1 & 2 & 3 \\ 4 & 5 & 6 \\ 7 & 8 & 9 \end{bmatrix}$$

$$\pi_2 A = \begin{bmatrix} 1 & 0 & 0 \\ 0 & 0 & 1 \\ 0 & 1 & 0 \end{bmatrix} \begin{bmatrix} 1 & 2 & 3 \\ 4 & 5 & 6 \\ 7 & 8 & 9 \end{bmatrix} = \begin{bmatrix} 1 & 2 & 3 \\ 7 & 8 & 9 \\ 4 & 5 & 6 \end{bmatrix}$$

That is, $\pi_2 A$ has performed the operation of interchanging rows 2 and 3.

Next,

$$\pi_2 A \pi_2^T = \begin{bmatrix} 1 & 2 & 3 \\ 7 & 8 & 9 \\ 4 & 5 & 6 \end{bmatrix} \begin{bmatrix} 1 & 0 & 0 \\ 0 & 0 & 1 \\ 0 & 1 & 0 \end{bmatrix} = \begin{bmatrix} 1 & 3 & 2 \\ 7 & 9 & 8 \\ 4 & 6 & 5 \end{bmatrix}$$

Thus, columns 2 and 3 have been interchanged.

In a similar way, the other π_i's can be shown to interchange rows when A is pre-multiplied by π, and interchange columns when A is post-multiplied by π^T.

(ii) Indecomposable matrices

Consider a matrix

$$A = \begin{bmatrix} 0 & 2 & 3 \\ 0 & 5 & 0 \\ 7 & 8 & 9 \end{bmatrix}$$

Let us interchange rows and columns using the permutation matrices so that the zeros will be brought down to the left-hand corner.

$$\pi A = \begin{bmatrix} 1 & 0 & 0 \\ 0 & 0 & 1 \\ 0 & 1 & 0 \end{bmatrix} \begin{bmatrix} 0 & 2 & 3 \\ 0 & 5 & 0 \\ 7 & 8 & 9 \end{bmatrix} = \begin{bmatrix} 0 & 2 & 3 \\ 7 & 8 & 9 \\ 0 & 5 & 0 \end{bmatrix}$$

$$\pi A \pi^T = \begin{bmatrix} 0 & 2 & 3 \\ 7 & 8 & 9 \\ 0 & 5 & 0 \end{bmatrix} \begin{bmatrix} 1 & 0 & 0 \\ 0 & 0 & 1 \\ 0 & 1 & 0 \end{bmatrix} = \begin{bmatrix} 0 & 3 & 2 \\ 7 & 9 & 8 \\ 0 & 0 & 5 \end{bmatrix}$$

Let us now partition $\pi A \pi^T$.

$$\pi A \pi^T = \begin{bmatrix} 0 & 3 & 2 \\ 7 & 8 & 9 \\ \hline 0 & 0 & 5 \end{bmatrix} = \begin{bmatrix} A_1 & A_2 \\ \hline A_3 & A_4 \end{bmatrix}$$

The characteristic of this partition is that A_1 and A_4 are square submatrices along the diagonal, whereas A_2 and A_3 are not necessarily square. Furthermore, A_3 is made up of zero elements in our present case. If we can find a π that will transform a matrix A into this form, we say A is *decomposable*. If no such π can be found, we say it is *indecomposable*. For example, let B be

$$B = \begin{bmatrix} 0 & 2 & 3 \\ 4 & 5 & 6 \\ 7 & 8 & 9 \end{bmatrix}$$

This is indecomposable. We can interchange row 1 and row 3 so that 0 will be brought down to the left-hand corner, but then we have to interchange column 1 and column 3, which will bring the 0 to the lower right-hand corner, which does not satisfy our requirements.

Next note that A_1 and A_4 of A are indecomposable. For example,

$$A_1 = \begin{bmatrix} 0 & 3 \\ 7 & 8 \end{bmatrix}$$

If we interchange rows, the 0 will be in the lower left-hand corner, but then we have also to interchange columns, which brings the 0 to the lower right-hand corner, and this does not satisfy our requirements.

Let us illustrate further with

$$C = \begin{bmatrix} 1 & 2 & 0 \\ 0 & 5 & 0 \\ 7 & 8 & 9 \end{bmatrix}$$

$$\pi C \pi^T = \begin{bmatrix} 1 & 0 & 0 \\ 0 & 0 & 1 \\ 0 & 1 & 0 \end{bmatrix} \begin{bmatrix} 1 & 2 & 0 \\ 0 & 5 & 0 \\ 7 & 8 & 9 \end{bmatrix} \begin{bmatrix} 1 & 0 & 0 \\ 0 & 0 & 1 \\ 0 & 1 & 0 \end{bmatrix}$$

$$= \begin{bmatrix} 1 & 2 & 0 \\ 7 & 8 & 9 \\ 0 & 5 & 0 \end{bmatrix} \begin{bmatrix} 1 & 0 & 0 \\ 0 & 0 & 1 \\ 0 & 1 & 0 \end{bmatrix} = \left[\begin{array}{cc|c} 1 & 0 & 2 \\ 7 & 9 & 8 \\ \hline 0 & 0 & 5 \end{array} \right] = \begin{bmatrix} A_1 & A_2 \\ A_3 & A_4 \end{bmatrix}$$

Note now that

$$A_1 = \begin{bmatrix} 1 & 0 \\ 7 & 9 \end{bmatrix}$$

is decomposable.

$$\pi A_1 \pi^T = \begin{bmatrix} 0 & 1 \\ 1 & 0 \end{bmatrix} \begin{bmatrix} 1 & 0 \\ 7 & 9 \end{bmatrix} \begin{bmatrix} 0 & 1 \\ 1 & 0 \end{bmatrix}$$

$$= \begin{bmatrix} 7 & 9 \\ 1 & 0 \end{bmatrix} \begin{bmatrix} 0 & 1 \\ 1 & 0 \end{bmatrix} = \begin{bmatrix} 9 & 7 \\ 0 & 1 \end{bmatrix} = A_5$$

Let us now combine the two steps.

$$\pi_1 \pi A \pi^T \pi_1^T = \begin{bmatrix} 0 & 1 & 0 \\ 1 & 0 & 0 \\ 0 & 0 & 1 \end{bmatrix} \begin{bmatrix} 1 & 0 & 0 \\ 0 & 0 & 1 \\ 0 & 1 & 0 \end{bmatrix} \begin{bmatrix} 1 & 2 & 0 \\ 0 & 5 & 0 \\ 7 & 8 & 9 \end{bmatrix} \begin{bmatrix} 1 & 0 & 0 \\ 0 & 0 & 1 \\ 0 & 1 & 0 \end{bmatrix} \begin{bmatrix} 0 & 1 & 0 \\ 1 & 0 & 0 \\ 0 & 0 & 1 \end{bmatrix}$$

$$= \begin{bmatrix} 0 & 0 & 1 \\ 1 & 0 & 0 \\ 0 & 1 & 0 \end{bmatrix} \begin{bmatrix} 1 & 2 & 0 \\ 0 & 5 & 0 \\ 7 & 8 & 9 \end{bmatrix} \begin{bmatrix} 0 & 1 & 0 \\ 0 & 0 & 1 \\ 1 & 0 & 0 \end{bmatrix} = \begin{bmatrix} 9 & 7 & 8 \\ 0 & 1 & 2 \\ 0 & 0 & 5 \end{bmatrix}$$

$$= \begin{bmatrix} A_5 & A_2 \\ A_3 & A_4 \end{bmatrix}$$

Thus,

$$\pi_1 \pi = \pi_2 = \begin{bmatrix} 0 & 0 & 1 \\ 1 & 0 & 0 \\ 0 & 1 & 0 \end{bmatrix}$$

is the permutation matrix that transforms A into the form

$$\pi_2 A \pi_2^T = \begin{bmatrix} A_5 & * \\ 0 & A_4 \end{bmatrix}$$

where along the diagonal we have indecomposable *square* matrices A_5 and A_4, zeros in the lower left-hand, and other elements in the upper right-hand corner.

(iii) Non-negative indecomposable matrices

We shall now present without the proofs results given by Debreu and Herstein (1953). Let A be an $n \times n$ indecomposable matrix, where $a_{ij} \geq 0$, i.e., $A \geq 0$. Let us find the characteristic roots from $|A - \lambda I| = 0$. Then, (1) we can find a characteristic root $\lambda_1 > 0$ such that (2) the characteristic vector v_1 associated with λ_1 may be taken to be positive, i.e., $v_1 > 0$ (which means that all the elements of v_1 are positive), and (3) this λ_1 will have the greatest absolute value. This theorem is also known as the *Theorem of Perron*. Let us illustrate it by letting

$$A = \begin{bmatrix} 2 & 3 \\ 2 & 1 \end{bmatrix}$$

Then $A \geq 0$ and is indecomposable. Let us find the λ_i.

$$|A - \lambda I| = \lambda^2 - 3\lambda - 4 = (\lambda + 1)(\lambda - 4) = 0$$

Thus, $\lambda_1 = 4$, $\lambda_2 = -1$, and $\lambda_1 = 4$ is the characteristic root that is positive and has the largest absolute value, i.e., $|\lambda_1| > |\lambda_2|$.

Next let us find v_1 and see if its elements are positive.

$$\begin{bmatrix} 2-4 & 3 \\ 2 & 1-4 \end{bmatrix} \begin{bmatrix} x_1 \\ x_2 \end{bmatrix} = \begin{bmatrix} 0 \\ 0 \end{bmatrix}$$

$$-2x_1 + 3x_2 = 0$$

$$2x_1 - 3x_2 = 0$$

$$x_1 = \tfrac{3}{2}x_2 = \tfrac{3}{2}m, \qquad x_2 = m$$

Thus, $v_1 = m(\tfrac{3}{2}, 1)$, where m is an arbitrary constant and, if we let $m > 0$, then $v_1 > 0$.

Now let us increase the value of an element of A and see what happens to λ_1. Let

$$A_1 = \begin{bmatrix} 2 & 4 \\ 2 & 1 \end{bmatrix}$$

where we have increased $a_{12} = 3$ to 4. Then,

$$|A_1 - \lambda I| = (2 - \lambda)(1 - \lambda) - 8 = \lambda^2 - 3\lambda - 6 = 0$$
$$\lambda_1 = \tfrac{1}{2}[3 + \sqrt{9 + 4 \times 6}] > \tfrac{1}{2}[3 + 5] = 4$$

The λ_1 has become larger than 4. In general, it can be shown that, when an element of A is increased, λ_1 will also increase.

Problems

1. Given the matrix $A > 0$, answer the following questions.

$$A = \begin{bmatrix} 1 & 4 \\ 4 & 7 \end{bmatrix}$$

(a) Find the characteristic root λ_1 with the largest absolute value.
(b) Find the characteristic vector v_1 associated with λ_1, and check to see that it is $v_1 > 0$.
(c) Increase any one of the elements of A by adding 1, and check to see whether λ_1 has increased.

2. Given the matrix $A \geq 0$, answer the following questions.

$$A = \begin{bmatrix} 0 & 4 \\ 2 & 7 \end{bmatrix}$$

(a) Is A decomposable?
(b) Find the characteristic root λ_1 with the largest absolute value.
(c) Find v_1, and see that v_1 may be positive.
(d) Increase any one of the elements of A by adding 1, and check to see whether λ_1 has increased.

(iv) Non-negative square matrices

Let us now see if we can apply what we stated in Section (iii) to non-negative square matrices. Since we have non-negative (and not positive) square matrices, some of the elements may be zero and thus the matrix A may be decomposable. If A should be decomposable, by use of the permutation matrices we can find a *similar* matrix B that will have indecomposable submatrices along its diagonal. A and B will have the same characteristic roots.

It can be shown that if we have a square matrix $A \geq 0$, (1) it will have a characteristic root λ_1 that is non-negative, i.e., $\lambda_1 \geq 0$ (in our previous case, $\lambda_1 > 0$), (2) the characteristic vector associated with λ_1 will be non-negative, i.e., $v_1 \geq 0$ (which means that some of the elements of v_1 may be zero), (3) this λ_1 will have the greatest absolute value, and (4) when an element of A is increased, λ_1 may stay the same or increase.

Let us illustrate. Let A be

$$A = \begin{bmatrix} 1 & 0 & 0 \\ 1 & 3 & 2 \\ 1 & 0 & 2 \end{bmatrix}$$

A is non-negative, and is decomposable. Thus,

$$\pi A \pi^T = \begin{bmatrix} 0 & 1 & 0 \\ 0 & 0 & 1 \\ 1 & 0 & 0 \end{bmatrix} \begin{bmatrix} 1 & 0 & 0 \\ 1 & 3 & 2 \\ 1 & 0 & 2 \end{bmatrix} \begin{bmatrix} 0 & 0 & 1 \\ 1 & 0 & 0 \\ 0 & 1 & 0 \end{bmatrix}$$

$$= \begin{bmatrix} 3 & 2 & 1 \\ 0 & 2 & 1 \\ 0 & 0 & 1 \end{bmatrix} = B$$

Note that $\pi^T = \pi^{-1}$, and also that π is an orthogonal matrix. (But π is not a modal matrix.) Thus, A and B are similar, i.e., the characteristic roots of A and B are equal.

Let B be partitioned as

$$B = \begin{bmatrix} A_1 & A_2 \\ 0 & A_3 \end{bmatrix} = \begin{bmatrix} 3 & 2 & \vdots & 1 \\ 0 & 2 & \vdots & 1 \\ \cdots & \cdots & & \cdots \\ 0 & 0 & \vdots & 1 \end{bmatrix}$$

A_1 and A_3 are indecomposable. Now let us find the characteristic roots and characteristic vectors of B.

$$|B - \lambda I| = \begin{vmatrix} A_1 - \lambda I & A_2 \\ 0 & A_3 - \lambda I \end{vmatrix}$$

$$= |A_1 - \lambda I| \, |A_3 - \lambda I|$$

Since A_1 and A_3 are indecomposable and non-negative square matrices, the results we discussed in Section (iii) can be applied to A_1 and A_3.

From $|A_1 - \lambda I|$, we have

$$\begin{vmatrix} 3 - \lambda & 2 \\ 0 & 2 - \lambda \end{vmatrix} = (3 - \lambda)(2 - \lambda)$$

Thus, $\lambda_1 = 3$, $\lambda_2 = 2$. From $|A_3 - \lambda I|$ we find $\lambda_3 = 1$, and 3 is the characteristic root with the greatest absolute value. The characteristic vector v_1 associated to $\lambda_1 = 3$ can be found from

$$[A - \lambda_1 I]v_1 = 0$$
$$-2x = 0$$
$$x + 2z = 0$$
$$x - z = 0$$

Thus, $v_1 = (x, y, z) = m(0, 1, 0)$. We can also find

$$\lambda_2 = 2: \qquad v_2 = m(0, -2, 1)$$
$$\lambda_3 = 1: \qquad v_3 = m(-1, -\tfrac{1}{2}, 1)$$

Thus, we find that $v_1 \geq 0$ when we take $m > 0$.

As is seen, v_1, v_2, and v_3 were obtained from A. Let us see if we can obtain them from the matrix B. For this we set up the equation

$$[B - \lambda_i I]v_i = 0$$

But we know that $B = \pi^{-1}A\pi$. Thus,

$$[\pi^{-1}A\pi - \lambda_i I]v_i = 0$$
$$\pi^{-1}[A - \lambda_i I]\pi v_i = 0$$

(Note: $\pi^{-1}\lambda_i I\pi = \lambda_i I\pi^{-1}\pi = \lambda_i I$)

$$\therefore \quad [A - \lambda_i I]\pi v_i = 0$$

where π is non-singular. But πv_i is simply interchanging the rows of v_i. Thus, when we solve for the v_i using B instead of A, we shall get the same answer, but the rows of v_i will be interchanged according to π. Let us check this. Solving for v_i using B, we find

$$\lambda_1 = 3: \quad v_1 = m(1, 0, 0)$$
$$\lambda_2 = 2: \quad v_2 = m(-2, 1, 0)$$
$$\lambda_3 = 1: \quad v_3 = m(\tfrac{1}{2}, -1, 1)$$

We know that

$$\pi = \begin{bmatrix} 0 & 1 & 0 \\ 0 & 0 & 1 \\ 1 & 0 & 0 \end{bmatrix}$$

Thus,

$$\pi v_1 = \begin{bmatrix} 0 & 1 & 0 \\ 0 & 0 & 1 \\ 1 & 0 & 0 \end{bmatrix}\begin{bmatrix} 0 \\ 1 \\ 0 \end{bmatrix} = \begin{bmatrix} 1 \\ 0 \\ 0 \end{bmatrix} = v_1^0$$

$$\pi v_2 = \begin{bmatrix} 0 & 1 & 0 \\ 0 & 0 & 1 \\ 1 & 0 & 0 \end{bmatrix}\begin{bmatrix} 0 \\ -2 \\ 1 \end{bmatrix} = \begin{bmatrix} -2 \\ 1 \\ 0 \end{bmatrix} = v_2^0$$

$$\pi v_3 = \begin{bmatrix} 0 & 1 & 0 \\ 0 & 0 & 1 \\ 1 & 0 & 0 \end{bmatrix}\begin{bmatrix} -1 \\ -\tfrac{1}{2} \\ 1 \end{bmatrix} = \begin{bmatrix} -\tfrac{1}{2} \\ 1 \\ -1 \end{bmatrix} = -v_3^0$$

Thus we see that v_i can be obtained from either A or B. But we are mainly interested in $v_1 \geq 0$ which is associated to $\lambda_1 \geq 0$ which has the largest absolute value.

(v) *Properties of* $(kI - A)$

The input-output model in Section (i) was shown by

$$(I - A)x = c$$

and we were interested in knowing whether or not this could be solved. Let us state the system in a more general form.

$$(kI - A)x = y$$

Then, the input-output model we have has $k = 1$. We are assuming A is a non-negative square matrix.

Let λ_1 be the characteristic root with the largest absolute value. Assume $k > \lambda_1$. Then, k is larger than all the other characteristic roots. Thus, $|kI - A| \neq 0$, that is, $(kI - A)$ is non-singular. Thus,

$$x = (kI - A)^{-1}y$$

That is, we can solve the system of equations.

In addition, for cases like the input-output system, we want $x \geq 0$, and $y \geq 0$, where y, which is the final output, is data that are given and we assume $y \geq 0$. If we can show that $(kI - A)^{-1} \geq 0$, then, since $x = (kI - A)^{-1}y$, x will also be $x \geq 0$, as we desire. Thus, the problem is to check whether $(kI - A)^{-1} \geq 0$, given conditions such as $A \geq 0, k > \lambda_1$. We shall next show that $(kI - A)^{-1} \geq 0$, given certain conditions, by illustrations, and without proofs. References are given for those interested in studying the proofs.

$A \geq 0$ *decomposable case.* If $A \geq 0$, $k > \lambda_1$, then $(kI - A)^{-1} \geq 0$. $A \geq 0$ implies A may have zero elements and thus may be decomposable. Let us illustrate this with

$$A = \begin{bmatrix} 1 & 0 \\ 2 & 3 \end{bmatrix}$$

This is decomposable. That is, we can find π such that

$$\pi A \pi^T = \begin{bmatrix} 0 & 1 \\ 1 & 0 \end{bmatrix}\begin{bmatrix} 1 & 0 \\ 2 & 3 \end{bmatrix}\begin{bmatrix} 0 & 1 \\ 1 & 0 \end{bmatrix} = \begin{bmatrix} 3 & 2 \\ 0 & 1 \end{bmatrix}$$

Next let us find the characteristic roots.

$$|A - \lambda I| = (1 - \lambda)(3 - \lambda) = 0$$

Thus, they are $\lambda_1 = 3, \lambda_2 = 1$. Let $k = 4$. Then, $k > \lambda_1$. Thus,

$$kI - A = \begin{bmatrix} 4 - 1 & 0 \\ -2 & 4 - 3 \end{bmatrix} = \begin{bmatrix} 3 & 0 \\ -2 & 1 \end{bmatrix}$$

The inverse will be

$$(kI - A)^{-1} = \tfrac{1}{3}\begin{bmatrix} 1 & 0 \\ 2 & 3 \end{bmatrix}$$

Thus, $(kI - A)^{-1} \geq 0$ when $k > \lambda_1$.

$A \geq 0$ *indecomposable case.* If $A \geq 0$ is indecomposable, and $k > \lambda_1$, then $(kI - A)^{-1} > 0$. Let us illustrate this with

$$A = \begin{bmatrix} 1 & 2 \\ 3 & 0 \end{bmatrix}$$

As is seen, we have a zero element, but it is indecomposable. From $|A - \lambda I| = 0$ we find the two characteristic roots as $\lambda_1 = 3$, $\lambda_2 = -2$, and λ_1 is the characteristic root that is positive and has the largest absolute value. Let $k = 4$. Then, $k = \lambda_1 + 1 > \lambda_1$ as required and

$$(kI - A) = \begin{bmatrix} 3 & -2 \\ -3 & 4 \end{bmatrix}$$

Thus, the inverse becomes

$$(kI - A)^{-1} = \tfrac{1}{6} \begin{bmatrix} 4 & 2 \\ 3 & 3 \end{bmatrix} > 0$$

as required. All elements in $(kI - A)^{-1}$ are positive. Note that in our previous example where

$$A = \begin{bmatrix} 1 & 0 \\ 2 & 3 \end{bmatrix}$$

we found a π such that

$$\pi A \pi^T = \begin{bmatrix} 3 & 2 \\ 0 & 1 \end{bmatrix} = B$$

Thus, A is decomposable. B cannot be rearranged any further. But we want to point out that B is also considered decomposable because

$$\pi B \pi^T = \begin{bmatrix} 1 & 0 \\ 0 & 1 \end{bmatrix} \begin{bmatrix} 3 & 2 \\ 0 & 1 \end{bmatrix} \begin{bmatrix} 1 & 0 \\ 0 & 1 \end{bmatrix} = \begin{bmatrix} 3 & 2 \\ 0 & 1 \end{bmatrix}$$

That is $\pi = I$ is also a permutation matrix. Thus, in this case, we have $B \geq 0$ and B is decomposable. Then $(kI - B)^{-1} \geq 0$. That is, the inverse may have zero elements.

In contrast, when we have

$$C = \begin{bmatrix} 3 & 2 \\ 1 & 0 \end{bmatrix}$$

this is indecomposable, although C has a zero element and $C \geq 0$. That is, there is no π, including $\pi = I$, that will rearrange the rows and columns of C so that the zeros will be brought down to the lower left-hand corner. In this case $(kI - C)^{-1} > 0$; i.e., all the elements in the matrix will be positive. Finally, if $A > 0$, then A is clearly indecomposable. Thus, we can immediately see that $(kI - A)^{-1} > 0$, when $k > \lambda_1$.

$A > 0$ *case.* If $A > 0$ and $\Sigma a_{ij} < 1$, i.e., the sum of the elements in each row is less than unity, then $(I - A)^{-1} > 0$. This implies that, when the above condition holds, $1 > \lambda_1$. For our input-output model, this is the case we are interested in. Let us illustrate that this holds by use of an example. Let

$$A = \begin{bmatrix} \frac{2}{4} & \frac{1}{4} \\ \frac{1}{5} & \frac{3}{5} \end{bmatrix}$$

Then $(I - A)^{-1}$ will be

$$(I - A)^{-1} = \tfrac{20}{3} \begin{bmatrix} \tfrac{2}{5} & \tfrac{1}{4} \\ \tfrac{1}{5} & \tfrac{2}{4} \end{bmatrix} > 0$$

as required.

For the input-output model, we need to assume that the sum of the technical coefficients in any row is less than unity.

Since proofs are beyond the level of this book, we have only explained the meaning of the theorems by use of simple illustrations. References for proofs and related topics are given at the end of the chapter.

Problems

1. Given the matrix

$$A = \begin{bmatrix} 2 & 0 \\ 2 & 4 \end{bmatrix}$$

(a) If decomposable, find π that will bring the zeros down to the left-hand corner so that it becomes indecomposable (other than by $\pi = I$).
(b) Find λ_1, the characteristic root with largest absolute value.
(c) Let $k = \lambda_1 + 1$. Then find $(kI - A)^{-1}$, and show that it is non-negative.

2. Given the matrix

$$A = \begin{bmatrix} 2 & 4 \\ 2 & 0 \end{bmatrix}$$

(a) Check its decomposability.
(b) Find λ_1.
(c) Let $k = \lambda_1 + 1$ and find $(kI - A)^{-1}$, and check whether it is positive or non-negative.

3. Given the matrix

$$A = \begin{bmatrix} 3 & 2 \\ 4 & 1 \end{bmatrix}$$

Find $(kI - A)^{-1}$ where $k = \lambda_1 + 1$, and show that it is positive.

4. Given the matrix

$$A = \begin{bmatrix} \tfrac{1}{6} & \tfrac{3}{6} \\ \tfrac{1}{4} & \tfrac{2}{4} \end{bmatrix}$$

Show that $(I - A)^{-1} > 0$.

Notes and References

Most of the topics in this chapter may be found under similar headings in the references listed at the end of Chapter 10. There are, however, several topics that need special comment. One is non-negative square matrices (11.16). They are used in connection with input-output analysis and also stability problems. Most matrix algebra texts do not have good discussions on this topic. Three references that are especially recommended are Gantmacher (1959) Vol. II, Chapter 13; Bellman (1960), Chapter 16; and Marcus-Minc (1964), pp. 121–138. Gantmacher (1959) proves Perron's theorem, and Frobenius' theorem which is a generalization of Perron's theorem. Bellman's (1960) Chapter 16 has illustrations of uses of non-negative matrices as applied to economic problems. Karlin (1959) also has a brief discussion on positive matrices in Chapter 8. Also see the articles by Debreu (1952), Debreu and Herstein (1953). Both articles are difficult.

For those who are mathematically competent and wish to read the original articles of Perron and Frobenius, and the subsequent mathematical work on this topic, they are referred to the Appendix in Morishima (1964). The student will find there a list of the articles concerning non-negative square matrices and a summary by Morishima.

For those who want a good non-technical discussion of how non-negative matrices are used in general equilibrium analysis, see Kuenne (1963), Chapter 1.

When studying general equilibrium analysis, not only will non-negative square matrices be necessary, but also fixed point theorems which we have not discussed. Fixed point theorems are used to prove the existence of solutions of systems of equations. An elementary explanation of the Brouwer fixed point theorem is in Courant and Robbins (1941), pp. 251–255; and Saltz (1965), pp. 100–104. A brief explanation is also in Debreu (1959). For advanced mathematical references, the reader is referred to Lefschetz (1949), pp. 117–119; Bers (1957), Chapter 4; Kakutani (1941).

For a general discussion of the existence and uniqueness of equilibrium, see Kuenne (1963), Chapter 9. The student will find an extensive list of references of the works of Arrow and Debreu on this problem in Kuenne (1963).

11.1–11.4 Murdoch (1957), Chapter 7; Perlis (1952), Chapter 9; Wade (1951), Chapter 8; Mirsky (1957), Chapter 7; Hadley (1961), Chapter 7; Johnston (1963), Chapter 3; and Goldberger (1964), Chapter 2.

11.5 Murdoch (1957), pp. 118–122; Cramer (1946), pp. 112–114; Ferrar (1941), Chapter 13; Mirsky (1957), Chapter 8; Hadley (1961), Chapter 7; Johnston (1963), Chapter 3; and Goldberger (1964), Chapter 2.

11.6 Murdoch (1957), pp. 144–149; Wade (1951), pp. 120–123; Mirsky (1957), Chapter 10; Hadley (1961), Chapter 7; Johnston (1963), Chapter 3; and Goldberger (1964), Chapter 2.

11.7 Bellman (1960), Chapter 3; Cramer (1946), pp. 114–116; Ferrar (1941), Chapter 11; Perlis (1952), Chapter 9; Mirsky (1957), Chapter 12,13; Hadley (1961), Chapter 7; Johnston (1963), Chapter 3; and Goldberger (1964), Chapter 2.

11.8 Allen (1938), Chapter 18, 19; Bellman (1960), Chapter 5; Debreu (1952); Hicks (1939), Mathematical Appendix; Samuelson (1947), Appendix A;

Mirsky (1957), Chapter 12, 13; Hadley (1961), Chapter 7; Johnston (1963), Chapter 3; and Goldberger (1964), Chapter 2.

11.9 See references of 11.8.

11.10–11.11 Wade (1951), pp. 126–130; Perlis (1952), pp. 13–16; Mirsky (1957), pp. 100–106; Hadley (1961), Chapter 3; Johnston (1963), Chapter 3; Goldberger (1964), Chapter 2; and Ayres (1962), Chapter 7.

11.12–11.13 Johnston (1963), Chapter 3; Goldberger (1964), Chapter 2; Courant (Vol. II, 1936), pp. 477–479; Ferrar (1941), pp. 25–26, 174–175; and Sokolnikoff (1939), pp. 147–161, 415–439.

11.14 Ayres (1962), Chapter 2; Johnston (1963), Chapter 2; Goldberger (1964), Chapter 2.

11.15–11.16 Hadley (1961), Chapter 3; Bellman (1960), Chapter 16; Birkhoff and MacLane (1952), pp. 214–216; Debreu and Herstein (1953); Karlin (Vol. I, 1959), pp. 246–265; Mirsky (1957), Chapter 11; Gantmacher (1959), Vol. II, Chapter 13; Morishima (1964), Appendix; Kuenne (1963), Chapter 1; and Goldberger (1964), Chapter 2.

Ayres, F. Jr., *Matrices*. New York: Schaum Publishing Co., 1962.

Bers, L., *Topology*. New York: New York University Institute of Mathematical Sciences, 1957. This is a mimeographed book.

Birkhoff, G. and MacLane, S., *A Survey of Modern Algebra*. New York: Macmillan rev. ed. 1953.

Debreu, G., *Theory of Value*. New York: John Wiley and Sons, 1959.
———, "Definite and Semidefinite Quadratic Forms." *Econometrica*, 1952, pp. 295–300.

Debreu, G. and Herstein, I. N., "Non-negative Square Matrices." *Econometrica*, 1953, pp. 597–607.

Gantmacher, F. R., *The Theory of Matrices*, Vol. II, translated by K. A. Hirsch. New York: Chelsea Publishing Company, 1959.

Kakutani, S., "A Generalization of Brouwer's Fixed Point Theorem." *Duke Mathematical Journal*, 1941.

Karlin, S., *Mathematical Methods and Theory in Games, Programming, and Economics*. Reading. Mass.: Addison-Wesley, 1959, Vol. I, Vol. II.

Kemeny, J. G., Morgenstern, O. and Thompson, G. L., "A Generalization of the Von Neumann Model of an Expanding Economy." *Econometrica*, 1956.

Kuenne, R. E., *The Theory of General Economic Equilibrium*. New Jersey: Princeton University Press, 1963.

Lefschetz, S., *Introduction to Topology*. Princeton, New Jersey: Princeton University Press, 1949.

McKenzie, L. W., "On the Existence of General Equilibrium for a Competitive Market." *Econometrica*, 1959, pp. 54–71.

Morishima, M. *Equilibrium, Stability, and Growth*. New York: Oxford University Press, 1964.

Saltz, D., *An Introduction to Analysis*. New Jersey: Prentice-Hall, Inc., 1965.

Von Neumann, J., "A Model of General Equilibrium." *Review of Economic Studies*, Vol. 13, 1945–46.

Wald, A., "On Some Systems of Equations of Mathematical Economics." *Econometrica*, 1951, pp. 368–403.

CHAPTER 12

Vectors and Matrices (Part III)

12.1 Introduction

The two main topics we shall consider in this chapter are *stability of equilibrium* and *convex sets*. We start our discussion with some preliminary definitions of equilibrium and stability of equilibrium. Then in Sections 12.2–12.12, various aspects of the stability problem are considered. The topic of convex sets is treated in Section 12.13.

Consider a commodity Q and its price p at time t. When the price p does not change over time, that is, stays constant, we shall say the price is in a *state of equilibrium*. To be more precise, we shall let dp/dt be called the velocity of price. This shows the change in price when there is a small change in time. Thus, for our concept of equilibrium, we need $dp/dt = 0$.

But consider, for example, a car that travels distance $y = t^2$ where t is time. Then the velocity of the car is

$$\frac{dy}{dt} = 2t$$

At time $t = 0$, the velocity is zero, but after the point $t = 0$, the velocity increases as time increases. This increase of velocity (i.e., acceleration) is shown by

$$\frac{d^2y}{dt^2} = 2$$

The acceleration is a constant 2. Thus, if the car is to be in a state of equilibrium and not move over time, we need to add the condition that the acceleration is zero;

$$\frac{d^2y}{dt^2} = 0$$

In terms of our price example,

$$\frac{dp}{dt} = 0, \qquad \frac{d^2p}{dt^2} = 0$$

512

This will assure us that the price not only has a velocity of zero at a given specific moment (in our car case, at $t = 0$), but also, in the subsequent time periods, the velocity will still be zero. Thus, we can say that prices will remain constant.

Let us express this idea of equilibrium mathematically as follows: Take p on the horizontal axis and dp/dt (velocity) on the vertical axis as in Figure 12-1. Then if at point p_0 we have $dp/dt = 0$, $d^2p/dt^2 = 0$, we shall call p_0 a singular point. These singular points correspond to states of equilibrium.

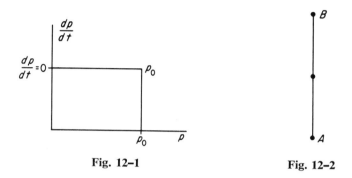

Fig. 12-1   Fig. 12-2

When this idea is generalized to n commodities, there are n prices and n velocities. Thus, instead of the two-dimensional space we had for the one commodity case, we have a $2n$-dimensional space which has n-price and n-velocity coordinates. (Such a space is usually called a *phase space*). Then, the state of equilibrium of a set of n prices can be characterized by saying: Let M be a point in this $2n$-dimensional space where $dp_i/dt = 0$ and $d^2p_i/dt^2 = 0$ $(i = 1, 2, \ldots n)$, then M is a singular point corresponding to a state of equilibrium.

The comparison of two singular points is the problem of *comparative statics*. The non-singular points in the phase space are called *representative points*, and each point represents a certain state of the given set of prices.

With this much background about equilibrium, let us next define *stability of equilibrium*. Following the illustration in Andronow and Chaikin (1949), let us consider a pendulum as in Figure 12-2. When the pendulum is in position A, it will stay in that position if there are no disturbances. This is also true for position B. When a small disturbance is applied to A, it will swing back and forth and eventually settle in position A. But for position B, the pendulum will not return to that position. Position A is stable whereas position B is unstable.

In a similar manner, when price deviates from the equilibrium price and during the subsequent periods of time the price returns "near" the equilibrium price, we say the equilibrium price is stable.

Let us now more precisely define stability of equilibrium. Let the price p_0 be in a state of equilibrium (Figure 12–3). Consider a small neighborhood around p_0 that has a diameter of ϵ and call it neighborhood N_1. Next, consider a small neighborhood N_2 that is in N_1. Let $p(t_0)$ be the price at time t_0 that is in neighborhood N_2. This is shown by

$$|p(t_0) - p_0| < \delta$$

where δ is a small positive number dependent on ϵ, i.e., $\delta = \delta(\epsilon)$. Thus, $p(t_0)$ is a small distance away from the state of equilibrium. The question

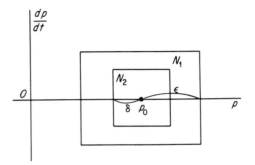

Fig. 12–3

is: What will happen to the price at time $t \geq t_0$? We shall say that the state of equilibrium is stable if the price at time t, (i.e., $p(t)$) is still in the neighborhood N_1. This is shown by

$$|p(t) - p_0| < \epsilon \quad \text{for} \quad t \geq t_0$$

The implication is: If we can find that after a certain lapse of time $t(t \geq t_0)$, the price $p(t)$ will remain close to p_0 and not deviate further away when the initial displacement from equilibrium is very small (i.e., $|p(t_0) - p_0| < \delta$), we say the state of equilibrium is stable. Or, more simply, when the initial displacement from equilibrium is small, the price will tend to return to the equilibrium price as $t \to \infty$.

What if the displacement is large? A distinction is usually made by saying that equilibrium is perfectly stable when no matter how large the displacement we eventually return to the state of equilibrium. But we shall consider only the case where the initial displacement is small. This is sometimes called locally stable.* In our subsequent discussion, stability will mean local stability.

Now that we have discussed the ideas of equilibrium and stability, let

* This condition is necessary for obtaining Liapounoff's equation of the first approximation. See, e.g., Andronow and Chaikin (1949), p. 147, Samuelson (1947), p. 263.

us relate these to difference and differential equations. We saw in Chapter 8 that the solution of a linear differential equation

(1) $$\frac{d^2y}{dx^2} + a_1 \frac{dy}{dx} + a_2y = 0$$

was a function that satisfied this equation identically and was of the form

(2) $$y = c_1 e^{m_1 x} + c_2 e^{m_2 x}$$

where m_1, m_2 were real roots of the auxiliary equation.

For y to be an equilibrium solution we need $dy/dx = 0$, $d^2y/dx^2 = 0$. For this to hold in our present case, y must be a constant. But, since we can assume $a_2 \neq 0$, from our differential equation (1) we see that the constant solution will be $y(x) = 0$. This $y(x) = 0$ is then the equilibrium solution.

Thus, for this equilibrium to be stable we need to show that as $x \to \infty$, y will become closer to $y(x) = 0$. But, as can be seen

$$\lim_{x \to \infty} (c_1 e^{m_1 x} + c_2 e^{m_2 x}) \to 0$$

only when the roots m_1 and m_2 are negative.

For the complex root case, we had

$$y = e^{ax}(c_1 \cos bx + c_2 \sin bx)$$

where a was the real part of the conjugate complex roots. (That is, $m = a \pm bi$.) So, for this case we need $a < 0$ for stability and the problem of stability for linear differential equations with constant coefficients becomes one of finding conditions where $m_1 < 0$, $m_2 < 0$, or $a < 0$.

In Chapter 9, we saw that, given a linear difference equation

(3) $$y_{t+2} + a_1 y_{t+1} + a_2 y_t = 0$$

the solution was of the form

(4) $$y_t = c_1 \beta_1^t + c_2 \beta_2^t$$

where β_1 and β_2 were the real roots of the auxiliary equation. Since we may assume that $a_2 \neq 0$, the equilibrium solution will be the constant $y_t \equiv 0$. Thus, the stability condition will be

$$y_t \to 0 \quad \text{as} \quad t \to \infty$$

which implies that we need $|\beta_1| < 1$, $|\beta_2| < 1$.

For the complex case, the solution was of the form

(5) $$y_t = A\rho^t \cos(\theta t + B)$$

Thus, the condition for a stable equilibrium solution will be $|\rho| < 1$.

The problem of stability for difference equations becomes one of finding conditions where the absolute value of the characteristic roots are less than unity for the real case, and where the absolute value of the amplitude is less than unity for the complex case.

The characteristic equations and auxiliary equations are polynomials, therefore, our problem boils down to one of solving polynomial equations or systems of polynomial equations and showing the necessary conditions for the roots to be negative or less than unity. What we wish to do now is to present in an elementary fashion some of these methods used by economists. This problem of finding such conditions is a difficult one and only simple illustrations have been worked out. The notes at the end of the chapter give references for further study.

Note that the ideas of equilibrium and stability of equilibrium are of a certain situation or state. The illustration of the pendulum or of the set of prices depicted a certain situation or state and we were concerned with the equilibrium and the stability of equilibrium of these situations.

A single or system of differential or difference equations is the mathematical expression of a certain situation or state. Thus, instead of concerning ourselves with a particular situation, such as the pendulum illustration, we shall set up a single or system of differential or difference equations and use it as a general expression for some given situation or state. Then the idea of stability (of equilibrium) may be expressed in terms of the differential or difference equations. We shall say that the system of differential or difference equations is stable, or simply that the system is stable. An alternative expression is to say that the zero solution is stable, or simply that the solution is stable. This second expression is obtained from the result that the equilibrium solution was zero. Both expressions will be used interchangeably.

Before investigating the conditions of stability, three preliminary topics necessary for subsequent discussion are taken up. The first is a rule concerning the sign of roots, the second is the expansion of a characteristic equation, and the third is the solution of simultaneous linear equations.

12.2 Descartes' rule of sign

Descartes' rule of sign is convenient for determining whether or not an equation has positive roots. Proof of this rule requires preliminary discussion of other topics in the theory of equations which cannot be treated in a short amount of space. Thus, we shall only state the rule.

Given a polynomial

$$f(x) = x^n + c_1 x^{n-1} + c_2 x^{n-2} + \ldots + c_n$$

the number of positive roots of $f(x)$ will be equal to the number of variations in the signs of the sequence of coefficients c_i minus an even number $k \geq 0$.

Let us illustrate this with several examples.

Example 1.

$$f(x) = x^2 - 2x - 3 = (x + 1)(x - 3)$$

The sequence of coefficients is $1, -2, -3$. Thus, the signs are $+, -, -$, and there is one variation in the sign, and one positive root. As can be seen, it is $x_1 = 3$.

Example 2.

$$f(x) = x^2 + 3x + 2 = (x + 1)(x + 2)$$

Here we have $+, +, +$. Thus, there are no variations, and so there are no positive roots. As can be seen, we have two negative roots.

Example 3.

$$f(x) = x^3 - 3x^2 + 2x = x(x - 1)(x - 2)$$

The signs of the coefficients are $+, -, +, +$ where the last $+$ is for $+0$. Thus, we have two variations, and so two positive roots. One of the roots is $x = 0$ and is not positive.

Problems

Check the number of positive roots of the following $f(x)$

1. $f(x) = x^3 - 2x^2 - 2x - 4$.

2. $f(x) = x^4 - 2x^3 + 3x^2 - 4x + 5$.

12.3 Expansion of a characteristic equation

Consider a matrix $A(3 \times 3)$. Then, its characteristic equation is

$$|\lambda I - A| = \begin{vmatrix} \lambda - a_{11} & -a_{12} & -a_{13} \\ -a_{21} & \lambda - a_{22} & -a_{23} \\ -a_{31} & -a_{32} & \lambda - a_{33} \end{vmatrix} = 0$$

This can be expanded and written as a polynomial of λ as

$$\Delta = \lambda^3 - D_1\lambda^2 + D_2\lambda - D_3 = 0$$

where the D_i are the sum of the i-th order minors about the principal diagonal. Thus, for D_1 we have

$$D_1 = a_{11} + a_{22} + a_{33}$$

which are first order minors about the diagonal. For D_2 it is

$$D_2 = \begin{vmatrix} a_{11} & a_{12} \\ a_{21} & a_{22} \end{vmatrix} + \begin{vmatrix} a_{22} & a_{23} \\ a_{32} & a_{33} \end{vmatrix} + \begin{vmatrix} a_{11} & a_{13} \\ a_{31} & a_{33} \end{vmatrix}$$

and, for D_3 we have

$$D_3 = \begin{vmatrix} a_{11} & a_{12} & a_{13} \\ a_{21} & a_{22} & a_{23} \\ a_{31} & a_{32} & a_{33} \end{vmatrix}$$

There are $n!/i!(n-i)!$ minors in each case. The sign is determined by $(-1)^i$. In general, when A is $n \times n$, we have

$$\Delta = \lambda^n + (-1)^1 D_1 \lambda^{n-1} + (-1)^2 D_2 \lambda_2^{n-2} \ldots + (-1)^n D_n = 0$$

Problems

1. Check the above expansion for a 2×2 matrix A.

2. Given a matrix

$$A = \begin{bmatrix} 1 & 2 & 3 \\ 2 & 3 & 4 \\ 2 & 0 & 1 \end{bmatrix}$$

Expand $|\lambda I - A|$ according to the above formula. Check the results by expanding it by the cross-multiplication scheme.

12.4 Solution of simultaneous linear equations

(i) Homogeneous case

Consider a system of homogeneous linear equations.

(1)
$$a_{11}x_1 + a_{12}x_2 = 0$$
$$a_{21}x_1 + a_{22}x_2 = 0$$

We can see by observation that $x_1 = x_2 = 0$ will be a set of solutions. This is a *trivial solution*. What are the conditions for a non-trivial solution? We shall only show how the necessary conditions for such a solution are obtained.

In matrix form (1) becomes

$$\begin{bmatrix} a_{11} & a_{12} \\ a_{21} & a_{22} \end{bmatrix} \cdot \begin{bmatrix} x_1 \\ x_2 \end{bmatrix} = \begin{bmatrix} 0 \\ 0 \end{bmatrix}$$

or

(2)
$$AX = 0$$

The adjoint of A which is denoted by A^* is

$$A^* = \begin{bmatrix} A_{11} & A_{21} \\ A_{12} & A_{22} \end{bmatrix}$$

where the A_{ij} are the signed minors. Now, using the properties related to expanding a determinant, we find

$$A*A = \begin{bmatrix} A_{11} & A_{21} \\ A_{12} & A_{22} \end{bmatrix} \begin{bmatrix} a_{11} & a_{12} \\ a_{21} & a_{22} \end{bmatrix}$$

$$= \begin{bmatrix} a_{11}A_{11} + a_{21}A_{21} & a_{12}A_{11} + a_{22}A_{21} \\ a_{11}A_{12} + a_{21}A_{22} & a_{12}A_{12} + a_{22}A_{22} \end{bmatrix}$$

$$= \begin{bmatrix} |A| & 0 \\ 0 & |A| \end{bmatrix} = |A| \cdot I$$

That is

(3) $$A*A = |A| \cdot I$$

(Also note that $AA* = A*A$.)

Let us premultiply (2) by $A*$. Then,

(4) $$A*AX = 0$$

But from (3) we see that (4) becomes

(5) $$A*AX = |A| \cdot I \cdot X = 0$$

When $|A| \neq 0$, then $X = 0$. That is, when $|A| \neq 0$, we get a trivial solution. For X to be $X \neq 0$, we need $|A| = 0$ for (5) to hold. *Thus $|A| = 0$ is a necessary condition for the linear homogeneous equations (1) to have a non-trivial solution.*

Example 1.

$$2x_1 + 3x_2 = 0$$

$$4x_1 + 6x_2 = 0$$

$$|A| = \begin{vmatrix} 2 & 3 \\ 4 & 6 \end{vmatrix} = 0$$

Thus, there will be a non-trivial solution and it is, $x_1 = m$, $x_2 = -\frac{2}{3}m$ where m is an arbitrary constant.

(ii) Non-homogeneous case

Consider a system of non-homogeneous equations

$$a_{11}x_1 + a_{12}x_2 + a_{13}x_3 = b_1$$

$$a_{21}x_1 + a_{22}x_2 + a_{23}x_3 = b_2$$

$$a_{31}x_1 + a_{32}x_2 + a_{33}x_3 = b_3$$

In matrix notation this is

$$AX = B$$

Similar to the previous case let A^* be the adjoint matrix. Then,

$$A^*AX = A^*B$$

$$|A| \cdot I \cdot X = A^*B$$

When $|A| \neq 0$, we find X as

$$X = \frac{1}{|A|} A^*B$$

Writing this out it becomes

$$\begin{bmatrix} x_1 \\ x_2 \\ x_3 \end{bmatrix} = \frac{1}{|A|} \begin{bmatrix} A_{11} & A_{21} & A_{31} \\ A_{12} & A_{22} & A_{32} \\ A_{13} & A_{23} & A_{33} \end{bmatrix} \begin{bmatrix} b_1 \\ b_2 \\ b_3 \end{bmatrix}$$

$$= \frac{1}{|A|} \begin{bmatrix} b_1A_{11} + b_2A_{21} + b_3A_{31} \\ b_1A_{12} + b_2A_{22} + b_3A_{32} \\ b_1A_{13} + b_2A_{23} + b_3A_{33} \end{bmatrix}$$

Thus, x_1 for example is

$$x_1 = \frac{1}{|A|} [b_1A_{11} + b_2A_{21} + b_3A_{31}]$$

But

$$b_1A_{11} + b_2A_{21} + b_3A_{31} = \begin{vmatrix} b_1 & a_{12} & a_{13} \\ b_2 & a_{22} & a_{23} \\ b_3 & a_{32} & a_{33} \end{vmatrix}$$

The x_2 and x_3 are obtained in a similar manner.

Therefore, the rule (*Cramer's rule*) is to first find the determinant of the coefficient matrix A and let that be $|A|$. When we are solving for x_1 we will replace the coefficients in the first column by the b's and let that determinant be $|A_{x_1}|$. The solution for x_1 is, providing $|A| \neq 0$,

$$x_1 = \frac{|A_{x_1}|}{|A|}$$

For x_2, replace the second column by the b's. Similarly for x_3. This rule is general.

Example.

$$2x + 3y = 13$$

$$4x - y = 5$$

$$x = \frac{\begin{vmatrix} 13 & 3 \\ 5 & -1 \end{vmatrix}}{\begin{vmatrix} 2 & 3 \\ 4 & -1 \end{vmatrix}} = 2, \quad y = \frac{\begin{vmatrix} 2 & 13 \\ 4 & 5 \end{vmatrix}}{\begin{vmatrix} 2 & 3 \\ 4 & -1 \end{vmatrix}} = 3$$

(iii) *General solution = homogeneous solution + particular solution*

In Chapters 8 and 9 we have stated that a general solution of a non-homogeneous linear differential or difference equation is the sum of a homogeneous solution and a particular solution. Let us outline the rationale of this statement with respect to a system of non-homogeneous linear equations.

Consider a system of linear equations

(1)
$$a_{11}x_1 + a_{12}x_2 + a_{13}x_3 = b_1$$
$$a_{21}x_1 + a_{22}x_2 + a_{23}x_3 = b_2$$

which in matrix form is

(2)
$$AX = b$$

The associated system of homogeneous equations is

(3)
$$AX = 0$$

Let X_1 be a solution of (2), and X_2 be any other solution of (2). Set

$$X_1 = X_2 + (X_1 - X_2) = X_2 + X_3.$$

Then,

$$AX_1 = A\{X_2 + (X_1 - X_2)\}$$
$$= AX_2 + AX_1 - AX_2 = b + b - b = b$$

Furthermore,

$$AX_3 = A(X_1 - X_2) = b - b = 0$$

Thus a solution of $AX = b$ is the sum of X_2 (a solution of $AX = b$) and X_3 (a solution of $AX = 0$).

Conversely, let X_4 be a solution of $AX = 0$ and X_5 be a solution of $AX = b$. Let $X_6 = X_4 + X_5$. Then,

$$AX_6 = A(X_4 + X_5) = 0 + b = b$$

That is, the sum of X_4 and X_5 is a solution of $AX = b$.

A similar argument may be applied to linear differential and difference equations. Usually the differential or difference equations are expressed in terms of linear operators (which we have not discussed) before applying an analysis similar to the one above.

Example. Consider the following system of non-homogeneous linear equations

$$x + 2y + 3z = 6$$
$$3x - y + z = 3$$

A solution of this system is

$$x = \tfrac{1}{7}(12 - 5m_1), \quad y = \tfrac{1}{7}(15 - 8m_1), \quad z = m_1$$

where m_1 is an arbitrary constant. For example, if $m_1 = 2$, then $x = \tfrac{2}{7}$,

$y = -\frac{1}{7}$, $z = 2$. This is a particular solution. A check will show that this satisfies the system.

The solution to the associated homogeneous system

$$x + 2y + 3z = 0$$
$$3x - y + z = 0$$

is

$$x = -\tfrac{5}{7}m_2, \quad y = -\tfrac{8}{7}m_2, \quad z = m_2$$

where m_2 is an arbitrary constant. Thus, if $m_2 = 7$ for example, $x = -5$, $y = -8$, $z = 7$. This is a homogeneous solution.

The general solution is

$$x_g = \tfrac{1}{7}(12 - 5m_1) - \tfrac{5}{7}m_2$$
$$y_g = \tfrac{1}{7}(15 - 8m_1) - \tfrac{8}{7}m_2$$
$$z_g = m_1 + m_2$$

Let us check this for the first equation.

$$x + 2y + 3z = \{\tfrac{1}{7}(12 - 5m_1) - \tfrac{5}{7}m_2\}$$
$$+ \{\tfrac{1}{7}(15 - 8m_1) - \tfrac{8}{7}m_2\} + (m_1 + m_2) = 6$$

That is, our general solution satisfies the first equation. A similar check holds true for the second equation.

For the particular case where $m_1 = 2$, $m_2 = 7$, we have

$$x = \tfrac{2}{7} - 5, \quad y = -\tfrac{1}{7} - 8, \quad z = 2 + 7$$

Substituting this into the first equation we find

$$x + 2y + 3z = (\tfrac{2}{7} - 5) + 2(-\tfrac{1}{7} - 8) + 3(2 + 7) = 6$$

Substitute the general solution into the second equation and check it.

Problems

1. Solve the following systems of homogeneous equations. First check whether the condition for a non-trivial solution is satisfied.

    (a) $x - 2y + 3z = 0$ (b) $x \quad\quad + 3z = 0$
            $3x + 3y \quad\quad = 0$ $x + 2y + 7z = 0$
            $x \quad\quad\quad + z = 0$ $y + 2z = 0$

2. Solve the following equations by use of Cramer's rule.

    (a) $x_1 - 2x_2 = -4$ (b) $x_1 - 2x_2 + 3x_3 = 5$
            $2x_1 + x_2 = 4$ $2x_1 + 3x_2 - x_3 = 6$
                                       $x_1 \quad\quad + 2x_3 = 4$
                                      Ans. $\tfrac{26}{7}$, $-\tfrac{3}{7}$, $\tfrac{1}{7}$.

12.5 Stability conditions (I)—Schur theorem

Consider a second-order difference equation

(1) $$y_{t+2} - y_{t+1} + \tfrac{2}{9}y_t = 0$$

The characteristic equation for this is, letting $y_t = \beta^t$

(2) $$\beta^2 - \beta + \tfrac{2}{9} = 0$$

From this we find the characteristic roots to be $\beta_1 = \tfrac{1}{3}$, $\beta_2 = \tfrac{2}{3}$. Then,

$$y_t = c_1\beta_1^t + c_2\beta_2^t = c_1(\tfrac{1}{3})^t + c_2(\tfrac{2}{3})^t$$

Thus, as $t \to \infty$, $y_t \to 0$ and the difference equation (1) is stable.

As can be seen, (2) is a polynomial of β. In our present case, it was easy to find the roots and show they were less than unity. But when we have higher-order equations, finding roots becomes difficult. It would be convenient if certain conditions could be found that would tell us without finding the roots explicitly whether or not they are less than unity. Fortunately the *Schur theorem* gives us this information and is presented next without proof.

Schur theorem. Consider a polynomial equation

$$f(x) = a_0x^n + a_1x^{n-1} + a_2x^{n-2} + \ldots + a_n = 0$$

The roots of this equation will be less than unity if and only if the following n determinants are positive.

$$\left|
\begin{array}{cccc:cccc}
a_0 & 0 & \ldots & 0 & a_n & a_{n-1} & \ldots & a_1 \\
a_1 & a_{0^-} & & 0 & 0 & a_n & & a_2 \\
\ldots & \ldots & & \ldots & \ldots & \ldots & \ldots & \ldots \\
a_{n-1} & a_{n-2} & \ldots & a_0 & 0 & 0 & \ldots & a_n \\
\hdashline
a_n & 0 & \ldots & 0 & a_0 & a_1 & \ldots & a_{n-1} \\
a_{n-1} & a_n & \ldots & 0 & 0 & a_0 & \ldots & a_{n-2} \\
\ldots & \ldots & \ldots & & \ldots & \ldots & & \ldots \\
a_1 & a_2 & \ldots & a_n & 0 & 0 & \ldots & a_0
\end{array}
\right|$$

where

$$\Delta_1 = \begin{vmatrix} a_0 & a_n \\ a_n & a_0 \end{vmatrix}$$

$$\Delta_2 = \left|
\begin{array}{cc:cc}
a_0 & 0 & a_n & a_{n-1} \\
a_1 & a_0 & 0 & a_n \\
\hdashline
a_n & 0 & a_0 & a_1 \\
a_{n-1} & a_n & 0 & a_0
\end{array}
\right|$$

and so forth.

This theorem holds for both the complex and real case. In the real case, the absolute values of the characteristic roots are less than unity, and the stability of y_t is clear.

For the complex case, we have as follows: Let the complex roots be

$$c = a + bi, \qquad \bar{c} = a - bi$$

Then, the Schur theorem says

$$|a + bi| < 1, \qquad |a - bi| < 1.$$

But we know that

$$|a + bi| = \sqrt{a^2 + b^2}$$

$$|a - bi| = \sqrt{a^2 + b^2}$$

We also know that the solution for the complex case is, in general form,

$$y_t = A\rho^t \cos(\theta t + B)$$

where

$$\rho = a^2 + b^2$$

Thus, when

$$|a + bi| \cdot |a - bi| < 1,$$

this implies $a^2 + b^2 < 1$, thus $\rho < 1$ and the difference equation is stable.

Example 1.

$$f(x) = x^2 - x + \tfrac{2}{9} = (x - \tfrac{1}{3})(x - \tfrac{2}{3})$$

$$a_0 = 1, \quad a_1 = -1, \quad a_2 = \tfrac{2}{9}.$$

Thus,

$$\Delta_1 = \begin{vmatrix} a_0 & a_2 \\ a_2 & a_0 \end{vmatrix} = \begin{vmatrix} 1 & \tfrac{2}{9} \\ \tfrac{2}{9} & 1 \end{vmatrix} = 1 - \tfrac{4}{81} > 0$$

$$\Delta_2 = \begin{vmatrix} a_0 & 0 & a_2 & a_1 \\ a_1 & a_0 & 0 & a_2 \\ a_2 & 0 & a_0 & a_1 \\ a_1 & a_2 & 0 & a_0 \end{vmatrix} = \begin{vmatrix} 1 & 0 & \tfrac{2}{9} & -1 \\ -1 & 1 & 0 & \tfrac{2}{9} \\ \tfrac{2}{9} & 0 & 1 & -1 \\ -1 & \tfrac{2}{9} & 0 & 1 \end{vmatrix} = \frac{1960}{6561} > 0$$

Thus, $f(x)$ has roots less than unity. And we know they are $x_1 = \tfrac{1}{3}$, $x_2 = \tfrac{2}{3}$.

Example 2.

$$f(x) = x^2 - 3x + 2 = (x - 1)(x - 2)$$

$$\Delta_1 = \begin{vmatrix} 1 & 2 \\ 2 & 1 \end{vmatrix} = 1 - 4 = -3 < 0$$

$$\Delta_2 = \begin{vmatrix} 1 & 0 & 2 & -3 \\ -3 & 1 & 0 & 2 \\ 2 & 0 & 1 & 1 \\ -3 & 2 & 0 & 1 \end{vmatrix} = 24 > 0$$

Thus, all of the roots of $f(x)$ are not less than unity.

Example 3.

$$f(x) = 2x^2 - 2x + 1$$

Let us first find the roots by the conventional method. Then,

$$x_1 = \tfrac{1}{2} + \tfrac{1}{2}i, \qquad x_2 = \tfrac{1}{2} - \tfrac{1}{2}i$$

We know that

$$|\tfrac{1}{2} \pm \tfrac{1}{2}i| = \sqrt{\tfrac{1}{4} + \tfrac{1}{4}} = \frac{1}{\sqrt{2}} < 1$$

Also,

$$|\tfrac{1}{2} + \tfrac{1}{2}i| \cdot |\tfrac{1}{2} - \tfrac{1}{2}i| = \frac{1}{\sqrt{2}} \cdot \frac{1}{\sqrt{2}} = \frac{1}{2} < 1$$

Let us apply the Schur conditions and check these results.

$$a_0 = 2, \qquad a_1 = -2, \qquad a_2 = 1$$

$$\Delta_1 = \begin{vmatrix} 2 & 1 \\ 1 & 2 \end{vmatrix} = 3 > 0$$

$$\Delta_2 = \begin{vmatrix} 2 & 0 & 1 & -2 \\ -2 & 2 & 0 & 1 \\ 1 & 0 & 2 & -2 \\ -2 & 1 & 0 & 2 \end{vmatrix} = 5 > 0$$

Thus, the Schur conditions tell us that $f(x)$ will have roots less than unity which is the same as the results we obtained by the conventional method.

Problems

Check the Schur conditions of the following equations and see if the roots are less than unity.

1. $f(x) = 6x^2 - 5x + 1 = 0$ \qquad\qquad $(\tfrac{1}{2}, \tfrac{1}{3})$

2. $f(x) = 10x^2 - 11x + 3 = 0$ \qquad\qquad $(\tfrac{1}{2}, \tfrac{3}{5})$

3. $f(x) = 24x^3 - 26x^2 + 9x + 1 = 0$ \qquad $(\tfrac{1}{2}, \tfrac{1}{3}, \tfrac{1}{4})$

4. $f(x) = 2x^3 + 7x^2 + 7x - 2 = 0$ \qquad $(1, 2, \tfrac{1}{2})$

Given the following difference equations, check their stability.

5. $6y_{t+2} - y_{t+1} - y_t = 0$

6. $18y_{t+3} + 9y_{t+2} - 5y_{t+1} - 2y_t = 0$

7. $3y_{t+2} - 2y_{t+1} + y_t = 0$

12.6 Translation of a higher-order difference equation to a lower order

In Section 12.5 the necessary and sufficient conditions for stability of a *single* difference equation were discussed. But in many economic problems, such as general equilibrium analysis, we have a *system* of difference equations. In Section 12.8 we shall see that with the help of matrix algebra the necessary conditions for stability of a system of first-order difference equations can be easily obtained. This implies that if there is a way of translating higher-order systems to first-order systems, it is only necessary to confine our attention to the first-order systems. Fortunately, this translation is not difficult and it is discussed in this section.

The methods of finding stability conditions discussed in subsequent sections do not require the explicit solution of difference equations. That is, instead of explicitly finding the characteristic roots, an indirect method of expressing the magnitude and sign of the characteristic roots is used to establish stability conditions. But there may be occasions where the actual solutions are desired, and since higher-order systems can be translated into lower-order systems, it is only necessary to show how first-order systems can be solved. This problem is discussed in Section 12.7. So let us first discuss these two preliminary topics before we get into Section 12.8.

(*i*) *Translation of second-order equation to first-order*

Consider a second-order difference equation

(1) $y_{t+2} - 5y_{t+1} + 6y_t = 0,$ $(t = 0, 1, 2, ...)$

Define a relation

$$x_t = y_{t+1}$$

Then,

$$x_{t+1} = y_{t+2}$$

Thus, the difference equation (1) becomes

$$x_{t+1} = 5x_t - 6y_t$$

$$y_{t+1} = x_t$$

which is a system of first-order difference equations. In matrix notation this is

$$\begin{bmatrix} x_{t+1} \\ y_{t+1} \end{bmatrix} = \begin{bmatrix} 5 & -6 \\ 1 & 0 \end{bmatrix} \cdot \begin{bmatrix} x_t \\ y_t \end{bmatrix}$$

$$V_{t+1} = AV_t$$

We can also first shift the origin of (1) from $t = 0$ to $t = 1$. Then,

$$y_{t+1} - 5y_t + 6y_{t-1} = 0, \qquad t = 1, 2, 3, ...$$

Then set $x_{t+1} = y_t$. Thus, $x_t = y_{t-1}$. Substituting this in we get

$$y_{t+1} = 5y_t - 6x_t$$
$$x_{t+1} = y_t$$

In matrix notation it is

$$\begin{bmatrix} y_{t+1} \\ x_{t+1} \end{bmatrix} = \begin{bmatrix} 5 & -6 \\ 1 & 0 \end{bmatrix} \cdot \begin{bmatrix} y_t \\ x_t \end{bmatrix}$$

The advantage of this is that when we find x_{t+1}, since $x_{t+1} = y_t$ we get y_t directly, which is what we were originally seeking. This will be illustrated later.

(ii) *Translation of third-order equation to first-order*

Let us apply this to a third-order equation

$$y_{t+3} + 3y_{t+2} - 4y_{t+1} + 5y_t = 6, \quad t = 0, 1, 2, \dots$$

Define

$$p_t = q_{t+1}, \quad q_t = y_{t+1}$$

Then we get the following set of equations

$$p_{t+1} = -3p_t + 4q_t - 5y_t - 6$$
$$q_{t+1} = p_t$$
$$y_{t+1} = q_t$$

In matrix notation it becomes

$$\begin{bmatrix} p_{t+1} \\ q_{t+1} \\ y_{t+1} \end{bmatrix} = \begin{bmatrix} -3 & 4 & -5 \\ 1 & 0 & 0 \\ 0 & 1 & 0 \end{bmatrix} \cdot \begin{bmatrix} p_t \\ q_t \\ y_t \end{bmatrix} + \begin{bmatrix} -6 \\ 0 \\ 0 \end{bmatrix}$$

or

$$V_{t+1} = AV_t + k$$

We have reduced a third-order equation to three first-order equations.

(iii) *Translation of two higher-order equations to first-order*

Consider the case where there are two equations

$$y_{t+3} + 3y_{t+2} - 4y_{t+1} + 5y_t - 6x_t = 7$$
$$y_{t+2} + 2y_{t+1} - 3y_t + 4x_{t+1} = 5$$

To reduce this, we set

$$p_t = q_{t+1}, \quad q_t = y_{t+1}$$

Then in matrix notation we get

$$\begin{bmatrix} p_{t+1} \\ q_{t+1} \\ x_{t+1} \\ y_{t+1} \end{bmatrix} = \begin{bmatrix} -3 & 4 & -5 & 6 \\ 1 & 0 & 0 & 0 \\ -1 & -2 & 3 & 0 \\ 0 & 1 & 0 & 0 \end{bmatrix} \cdot \begin{bmatrix} p_t \\ q_t \\ x_t \\ y_t \end{bmatrix} + \begin{bmatrix} 7 \\ -5 \\ 0 \\ 0 \end{bmatrix}$$

These techniques of translating higher-order difference equations to first-order equations that we illustrated are general and can be applied to other higher-order difference equations.

12.7 Solving simultaneous difference equations

Since higher-order difference equations can be translated into a first-order system, we may confine our discussion to the solution of a system of first-order difference equations. Therefore, let us consider

(1)
$$y_{t+1} = a_{11}y_t + a_{12}x_t$$
$$x_{t+1} = a_{21}y_t + a_{22}x_t$$

In matrix notation it becomes

$$\begin{bmatrix} y_{t+1} \\ x_{t+1} \end{bmatrix} = \begin{bmatrix} a_{11} & a_{12} \\ a_{21} & a_{22} \end{bmatrix} \cdot \begin{bmatrix} y_t \\ x_t \end{bmatrix}$$

or

$$V_{t+1} = AV_t$$

Let $t = 0$. Then,

$$V_1 = AV_0$$

where

$$V_0 = \begin{bmatrix} y_0 \\ x_0 \end{bmatrix}$$

are given by initial conditions. Then,

$$V_2 = AV_1 = A(AV_0) = A^2V_0$$

When this process is continued, we get

(2)
$$V_t = A^tV_0$$

Thus, the solution V_t is obtained when we find A^t.

To find A^t, let

$$f(\lambda) = |A - \lambda I| = c_0 + c_1\lambda + c_2\lambda^2 = 0$$

be the characteristic equation of A, where λ is the characteristic root. Let us divide λ^2 by $f(\lambda)$.

$$
\require{enclose}
\begin{array}{r}
\dfrac{1}{c_2} \\[2mm]
c_2\lambda^2 + c_1\lambda + c_0 \enclose{longdiv}{\lambda^2 } \\[2mm]
\lambda^2 + \dfrac{c_1}{c_2}\lambda + \dfrac{c_0}{c_1} \\[2mm]
\hline
-\dfrac{c_1}{c_2}\lambda - \dfrac{c_0}{c_1}
\end{array}
$$

Thus,

$$\lambda^2 = \frac{1}{c_2}(c_2\lambda^2 + c_1\lambda + c_0) + \left(-\frac{c_1}{c_2}\lambda - \frac{c_0}{c_1}\right)$$

This may be written as

$$\lambda^2 = f(\lambda)q(\lambda) + r(\lambda)$$

where $q(\lambda)$ is the quotient and $r(\lambda)$ is the remainder. As is seen, $r(\lambda)$ is a polynomial of λ of degree 1. If we divide λ^t by $f(\lambda)$, since $f(\lambda)$ is of degree two, the remainder $r(\lambda)$ will also be, at most, of degree 1. If we have a matrix A that is 3×3, then $f(\lambda)$ will be of degree 3 and then $r(\lambda)$ will be, at most, of degree 2. In general, if A is of $n \times n$, then $r(\lambda)$ will be, at most, of degree $(n - 1)$. Let us assume we have divided λ^t by $f(\lambda)$ which is of degree 2. Then,

(3) $$\lambda^t = f(\lambda)q(\lambda) + r(\lambda)$$

But $f(\lambda) = 0$. Thus, since $r(\lambda)$ is at most of degree 1,

(4) $$\lambda^t = r(\lambda) = \alpha_1 + \alpha_2\lambda$$

where α_1 and α_2 are constants. It can be shown* that we may replace λ by A. Then,

(5) $$A^t = \alpha_1 I + \alpha_2 A$$

Thus, to find A^t, we need to find α_1 and α_2. This can be done by using (4). Let λ_1, λ_2 be the two characteristic roots of A. Then from (4) we have

$$\alpha_1 + \alpha_2\lambda_1 = \lambda_1^t$$

$$\alpha_1 + \alpha_2\lambda_2 = \lambda_2^t$$

Using Cramer's rule, we find

$$\alpha_1 = \frac{1}{\Delta}\begin{vmatrix} \lambda_1^t & \lambda_1 \\ \lambda_2^t & \lambda_2 \end{vmatrix}, \qquad \alpha_2 = \frac{1}{\Delta}\begin{vmatrix} 1 & \lambda_1^t \\ 1 & \lambda_2^t \end{vmatrix}, \qquad \Delta = \begin{vmatrix} 1 & \lambda_1 \\ 1 & \lambda_2 \end{vmatrix}$$

provided $\Delta \neq 0$. Thus, once α_1 and α_2 are determined, we find A^t from (5), and when A^t is found, we can obtain the solution of V_t from (2).

Example 1. Consider a second-order equation

(6) $$y_{t+2} - 6y_{t+1} + 8y_t = 0 \qquad (t = 0, 1, 2, \ldots)$$

where $y_0 = 1$, $y_1 = 2$. This can be rewritten by shifting the origin as

(7) $$y_{t+1} - 6y_{t+1} + 8y_{t-1} = 0 \qquad t = 1, 2, \ldots$$

where $y_0 = 1$, $y_1 = 2$.

---

* See Halmos (1958) pp. 59–60; Frazer, Duncan and Coller (1938), Chapter 2; MacDuffee (1943), Chapter 4; Finkbeiner (1960), pp. 134–136.

Next, let $y_t = x_{t+1}$. Then we have the following set of first order equations.

$$y_{t+1} = 6y_t - 8x_t$$
(8)
$$x_{t+1} = y_t$$

We wish to find a solution

$$y_t = c_1\beta_1^t + c_2\beta_2^t$$

The equations of (8) can be written in matrix form as

$$\begin{bmatrix} y_{t+1} \\ x_{t+1} \end{bmatrix} = \begin{bmatrix} 6 & -8 \\ 1 & 0 \end{bmatrix} \cdot \begin{bmatrix} y_t \\ x_t \end{bmatrix}$$

or

$$V_{t+1} = AV_t$$

We have seen that $V_{t+1} = A^t V_1$ where

$$V_1 = \begin{bmatrix} y_t \\ x_t \end{bmatrix} = \begin{bmatrix} y_t \\ y_{t-1} \end{bmatrix} = \begin{bmatrix} y_1 \\ y_0 \end{bmatrix} = \begin{bmatrix} 2 \\ 1 \end{bmatrix}$$

To find A^t, we need to find a and b (i.e. α_1 and α_2 of (5)) for $A^t = aI + bA$ which are found by solving

$$\lambda_1^t = a + b\lambda_1$$
(9)
$$\lambda_2^t = a + b\lambda_2$$

where λ_1 and λ_2 are the characteristic roots of A. We find

$$|A - \lambda I| = \begin{vmatrix} 6 - \lambda & -8 \\ 1 & -\lambda \end{vmatrix} = (\lambda - 2)(\lambda - 4) = 0$$

Substituting $\lambda_1 = 2$, $\lambda_2 = 4$ into (9) gives us

$$2^t = a + 2b$$
$$4^t = a + 4b$$

Solving for a and b we find

$$a = 2 \cdot 2^t - 4^t$$
(10)
$$b = -\tfrac{1}{2} \cdot 2^t + \tfrac{1}{2} \cdot 4^t$$

The A^t in terms of a and b is

$$A^t = aI + bA = \begin{bmatrix} a & 0 \\ 0 & a \end{bmatrix} + \begin{bmatrix} 6b & -8b \\ b & 0 \end{bmatrix}$$

$$= \begin{bmatrix} a + 6b & -8b \\ b & a \end{bmatrix}$$

Using this result V_t becomes

$$V_{t+1} = A^t V_1 = \begin{bmatrix} a + 6b & -8b \\ b & a \end{bmatrix} \cdot \begin{bmatrix} 2 \\ 1 \end{bmatrix}$$

$$\begin{bmatrix} y_{t+1} \\ x_{t+1} \end{bmatrix} = \begin{bmatrix} 2a + 12b - 8b \\ 2b + a \end{bmatrix} = \begin{bmatrix} 2a - 4b \\ a + 2b \end{bmatrix}$$

Thus, the y_t we seek is, using the a and b found in (10),
$$y_t = x_{t+1} = a + 2b = 2^t + 0 \cdot 4^t$$

Check.
$$y_{t+2} - 6y_{t+1} + 8y_t = 0$$
$$\beta^2 + 6\beta + 8 = 0$$
$$\beta_1 = 2, \qquad \beta_2 = 4$$
$$y_t = c_1 2^t + c_2 4^t$$
From $y_0 = 1$ and $y_1 = 2$, we find: $c_1 = 1, c_2 = 0$. Thus,
$$y_t = 2^t + 0 \cdot 4^t$$

Example 2. Consider a third order equation:

(11) $\qquad y_{t+3} - 6y_{t+2} + 11y_{t+1} - 6y_t = 0, \qquad t = 0, 1, 2, \ldots$

where $y_0 = 1, y_1 = 2, y_3 = 3$. Let us shift the origin to facilitate computations.

(12) $\qquad y_{t+2} - 6y_{t+1} + 11y_t - 6y_{t-1} = 0, \qquad t = 1, 2, \ldots$

Next, reduce this to first-order linear equations by setting $y_{t+1} = x_t$, $z_{t+1} = y_t$. Then,

(13)
$$\begin{aligned} x_{t+1} &= 6x_t - 11y_t + 6z_t \\ y_{t+1} &= x_t \\ z_{t+1} &= y_t \end{aligned}$$

In matrix notation this is
$$\begin{bmatrix} x_{t+1} \\ y_{t+1} \\ z_{t+1} \end{bmatrix} = \begin{bmatrix} 6 & -11 & 6 \\ 1 & 0 & 0 \\ 0 & 1 & 0 \end{bmatrix} \cdot \begin{bmatrix} x_t \\ y_t \\ z_t \end{bmatrix}$$
or

(14) $\qquad V_{t+1} = AV_t = A^t V_1$

A^t is found by setting

(15) $\qquad A^t = aI + bA + cA^2$

The a, b, and c are found from
$$\begin{aligned} \lambda_1^t &= a + b\lambda_1 + c\lambda_1^2 \\ \lambda_2^t &= a + b\lambda_2 + c\lambda_2^2 \\ \lambda_3^t &= a + b\lambda_3 + c\lambda_3^2 \end{aligned}$$
where $\lambda_1, \lambda_2, \lambda_3$ are the characteristic roots of A. So let us first find the λ's. We have
$$|A - \lambda I| = \begin{vmatrix} 6-\lambda & -11 & 6 \\ 1 & -\lambda & 0 \\ 0 & 1 & -\lambda \end{vmatrix} = -(\lambda-1)(\lambda-2)(\lambda-3) = 0$$

Thus, $\lambda_1 = 1$, $\lambda_2 = 2$, $\lambda_3 = 3$. Substitute this into (16). Then,

$$1^t = a + b + c$$
$$2^t = a + 2b + 4c$$
$$3^t = a + 3b + 9c$$

Solving this set of equations we find

$$a = -3 \cdot 2^t + 3^t + 3$$
$$b = 4 \cdot 2^t - \tfrac{3}{2} \cdot 3^t - \tfrac{5}{2}$$
$$c = -2^t + \tfrac{1}{2} \cdot 3^t + \tfrac{1}{2}$$

Next, note that

$$A^2 = AA = \begin{bmatrix} 25 & 60 & 36 \\ 6 & -11 & 6 \\ 1 & 0 & 0 \end{bmatrix}$$

Substituting these results into (15) gives us

$$A^t = aI + bA + cA^2$$
$$= \begin{bmatrix} a + 6b + 25c & -11b + 60c & 6b + 36c \\ b + 6c & a - 11c & 6c \\ c & b & a \end{bmatrix}$$

Thus, from (14) we get

$$\begin{bmatrix} x_{t+1} \\ y_{t+1} \\ z_{t+1} \end{bmatrix} = \begin{bmatrix} a + 6b + 25c & -11b + 60c & 6b + 36c \\ b + 6c & a - 11c & 6c \\ c & b & a \end{bmatrix} \cdot \begin{bmatrix} x_1 \\ y_1 \\ z_1 \end{bmatrix}$$

Since $z_{t+1} = y_t$, we find that

$$z_{t+1} = y_t = cx_1 + by_1 + az_1$$

But $x_1 = y_2 = 3$, $y_1 = 2$, and $z_1 = y_0 = 1$. Thus, y_t becomes, after substituting in the values of a, b, and c just computed

$$y_t = 3c + 2b + a$$
$$y_t = -\tfrac{1}{2} + 2 \cdot 2^t - \tfrac{1}{2} \cdot 3^t$$

This is our desired solution.

Let us as a check now find the solution by the method studied in Chapter 9. For that, let $y_t = \beta^t$. Then the auxiliary equation becomes from (11)

$$\beta^3 - 6\beta^2 + 11\beta - 6 = 0$$
$$(\beta - 1)(\beta - 2)(\beta - 3) = 0$$

Thus, the solution is

$$y = c_1 1^t + c_2 2^t + c_3 3^t$$

From the initial conditions we find

$$1 = c_1 + c_2 + c_3$$
$$2 = c_1 + 2c_2 + 3c_3$$
$$3 = c_1 + 4c_2 + 9c_3$$

Solving this gives us

$$y_t = -\tfrac{1}{2} + 2 \cdot 2^t - \tfrac{1}{2} \cdot 3^t$$

which is what we have above.

PROBLEMS

Given the following difference equations, translate them into systems of linear first-order difference equations. Then, solve these systems following the procedure in Section 12.7.

1. $y_{t+2} - 7y_{t+1} + 12y_t = 0$

2. $y_{t+2} - 3y_{t+1} + 2y_t = 0$

3. $y_{t+3} + 2y_{t+2} - y_{t+1} - 2y_t = 0$

12.8 Stability conditions (II)

Let us now return to our main line of argument and seek the necessary stability conditions for a system of linear difference equations using matrix algebra. Consider the following system.

$$x_{t+1} = a_{11}x_t + a_{12}y_t + a_{13}z_t$$
$$y_{t+1} = a_{21}x_t + a_{22}y_t + a_{23}z_t$$
$$z_{t+1} = a_{31}x_t + a_{32}y_t + a_{33}z_t$$

In matrix notation this is

$$\begin{bmatrix} x_{t+1} \\ y_{t+1} \\ z_{t+1} \end{bmatrix} = \begin{bmatrix} a_{11} & a_{12} & a_{13} \\ a_{21} & a_{22} & a_{23} \\ a_{31} & a_{32} & a_{33} \end{bmatrix} \cdot \begin{bmatrix} x_t \\ y_t \\ z_t \end{bmatrix}$$

or

$$V_{t+1} = AV_t = A^t V_1$$

Now let us perform a transformation

$$D = P^{-1}AP$$

where P is a modal matrix and D is a diagonal matrix with the characteristic roots in the diagonal.

The *trace* of a square matrix A is defined as $\operatorname{tr} A = \sum\limits_{i=1}^{n} a_{ii}$. Thus, in our present case it is

$$\operatorname{tr} A = a_{11} + a_{22} + a_{33}$$

It can also be shown very simply that

$$\text{tr}\,(A + B) = \text{tr}\,A + \text{tr}\,B$$

and

$$\text{tr}\,AB = \text{tr}\,BA.$$

Applying this to our transformation above, we have

$$\text{tr}\,D = \text{tr}\,P^{-1}AP = \text{tr}\,P^{-1}(AP) = \text{tr}\,APP^{-1}$$
$$= \text{tr}\,A$$

But $\text{tr}\,D$ is the sum of the characteristic roots. Thus, we have shown that

$$\text{tr}\,A = \text{tr}\,D = \text{sum of the characteristic roots}$$

Next, let us take the determinants on both sides. Then,

$$|D| = |P^{-1}| \cdot |A| \cdot |P| = |A| \cdot |P|^{-1} \cdot |P| = |A|$$

But $|D| = \prod_i \lambda_i$. Thus, we have shown that the determinant $|A|$ is equal to the product of the characteristic roots, i.e.,

$$|A| = |D| = \prod_i \lambda_i$$

Since the solution of the system is of the form, for y_t, for example,

$$y_t = c_1\lambda_1^t + c_2\lambda_2^t + c_3\lambda_3^t$$

we can see that y_t will converge as $t \to \infty$ when $|\lambda_i| < |$. But this implies that

$$\sum_{i=1}^{n} |\lambda_i| < n$$

$$\prod_{i=1}^{n} |\lambda_i| < 1$$

where $n = 3$ in our present case. In terms of what was just derived, this means

$$-n < \text{tr}\,A < n$$
$$-1 < |D| < 1$$

This, then, can be considered the (necessary) stability conditions for the system we have.

Example. Let us use our previous example to illustrate.

$$\begin{bmatrix} x_{t+1} \\ y_{t+1} \\ z_{t+1} \end{bmatrix} = \begin{bmatrix} 6 & -11 & 6 \\ 1 & 0 & 0 \\ 0 & 1 & 0 \end{bmatrix} \begin{bmatrix} x_t \\ y_t \\ z_t \end{bmatrix}$$

We know that $\lambda_1 = 1$, $\lambda_2 = 2$, $\lambda_3 = 3$. Thus,

$$D = \begin{bmatrix} 1 & & \\ & 2 & \\ & & 3 \end{bmatrix}$$

Then,

$$\operatorname{tr} A = 6 + 0 + 0 = 6$$
$$\operatorname{tr} D = 1 + 2 + 3 = 6$$
$$\therefore \quad \operatorname{tr} A = \operatorname{tr} D$$

Next,

$$|D| = \begin{vmatrix} 1 & & \\ & 2 & \\ & & 3 \end{vmatrix} = 1 \cdot 2 \cdot 3 = 6$$

$$|A| = 6$$
$$\therefore \quad |D| = |A|$$

A is a 3×3 matrix, that is, $n = 3$. Thus, since $\operatorname{tr} A = 6 > 3$ and $|D| = 6 > 1$, the stability conditions do not hold.

12.9 Stability conditions (III)

We can also apply the Schur theorem to systems of equations in the following way. Consider the following system of linear difference equations.

$$\begin{bmatrix} x_{t+1} \\ y_{t+1} \\ z_{t+1} \end{bmatrix} = \begin{bmatrix} a_{11} & a_{12} & a_{13} \\ a_{21} & a_{22} & a_{23} \\ a_{31} & a_{32} & a_{33} \end{bmatrix} \begin{bmatrix} x_t \\ y_t \\ z_t \end{bmatrix}$$

Recall that $D = P^{-1}AP$ and $D^t = P^{-1}A^tP$. Thus,

$$A^t = PD^tP^{-1}$$

Furthermore,

$$V_{t+1} = A^t V_1$$

so that if $A^t \to 0$ as $t \to \infty$, then we have stability. But, since

$$D^t = \begin{bmatrix} \lambda_1^t & & \\ & \lambda_2^t & \\ & & \lambda_3^t \end{bmatrix}$$

if $|\lambda_1| < 1$, $|\lambda_2| < 1$, $|\lambda_3| < 1$, then when $t \to \infty$, $D^t \to 0$ and also $A^t \to 0$. Thus, if the absolute value of the characteristic roots are less than unity, i.e., $|\lambda_i| < 1$, then the system will be stable. But what are the conditions for $|\lambda_i| < 1$?

We have seen in Section 12.2 that when given a polynomial, the Schur conditions were necessary and sufficient for the absolute values of the roots to be less than unity. We have also seen in Section 12.3 how a characteristic equation is expanded. In our present case, we have

$$|\lambda I - A| = \lambda^3 - D_1\lambda^2 + D_2\lambda - D_3 = 0$$
$$\equiv C_0\lambda^3 + C_1\lambda^2 + C_2\lambda + C_3 = 0$$

where we have set $C_i = (-1)^i D_i$, where the D_i are the sum of the i-th order minors about the principal diagonal. Then the Schur conditions can be shown as

$$\Delta_1 = \begin{vmatrix} C_0 & C_3 \\ C_3 & C_0 \end{vmatrix} > 0, \qquad \Delta_2 = \begin{vmatrix} C_0 & 0 & C_3 & C_2 \\ C_1 & C_0 & 0 & C_3 \\ C_3 & 0 & C_0 & C_1 \\ C_2 & C_3 & 0 & C_0 \end{vmatrix} > 0$$

$$\Delta_3 = \begin{vmatrix} C_0 & 0 & 0 & C_3 & C_2 & C_1 \\ C_1 & C_0 & 0 & 0 & C_3 & C_2 \\ C_2 & C_1 & C_0 & 0 & 0 & C_3 \\ C_3 & 0 & 0 & C_0 & C_1 & C_2 \\ C_2 & C_3 & 0 & 0 & C_0 & C_1 \\ C_1 & C_2 & C_3 & 0 & 0 & C_0 \end{vmatrix} > 0$$

Thus, $|\lambda_i| < 1$, when $\Delta_1 > 0$, $\Delta_2 > 0$, $\Delta_3 > 0$,

Let us next consider two special cases.

(i) When A is a non-negative square matrix

When dealing with a general equilibrium system or input-output system, we usually have non-negative square matrices. Thus, let us assume $A \geq 0$ and see what conditions are necessary for a stable system.

Recall that when v is a characteristic vector obtained from a characteristic root λ we have

$$Av = \lambda v$$

Let $v = (\alpha_1, \alpha_2, \alpha_3)$. Then,

$$a_{11}\alpha_1 + a_{12}\alpha_2 + a_{13}\alpha_3 = \lambda\alpha_1$$
$$a_{21}\alpha_1 + a_{22}\alpha_2 + a_{23}\alpha_3 = \lambda\alpha_2$$
$$a_{31}\alpha_1 + a_{32}\alpha_2 + a_{33}\alpha_3 = \lambda\alpha_3$$

Using the properties of inequalities, we have

$$|\lambda| \cdot |\alpha_1| \leq |a_{11}\alpha_1| + |a_{12}\alpha_2| + |a_{13}\alpha_3|$$
$$|\lambda| \cdot |\alpha_2| \leq |a_{21}\alpha_1| + |a_{22}\alpha_2| + |a_{23}\alpha_3|$$
$$|\lambda| \cdot |\alpha_3| \leq |a_{31}\alpha_1| + |a_{32}\alpha_2| + |a_{33}\alpha_3|$$
$$\therefore \quad |\lambda| \cdot [|\alpha_1| + |\alpha_2| + |\alpha_3|] \leq (a_{11} + a_{21} + a_{31}) \cdot |\alpha_1|$$
$$+ (a_{12} + a_{22} + a_{32}) \cdot |\alpha_2| + (a_{13} + a_{23} + a_{33}) \cdot |\alpha_3|$$

Therefore, if the sum of the elements in each column are less than 1, then,

$$|\lambda| \cdot [|\alpha_1| + |\alpha_2| + |\alpha_3|] < |\alpha_1| + |\alpha_2| + |\alpha_3|$$
$$\therefore \quad |\lambda| < 1$$

Similarly, the other characteristic roots of the matrix are less than 1. Then,

$$D^t \to 0, \quad \text{as} \quad t \to \infty$$

i.e. $$V_{t+1} \to 0$$

To summarize: When A is a non-negative square matrix and the sum of the elements of each column are less than 1, the characteristic roots are less than 1. This can be considered as a necessary stability condition.

(*ii*) *When $A > 0$ and $\Sigma\, a_{ij} < 1$*

In Section 11.10(e) we stated without proof that when $A > 0$, $\Sigma\, a_{ij} < 1$, then $(I - A) > 0$ and $\lambda_1 < 1$, where λ_1 was the root with the largest absolute value. The result is consistent with the result we arrived at in (1) above.

12.10 Stability conditions (IV)—Routh theorem

Let us now discuss the stability of differential equations. We shall first consider a *single* differential equation, and then *systems* of equations.

The general form of the solution for differential equations was

$$y = c_0 + c_1 e^{m_1 x} + c_2 e^{m_2 x} \qquad \text{(real case)}$$
$$y = e^{ak} (c_1 \cos bx + c_2 \sin bx) \qquad \text{(complex case)}$$

and the stability of y required that $m_1 < 0$, $m_2 < 0$ for the real case, and $a < 0$ for the complex case.

Samuelson (1947) has presented the Routh theorem that gives us the necessary and sufficient conditions for the real parts of the roots to be negative. Let us illustrate this.

(*i*) *Routh theorem*

Consider a polynomial

$$f(x) = a_0 x^4 + a_1 x^3 + a_2 x^2 + a_3 x + a_4 = 0$$

where we assume $a_0 > 0$. Then the Routh Theorem says that the necessary and sufficient conditions for the real parts of the roots to be negative is that the following sequence of determinants all be positive.

$$\Delta_1 = |a_1|, \quad \Delta_2 = \begin{vmatrix} a_1 & a_3 \\ a_0 & a_2 \end{vmatrix}, \quad \Delta_3 = \begin{vmatrix} a_1 & a_3 & 0 \\ a_0 & a_2 & a_4 \\ 0 & a_1 & a_3 \end{vmatrix}, \quad \Delta_4 = \begin{vmatrix} a_1 & a_3 & 0 & 0 \\ a_0 & a_2 & a_4 & 0 \\ 0 & a_1 & a_3 & 0 \\ 0 & a_0 & a_2 & a_4 \end{vmatrix}$$

Notice carefully the way the coefficients and the zeros are placed in the determinants. For example, in the first row of Δ_3, we should have a_1, a_3, and a_5. But a_5 does not exist, so we insert a zero. In the first column, we should have, a_1, a_0, a_{-1}. But a_{-1} does not exist so we insert a zero. Similarly for Δ_4.

The Δ_4 can be shown as

$$\Delta_4 = a_4 \begin{vmatrix} a_1 & a_3 & 0 \\ a_0 & a_2 & a_4 \\ 0 & a_1 & a_3 \end{vmatrix} = a_4 \cdot \Delta_3$$

But $\Delta_3 > 0$ so that, $a_4 > 0$. Therefore, the conditions can be stated as

$$\Delta_1 > 0, \quad \Delta_2 > 0, \quad \Delta_3 > 0, \quad a_4 > 0$$

We have illustrated the Routh theorem for a 4-th-degree polynomial but as is seen, it can easily be extended to the n-th-degree case.

Example.

$$f(x) = x^3 + 6x^2 + 11x + 6 = (x + 1)(x + 2)(x + 3)$$

Apply Routh's theorem.

$$\Delta_1 = 6 > 0$$

$$\Delta_2 = \begin{vmatrix} a_1 & a_3 \\ a_0 & a_2 \end{vmatrix} = \begin{vmatrix} 6 & 6 \\ 1 & 11 \end{vmatrix} = 60 > 0$$

$$\Delta_3 = \begin{vmatrix} a_1 & a_3 & 0 \\ a_0 & a_2 & 0 \\ 0 & a_1 & a_3 \end{vmatrix} = \begin{vmatrix} 6 & 6 & 0 \\ 1 & 11 & 0 \\ 0 & 6 & 6 \end{vmatrix} = 6 \cdot \Delta_2 > 0$$

Thus, $f(x)$ has negative roots. We know they are $-1, -2, -3$.

(ii) *Application to differential equations*

Given the differential equation,

(1)
$$\frac{d^3y}{dt^3} + 6\frac{d^2y}{dt^2} + 11\frac{dy}{dt} + 6y = 0$$

Let

$$y = e^{mt}$$

$$\therefore \quad \frac{d^3y}{dt^3} = m^3 e^{mt}, \quad \frac{d^2y}{dt^2} = m^2 e^{mt}, \quad \frac{dy}{dt} = me^{mt}$$

Then the auxiliary equation becomes

$$m^3 + 6m^2 + 11m + 6 = 0$$

Applying Routh's theorem we find (since this auxiliary equation is the same as our example above)

$$\Delta_1 = 6 > 0, \quad \Delta_2 = 60 > 0, \quad \Delta_3 = 6\Delta_2 > 0$$

Thus, all the characteristic roots are negative and the solution is stable.

Let us check this. We know that $m_1 = -1$, $m_2 = -2$, $m_3 = -3$. Therefore the solution is

$$y = c_1 e^{-t} + c_2 e^{-2t} + c_3 e^{-3t}$$

and as $t \to \infty$, then $y \to 0$, and we have a stable solution.

(iii) Application of Descartes' rule

We can apply Descartes' rule of signs to equation (1). Since there are no variations of signs of coefficients, there are no positive roots. Thus, we have a stable equation.

Problems

1. Given the polynomial

$$f(x) = a_0 x^5 + a_1 x^4 + a_2 x^3 + a_3 x^2 + a_4 x + a_5 = 0$$

where $a_0 > 0$, write out the Routh conditions for the roots to be negative.

2. Given the polynomial

$$f(x) = x^5 + 2x^4 + x^3 + 3x^2 + x + 2 = 0$$

check whether it has negative roots or not by use of Routh's theorem.

3. Given the polynomial

$$f(x) = x^3 + 3x^2 + 4x + 2 = 0$$

check whether the roots are negative or not by use of Routh's theorem. (The roots are $-1 + i$, $-1 - i$, -1.)

4. Given the following differential equations check their stability.

(a) $\dfrac{d^5x}{dy^5} + 2\dfrac{d^4x}{dy^4} + \dfrac{d^3x}{dy^3} + 3\dfrac{d^2x}{dy^2} + \dfrac{dx}{dy} + 2y = 0.$

(b) $\dfrac{d^3x}{dy^3} + 3\dfrac{d^2x}{dy^2} + 4\dfrac{dx}{dy} + 2y = 0.$

(c) $\dfrac{d^3x}{dy^3} + 7\dfrac{d^2x}{dy^2} + 14\dfrac{dx}{dy} + 8y = 0.$

$$(-1, -2, -4)$$

12.11 Stability conditions (V)

Let us now consider the stability of a first order differential equation system. A system of three equations is considered for simplicity, but the results are general.

(i) The solution and necessary conditions for stability

Consider

$$\frac{dy_1}{dt} = a_{11}y_1 + a_{12}y_2 + a_{13}y_3$$

(1)
$$\frac{dy_2}{dt} = a_{21}y_1 + a_{22}y_2 + a_{23}y_3$$

$$\frac{dy_3}{dt} = a_{31}y_1 + a_{32}y_2 + a_{33}y_3$$

Let us set the form of the solution as

$$y_1 = ae^{mt}, \qquad y_2 = be^{mt}, \qquad y_3 = ce^{mt}$$

Then,

$$\frac{dy_1}{dt} = ame^{mt}, \qquad \frac{dy_2}{dt} = bme^{mt}, \qquad \frac{dy_3}{dt} = cme^{mt}$$

Substitute these into (1) and rearrange terms. Then we get in terms of matrices

(2)
$$\begin{bmatrix} a_{11} - m & a_{12} & a_{13} \\ a_{21} & a_{22} - m & a_{23} \\ a_{31} & a_{32} & a_{33} - m \end{bmatrix} \cdot \begin{bmatrix} a \\ b \\ c \end{bmatrix} = 0$$

If y_1, y_2, y_3 are to have a non-trivial solution, all of a, b, c cannot be zero. Thus, according to the results in Section 12.4 concerning solution of homogeneous equations, we need

(3)
$$\begin{vmatrix} a_{11} - m & a_{12} & a_{13} \\ a_{21} & a_{22} - m & a_{23} \\ a_{31} & a_{32} & a_{33} - m \end{vmatrix} = 0$$

This (3) is the *characteristic (auxiliary) equation* when we have a system of equations. Upon solving it, we find m_1, m_2, and m_3.

Thus, we find as solutions:

(4)
$$\begin{aligned} y_{11} &= a_1 e^{m_1 t} & y_{12} &= a_2 e^{m_2 t} & y_{13} &= a_3 e^{m_3 t} \\ y_{21} &= b_1 e^{m_1 t} & y_{22} &= b_2 e^{m_2 t} & y_{23} &= b_3 e^{m_3 t} \\ y_{31} &= c_1 e^{m_1 t} & y_{32} &= c_2 e^{m_2 t} & y_{33} &= c_3 e^{m_3 t} \end{aligned}$$

The general solutions are

(5)
$$\begin{aligned} y_1 &= y_{11} + y_{12} + y_{13} = a_1 e^{m_1 t} + a_2 e^{m_2 t} + a_3 e^{m_3 t} \\ y_2 &= y_{21} + y_{22} + y_{23} = b_1 e^{m_1 t} + b_2 e^{m_2 t} + b_3 e^{m_3 t} \\ y_3 &= y_{31} + y_{32} + y_{33} = c_1 e^{m_1 t} + c_2 e^{m_2 t} + c_3 e^{m_3 t} \end{aligned}$$

How will y_1, y_2, and y_3 behave as $t \to \infty$? As is seen, it will depend on m_1, m_2, and m_3. When these three characteristic roots are negative, y_1, y_2, and y_3 will converge to a stable value. That is, the necessary condition for the system to be stable is for the characteristic roots to be negative.

(ii) A matrix presentation of the results

Let us now reinterpret our results as follows: The system of equations can be shown as

$$\begin{bmatrix} y_1' \\ y_2' \\ y_3' \end{bmatrix} = \begin{bmatrix} a_{11} & a_{12} & a_{13} \\ a_{21} & a_{22} & a_{23} \\ a_{31} & a_{32} & a_{33} \end{bmatrix} \cdot \begin{bmatrix} y_1 \\ y_2 \\ y_3 \end{bmatrix}$$

Or, for brevity

(7) $$y' = Ay$$

According to our results of (i) above, the necessary condition for the system to be stable was that

(8) $$|A - mI| = 0$$

and the roots m_1, m_2, m_3 be negative.

The important point to note is the following three steps: One, the system of linear differential equations (1) is rearranged into a system of linear *homogeneous* equations (2). Two, the necessary condition for a non-trivial solution is stated as (3) which turns out to be the characteristic determinant of the matrix of coefficients. Three, the characteristic roots of this characteristic determinant are the roots we seek of the differential equation system.

Thus, in terms of our matrix presentation, solving the differential equation system (1) becomes equivalent to finding the characteristic roots of (8) which is the characteristic determinant of the matrix A. Using this result, the stability problem can be discussed in terms of the characteristic roots m_1, m_2 and m_3 of A.

We have seen in Section 12.8 how a diagonal matrix $D = P^{-1}AP$, and that

$$\operatorname{tr} A = \operatorname{tr} D = m_1 + m_2 + m_3$$

$$|A| = |D| = m_1 m_2 m_3$$

Thus, we can state that the necessary conditions for a system of linear differential equations to be stable are: (1) the $\operatorname{tr} A < 0$, and, (2) $|A| < 0$ when we have an odd number of equations and variables in the system and $|A| > 0$ when we have an even number.

Example.

$$y_1' = y_1 - 2y_2$$
$$y_2' = 3y_1 - 4y_2$$

We shall first solve the system completely, and then use the alternative method and show that the roots are negative.

First method. Let

$$y_1 = ae^{mt}, \qquad y_2 = be^{mt}.$$

Then, the auxiliary equation for the system becomes

$$f(m) = \begin{vmatrix} 1 - m & -2 \\ 3 & -4 - m \end{vmatrix} = m^2 + 3m + 2 = 0$$

and the characteristic roots are $m_1 = -1$, $m_2 = -2$. This gives us

$$\begin{aligned} y_{11} &= a_1 e^{-t} & y_{12} &= a_2 e^{-2t} \\ y_{21} &= b_1 e^{-t} & y_{22} &= b_2 e^{-2t} \end{aligned}$$

and the general solutions are

$$\begin{aligned} y_1 &= y_{11} + y_{12} = a_1 e^{-t} + a_2 e^{-2t} \\ y_2 &= y_{21} + y_{22} = b_1 e^{-t} + b_2 e^{-2t} \end{aligned}$$

As can be seen, as $t \to \infty$, the system will be stable.

Let us find the constants a's and b's. For $m_1 = -1$, we have

$$\begin{bmatrix} 1 - (-1) & -2 \\ 3 & -4 - (-1) \end{bmatrix} \begin{bmatrix} a_1 \\ b_1 \end{bmatrix} = 0$$

$$2a_1 - 2b_1 = 0$$
$$3a_1 - 3b_1 = 0$$

$$a_1 = b_1, \qquad b_1 = k_1$$

where k_1 is an arbitrary constant. For $m_2 = -2$, we get

$$3a_2 - 2b_2 = 0$$
$$3a_2 - 2b_2 = 0$$
$$a_2 = \tfrac{2}{3} b_2, \qquad b_2 = k_2$$

where k_2 is an arbitrary constant. Then,

$$\begin{aligned} y_1 &= k_1 e^{-t} + \tfrac{2}{3} k_2 e^{-2t} \\ y_2 &= k_1 e^{-t} + k_2 e^{-2t} \end{aligned}$$

Check. The first equation of the system is

$$\text{l.h.s.} = y' = \frac{d}{dt}(k_1 e^{-t} + \tfrac{2}{3} k_2 e^{-2t})$$

$$= -k_1 e^{-t} - \tfrac{4}{3} k_2 e^{-2t}$$

$$\text{r.h.s.} = y_1 - 2y_2$$

$$= k_1 e^{-t} + \tfrac{2}{3} k_2 e^{-2t} - 2k_1 e^{-t} - 2k_2 e^{-2t}$$

$$= -k_1 e^{-t} - \tfrac{4}{3} k_2 e^{-2t}$$

Thus, l.h.s. = r.h.s. The second equation is checked in a similar manner.

Second method. Let us now use the alternative method. The necessary conditions for stability are tr $A < 0$ and $|A| > 0$ since there are an even number of equations. From the matrix A we find

$$A = \begin{bmatrix} 1 & -2 \\ 3 & -4 \end{bmatrix}$$

$$\text{tr } A = 1 - 4 = -3 < 0, \quad |A| = 2 > 0$$

Thus, we have the necessary conditions for negative roots. Note that

$$\text{tr } A = m_1 + m_2 = -1 - 2 = -3$$

which checks with the above result.

Problems

Given the following systems of linear differential equations, check the stability of the system by solving the system completely, and then check it by the alternative method of using the trace of the associated matrix and the value of the determinant of the matrix.

1. $\quad y_1' = y_1 - 4y_2$
$\quad\quad y_2' = 2y_1 - 5y_2$

2. $\quad y_1' = 2y_1 - 5y_2$
$\quad\quad y_2' = 4y_1 - 7y_2$

3. In the following check the necessary conditions of stability by use of the trace and value of the determinant.

$$y_1' = y_1 + 2y_2$$

$$y_2' = 2y_1 - 5y_2$$

$$y_3' = y_1 + 5y_2 + 2y_3$$

12.12 Stability conditions (VI)

Let us present an alternative way of determining the stability of a system of linear first-order differential equations. Consider

$$\frac{dy_1}{dt} = a_{11}y_1 + a_{12}y_2 + a_{13}y_3$$

(1) $$\frac{dy_2}{dt} = a_{21}y_1 + a_{22}y_2 + a_{23}y_3$$

$$\frac{dy_3}{dt} = a_{31}y_1 + a_{32}y_2 + a_{33}y_3$$

We saw in Section 12.11 that the characteristic roots of the characteristic equation $|A - mI| = 0$ need to be negative for stability. We know from Section 12.3 that the characteristic equation can be expanded as

$$|mI - A| = m^2 - D_1 m^2 + D_2 m - D_3 = 0$$

Therefore, if $D_1 < 0$, $D_2 > 0$, $D_3 < 0$, then by Descartes' rule of sign the roots will be negative or zero.

Let us further investigate this equation. We know

$$D_1 = a_{11} + a_{22} + a_{33} = \operatorname{tr} A$$

$$D_2 = \begin{vmatrix} a_{11} & a_{12} \\ a_{21} & a_{22} \end{vmatrix} + \begin{vmatrix} a_{22} & a_{23} \\ a_{32} & a_{33} \end{vmatrix} + \begin{vmatrix} a_{33} & a_{31} \\ a_{13} & a_{11} \end{vmatrix}$$

$$D_3 = \begin{vmatrix} a_{11} & a_{12} & a_{13} \\ a_{21} & a_{22} & a_{23} \\ a_{31} & a_{32} & a_{33} \end{vmatrix}$$

Let us abbreviate these determinants by

$$a_{ii}, \qquad \begin{vmatrix} a_{ii} & a_{ij} \\ a_{ji} & a_{jj} \end{vmatrix}, \qquad \begin{vmatrix} a_{ii} & a_{ij} & a_{ik} \\ a_{ji} & a_{jj} & a_{jk} \\ a_{ki} & a_{kj} & a_{kk} \end{vmatrix}$$

Thus, we can say, the condition for the characteristic equation to have negative and/or zero roots is that the above determinants alternate in sign, the first one being negative. For example, $a_{ii} < 0$ would mean, $a_{11} < 0$, $a_{22} < 0$, $a_{33} < 0$. Then, obviously $D_1 < 0$, and similarly for the other D_i's.

Example. Hicks' (1939) perfect stability conditions use this technique. Consider

$$x_1 = D_1(P_1, P_2, P_3) - S_1(P_1, P_2, P_3)$$
$$x_2 = D_2(P_1, P_2, P_3) - S_2(P_1, P_2, P_3)$$
$$x_3 = D_3(P_1, P_2, P_3) - S_3(P_1, P_2, P_3)$$

where x_i shows excess demand, D_i, S_i are the demand and supply functions, P_i are prices. Let there be a small change in P_1. Then,

$$\frac{dx_1}{dP_1} = \frac{\partial(D_1 - S_1)}{\partial P_1} + \frac{\partial(D_1 - S_1)}{\partial P_2}\frac{dP_2}{dP_1} + \frac{\partial(D_1 - S_1)}{\partial P_3}\frac{dP_3}{dP_1}$$

$$0 = \frac{\partial(D_2 - S_2)}{\partial P_1} + \frac{\partial(D_2 - S_2)}{\partial P_2}\frac{dP_2}{dP_1} + \frac{\partial(D_2 - S_2)}{\partial P_3}\frac{dP_3}{dP_1}$$

$$0 = \frac{\partial(D_3 - S_3)}{\partial P_1} + \frac{\partial(D_3 - S_3)}{\partial P_2}\frac{dP_2}{dP_1} + \frac{\partial(D_3 - S_3)}{\partial P_3}\frac{dP_3}{dP_1}$$

Let us rewrite this as

$$\frac{dx_1}{dP_1} = a_{11} + a_{12}\frac{dP_2}{dP_1} + a_{13}\frac{dP_3}{dP_1}$$

$$0 = a_{21} + a_{22}\frac{dP_2}{dP_1} + a_{23}\frac{dP_3}{dP_1}$$

$$0 = a_{31} + a_{32}\frac{dP_2}{dP_1} + a_{33}\frac{dP_3}{dP_1}$$

Using Cramer's rule, we find

$$1 = \frac{\begin{vmatrix} \dfrac{dx_1}{dP_1} & a_{12} & a_{13} \\ 0 & a_{22} & a_{23} \\ 0 & a_{32} & a_{33} \end{vmatrix}}{\begin{vmatrix} a_{11} & a_{12} & a_{13} \\ a_{21} & a_{22} & a_{23} \\ a_{31} & a_{32} & a_{33} \end{vmatrix}} = \frac{\dfrac{dx_1}{dP_1}\begin{vmatrix} a_{22} & a_{23} \\ a_{32} & a_{33} \end{vmatrix}}{|A|}$$

$$\therefore\quad \frac{dx_1}{dP_1} = |A| \div \begin{vmatrix} a_{22} & a_{23} \\ a_{32} & a_{33} \end{vmatrix}$$

Similarly, for

$$\frac{dx_2}{dP_2} = |A| \div \begin{vmatrix} a_{11} & a_{13} \\ a_{31} & a_{33} \end{vmatrix}$$

$$\frac{dx_3}{dP_3} = |A| \div \begin{vmatrix} a_{11} & a_{12} \\ a_{21} & a_{22} \end{vmatrix}$$

Here we have considered three markets. But perfect stability implies this must hold when we consider two markets holding the other constant, or one market holding the other two constant. In each case we need the condition that excess demand decreases when prices increase. That is,

$$\frac{dx_i}{dP_i} < 0$$

For this to hold for all markets as mentioned above, we need

$$a_{ii}, \quad \begin{vmatrix} a_{ii} & a_{ij} \\ a_{ji} & a_{jj} \end{vmatrix}, \quad \begin{vmatrix} a_{ii} & a_{ij} & a_{ik} \\ a_{ji} & a_{jj} & a_{jk} \\ a_{ki} & a_{kj} & a_{kk} \end{vmatrix}$$

to alternate in sign. For example, we need $a_{11} < 0$, $a_{22} < 0$, $a_{33} < 0$, and so forth. Note that

$$a_{ii} = \frac{\partial(D_i - S_i)}{\partial P_i} = \frac{\partial x_i}{\partial P_i}$$

Therefore, the determinants are Jacobian determinants.

12.13 Convex sets

The postwar development of linear programming and its increasing application to various economic problems such as the theory of the firm, input-output analysis, and welfare economics have made it necessary for the economist to acquire an understanding of this mathematical technique. To understand linear programming, it is convenient to distinguish between its theoretical and computational aspects. As we shall see, linear programming involves large numbers of equations. The computational aspects are mainly concerned with the various methods that have been devised to solve these systems, especially with the help of computers.

There are a number of excellent books on the theoretical aspects that are appropriate for economists who are not professional mathematicians (see Notes and References). Of the mathematical techniques used in these books, the two important topics are *matrix algebra* and *convex sets*. In this section a brief survey of some elementary ideas of convex sets are presented to serve as background material for further study in linear programming. The problem of linear programming is stated but not discussed. The computational aspects are also not discussed. For a full treatment of these problems the reader is referred to the references at the end of the chapter.

(i) Convex sets

Let us first discuss a few ideas in terms of a two-dimensional Cartesian coordinate system. Consider two vectors

$$P_1 = \begin{bmatrix} 4 \\ 1 \end{bmatrix}, \quad P_2 = \begin{bmatrix} 1 \\ 4 \end{bmatrix}$$

Let us select a point P on the line $\overline{P_1P_2}$. Furthermore, let $\overline{P_1P} : \overline{P_2P} = 1 : 2 = \mu : (1 - \mu)$ where $\mu = \frac{1}{3}$. In vector notation we have

$$\frac{\|P_1 - P\|}{\|P - P_2\|} = \frac{\mu}{1 - \mu}$$

Thus,

$$(1 - \mu)P_1 - (1 - \mu)P = \mu P - \mu P_2$$

which becomes

$$P = (1 - \mu)P_1 + \mu P_2$$

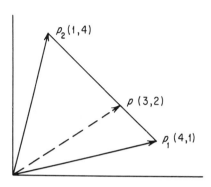

Fig. 12–4

This result may be summarized as follows: Given two vectors P_1 and P_2, select a point P on the vector $P_1 - P_2$ so that it divides the vector into two parts with a ratio of

$$\|P_1 - P\| : \|P - P_2\| = \mu : 1 - \mu,$$

then,

$$P = (1 - \mu)P_1 + \mu P_2 \qquad 0 \le \mu \le 1$$

Thus, every point on the line $\overline{P_1P_2}$ can be shown as a linear combination of P_1 and P_2 by letting μ take values between $0 \le \mu \le 1$.

In our present case we have

$$P = (1 - \tfrac{1}{3}) \begin{bmatrix} 4 \\ 1 \end{bmatrix} + \tfrac{1}{3} \begin{bmatrix} 1 \\ 4 \end{bmatrix} = \begin{bmatrix} 3 \\ 2 \end{bmatrix}$$

Thus, the norm becomes

$$\|P_1 - P\| = [(P_1 - P)'(P_1 - P)]^{1/2}$$

$$= \left\{ \left(\begin{bmatrix} 4 \\ 1 \end{bmatrix} - \begin{bmatrix} 3 \\ 2 \end{bmatrix} \right) \left(\begin{bmatrix} 4 \\ 1 \end{bmatrix} - \begin{bmatrix} 3 \\ 2 \end{bmatrix} \right) \right\}^{1/2}$$

$$= \sqrt{2}$$

$$\|P - P_2\| = \sqrt{8}$$

and we get

$$\frac{\|P_1 - P\|}{\|P - P_2\|} = \frac{\sqrt{2}}{\sqrt{8}} = \frac{1}{2}$$

The vector point P was $P = (1 - \mu)P_1 + \mu P_2$ where $0 \le \mu \le 1$. Thus, $\{(1 - \mu)P_1 + \mu P_2\}$ where $0 \le \mu \le 1$ shows us the set of points that form the vector $P_1 - P_2$ or in terms of geometry the line $\overline{P_1P_2}$. Let us call this line a *segment* joining P_1 and P_2.

P is a *linear combination* of P_1 and P_2. When the coefficients of P_1 and P_2 add up to 1, we call it a *convex linear combination*.

Let S be a set and P_1 and P_2 be points of S. If P is a convex linear combination of P_1 and P_2 and belongs to the set S, then the set S is said to be a

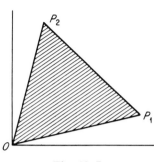

convex set C. The Figure 12–5 is a convex set. As is seen, any point that is a convex linear combination of two points in the shaded triangle will also be in the triangle. Or we can say that if we have two points in the set and the segment joining the two points is also in the set, then we have a convex set. Figures 12–6(a) and (b) are examples of convex sets. Figure 12–6(c) is not a convex set. Let us extend this to three dimensions. Let P_1, P_2, P_3 be three points. They will define a plane. Let P be a point in this plane. Draw a line from P_1 through P and let it intersect

Fig. 12–5

$\overline{P_2P_3}$ at P' where the ratio of $\overline{P_2P'} : \overline{P_3P'} = \mu : 1 - \mu$ where $0 \leq \mu \leq 1$. Then, P' is a linear combination of P_2 and P_3; i.e.,

$$P' = (1 - \mu)P_2 + \mu P_3$$

Next let $\overline{P'P} : PP_1 = (1 - \lambda) : \lambda$. Then,

$$P = (1 - \lambda)P_1 + \lambda P'$$
$$= (1 - \lambda)P_1 + \lambda(1 - \mu)P_2 + \lambda\mu P_3$$

(a)   (b)   (c)

Fig. 12–6

This shows that P is a linear combination of P_1, P_2, P_3. But we see that the sum of the coefficients is 1; i.e.,

$$(1 - \lambda) + \lambda(1 - \mu) + \lambda\mu = 1$$

Therefore, P is a convex linear combination of P_1, P_2, P_3. Let the coefficients be denoted by a_1, a_2, and a_3. Then,

$$P = a_1P_1 + a_2P_2 + a_3P_3$$

where $\Sigma\, a_i = 1$, $a_i \geq 0$.

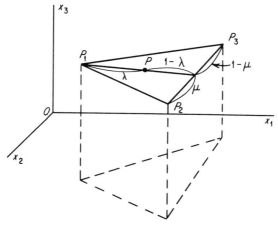

Fig. 12–7

This can be generalized. When we have an n-dimensional vector space R_n and $m(\leq n)$ points $P_1, P_2, \ldots, P_m$, these points will define a hyperplane in R_n. Then, a point P on this hyperplane can be shown as a convex linear combination of the P_i, $(i = 1, 2, \ldots, m)$; i.e.,

$$P = a_1 P_1 + a_2 P_2 + \ldots + a_m P_m$$

where $\Sigma\, a_i = 1$, $a_i \geq 0$. If all the points P are in the same set as the points $P_1, \ldots, P_m$, then we have a convex set. The vector $[a_1, a_2, \ldots, a_m]$ is called a probability vector.

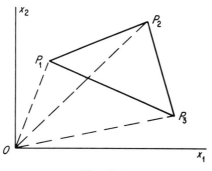

Fig. 12–8

(ii) *Convex hull*

Consider a triangle $P_1 P_2 P_3$ as in Figure 12–8. Let S be the set of three points P_1, P_2, and P_3; i.e.,

$$S = \{P_1, P_2, P_3\}$$

Select two points P_1 and P_2 and make a line $\overline{P_1P_2}$. Then the set of points that make up the line $\overline{P_1P_2}$ is shown as the convex linear combination of P_1 and P_2, i.e.,

$$\{P : P = a_1P_1 + a_2P_2\}$$

where $\Sigma\ a_i = 1$, $a_i \geq 0$. In a similar manner, the points on $\overline{P_2P_3}$ ($\overline{P_3P_1}$) will be convex linear combinations of vector points P_2 and P_3 (P_3 and P_1). Thus, we have three new sets of points corresponding to the three line segments $\overline{P_1P_2}$, $\overline{P_2P_3}$, and $\overline{P_3P_1}$.

Let us now select a point on $\overline{P_1P_2}$ and one on $\overline{P_2P_3}$. Then, the set of points obtained from the convex linear combination of these two points will be shown by the line segment joining them. Furthermore, the line segment is in the triangle $P_1P_2P_3$. After this process is repeated many times for the other points, we can see intuitively that all the points that are generated in this manner will give us the points in the triangle $P_1P_2P_3$. The set of points that make up this triangle is called the *convex hull* of the set $S = \{P_1, P_2, P_3\}$. Or, we may say, the convex hull K of the set $S = \{P_1,, P_2\,P_3\}$ is the set of points obtained as convex linear combinations of the points S. Clearly, $S = \{P_1, P_2, P_3\}$ is a subset of K.

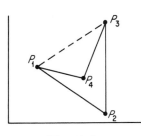

Fig. 12–9

The extreme points of a convex set S are the points which are not on a segment between any two points of S. The points P_1, P_2, and P_3 are the extreme points of the set S.

Now let us have a set $S = \{P_1, P_2, P_3, P_4\}$ such as in Figure 12–9. As can be seen, S is not a convex set. When we construct a convex hull K, K will be the triangle $P_1P_2P_3$ which is convex.

(iii) Convex cone

Consider a convex set $S = \{P_1, P_2, P_3\}$ where P_i are vector points. The *ray* through P is defined as the vector μP_1 that goes through P_1 from 0. As is seen, when $0 \leq \mu \leq 1$, the ray is a vector between 0 and P_1. When $\mu = 1$, the ray is the vector $\overrightarrow{0P_1}$, and when $\mu > 1$, then the ray extends beyond P_1.

Three rays can be drawn corresponding to the three points P_1, P_2, and P_3. Let P be an arbitrary point within the confines of the rays. Then we see that any point μP ($\mu \geq 0$) will also be within these confines. In a case where all points μp ($\mu \geq 0$) are in the set of points from which P was taken, the set is called a *cone*. When the set of points P_i are a convex set we have a *convex cone*. A convex linear combination of two points in the convex cone will also be in the cone.

If μ is allowed to become negative, then we may have as in Figure 12–11.

Fig. 12–10

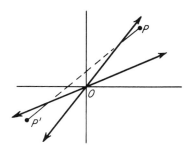

Fig. 12–11

This is also a cone in the sense that for every point P in the cone, the point μP will also be in the cone. But since μ may be negative, we can select a point P' such that the segment joining P and P' will not be in the cone. This cone is, therefore, not a convex set. But when we add the restriction $\mu \geq 0$, then it is only the part in the first quadrant that is being considered and as can be seen this will be a convex set.

A convex set generated from a finite number of points such as in Figure 12–10 is called a *convex polyhedron*. A convex cone generated by a convex polyhedron is called a *convex polyhedral cone*.

(iv) Half spaces

Let $\{P_1, P_2, P_3\}$ be a convex set. The line $\overline{P_1 P_2}$ in Figure 12–12 divides the plane into two parts. Let us call these *half spaces*. Let this line be shown by

$$a_{11}x_1 + a_{12}x_2 = w_1$$

Then,

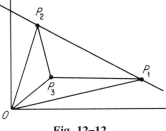

Fig. 12–12

$a_{11}x_1 + a_{12}x_2 > w_1$ ... northeast half space

$a_{11}x_1 + a_{12}x_2 < w_1$ ... southwest half space

Similarly the lines $\overline{P_2 P_3}$, $\overline{P_3 P_1}$ divide the plane into two parts. The triangle $P_1 P_2 P_3$ (convex set) is enclosed by these three lines. Or we can say that the convex set is the intersection of three half spaces generated by the three lines. This can be shown as

$$\overline{P_1 P_2} : a_{11}x_1 + a_{12}x_2 \leq w_1$$
$$\overline{P_2 P_3} : a_{21}x_1 + a_{22}x_2 \geq w_2$$
$$\overline{P_3 P_1} : a_{31}x_1 + a_{32}x_2 \geq w_3$$

and may be written

$$\begin{bmatrix} a_{11} & a_{12} \\ -a_{21} & -a_{22} \\ -a_{31} & -a_{32} \end{bmatrix} \begin{bmatrix} x_1 \\ x_2 \end{bmatrix} \leq \begin{bmatrix} w_1 \\ -w_2 \\ -w_3 \end{bmatrix}$$

or simply $AX \leq w$. We shall generalize this result as follows: Let there be five lines in the two-dimensional space as in Figure 12–13 forming a convex set C. Then this is shown as

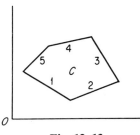

$$AX \leq w$$

where A is a 5×2 matrix of the coefficients, X is a 2×1 matrix, and w is a 5×1 matrix.

If we have n lines and thus $2n$-half spaces, then their intersection will also be a convex set which can be shown by $AX \leq w$ where A is an $n \times 2$ matrix, X is a 2×1 and w is an $n \times 1$ matrix.

Fig. 12–13

As can be seen, solving $AX \leq w$ will mean, geometrically, finding values of $X = [x_1, x_2]$ that give us points in C. Solving $AX = w$ will mean finding values of X at the intersection of the lines; i.e., the extreme points.

If we have a three-dimensional space then the dividing line becomes a dividing plane. For four-dimensional space it becomes a hyperplane. We can also express this in vector notation by letting $A = [v_1, v_2]$ where v_1 and v_2 are column vectors. Then,

$$AX = [v_1, v_2] \begin{bmatrix} x_1 \\ x_2 \end{bmatrix} = v_1 x_1 + v_2 x_2$$

Thus, the equation $AX \leq w$ becomes

$$v_1 x_1 + v_2 x_2 \leq w$$

(v) Simplex

When we have a two-dimensional space, $2 + 1 = 3$ extreme points give us a convex set that is a triangle. In three-dimensional space, $3 + 1 = 4$ extreme points give us a tetrahedron. Such convex sets are called *simplices*. The triangle is a two-simplex, the tetrahedron is a three-simplex. In n-dimensional space, $n + 1$ extreme points give us an n-simplex.

Fig. 12–14

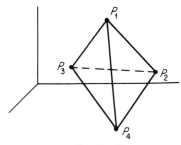

Fig. 12–15

(vi) The linear programming problem

Given a linear function

(1) $$f(y_1, y_2) = 2y_1 - 2y_2$$

subject to the linear constraints

(2)
$$4y_1 + y_2 \leqq 12$$
$$y_1 + y_2 \leqq 9$$
$$y_1 + 4y_2 \leqq 18$$

find a set of non-negative (y_1, y_2) such that (1) is maximized. This is a linear programming problem.

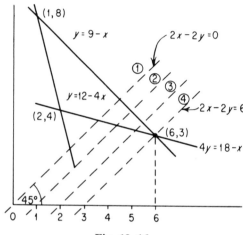

Fig. 12–16

Let us now interpret this problem in terms of convex sets. The linear constraints of (2) divide a two-dimensional plane into half spaces and generate a convex set as in Figure 12–16. Then, the points (y_1, y_2) that are to maximize (1) (the linear functional or objective function) must be points in this convex set.

The objective function (1) in our present example can be shown as a set of parallel lines. We wish to find the one that intersects the convex set that has a maximum value. In our present case, we can see that

$$f(y_1, y_2) = 2y_1 - 2y_2 = 0$$

is line one in the diagram that goes through the origin. $f(y_1, y_2) = 2, 4, 6$ are lines 2, 3, and 4. As is seen, when $f(y_1, y_2) = 6$, the line passes through (6, 3) and $f(y_1, y_2)$ reaches a maximum. For any value greater than 6 (i.e., $2y_1 - 2y_2 > 6$) the line will pass outside the convex set. Thus, the extreme point (6, 3) maximizes the linear functional (objective function). That is, the non-negative solution we seek is $(y_1, y_2) = (6, 3)$.

Let us now restate the linear programming problem schematically as shown below.

	$c_1 = 12$	$c_2 = -9$	$c_3 = -18$
	x_1	x_2	x_3
$b_1 = 2y_1$	$a_{11} = 4$	$a_{12} = -1$	$a_{13} = -1$
$b_2 = -2y_2$	$a_{21} = 1$	$a_{22} = -1$	$a_{23} = -4$

Maximize the linear function

$$f = b_1 y_1 + b_2 y_2 = 2y_1 - 2y_2$$

subject to the linear constraints,

$$a_{11} y_1 + a_{21} y_2 \leq c_1$$
$$a_{12} y_1 + a_{22} y_2 \leq c_2$$
$$a_{13} y_1 + a_{23} y_2 \leq c_3$$

which is

$$4y_1 + y_2 \leq 12$$
$$-y_1 - y_2 \leq -9$$
$$-y_1 - 4y_2 \leq -18$$

where the y_i are non-negative. The solution we have obtained was $(y_1, y_2) = (6, 3)$ and the maximum value of the linear function was

$$f = 2y_1 - 2y_2 = 12 - 6 = 6$$

To this maximum problem, we can find a minimum problem called the *dual of the maximum problem*. This is stated as follows.

Find a set of non-negative (x_1, x_2, x_3) that minimizes

$$g = c_1 x_1 + c_2 x_2 + c_3 x_3$$

subject to the linear constraints

$$a_{11} x_1 + a_{12} x_2 + a_{13} x_3 \geq b_1$$
$$a_{21} x_1 + a_{22} x_2 + a_{23} x_3 \geq b_2$$

In terms of our example, this is as follows: minimize

$$g = 12x_1 - 9x_2 - 18x_3$$

subject to the linear constraints

$$4x_1 - x_2 - x_3 \geq 2$$
$$x_1 - x_2 - 4x_3 \geq -2$$

It can be shown that the minimum g is 6; i.e., the same value as the maximum f found above.

We have only stated the problem of linear programming. For further study, see the references at the end of the chapter.

Notes and References

The topic concerning stability is very difficult and the mathematical references are usually of an advanced nature. But the following three steps are suggested:

(1) First, as a general background, see Bushaw and Clower (1957), pp. 51–62; Andronow and Chaikin (1949), pp. 6–10, 11–15, and 147–148; and Samuelson (1947), pp. 257–263. Our discussion of equilibrium and stability was based on A. M. Liapounov's definition of stability. The three references just mentioned also base their discussion on Liapounov's ideas.

(2) Then, as a second step, which will introduce the student to the technical aspects of the problem, see Bushaw and Clower (1957), pp. 284–313; Samuelson (1947), Chapter 9; Allen (1956), Sections 1.8, 10.5, 14.6; Metzler (1945); and the present chapter of this book plus the various references listed below which correspond with the topics in this chapter. This should provide a survey of the various techniques that have been used and their applications to economics.

(3) As a third step see the excellent discussion of these topics of stability in Gantmacher (1959) Vol. II, p. 120 and Chapter 15. He first gives a brief historical discussion of the development of the problem and then provides the various proofs and discussions that we have left out. He also has an excellent bibliography. Also see Bellman (1953); and Bellman (1960), Chapter 13. Finally, see Samuelson (1947), Chapter 9, 10 and 11.

The problem of stability in economics at a more general level than those treated in the above mentioned references can be found in issues of Econometrica 1954–1960. But as a first step, Chapter 9 of Karlin (1959), Vol. I is recommended. For examples of articles see Wald (1951); von Neumann (1945–56); Arrow and Debreu (1954); Kemeny, Morgenstern and Thompson (1956); Arrow and Hurwicz (1958); Arrow, Block, and Hurwicz (1959); Nikaido (1959); Arrow and Hurwicz (1960). Two other books that are recommended are Debreu (1959) and Koopmans (1957).

The first book that is recommended to students planning to study linear programming is Gale (1960), *The Theory of Linear Economic Models*, Chapters 1, 2, and 3. These three chapters will provide the necessary mathematical and theoretical background of linear programming. As a second step it is recommended that chapters from the following books be selected to suit one's need: Gale (1960); Gass (1958); Dorfman, Samuelson, and Solow (1958); and Karlin (1958), Vol. I, Part II. For advanced treatment of various aspects of linear and non-linear programming, see the following books:

(a) Kuhn and Tucker (1956). This is a collection of 18 papers by various authors of which several concern linear programming. The fourth paper by Goldman, A. J. and Tucker, A. W., "Theory of Linear Programming" is recommended.

(b) Dennis (1959), which contains discussions of linear programming techniques applied to Lagrange Multipliers. See especially Chapter 2 and the appendices at the end of the book.

(c) Koopmans (Ed.) (1951) contains papers related to the problems of production and allocation of resources.

(d) Arrow, Hurwicz, and Uzawa (1958).

12.2   Weisner (1938), pp. 88–90.

12.3   Aitken (1956), pp. 87–88; Chipman (1950), p. 101; MacDuffee (1949), p. 84; Metzler (1945), p. 289.

12.4   Aitken (1956), pp. 55–71; Ferrar (1941), pp. 30–35; Kemeny (1958), pp. 223–240; Murdoch (1957), pp. 48–53.

12.5   Chipman (1950), pp. 118–121 (gives a brief historical background and lists various sources of proofs); Samuelson (1941).

12.6   Baumol (1959), pp. 332–333.

12.7   Baumol (1959), pp. 327–331, and Chapter 16; Goldberg (1958), pp. 222–238.

12.8   Baumol (1959), pp. 356–365.

12.10 Bellman (1960), pp. 244–245 (has a bibliography at the end of Chapter 13 on stability theory); Baumol (1959), pp. 365–370; Samuelson (1947), pp. 429–435.

12.11 Baumol (1959), Chapters 14, 15 and 16.

12.12 Allen (1959), pp. 19–23, 325–329, 480–483; Hicks (1939), Mathematical Appendix.

12.13 Charnes, Cooper, and Henderson (1953), Part II; Kemeny (1958), Chapter 5; Gass (1958), Chapters 1–3; Gale (1960), Chapters 1–3.

STABILITY REFERENCES

Andronow, A. A. and Chaikin, C. E., *Theory of Oscillations*. Princeton, N. J.: Princeton University Press, 1949.

Arrow, K. J., Block, H. D. and Hurwicz, L., "On the Stability of the Competitive Equilibrium, II," *Econometrica*, pp. 82–109, 1959.

Arrow, K. J. and Debreu, G., "Existence of an Equilibrium for a Competitive Economy," *Econometrica*, pp. 265–290, 1954.

Arrow, K. J. and Hurwicz, L., "On the Stability of the Competitive Equilibrium, I," *Econometrica*, pp. 522–552, 1958.

Arrow, K. J. and Hurwicz, L., "Some Remarks on the Equilibrium of Economic Systems," *Econometrica*, pp. 640–646, 1960.

Bellman, R., *Stability Theory of Differential Equations*. New York: McGraw-Hill Book Co., Inc., 1953.

Bushaw, D. W. and Clower, R. W., *Introduction to Mathematical Economics*. Homewood, Ill.: Richard D. Irwin, Inc., 1957.

Chipman, J. S., *The Theory of Inter-Sectoral Money Flows and Income Formation*. Baltimore, Md.: John Hopkins Press, 1950.

Ferrar, W. L., *Finite Matrices*, New York: Oxford University Press, 1951.

Finkbeiner II, D. T., *Introduction to Matrices and Linear Transformations*. San Francisco: W. H. Freeman and Company, 1960.

Gantmacher, F. R., *The Theory of Matrices*, Vol. II. New York: Chelsea Publishing Company, 1959. Translated from the Russian by K. A. Hirsch.

Kemeny, J. G., Morgenstern, O. and Thompson, G. L., "A Generalization of the Von Neumann Model of an Expanding Economy," *Econometrica*, pp. 115–135, 1956.

Metzler, L. A., "Stability of Multiple Markets: The Hicks Conditions," *Econometrica*, pp. 277–292, 1945.

Nikaido, H., "Stability of Equilibrium by Brown-Von Neumann Differential Equation," *Econometrica*, pp. 654–671, 1959.

Samuelson, P. A., "Conditions that the Root of a Polynomial be less than Unity in Absolute Value," *Annals of Mathematical Statistics*, pp. 360–364, 1941.

Von Neumann, J., "A Model of General Economic Equilibrium," *Review of Economic Studies*," pp. 1–9, 1945–46. This is a translation of his German article.

Wald, A., "On Some Systems of Equations of Mathematical Economics," *Econometrica*, pp. 368–403, 1951. This is a translation of his German article.

LINEAR PROGRAMMING REFERENCES

Arrow, K. J., Hurwicz, L., and Uzawa, H., *Studies in Linear and Non-Linear Programming*. California: Stanford University Press, 1958.

Charnes, A., Cooper, W. W. and Henderson, A., *An Introduction to Linear Programming*. New York: John Wiley & Sons, Inc., 1953.

Dennis, J. B., *Mathematical Programming and Electrical Networks*. New York: John Wiley & Sons, Inc., 1959.

Dorfman, R., Samuelson, P. A. and Solow, R. M., *Linear Programming and Economic Analysis*. New York: McGraw-Hill Book Co., Inc., 1958.

Gale, D., *The Theory of Linear Economic Model*. New York: McGraw-Hill Book Co., Inc., 1960.

Gass, S. I., *Linear Programming*. New York: McGraw-Hill Book Co., Inc., 1958.

Koopmans, T. C., (Ed.), *Activity Analysis of Production and Allocation*. New York: John Wiley & Sons, Inc., 1951.

Kuhn, H. W. and Tucker, A. W., *Linear Inequalities and Related Systems*. New Jersey: Princeton University Press, 1956.

CHAPTER 13

Probability and Distributions

Three main topics, calculus, difference equations, and matrix algebra have been covered. In the next four chapters we will discuss probability and statistics confining ourselves to some basic ideas, and will approach the subject theoretically, although at an elementary level.

In this chapter we shall present some basic ideas of probability and distributions. Since much of this material is usually covered in statistics courses, detailed discussions have been omitted. This chapter is intended to serve as a review for the subsequent chapters and may be skipped by those familiar with the topics.

13.1 Sample space

Let us perform an *experiment* of tossing a die. The six possible outcomes are denoted by a capital X, and each individual outcome is denoted by a small x_i. Then we can write

$$R: \{x_1 = 1,\ x_2 = 2,\ x_3 = 3,\ x_4 = 4,\ x_5 = 5,\ x_6 = 6\}$$

This can be shown graphically as in Figure 13–1. The outcomes or results of the experiment are called *events*.

Fig. 13–1

As is seen, these events have been plotted on a straight line and shown by points. These points which represent the events are called *sample points*, and the six points on the line will be called the sample space which we denote by R.

What we have done is to take an experiment and translate it into terms of points and sets. Our intention is to use various operations concerning points and sets to analyze the experiment. But before going further, let us consider another experiment.

Consider tossing two dice. How can this experiment be translated into ideas of points and sets? There are 36 outcomes or, we can say, 36 events, which is shown two-dimensionally in Figure 13–2. Each of the 36 points is a *sample point*, and the aggregate of all 36 points is the *sample space R*.

But note that if we ask for the event
E that "the sum of two dice be 5,"
we have the points (1, 4), (2, 3), (3, 2),
and (4, 1). Then the event *E* is made
up of the following 4 events:

$$E: \{(1, 4), (2, 3), (3, 2) (4, 1)\}$$

Each of the 4 events that make up *E*
cannot be decomposed into smaller
events, whereas *E* can be decomposed
into these four indecomposable events
which are called *simple events*. Events
such as *E* that can be decomposed
are called *compound events*.

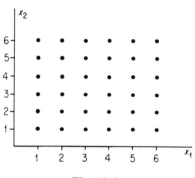

Fig. 13–2

When we say sample points, we mean *simple* events. Thus a sample space is made up of *simple* events.

13.2 A class of sets

The experiment of tossing a die generated a sample space *R* of six points. Let us now ask, "How many different subsets can be selected from this sample space?" This will be

$$\{1\}, \quad \{2\}, \quad \{3\}, \quad \{4\}, \quad \{5\}, \quad \{6\}$$

$$\{1, 2\}, \quad \{1, 3\}, \quad \{1, 4\} \ldots\ldots\ldots\ldots$$

$$\ldots\ldots\ldots\ldots\ldots \{1, 2, 3, 4, 5, 6\}$$

If we include 0 as a null subset, then the total number of subsets will be

$$\binom{6}{0} + \binom{6}{1} + \binom{6}{2} + \binom{6}{3} + \binom{6}{4} + \binom{6}{5} + \binom{6}{6} = (1 + 1)^6 = 2^6 = 64$$

Thus we have a collection of 64 subsets taken from *R*. Instead of saying a *collection* of subsets, we shall say we have a *class* of subsets, (some use the word *system*) and denote it by *G*.

It is possible to qualify these subsets by some characteristic. For example we can select subsets such that the sum of the numbers will be even. Or such that the sum of numbers will be odd. Or such that the sum of numbers will exceed 10. And so forth. We say we have different classes of subsets.

The characteristics of the 64 subsets we selected are:

(1) The union of any number of these subsets will produce a subset that is a member of this class of subsets.

(2) The intersection of any number of these subsets will produce a subset that is a member of this class of subsets.

(3) The difference of any two subsets is a member of this class of subsets.

(4) The complement of any subset is a member of this class of subsets.

Thus we have a *closed* system, and this class of subsets can be thought of as a *field* which is denoted by *F*.

Let us illustrate these operations by an example. Let

$$A = \{1, 2\}, \qquad B = \{3, 4\}, \qquad C = \{2, 3, 4\}$$

Then the union of *A* and *B* is

$$A \cup B = \{1, 2\} \cup \{3, 4\} = \{1, 2, 3, 4\}$$

which is clearly a subset of *R*. In terms of our experiment, we say that the *events A or B or both occur.*

The intersection of *A* and *B* will be

$$A \cap B = \{1, 2\} \cap \{3, 4\} = 0$$

which is also a subset of *R*. This can be interpreted to mean *events A and B both occur.* In our present case $A \cap B = \{\ \} = 0$ means the event $A \cap B$ is impossible. For this case we say events *A* and *B* are *mutually exclusive.* In set terminology we said that *A* and *B* are *disjoint sets.*

The difference and complement of subsets can also be illustrated in a similar manner.

Problems

1. Given a four sided die explain the following.
   (a) What is the sample space?
   (b) How many subsets can be generated from this sample space?
   (c) Write out the subsets.
   (d) Explain the four operations that can be performed on this class of subsets by use of an example.
2. Perform an experiment of tossing two coins.
   (a) Explain the sample space by use of a graph.
   (b) How many subsets can be generated from this sample space? Write out the subsets.
   (c) Explain the four operations that can be performed on this class of subsets.
3. Perform the experiment of tossing a coin three times.
   (a) Explain the sample space.
   (b) How many subsets can be generated?

13.3 Axioms

Let *R* be a sample space made up of sample points (simple events). Let *F* be the field that has been generated from *R*. The elements of *F* will be simple and compound events. Let the sample points in R be denoted by E_1, E_2, ... E_n. Then we state the following axioms:

(1) To each sample point E_i we associate a non-negative real number and call it the probability of the event E_i. This will be denoted by $P(E_i) \geq 0$.

(2) $P(R) = 1$

(3) If two events A and B of the field F have no elements (sample points) in common, then,

$$P(A \cup B) = P(A) + P(B)$$

From this we see immediately that since

$$R = E_1 \cup E_2 \cup ... \cup E_n$$

we get

$$P(E_1) + P(E_2) + ... + P(E_n) = 1$$

$A \cup B$ is also written $A + B$ when $AB = 0$.

Let us summarize what we have done so far. First an experiment was conducted. Second, this was translated into a mathematical model of points and sets. Third, non-negative real numbers called probabilities were assigned to the sample points and axioms which give us the basic rules of calculations were stated.

Let us illustrate. When a die is tossed, we have a sample space of six sample points which we denote by E_1, E_2, ... E_6. Let us assign non-negative numbers $\frac{1}{6}$ to each of these points. This is written

$$P(E_i) = \tfrac{1}{6}$$

Then,

$$P(R) = P(E_1) + P(E_2) + ... + P(E_6) = \tfrac{1}{6} + ... + \tfrac{1}{6} = 1$$

Next let A be the event that 1 or 2 or both occur. Then,

$$A = E_1 \cup E_2$$

But since 1 and 2 cannot both occur at the same time $E_1 E_2 = 0$. Thus,

$$A = E_1 + E_2$$

i.e., either 1 or 2 occurs. Let B be the event that either E_3 or E_4 occurs. Then, we have

$$P(A) = P(E_1) + P(E_2) = \tfrac{1}{6} + \tfrac{1}{6} = \tfrac{2}{6}$$

$$P(B) = P(E_3) + P(E_4) = \tfrac{2}{6}$$

The probability that either A or B occurring is

$$P(A \cup B) = P(A) + P(B) = \tfrac{2}{6} + \tfrac{2}{6} = \tfrac{4}{6}$$

In common sense terminology, we are saying that when a die is tossed the probability of a 1, 2, 3 or 4 occurring is $\frac{4}{6}$.

Problems

1. Let $A + \bar{A} = R$. Then prove that
$$P(\bar{A}) = 1 - P(A)$$

2. Note that $\bar{R} = 0$. Then prove that
$$P(0) = 0$$

3. If A and B are not disjoint, prove that
$$P(A \cup B) = P(A) + P(B) - P(AB)$$

13.4 Random variable (Part I)

When a die was tossed, the six outcomes were denoted by the variable capital X and the individual outcomes were denoted by the small x_i's. This capital X is called a *random variable*.

Let us toss the die twice. Then we have 36 sample points. The random variable X expresses these 36 outcomes. Each individual outcome is shown by x_i, and can be interpreted as a vector point which is of order two. For example, the outcome (3, 5) is a vector point in the two-dimensional sample space. Thus, the random variable (which will be abbreviated by r.v.) indicates the coordinates of the sample point in the two-dimensional sample space. It may thus be called a two dimensional r.v.

If we toss the die three times, we get a three-dimensional sample space and $6^3 = 216$ sample points. The r.v. X is a three-dimensional r.v. that expresses these 216 points. The individual points are shown by x_i, ($i = 1$, 2, ... 216) where the x_i can be considered as a vector point of order 3.

If we have 100 students and conduct the experiment of finding whether or not they smoke, we have two possible outcomes: $x_1 =$ smokers, $x_2 =$ non-smokers. The r.v. X is one-dimensional and expresses these two possible outcomes.

When a die was tossed, we assumed in our previous illustration that the event A was the occurrence of either 1 or 2. This can be shown in set notation, using the r.v. X, as
$$X \subset A$$

Thus the probability of event A which we wrote as $P(A)$ can be shown as
$$P(A) = P(X \subset A)$$

The probability that either A or B occurs will be shown as
$$P(A \cup B) = P(X \subset A \cup B)$$

We shall discuss other aspects of the r.v. X in Section 13.10.

13.5 Conditional probability

(i) Conditional probability

As the reader may have noticed, we have defined operations of addition concerning probabilities but have said nothing about multiplication. Let us now take this up. For this we first define conditional probability, and then, using that, define the operation of multiplication of probabilities.

Consider a situation as given by Table 13–1 between smokers, non-smokers, males, and females. Let X_1 be the r.v. that indicates smokers and non-smokers, X_2 be the r.v. that indicates male and female. Then the sample

Table 13–1

	Male	Female	
Smokers	40	20	60
Non-smokers	10	30	40
	50	50	100

space can be shown as in Figure 13–3.

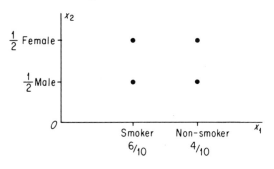

Fig. 13–3

Let us consider the following situations:

A: the event of selecting a smoker
B: the event of selecting a male

(i) $P(A) = P(\text{smoker}) = 60/100$

(ii) $P(B) = P(\text{male})\ \ \ = 50/100$

(iii) $P(AB)$

This is the probability of selecting a smoker who is a male. We know there are 40 male smokers. Thus,

$$P(AB) = 40/100$$

(iv) $P(B \mid A) = P(\text{male} \mid \text{smoker})$

What is the probability of selecting a male, given that a smoker is selected first? Since a smoker is selected first, we have confined our population to the *subpopulation* of smokers, and from this subpopulation, we wish to find the probability of selecting a male. We know that there are 60 smokers, and of them, 40 are males. Thus,

$$P(B \mid A) = \tfrac{40}{60} = \frac{\tfrac{40}{100}}{\tfrac{60}{100}} = \frac{P(AB)}{P(A)}$$

Using this line of reasoning, let us now formally define as follows: The *conditional probability* of B, given the hypothesis A is

(1)
$$P(B \mid A) = \frac{P(AB)}{P(A)}$$

where $P(A) > 0$.

From the definition of conditional probability, we obtain

(2)
$$P(AB) = P(A) \cdot P(B \mid A)$$

That is, the probability of A and B both occurring is equal to the product of the probability of A occurring and the probability of B occurring, given A has occurred. Note also that

(3)
$$P(AB) = P(B) \cdot P(A \mid B)$$

Formulas (2) and (3) are the first rules of *multiplication* of probabilities we obtain.

Problem

Show that
$$P(ABC) = P(A) \cdot P(B \mid A) \cdot P(C \mid AB)$$

(ii) Statistical independence

Consider an experiment of tossing a coin and a die. Let X_1 and X_2 be the r.v.'s associated to the coin and die respectively. The sample space has $2 \times 6 = 12$ sample points and is shown in Figure 13–4.

Let us now consider the following:

A: the event of getting a head
B: the event of getting an even number

$$P(A) = P(X_1 = H) = \tfrac{1}{2}$$
$$P(B) = P(X_2 = 2, 4, \text{ or } 6) = \tfrac{3}{6}$$
$$P(AB) = P(X_1 = H \text{ and } X_2 = 2, 4, \text{ or } 6)$$
$$= P((H, 2), (H, 4) \text{ or } (H, 6)) = \tfrac{3}{12}$$
$$P(B \mid A) = P(\text{even number} \mid \text{head}) = ?$$

We know intuitively that the toss of a coin will have no affect on the toss of a die. Thus the probability of getting an even number, given that we got a head, will be the same as simply the probability of getting an even number. That is,

$$P(B \mid A) = P(B) = \tfrac{3}{6}$$

This is consistent with the conditional probability definition

$$P(B \mid A) = \frac{P(AB)}{P(A)} = \tfrac{3}{12} \times \tfrac{2}{1} = \tfrac{3}{6}$$

When information of the outcome of A does not influence the probability associated to B, we say A and B are *statistically independent*. As we see, since $P(B \mid A) = P(B)$, the conditional probability formula gives us

(4) $$P(AB) = P(A) \, P(B)$$

Using this we shall define that: When there are two events A and B, and the above formula (4) holds, A and B are said to be statistically independent. We have thus obtained a second multiplication rule.

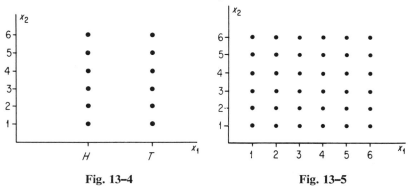

Fig. 13–4   Fig. 13–5

(iii) Independent trials

Let us illustrate how the idea of statistical independence and the multiplication rule can be used. In the process we shall define the idea of independent trials. The sample space when a die is tossed twice is shown in Figure 13–5. What probabilities should we assign to each of these 36 sample points? First note that the first and second toss are independent. Thus, according to the multiplication rule, we get

$$P(X_{1i} \cdot X_{2j}) = p_i \cdot p_j = \tfrac{1}{6} \times \tfrac{1}{6} = \tfrac{1}{36}, \qquad i, j = 1, 2, \ldots, 6$$

where X_{1i} indicates the outcome of the first toss and X_{2j} that of the second. For example, $X_{11} = x_1 = 1$ means a 1 occurs. $X_{23} = x_3 = 3$ means a 3 occurs. Thus $P(X_{11}, X_{23})$ is the probability of a 1 and 3 occurring on the first and second toss.

We have assigned probabilities of $p_i p_j = \frac{1}{36}$, but for this to be legitimate probabilities, we need $P(R) = 1$, where R is the 36 sample points. Let us check this.

$$P(R) = P(E_1) + P(E_2) + \ldots + P(E_{36})$$
$$= p_1 p_1 + p_1 p_2 + \ldots + p_1 p_6$$
$$\quad + p_2 p_1 + p_2 p_2 + \ldots + p_2 p_6$$
$$\ldots$$
$$\quad + p_6 p_1 + p_6 p_2 + \ldots + p_6 p_6$$
$$= p_1(p_1 + p_2 + \ldots + p_6)$$
$$\quad + p_2(p_1 + p_2 + \ldots + p_6)$$
$$\ldots$$
$$\quad + p_6(p_1 + p_2 + \ldots + p_6)$$
$$= (p_1 + p_2 + \ldots + p_6)(p_1 + p_2 + \ldots + p_6) = 1 \times 1 = 1$$

Fig. 13–6

Thus, we have found a way to assign probabilities to sample points when we have a sample space generated by combinations of experiments that are independent of each other. When the experiments (such as tossing a die twice, or tossing a coin three times) are successive experiments independent of each other, and when probabilities can be assigned to the sample points that have been generated by these experiments according to the second multiplication rule, they are called *independent trials*.

Random sampling is an illustration of *repeated independent trials*. Assume 10 students. Select a sample of size $n = 2$ with replacement. Then, the first selection is the first trial, and the second selection the second trial. There are $10^2 = 100$, possible outcomes. This is shown in Figure 13–6. Each sample point is a sample of size 2 and to each point we assign a probability according to the second multiplication rule, and that will be

$$P(X_1, X_2) = P(X_1) \times P(X_2) = \frac{1}{10} \times \frac{1}{10} = \frac{1}{100}$$

Note that we are sampling with replacement and that the sample space considers the order by which the student has been selected. That is, point (2, 3) and point (3, 2) are different in the sample space, but both are samples made up of the second and third student.

Problems

Given the following data, answer the following:

	soap K	soap L	soap M	Total
Male	10	20	30	60
Female	30	10	20	60
	40	30	50	120

A = the event of selecting a male.
B = the event of selecting a user of soap K
C = the event of selecting a female.
D = the event of selecting a user of soap M.

1. Find $P(A)$, $P(B)$, $P(AB)$

2. Find $P(C)$, $P(D)$, $P(CD)$

3. Find $P(A \mid B)$, $P(B \mid A)$. Explain the meaning of these probabilities.

13.6 Distribution function

So far probabilities have been discussed in terms of a sample space, that is, in terms of set theory. But, as we know, for ordinary calculations calculus is used, which is based on point functions. What we wish to do now is to establish a relationship between the set theory we have been using and calculus so that probabilities can be calculated with calculus. Let us develop our discussion using an illustration.

(i) Probability function

Consider again the experiment of tossing a die which generates a sample space

R:	$\{x_1 = 1,$	$x_2 = 2,$	$x_3 = 3,$	$x_4 = 4,$	$x_5 = 5,$	$x_6 = 6\}$
Fair die	1/6	1/6	1/6	1/6	1/6	1/6
Loaded die	2/6	0	2/6	0	2/6	0

with 6 sample points. We associate the probabilities $P(X = x_i)(i = 1, 2, ... 6)$ to the r.v. X. If the die is fair, $P(X = x_i) = 1/6$ for all i. If the die is loaded so that only odd numbers appear with equal probabilities, then

$$P(X = x_i) = \tfrac{2}{6} \qquad i = 1, 3, 5$$
$$= 0 \qquad i = 2, 4, 6$$

Depending on how the die is loaded, various probabilities are assigned to the sample points. We shall call these assignments of probabilities to the sample points, the *distribution of probabilities* over the sample space. Once we find the distribution of probabilities associated to a sample space, that is, associated to a r.v. X, a great deal of information has been obtained about X and thus about the experiment. Finding the distribution of probabilities is, therefore, one of the main objects.

When the die is tossed twice, we have a distribution of probabilities over a two-dimensional sample space. In general, when it is tossed n-times, we have a distribution of probabilities over an n-dimensional sample space.

Next, let A be the event that a 1, 2, or 3 occurs. Then, this is expressed as, assuming a fair die,

$$P(X \subset A) = P(X \leq x_3)$$

$$= P(X = x_1) + P(X = x_2) + P(X = x_3) = \tfrac{3}{6}$$

$P(X \subset A)$ or $P(X \leq x_3)$ is called a *probability function* and it is a set function that assigns probabilities to sets of sample points. (In our present case X is a one-dimensional random variable.) The various operations we have established were based on the properties of set theory. Let us now see how we can define a point function that will correspond to the probability function.

(*ii*) *Distribution function*

Let us *define* a point function as

$$F(x:k) = \begin{cases} P(k < X \leq x) & \text{for} \quad x > k \\ 0 & \text{for} \quad x = k \\ -P(x < X \leq k) & \text{for} \quad x < k \end{cases}$$

This means diagrammatically, if we have x to the right of the constant k, then,

$$F(x:k) = P(k < X \leq x)$$

Thus, F is a function of x and as x moves along the R_1, the value of F will be equal to the set function $P(k < X \leq x)$ where the argument of this set function is the set given by $k < X \leq x$ which changes as x moves along R_1. When x coincides with k, then $F = 0$, and when x goes to the left of k, then F is defined to take the value given by the set function $P(x < X \leq k)$ with a negative sign. This set function, it will be recalled, was non-negative.

Therefore, if we have an interval (a, b) as in the diagram, then,

$$F(b:k) = P(k < X \leq b)$$

$$F(a:k) = -P(a < X \leq k)$$

$$F(k:k) = 0$$

Thus,

$$F(b:k) - F(a:k) = P(k < X \leq b) + P(a < X \leq k)$$
$$= P(a < X \leq b)$$

What about the case when both points a and b are to the right of k?

We have

```
———————————————————
   k       a       b
```

$$F(b:k) = P(k < X \leq b)$$
$$F(a:k) = P(k < X \leq a)$$
$$F(b:k) - F(a:k) = P(k < X \leq b) - P(k < X \leq a)$$
$$= P(a < X \leq b)$$

and similarly for the case where both points a and b are to the left of k.

Thus, in general, no matter where we have k, we have

$$F(b:k) - F(a:k) = P(a < X \leq b)$$

Since it does not matter where we have k, we can omit it from F and write simply

$$F(b) - F(a) = P(a < X \leq b)$$

Thus, the set function $P(a < X \leq b)$ has been represented by the point function $F(x)$ and we have obtained our desired result. We can thus use the point function for further investigations and apply the conventional methods of calculus we already know.

Let us now formally introduce the following conditions.

$$F(x) = P(-\infty < X \leq x) = P(X \leq x)$$
$$0 \leq F(x) \leq 1$$
$$F(-\infty) = 0, \qquad F(+\infty) = 1$$

This $F(x)$ will be called a *distribution function*.

Example. Consider the following distribution of wages. Figure 13–7 is a histogram.

Wages	Frequency	Cumulative
$40	1	1
50	2	3
60	3	6
70	4	10
80	6	16
90	3	19
100	2	21
110	1	22
	——	
	22	

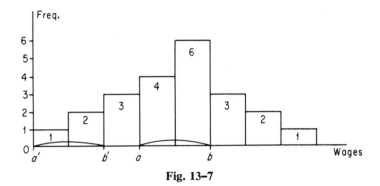

Fig. 13-7

As the histogram shows, between a' and b' we have three wage earners, whereas between a and b we have ten wage earners. If each wage earner is considered as a point on the horizontal axis, since the intervals (a', b') and (a, b) are equal, the density of the points in (a, b) will be greater than that of (a', b'). How are we going to measure this density? When probabilities are used to measure the density, this can be shown by the set functions as

$$P(a < X \le b) \quad \text{and} \quad P(a' < X \le b')$$

where the r.v. X indicates wages. We can see heuristically that $P(a < X \le b)$ will be larger (since it contains more points) than $P(a' < X \le b')$.

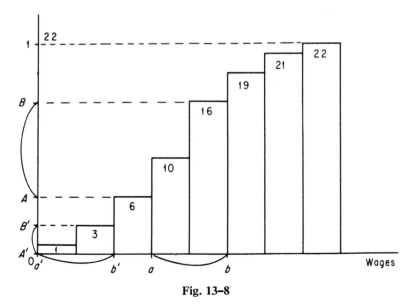

Fig. 13-8

Let us now change this set function into a point function, that is, find the distribution function $F(x)$. For this first draw a histogram as in Figure 13-8, and show the cumulative frequencies on the vertical axis. Then change the scale of this vertical axis to relative terms. Since the total number of wage earners is 22, if we divide by 22, the scale will be in relative terms from 0 to 1. The intervals (a', b') and (a, b) on the horizontal axis have been translated to (A', B') and (A, B) on the vertical axis. Let this relation be shown by

$$P(a' < X \leq b') = F(b') - F(a') = B' - A' = \tfrac{3}{22} - 0 = \tfrac{3}{22}$$

$$P(a < X \leq b) = F(b) - F(a) = B - A = \tfrac{16}{22} - \tfrac{6}{22} = \tfrac{10}{22}$$

This $\tfrac{3}{22}$ and $\tfrac{10}{22}$ shows the densities of the two intervals (a', b') and (a, b). Also note that

$$F(x = 22) = 1, \qquad F(x = 0) = 0$$

or

$$F(x = 22) - F(x = 0) = 1 - 0 = 1$$

shows the whole horizontal axis, i.e. $P(R)$ where R is the whole sample space of 22 points.

(iii) *Probability density*

The distribution function $F(x)$ showed the probability of a set from $-\infty$ to x. It is cumulative. That is,

$$F(x) = P(-\infty < X \leq x)$$

Let us now consider the probability within a small interval $(x, x + \Delta x)$. Then,

$$P(x < X \leq x + \Delta x) = F(x + \Delta x) - F(x)$$

If we let $\Delta x \to 0$, then this will approach the probability at the point x. This leads to

$$\lim_{\Delta x \to 0} \frac{F(x + \Delta x) - F(x)}{\Delta x} \Delta x = F'(x)\Delta x$$

where $F'(x)$ is the derivative of $F(x)$. Let us denote this by $F'(x) = f(x)$. We are assuming the derivative exists. Then this $f(x)$ will express the density at the point x. Hence, for a small interval Δx, the probability can be expressed as $f(x)\Delta x$. Thus, let us write

$$P(x < X \leq x + \Delta x) = f(x)\Delta x$$

This $f(x)$ is called the *probability density* or *density function* when the data is continuous, and is called the *frequency function* when the data is discrete. $f(x)\Delta x$ will be called the *probability element*.

Example. The density function for a normal distribution is

$$f(x) = \frac{1}{\sqrt{2\pi}\sigma} e^{-(x-\mu)^2/2\sigma^2}$$

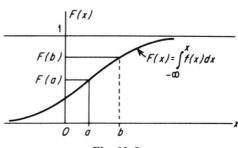

Fig. 13–9

Then,

$$F(x) = \int_{-\infty}^{x} \frac{1}{\sqrt{2\pi}\sigma} e^{-(x-\mu)^2/2\sigma^2} \, dx$$

This is shown in Figure 13–9. As we know from elementary statistics, the r.v. X ranges from $(-\infty, +\infty)$. Let us take an interval (a, b) as in the diagram. Then,

$$P(a < X \le b) = F(b) - F(a) = \int_{a}^{b} f(x) \, dx$$

$$P(-\infty < X \le a) = F(a) - F(-\infty) = F(a) = \int_{-\infty}^{a} f(x) \, dx$$

$$P(b \le X < \infty) = F(\infty) - F(b)$$

$$= 1 - \int_{-\infty}^{b} f(x) \, dx = \int_{b}^{\infty} f(x) \, dx$$

13.7 Expectation, variance

(i) *Expectation*

The expected value of a r.v. X which has a probability density $f(x)$ (continuous case) or p_i (discrete case) is defined as

$$E(X) = \sum x_i p_i \quad \text{(discrete case)}$$

$$E(X) = \int_{-\infty}^{\infty} x f(x) \, dx \quad \text{(continuous case)}$$

As can be seen, $E(X)$ can be interpreted as the weighted mean.

Example. Let X be the number that appears when a die is tossed. Then,

$$E(X) = \sum x_i p_i = (1)(\tfrac{1}{6}) + (2)(\tfrac{1}{6}) + \dots + (6)(\tfrac{1}{6}) = \tfrac{21}{6}$$

(ii) *Properties of $E(X)$*

Two properties of $E(X)$ are listed.

(a)
$$E(aX) = \sum a x_i f(x_i) = a \sum x_i f(x_i) = aE(X)$$

$$\therefore \quad E(aX) = aE(X)$$

where a is a constant.

(b)
$$E(X_1 + X_2) = \sum_i \sum_j (x_i + x_j) f(x_i, x_j)$$
$$= \sum \sum x_i f(x_i, x_j) + \sum \sum x_j f(x_i, x_j)$$
$$= E(X_1) + E(X_2)$$
$$\therefore \quad E(X_1 + X_2) = E(X_1) + E(X_2)$$

In general,

$$E(X_1 + X_2 + \ldots + X_n) = E(X_1) + E(X_2) + \ldots + E(X_n)$$

(*iii*) *The variance*

Moments. For the discrete case, the rth moment about the origin is defined as

$$E(X^r) = \sum x_i^r f(x_i)$$

i.e., it is the expectation of the r.v. X^r. The rth moment about a constant a is

$$E(X - a)^r = \sum (x_i - a)^r f(x_i)$$

For the continuous case it is

$$E(X^r) = \int_{-\infty}^{\infty} x^r f(x)\, dx$$

$$E(X - a)^r = \int_{-\infty}^{\infty} (x - a)^r f(x)\, dx$$

Variance. The first moment about the origin as can be easily seen is the mean

$$\mu = E(X) = \sum x_i f(x_i)$$

The second moment about the mean,

$$E[(X - \mu)^2] = \sum (x_i - \mu)^2 f(x_i)$$

is called the *variance.* For the continuous case we have

$$E[(X - \mu)^2] = \int_{-\infty}^{\infty} (x - \mu)^2 f(x)\, dx$$

The variance is usually denoted by σ^2. We shall write

$$\text{Var}(X) = E[(X - \mu)^2] = \sigma^2$$

The positive square root of the Var (X), i.e., σ is called the standard deviation of X.

The variance σ^2 or the σ is a measure of dispersion of the distribution. This measure of dispersion was taken around the mean. It could have been taken around any other constant. But, it turns out, it is at a minimum when taken around the mean, i.e.,

$$E[(X - a)^2] = E[(X - \mu + \mu - a)^2] = E(X - \mu)^2 + E(\mu - a)^2$$
$$= \sigma^2 + (\mu - a)^2$$

Thus it is at a minimum when $\mu = a$

(iv) *Some useful properties*

(a)
$$\text{Var}(X + a) = E[(X + a - E(X + a))^2]$$
$$= E[(X + a - E(X) - E(a))^2]$$
$$= E[(X + a - \mu - a)^2]$$
$$= E[(X - \mu)^2] = \text{Var}(X)$$

$$\therefore \quad \text{Var}(X + a) = \text{Var}(X)$$

(b)
$$\text{Var}(bX) = E[(bX - E(bX))^2]$$
$$= E[(bX - b\mu)^2]$$
$$= b^2 E(X - \mu)^2$$
$$= b^2 \text{Var}(X)$$

(c) $\quad \text{Var}(X_1 + X_2) = E[\{(X_1 + X_2) - E(X_1 + X_2)\}^2]$
$$= E[(X_1 - \mu_1) + (X_2 - \mu_2)]^2$$
$$= E[(X_1 - \mu_1)^2 + (X_2 - \mu_2)^2 + 2(X_1 - \mu_1)(X_2 - \mu_2)]$$
$$= \sigma_1^2 + \sigma_2^2 + 2E(X_1 - \mu_1)(X_2 - \mu_2)$$

If X_1 and X_2 are independent, then,

$$E(X_1 - \mu_1)(X_2 - \mu_2) = E(X_1 - \mu_1)E(X_2 - \mu_2) = 0$$

Thus,

$$\text{Var}(X_1 + X_2) = \sigma_1^2 + \sigma_2^2$$

In general if $X_1, X_2, \ldots X_n$ are independent,

$$\text{Var}(X_1 + X_2 + \ldots + X_n) = \sigma_1^2 + \sigma_2^2 + \ldots + \sigma_n^2$$

Example. Let $X_1, X_2, \ldots X_n$ be a sequence of random variables having the same distribution. Thus, they all have mean μ and variance σ^2. We can consider this as a sample of size n. Let

$$\bar{X} = \frac{1}{n}(X_1 + X_2 + \ldots + X_n)$$

A combination of random variables is also a random variable. Thus, $\bar{X}$ is a random variable. We do not know its distribution but let it be, say, $g(\bar{x})$. Then the mean and variance of $\bar{X}$ will be

$$E(\bar{X}) = \frac{1}{n} E(X_1 + X_2 + ... + X_n)$$

$$= \frac{1}{n} (\mu + \mu + ... + \mu) = \mu$$

$$\text{Var} (\bar{X}) = \frac{1}{n^2} (\sigma^2 + \sigma^2 + ... + \sigma^2)$$

$$= \frac{\sigma^2}{n}$$

We shall see in section 13.9 that, due to the *central limit theorem*, $\bar{X}$ will have a normal distribution. We have just seen that the mean and variance will be μ and σ^2/n.

Problems

1. Show $\text{Var}(aX + b) = a^2 \text{Var}(X)$.

2. Show $E(X - \mu) = 0$.

3. Let $E(X - \mu)^2 = \sigma^2$. Then $X^* = \dfrac{X - \mu}{\sigma}$, where X^* is called a normalized (or standardized) variable. Show that $E(X^*) = 0$ and $\text{Var}(X^*) = 1$.

4. Show $E[(X - \mu)^2] = E(X^2) - \mu^2$.

5. Show $E[(X - a)^2] = \sigma^2 + (\mu - a)^2$.

13.8 Distributions

Two distributions are mentioned, mainly for reference.

(i) Binomial probability distribution

Consider an experiment of tossing a coin. The characteristics of this experiment are as follows:

(1) Each experiment (toss) has only two possible outcomes; i.e., either head or tail.
(2) The probability of heads (p) and that of tails ($q = 1 - p$) is the same at each trial. That is, it does not change.

We will call such repeated independent trials, *Bernoulli trials*.

When a die is tossed, it has 6 possible outcomes so it is not a Bernoulli trial. But if the outcome of the experiment is defined to be either an odd or even number, then we have a Bernoulli trial.

When a coin is tossed once, we get either heads (success) or tails (failure), and the outcome can be shown as in Figure 13–10. When it is tossed twice, the outcomes are

Fig. 13–10

$$SS, SF, FS, FF$$

There are $2^2 = 4$ points in two-dimensional space (Figure 13–11). When the coin is tossed n times, it will generate an n-dimensional sample space and have 2^n points or possible outcomes.

Fig. 13–11

Each point in a, say, three-dimensional sample space, is a succession of S's and F's,

$$SSS, SFS, SFF, \ldots , FFF$$

There are $2^3 = 8$ different such points. We can define a r.v. k that will be the number of successes. Let us consider $k = 2$. Then we have

$$(SSF), (SFS), (FSS)$$

That is, 2 successes in three tosses will occur in $\binom{3}{2} = 3$ different ways.

The probability associated to each point is, from our assumptions of the Bernoulli trials, for 2 successes and 1 failure,

$$p^2q^1$$

Since there are $\binom{3}{2} = 3$ such points we have

$$P(X = k = 2) = \binom{n}{k} p^k q^{n-k} = \binom{3}{2} p^2 q^1$$

Another way of expressing it is

$$b(k : n, p) = \binom{n}{k} p^n q^{n-k}$$

which shows n and p explicitly on the left side of the formula. This is called the *binomial distribution*.

(*ii*) *The normal distribution*

The normal density function is shown in Figure 13–12 and defined as

$$n(x) = \frac{1}{\sqrt{2\pi}\sigma} e^{-(x-\mu)^2/2\sigma^2} \qquad -\infty < x < \infty$$

where

$$E(X) = \mu, \qquad \text{Var}\,(X) = \sigma^2$$

Fig. 13–12

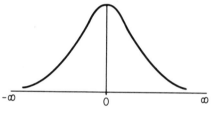

Fig. 13–13

If we use a normalized variable,

$$X^* = \frac{X - \mu}{\sigma}$$

then since $E(X^*) = 0$, $\text{Var}\,(X^*) = 1$ we have (Figure 13–13)

$$n(x^*) = \frac{1}{\sqrt{2\pi}} e^{-(x^*)^2/2}$$

The normal distribution function will be

$$F(x^*) = \int n(x^*)\,dx^* = \frac{1}{\sqrt{2\pi}} \int_{-\infty}^{t} e^{-t^2/2}\,dt$$

The normal distribution is usually indicated symbolically as $N(x; \mu, \sigma^2)$. We shall use this notation. When we have "normalized" or standardized the distribution, we write, $N(x; 0, 1)$. This may be abbreviated $N(0, 1)$.

The normal distribution function must satisfy the condition that

$$N(x) = \int_{-\infty}^{\infty} \frac{1}{\sqrt{2\pi}} e^{-t^2/2}\,dt = 1$$

This can be easily proven. (See Notes and References)

13.9 The central limit theorem

In elementary statistics we learn that when a random sample of size n is taken, the sample mean $\bar{X}$ will have a normal distribution with $E(\bar{X}) = \mu$ (the population mean) and Var $(\bar{X}) = \sigma^2/n$ (σ^2 is the population variance). Although it is not mentioned by name, this is one of the various forms of the central limit theorem. What we wish to do is to sketch the proof of this theorem. For this we need several preliminaries. First we shall define a moment generating function of the random variable X. Second, we shall find the moment generating function of a normally distributed random variable. Third, we shall find the moment generating function of $\bar{X}$. It turns out that the moment generating function of $\bar{X}$ has the same form as that of a random variable that has a normal distribution. Thus, we shall conclude that $\bar{X}$ has a normal distribution.

(i) Moment generating functions

Consider a function e^t where t is a continuous variable. Let X be the random variable under consideration. Raise e^t to the power X; i.e., e^{tX}. Then, the expected value of e^{tX} which will be a function of t is called the *moment generating function* of the variable X

$$M_X(t) = E(e^{tX}) = \int_{-\infty}^{\infty} e^{tx} f(x) \, dx$$

Using the results of Chapter 7, we can expand the exponential as

$$M_X(t) = E\left[1 + Xt + \frac{1}{2!}(Xt)^2 + \frac{1}{3!}(Xt)^3 + \cdots\right]$$

$$= 1 + E(X)t + \frac{1}{2!}E(X^2)t^2 + \frac{1}{3!}E(X^3)t^3 + \cdots$$

$$= 1 + \mu_1' t + \frac{1}{2!}\mu_2' t^2 + \frac{1}{3!}\mu_3' t^3 + \cdots$$

where μ_i' is the ith moment of X around the origin. Let us differentiate $M_X(t)$ with respect to t. Then,

$$\frac{d}{dt}M_X(t) = \mu_1' + \frac{2}{2!}\mu_2' t + \frac{3}{3!}\mu_3' t^2 + \cdots$$

Thus, when we set $t = 0$

$$\frac{d}{dt}M_X(0) = \mu_1'$$

As can be seen, when differentiated k-times,

$$\frac{d^k}{dt^k} M_X(0) = \mu_k'$$

(ii) *Two properties of the moment generating function*

Let X be a random variable with a distribution of $f(x)$. The moment generating function of cX where c is a constant is

$$M_{cX}(t) = E(e^{cXt}) = E(e^{Xct}) = M_X(ct)$$

This is the first property.

Next let $Y = X + c$ where c is a constant. Then,

$$M_{X+c}(t) = E(e^{(X+c)t})$$
$$= E(e^{Xt}e^{ct})$$
$$= e^{ct} M_X(t)$$

This is the second property.

(iii) *The moment generating function of a random variable X having a normal distribution*

Let the random variable X have a normal distribution with mean μ and standard deviation σ. Then,

$$f(x) = \frac{1}{\sqrt{2\pi}\sigma} e^{-(x-\mu)^2/2\sigma^2}$$

We wish to find the moment generating function of X, but to find it directly involves tedious computations. So let us first set

$$Y = \frac{X - \mu}{\sigma}$$

and find the moment generating function of Y which is normal with $E(Y) = 0$, Var $(Y) = 1$. We find

$$M_Y(t) = E(e^{Yt})$$

$$= \int_{-\infty}^{\infty} e^{yt} f(y)\, dy = \int_{-\infty}^{\infty} e^{yt} \left(\frac{1}{\sqrt{2\pi}} e^{-y^2/2} \right) dy$$

$$= e^{t^2/2} \frac{1}{\sqrt{2\pi}} \int_{-\infty}^{\infty} e^{-\frac{1}{2}(y-t)^2}\, d\,(y - t)$$

$$= e^{t^2/2}$$

Now let

$$X = \sigma Y + \mu$$

Then, using the two properties of the moment generating function of (ii), we find

$$M_X(t) = M_{\sigma Y + \mu}(t) = E(e^{(\sigma Y + \mu)t})$$

$$= e^{\mu t} M_{\sigma Y}(t)$$

$$= e^{\mu t} \cdot M_Y(\sigma t)$$

$$= e^{\mu t} \cdot e^{\sigma^2 t^2 / 2}$$

$$= e^{\mu t + \frac{1}{2}\sigma^2 t^2}$$

(iv) The moment generating function of $\overline{X}$

What we want to show is that the moment generating function of $\overline{X}$ is equal to the moment generating function of a random variable which is normally distributed.

Let X be a random variable with a distribution $f(x)$ which may not be normal, with mean μ and standard deviation σ. Take a random sample of size n and let the sample mean be $\overline{X}$. The $\overline{X}$ will have a distribution say $g(\bar{x})$, with mean μ and variance σ^2/n (see page 417). Let us standardize $\overline{X}$ as follows

$$Z = \frac{\overline{X} - \mu}{\dfrac{\sigma}{\sqrt{n}}} = \frac{\sqrt{n}(\overline{X} - \mu)}{\sigma} = \sum \frac{(X_i - \mu)}{\sigma\sqrt{n}}$$

Thus instead of showing the equality of $M_X(t)$ and $M_{\bar{X}}(t)$, we can show the equality of $M_Y(t)$ and $M_Z(t)$.

$$M_Z(t) = E(e^{Zt}) = E(e^{t\Sigma(X_i - \mu)/(\sigma/\sqrt{n})})$$

$$= [E(e^{t(X_i - \mu)/\sigma\sqrt{n}})]^n$$

since the X_i are independent. Let us expand the exponential.

$$e^{t(X_i - \mu)/\sigma\sqrt{n}} \equiv e^{t\theta} = 1 + \frac{\theta}{1}t + \frac{\theta^2}{2!}t^2 + \frac{\theta^3}{3!}t^3 + \cdots$$

$$= 1 + \frac{(X_i - \mu)}{1!} \cdot \frac{1}{\sigma}\left(\frac{t}{\sqrt{n}}\right) + \frac{(X_i - \mu)^2}{2!}\frac{1}{\sigma^2}\left(\frac{t}{\sqrt{n}}\right)^2 + \cdots$$

Thus if we take the expectation, we get

$$E(e^{t(X_i - \mu)/\sigma\sqrt{n}}) = 1 + 0 + \frac{\sigma^2}{2!} \cdot \frac{1}{\sigma^2} \cdot \left(\frac{t}{\sqrt{n}}\right)^2 + \frac{\mu_3}{3!}\frac{1}{\sigma^3}\left(\frac{t}{\sqrt{n}}\right)^3 + \cdots$$

where μ_3, μ_4, ... are the third, fourth, ... moments. This becomes

$$E(e^{t(X_i - \mu)/\sigma\sqrt{n}}) = 1 + \frac{1}{n}\left[\frac{1}{2}t^2 + \frac{\mu_3}{3!}\frac{1}{\sigma^3\sqrt{n}}t^3 + \frac{\mu_4}{4!}\frac{1}{\sigma^4 n}t^4 + \cdots\right]$$

$$= 1 + \frac{1}{n}h$$

where h is the part in the parenthesis. Thus,

$$M_Z(t) = \left(1 + \frac{h}{n}\right)^n$$

If we let $n \to \infty$, then,

$$\lim_{n \to \infty} M_Z(t) = e^h$$

But when $n \to \infty$, all the terms in h except $\frac{1}{2}t^2$ will approach zero. Thus,

$$\lim_{n \to \infty} M_Z(t) = e^{t^2/2}$$

But note that in section (ii), the moment generating function of the standardized normal random variable Y was $e^{t^2/2}$.

We state without proof that if the moment generating functions of two distributions exist and are equal, they will have the same distribution.

Then since $M_Z(t)$ and $M_Y(t)$ are equal

$$Y = \frac{X - \mu}{\sigma}, \qquad Z = \frac{\bar{X} - \mu}{\dfrac{\sigma}{\sqrt{n}}}$$

both have normal distributions. Thus $\bar{X}$ has a normal distribution with mean μ and variance σ^2/n.

Let us now state the results as a theorem:

Let X_1, X_2, ... X_n be a sequence of n identically distributed independent random variables with mean μ and variance σ^2. Then the mean $\bar{X} = \frac{1}{n}\Sigma X_i$ is asymptotically normal with mean μ and variance σ^2/n.

This is called the central limit theorem. There are various other forms of the central limit theorem and we have only presented one. By saying asymptotically normal, we mean that the distribution of $\bar{X}$ approaches a normal distribution as $n \to \infty$. Generally, when $n > 50$, we have a good approximation.

13.10 Random variable (Part II)

In Section 13.4 the r.v. was discussed in a descriptive way. We now take it up again in a more formal manner. A r.v. is defined as a real valued function defined on a sample space. Let us explain this by use of an illustration.

When two dice are tossed the possible outcomes of this experiment are shown, as in Figure 13–14, by the 36 sample points which make up the sample space R. These 36 points generate a class of subsets denoted by F_1. There are 2^{36} such subsets in F_1 and R_1 is one of them. That is, $R_1 \subset F_1$.

To each sample point in R_1 probabilities are assigned according to the multiplication rule. This will be $p = \frac{1}{36}$ for each point.

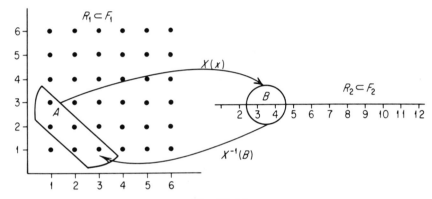

Fig. 13–14

Next consider a single valued real function $X(x)$ which maps the 36 sample points into a one-dimensional space R_2. Furthermore, assume that the rule of mapping is given by

$$X(x) = X_1 + X_2$$

where X_1, X_2 are the coordinates of the sample points in the sample space R_1. The $X(x)$ indicates the corresponding points on R_2. For example, the point $(x_1, x_2) = (1, 1)$ will be mapped into

$$X(x) = X_1 + X_2 = 1 + 1 = 2$$

on R_2; the point $(x_1, x_2) = (2, 6)$ will become $X(x) = 8$, and so forth. Thus, the points in R_2 will be

$$R_2: \quad \{2, 3, 4, 5, 6, 7, 8, 9, 10, 11, 12\}$$

as shown in Figure 13–14.

We have mapped the 36 sample points into R_2 which becomes a new sample space of 11 points. These 11 points will generate 2^{11} subsets. Let us denote this by F_2.

The 2^{36} subsets in F_1 can also be mapped into F_2. Let us illustrate with an example. Let A be an event in F_1,

$$A = A_1 + A_2 + A_3 + A_4 + A_5$$

where $A_1 = (1, 2)$, $A_2 = (1, 3)$ $A_3 = (2, 1)$, $A_4 = (2, 2)$, $A_5 = (3, 1)$

The transformation we used can be shown in matrix form as

$$X = [1, 1]$$

Applying the transformation X to A we find, using only A_1 and A_2 as an example,

$$X(A_1 + A_2)^T = XA_1^T + XA_2^T$$

$$= Y_1 + Y_2$$

This shows that A_1 maps into Y_1 which is

$$Y_1 = XA_1^T = [1, 1]\begin{bmatrix} 1 \\ 2 \end{bmatrix} = 1 + 2 = 3$$

and A_2 maps into Y_2 which is

$$Y_2 = XA_2^T = [1, 1]\begin{bmatrix} 1 \\ 3 \end{bmatrix} = 4$$

Therefore $A = A_1 + A_2$ maps into $Y_1 = 3$, $Y_2 = 4$ of R_2. Let the two points in R_2 be denoted by the set B. Then we can show the relation as

$$X^{-1}(B) = \{x : X(x) = B\}$$

What we have in the bracket is the set of points $x = (x_1, x_2)$ of sample space R_1 that maps into B of R_2. $X^{-1}(B)$ is the inverse function that gives the points in R_1 that map into B. These points in R_1 are A_1, A_2, A_3, A_4 and A_5.

Thus, we see that in a similar manner all the subsets in F_1 can be mapped into F.

The next step is to set up a correspondence between the probabilities of sample space R_1 and R_2. Using our illustration let us discuss this point. We know that

$$P(A) = P(\{(1, 2), \ldots (3, 1)\}) = \tfrac{5}{36}$$

Using this, we want to define probabilities for the space R_2, and in our present example, for the set B. It is natural that we would want to have the probability of A be equal to that of B. Thus, we shall define

$$Q(B) = P[X^{-1}(B)] = P(A)$$

where $Q(B)$ is the probability of B. When $X(x)$ establishes this relation, we shall call $X(x)$ a *random variable* (chance variable, stochastic variable, or random variate).

Thus the r.v. $X(x)$ is a function defined on R_1 that has generated a new space R_2 and furthermore probabilities have been assigned to the points in B by the relationship

$$Q(B) = P[X^{-1}(B)] = P(A)$$

R_2 becomes the range of the r.v. $X(x)$. When $X(x) = X$, we map onto the same space, and X simply denotes the 36 outcomes. When $X(x) = \frac{1}{2}(x_1 + x_2)$ this can be interpreted as taking the mean of each sample point and mapping this mean into a new space R_2.

Example 1. Let us toss a coin 3 times. This will generate a three-dimensional space with $2^3 = 8$ points, each point being a combination of S (successes) and F (failures). For example,

$$SSS, \ SSF, \ SFF, \ ... \ , \ FFF$$

Denote this space by R_1. We can take $2^8 = 256$ subsets from R_1 and form a class of subsets and call it G_1.

The probability p associated to each point in R_1 is

$$p = \tfrac{1}{8}.$$

Define a r.v. X on R_1 and let it denote the number of successes. Then,

$$X(x) = k, \qquad k = 0, 1, 2, 3$$

We have mapped R_1 into a new space, say R_2

$$R_2: \quad \{0, 1, 2, 3\}$$

by this random variable $X(x) = k$. G_2 is the collection of subsets that can be obtained from R_2. There are $2^4 = 16$ subsets. The probability is obtained by the relation

$$Q(B) = P[X^{-1}(B)]$$

where $B \in G_2$.

This may be shown diagrammatically as in Figure 13–15. The points of R_1 mapped into $\{0\}$ of R_2 by X is the single point (FFF). Thus,

$$Q(B = \{0\}) = P[X^{-1}(B)] = P(FFF) = \tfrac{1}{8}$$

Similarly,

$$Q(B = \{1\}) = P[X^{-1}(B)] = P[(SFF), (FSF), (FFS)]$$
$$= \tfrac{1}{8} + \tfrac{1}{8} + \tfrac{1}{8} = \tfrac{3}{8}$$
$$Q(B = \{2\}) = P(X^{-1}(B)) = \tfrac{3}{8}$$
$$Q(B = \{3\}) = P(X^{-1}(B)) = \tfrac{1}{8}$$
$$Q(B = \{2, 3\}) = P(X^{-1}(B)) = \tfrac{3}{8} + \tfrac{1}{8} = \tfrac{1}{2}$$

and so forth.

The above was carried out in terms of a set function but, as was discussed earlier, we can use a point function viz., the distribution function, to work

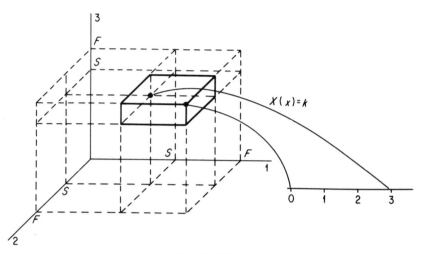

Fig. 13–15

this out. Usually the mapping process is abbreviated and, instead of $Q(B)$, we simply write

$$P(X = x) = f(x)$$

where $f(x)$ is the *probability density* or *density function* of the r.v. X. In our present case this is

$$f(k) = \binom{n}{k} p^k q^{n-k} = \binom{3}{k} \left(\frac{1}{2}\right)^k \left(\frac{1}{2}\right)^{3-k}$$

Thus, e.g.,

$$P(X = 0) = \binom{3}{0} \left(\frac{1}{2}\right)^0 \left(\frac{1}{2}\right)^{3-0} = \frac{1}{8}$$

$$P(X = 2) = \binom{3}{2} \left(\frac{1}{2}\right)^2 \left(\frac{1}{2}\right)^{3-2} = \frac{3}{8}$$

Example 2. Another example is obtained by defining X to be the number of failures in the previous problem.

One important thing to note here is that the new probability distribution associated to the new space is called a *derived distribution*. For example, if we take a sample of size 5, each sample will be a sample point in five-dimensional space. If we define the r.v. X to be

$$X(x) = \tfrac{1}{5} \sum X_i = \bar{X}$$

then the new sample space is made up of sample means. This derived distribution is usually called the *sampling distribution* of the sample mean.

Other examples are the χ^2-distribution, the t-distribution, and so forth.

Problems

1. Define X to be the number of failures in example 1 and work out the mapping process of the random variable.

2. Toss a coin twice. Construct a sample space, define the r.v. $X = k$ to be the number of successes, and explain the mapping process following the example above. Draw a diagram. Enumerate all cases.

13.11 Jacobian transformations

Let a set of random variables $(Y_1, Y_2, \ldots, Y_k)$ be related to another set of random variables $(X_1, X_2, \ldots, X_k)$ that has a density function $f(x_1, x_2, \ldots, x_k)$. Is there any way of finding the probability element of the set of random variables $(Y_1, Y_2, \ldots, Y_k)$? That is, is there any way of performing this transformation from one set of variables to another? Under certain conditions this transformation is possible by use of the Jacobian transformation. The proof of the Jacobian transformation is difficult and is not discussed. Only simple illustrations are used to explain the process. For those interested in the proofs, see the references cited at the end of the chapter.

(i) CASE 1

Let X be a random variable that is $N(\mu, \sigma^2)$. Let Z be

$$(1) \qquad Z = \frac{X - \mu}{\sigma}$$

Z is the standardized normal variable and the distribution is $N(0, 1)$. This transformation from X to Z is shown as follows by use of the Jacobian.

Equation (1) can be expressed as

$$(1') \qquad z = f(x)$$

Equation (1) shows that there is a one-to-one correspondence between X and Z. Thus we can find the inverse

$$(2) \qquad x = g(z)$$

In our present case this is from (1),

$$(2') \qquad X = \mu + \sigma Z$$

We state without proof that: the probability element of Z is

$$(3) \qquad f(g(z)) \cdot |J| \cdot dz$$

where J is the Jacobian of x with respect to z. That is,

$$|J| = \left| \frac{\partial x}{\partial z} \right| = \left| \frac{\partial (\mu + \sigma z)}{\partial z} \right| = \sigma$$

Then the probability element of Z is

$$f(g(z)) \cdot |J| \cdot dz = \frac{1}{\sqrt{2\pi}\sigma} e^{-(x-\mu)^2/2\sigma^2} \sigma \, dz$$

$$= \frac{1}{\sqrt{2\pi}} e^{-z^2/2} \, dz$$

This shows that Z is $N(0, 1)$ as we expected.

(ii) Case 2

Consider two random variables X and Y with a joint density function $f(x, y)$ and probability element $f(x, y) \, dx \, dy$. Let U and V be random variables such that

(4)
$$u = u(x, y)$$

$$v = v(x, y)$$

Assume a one-to-one correspondence between (X, Y) and (U, V). This means we can find the inverse functions

(5)
$$x = x(u, v)$$

$$y = y(u, v)$$

Then the probability element of U and V will be

$$h(u, v) \, du \, dv = f\,[x(u, v), y(u, v)] \cdot |J| \cdot du \, dv$$

where J is the Jacobian of the transformation (5), i.e.,

$$J = \frac{\partial(x, y)}{\partial(u, v)}$$

provided the partial derivatives of J exist.

As an illustration consider the joint density function

(6)
$$f(x, y) = \frac{1}{2\pi\sigma_x\sigma_y\sqrt{1-\rho^2}} \exp\left[\frac{-1}{2(1-\rho^2)}\left(\left(\frac{x-\mu_x}{\sigma_x}\right)^2 - 2\rho\frac{x-\mu_x}{\sigma_x}\frac{y-\mu_y}{\sigma_y} + \left(\frac{y-\mu_y}{\sigma_y}\right)^2\right)\right]$$

This is a bivariate normal distribution with means μ_x, μ_y and variances σ_x^2, σ_y^2 (Note that exp is an abbreviation for exponential e, i.e., $e^u = \exp u$). Consider the transformation

(7)
$$U = \frac{X - \mu_x}{\sigma_x}$$

$$V = \frac{Y - \mu_y}{\sigma_y}$$

To obtain the probability element of (U, V), we first find the Jacobian of the transformation (7).

$$|J| = \left| \frac{\partial(x, y)}{\partial(u, v)} \right| = \begin{vmatrix} \dfrac{\partial x}{\partial u} & \dfrac{\partial y}{\partial u} \\[2mm] \dfrac{\partial x}{\partial v} & \dfrac{\partial y}{\partial v} \end{vmatrix} = \begin{vmatrix} \sigma_x & 0 \\ 0 & \sigma_y \end{vmatrix} = \sigma_x \sigma_y$$

Then the probability element of (U, V) is

(8) $f[x(u, v), y(u, v)] \cdot |J| \cdot du\, dv$

$$= \frac{1}{2\pi \sqrt{1 - \rho^2}} \exp \left[\frac{-1}{2(1 - \rho^2)} (u^2 - 2\rho u v + v^2) \right] du\, dv$$

Note that ρ (correlation coefficient) in the equation has become

$$\rho = \frac{E(X - \mu_x)(Y - \mu_y)}{\sigma_x \sigma_y} = \frac{E(\sigma_x U)(\sigma_y V)}{\sigma_x \sigma_y} = E(UV)$$

Equation (8) shows that the joint density function of U and V is a bivariate normal distribution with mean zero and variance unity for both variables.

Let us restate the results as a theorem. *Theorem*: Let a set of random variables Y_1, Y_2 be related by a one-to-one transformation to a set of random variables X_1, X_2 which have a joint density function $f(x_1, x_2)$. Let

(9)
$$y_1 = y_1(x_1, x_2)$$
$$y_2 = y_2(x_1, x_2)$$

Since the relation is one-to-one, the inverse function can be shown as

(10)
$$x_1 = x_1(y_1, y_2)$$
$$x_2 = x_2(y_1, y_2)$$

Then the probability element of Y_1, Y_2 is

(11) $g(y_1, y_2)\, dy_1\, dy_2 = f(x_1(y_1, y_2), x_2(y_1, y_2)) \cdot |J| \cdot dy_1\, dy_2$

where J is the Jacobian of the transformation (10), i.e.,

$$|J| = \left| \frac{\partial(x_1, x_2)}{\partial(y_1, y_2)} \right| = \begin{vmatrix} \dfrac{\partial x_1}{\partial y_1} & \dfrac{\partial x_2}{\partial y_1} \\[2mm] \dfrac{\partial x_1}{\partial y_2} & \dfrac{\partial x_2}{\partial y_2} \end{vmatrix}$$

provided the partial derivatives exist.

This result may be generalized to k variables. This transformation technique will be used in Chapter 16, Regression Analysis.

Notes and References

13.1 Feller (1957), Chapter 1; Munroe (1951), Chapter 2.

13.3 Feller (1957), Chapter 1; Cramer (1946), Chapter 13; Kolmogorov (1956), pp. 1–6.

13.4–13.5 Cramer (1946), Chapter 14; Feller (1957), Chapter 5.

13.6 Cramer (1946), Chapter 6 and 15; Feller (1957), pp. 199–207; Fraser (1958), Chapter 4; Hoel (1954), pp. 16–27; Neyman (1950), pp. 164–179.

13.7 Feller (1957), Chapter 9.

13.8 Fraser (1958), Chapters 3 and 4; Cramer (1946), Chapters 16 and 17.

13.9 Cramer (1946), Chapter 17; Feller (1957), Chapters 7 and 10; Fraser (1958), Chapter 6.

13.10 Neyman (1950), Chapter 4; Cramer (1946), Chapters 13 and 14.

13.11 Wilks (1950), pp. 23–29; Cramer (1946), pp. 292–294.

The approach to probability theory used in this chapter is that of Kolmogorov (1956). It is an axiomatic approach based on set theory and then transformed into calculus by use of the Lebesgue-Stieltjes integral. To discuss probability theory rigorously using Lebesgue-Stieltjes integral requires extensive background in real variable theory, and, in particular, measure theory. For those interested see the following references. The basic book is Kolmogorov (1956) which is a translation of his German monograph of 1933. Two books on measure theory are Halmos (1950) and Munroe (1953). Both are very difficult, but a compact summary of probability theory using measure theory is in Halmos (1950), Chapter 9 which is recommended. An advanced text in probability theory in Loeve (1955).

Intermediate references which do not require measure theory as a background are Parzen (1960), Munroe (1951), and Feller (1957). Feller (1957) restricts his discussion to discrete sample spaces, and is an excellent book.

The books mentioned above on probability theory and measure theory are concerned with those topics per se whereas economists in most cases are interested in probability theory as a background to statistics. Five books that treat probability theory in connection with statistics are Cramer (1946); Cramer (1955); Neyman (1950); Savage (1954); and Schlaifer (1959). Cramer's (1946) book is probably the best source to obtain an overall picture of the relation between set theory, measure theory, Lebesgue-Stieltjes integral, and its transition to mathematical statistics. The treatment is at an advanced level. Chapters 13 and 14 of Cramer (1946) are especially recommended in connection with this chapter because they give a frequency interpretation of the probability axioms we have stated. Cramer (1955) is an elementary version of the first part of Cramer's (1946) book and can be read with only an elementary background of calculus. Neyman (1950) can also be read with an elementary calculus background and is an excellent book with many interesting problems.

Savage (1954) distinguishes three views on the interpretation of probability; objectivistic, personalistic, and necessary view. He develops the personalistic view to serve as a foundation of statistics. Schlaifer (1959) and Raiffa and Schlaifer (1961) adopt this approach in their discussions of statistics. The Kolmogorov approach we have discussed is classified as an objectivistic view. Savage (1954) has an excellent annotated bibliography for those interested in studying probability theory and these various views.

The following books are recommended for study of the various probability distributions. For the binomial, hypergeometric, and Poisson distribution, see Feller (1957) and Schlaifer (1959). For the normal distribution see Feller (1957), Schlaifer (1959), and Cramer (1946). For the t-distribution, chi-square distribution, and F-distribution, see Cramer (1946), Mood (1950), Hoel (1954), and Fraser (1958).

Cramer, H., *Mathematical Methods of Statistics*. Princeton, New Jersey: Princeton University Press, 1946.

Cramer, H., *The Elements of Probability Theory and Some of Its Applications*. New York: John Wiley & Sons, Inc., 1955.

Feller, W., *An Introduction to Probability Theory and Its Applications*. 2nd ed. New York: John Wiley & Sons, Inc., 1957.

Fraser, D. A. S., *Statistics: An Introduction*. New York: John Wiley & Sons, Inc., 1958.

Halmos, P. R., *Measure Theory*. New Jersey: D. Van Nostrand Company, Inc., 1950.

Hoel, P. G., *Introduction to Mathematical Statistics*, New York: John Wiley & Sons, Inc., 1954.

Kolmogorov, A. N., *Foundations of the Theory of Probability*. Translated from German by N. Morrison. New York: Chelsea Publishing Co., 1956.

Loeve, M., *Probability Theory*. New Jersey: D. Van Nostrand Company, Inc., 1955.

Mood, A. M., *Introduction to the Theory of Statistics*. New York: McGraw-Hill Book Co., Inc., 1950.

Munroe, M. E., *Introduction to Measure and Integration*. Cambridge, Mass: Addison-Wesley Publishing Co., Inc., 1953.

Munroe, M. E., *Theory of Probability*. New York: McGraw-Hill Book Co., Inc., 1951.

Neyman, J., *First Course in Probability and Statistics*. New York: Henry Holt & Co., Inc., 1950.

Parzen, E., *Modern Probability Theory and Its Applications*. New York: John Wiley & Sons, Inc., 1960.

Raiffa, H., and Schlaifer, R., *Applied Statistical Decision Theory*. Boston, Mass: Harvard Business School, 1961.

Savage, L. J., *The Foundations of Statistics*. New York: John Wiley & Sons, Inc., 1954.

Schlaifer, R., *Probability and Statistics for Business Decisions*. New York: McGraw-Hill Book Co., Inc., 1959.

Wilks, S. S., *Mathematical Statistics*. New Jersey: Princeton University Press, 1950.

CHAPTER 14

Statistical Concepts—Estimation

In the next two chapters, we take up two important statistical concepts, *estimation* and *testing hypothesis*.

14.1 Introduction

Consider a large group of students that have been given an I.Q. test and assume that we know from past experience that the distribution of I.Q.'s are normal, but do not know specifically the mean and standard deviation.

For simplicity, let the possible outcomes of the I.Q. test be shown as

$$\Omega: \quad \{100, 101, 102, \ldots \quad \ldots 138, 139, 140\}$$

To this is associated a density function $f(x)$ which we assumed is a normal density function. Denote the mean and variance by

$$E(X) = \mu, \qquad \text{Var}(X) = \sigma^2$$

Thus, we will say that the r.v. X is defined on Ω with a normal density function $f(x)$. μ and σ are the *parameters* of this distribution.

What we want to do is to take a sample of values from the population and, using these values *estimate* the parameters. For example, when we wish to estimate μ, we can take, say, n values of X from the population and find the sample mean $\bar{X}$ and use that as an *estimator*. As we know

$$\bar{X} = \frac{1}{n} \sum X_i$$

Thus if we let $\hat{\mu}$ stand for an estimator of μ, we can write

$$\hat{\mu} = \bar{X} = \frac{1}{n} \sum X_i$$

i.e., $\hat{\mu} = \bar{X}$ is an estimator of μ.

To show that $\hat{\mu}$ is a function of the sample values, we can write it as

$$\hat{\mu}(x_1, x_2, \ldots , x_n) = \bar{X}$$

Let us generalize the notation a step further. $\hat{\mu}$ was the estimator for μ, but now let $\hat{\theta}$ be an estimator for a parameter θ. Then,

$$\hat{\theta}(x_1, x_2, \ldots , x_n) = \hat{\theta}$$

We have shown that the sample mean

$$\hat{\theta}(x_1, x_2, \ldots , x_n) = \frac{1}{n} \sum X_i = \bar{X}$$

can be looked upon as "estimator" for μ. But how about the median of the sample, the mode, or the average of the largest and smallest values in the sample? Can they be looked upon as estimators of μ? The answer is, yes.

Then, the question arises, which of these various estimators will be the "best" estimator of μ? What are the characteristics of a "good estimator"? The first characteristic we discuss is unbiasedness.

14.2 Unbiasedness

An estimator $\hat{\theta}(x_1, x_2, \ldots , x_n)$ is said to be "unbiased" if

$$E(\hat{\theta}) = \theta$$

As an example, we know that

$$E(\bar{X}) = \mu$$

Thus, $\bar{X}$ is an unbiased estimator of μ.

An example of a biased estimator is the sample variance as an estimator of the population variance

$$E(s^2) = \frac{n-1}{n} \sigma^2 = \sigma^2 + \left(-\frac{1}{n} \sigma^2 \right)$$

Thus, s^2 is a biased estimator of σ^2 and $(-1/n)\sigma^2$ is called the *bias*. If the bias $(-1/n)\sigma^2$ is small compared to the variance of the sampling distribution of s^2, then this bias is not very important. That is, if the bias is small compared to the variance of the sampling distribution of the estimator, the usefulness of the estimator will not be greatly damaged.

14.3 Consistency

A second characteristic for a good estimator is consistency. An estimator $\hat{\theta}(x_1, x_2, \ldots , x_n)$ of θ is said to be a *consistent* estimator if

$$P[|\hat{\theta} - \theta| \leq \epsilon] \to 1 \quad \text{as} \quad n \to \infty$$

or

$$P[\theta - \epsilon \leq \hat{\theta} \leq \theta + \epsilon] \rightarrow 1 \quad \text{as} \quad n \rightarrow \infty$$

where ϵ is an arbitrarily small positive number. This means that as $n \rightarrow \infty$, $\hat{\theta}$ converges toward θ stochastically with probability unity.

Using the sample mean $\bar{X}$ as an example again, it is quite obvious that as the sample size $n \rightarrow \infty$, or as it approaches the population size, the $\bar{X}$ will approach the population mean μ. Thus, $\bar{X}$ satisfies the criterion of consistency.

Let us also consider

$$\bar{X} + \frac{1}{n} \quad \text{or} \quad \bar{X} + \frac{1}{2n}$$

If we have an infinite population, we can see that as $n \rightarrow \infty$, these will also approach μ and satisfy the criterion of consistency. Thus, all three $\bar{X}$, $\bar{X} + 1/n$ and $\bar{X} + 1/2n$ are consistent estimators.

We also notice that when $n \rightarrow \infty$, each is also an unbiased estimator. Consistent estimators are also unbiased estimators when $n \rightarrow \infty$.

Note that the idea of consistency is tied in with the idea of letting the sample size $n \rightarrow \infty$. The idea of unbiasedness is for a fixed sample size n. The $\bar{X} + 1/n$ and $\bar{X} + 1/2n$ are biased estimators of μ for a finite sample size n.

But now a question arises, which of these should we use as an estimator? What we want is an estimator that will be as close as possible to μ. Furthermore, we would like to accomplish this estimation with as small a sample as possible. These requirements lead to the following additional criteria.

14.4 Efficiency

(i) Relative efficiency

An estimator that is concentrated near the parameter is more desirable than one that is less so. We may determine whether or not an estimator is concentrated near the parameter by the variance of the estimator. For example, the degree of concentration of $\bar{X}$ as an estimator of μ is shown by

$$\text{Var}(\bar{X}) = \sigma_{\bar{X}}^2 = \frac{\sigma^2}{n}$$

Another estimator of μ is the median of a sample. It is known that

$$\text{Var}(X_{\text{Med}}) = \sigma_{\text{Med}}^2 = \frac{\pi \sigma^2}{2n}$$

Which of the two estimators is more concentrated near μ? For this we compare the variances. We say the *efficiency* of the median *relative to* the $\bar{X}$ is

$$\frac{\text{Var}(\bar{X})}{\text{Var}(X_{\text{Med}})} = \frac{\sigma^2/n}{\pi\sigma^2/2n} = \frac{2}{\pi} = 0.64$$

Here we have found the *relative efficiency*. Our result says that

$$\text{Var}(\overline{X}) = \text{Var}(X_{\text{Med}}) \times 64 \text{ per cent}$$

i.e., the variance of $\overline{X}$ is only 64 per cent of the variance of the median when they both have a sample size of n.

If efficiency is considered in terms of sample size, we can say that the variance of the median from samples of size 100 is about the same as that of sample means from samples of size 64.

We can also say that if the median is used instead of the mean, for a given sample size, there is a loss of $100 - 64 = 36$ per cent of the available information.

To summarize; if we have two estimators $\hat{\theta}_1$ and $\hat{\theta}_2$ and

$$\text{Var}(\hat{\theta}_1) < \text{Var}(\hat{\theta}_2)$$

then the efficiency of $\hat{\theta}_2$ relative to $\hat{\theta}_1$ is given by

$$E_f = \frac{\text{Var}(\hat{\theta}_1)}{\text{Var}(\hat{\theta}_2)}$$

Note that we put the variance of the estimator that is smaller in the numerator. Thus,

$$0 \leq E_f \leq 1$$

(ii) Efficient estimators

We have defined efficiency in relative terms and put the variance of the estimator that is smaller in the numerator. The efficiency was defined relative to this smaller variance estimator. But if we could find an estimator with a variance that is smaller than the variance of any other estimator, then we could use this smallest variance as the basis to measure efficiency, and in terms of efficiency, we could say that this estimator with the smallest variance is an *efficient estimator*.

Then a question arises: How small can the variance of an estimator become? If we can show that the variance cannot become smaller than a certain lower bound, and if we can find an estimator with a variance that is equal to this lower bound, then that variance will be the smallest variance. We shall use the word *minimum* instead of smallest and call it the *minimum variance*.

Furthermore, the estimator that has this minimum variance will be called the *minimum variance estimator*.

It turns out that there is a lower bound. It is called the *Cramer-Rao inequality*. We shall merely state it. Let us take a sample of size n and calculate an estimator

$$\theta(x_1, x_2, \ldots, x_n) = \hat{\theta}$$

Let

$$E(\hat{\theta}) = \theta + b(\theta)$$

where $b(\theta)$ is the bias. Let $f(x)$ be the density function. Then the Cramer-Rao inequality is given as

$$E[(\hat{\theta} - \theta)^2] \geq \frac{(1 + b'(\theta))^2}{nE\left[\left(\frac{\partial \log f}{\partial \theta}\right)^2\right]}$$

$E[(\hat{\theta} - \theta)^2]$ is the second moment around θ. When we have an unbiased estimator, then

$$E(\hat{\theta}) = \theta \quad \text{and} \quad b(\theta) = 0$$

Thus,

$$E[(\hat{\theta} - \theta)^2] = E[(\hat{\theta} - E(\hat{\theta}))^2] = \text{Var}\,(\hat{\theta})$$

Thus, when we have an unbiased estimator,

$$\text{Var}\,(\hat{\theta}) \geq \frac{1}{nE\left[\left(\frac{\partial \log f}{\partial \theta}\right)^2\right]}$$

For example, let

$$f(x) = \frac{1}{\sigma\sqrt{2\pi}}\, e^{-(x-m)^2/2\sigma^2}$$

which is a normal density function. Then,

$$\log f(x) = \log \left(\frac{1}{\sigma\sqrt{2\pi}}\right) - \frac{(x-m)^2}{2\sigma^2}$$

$$\frac{\partial \log f(x)}{\partial m} = \frac{x-m}{\sigma^2}$$

$$\therefore \quad E\left(\frac{\partial \log f}{\partial m}\right)^2 = \int_{-\infty}^{\infty} \left(\frac{x-m}{\sigma^2}\right)^2 \cdot f\,dx = \frac{1}{\sigma^2}$$

Thus,

$$\text{Var}\,(\hat{\theta}) = \text{Var}\,(\bar{X}) \geq \frac{1}{n\dfrac{1}{\sigma_2}} = \frac{\sigma^2}{n}$$

i.e.,

$$\text{Var}\,(\bar{X}) \geq \frac{\sigma^2}{n}$$

We know that for the $\bar{X}$ the equality holds, i.e.,

$$\text{Var}\,(\bar{X}) = \frac{\sigma^2}{n}$$

Thus, this is the minimum variance, and $\bar{X}$ is the minimum variance estimator.

Problems

1. Let

$$f(x) = \frac{1}{\sigma\sqrt{2\pi}}\, e^{-(x-m)^2/2\sigma^2}$$

Show that

$$\log f(x) = \log\left(\frac{1}{\sigma\sqrt{2\pi}}\right) - \frac{(x-m)^2}{2\sigma^2}$$

2. Show that

$$\frac{\partial \log f}{\partial m} = \frac{x-m}{\sigma^2}$$

3. Show that

$$E\left(\frac{\partial \log f}{\partial m}\right)^2 = \frac{1}{\sigma^2}$$

Hint: Note that $E(x-m)^2 = \int (x-m)^2 f\, dx = \mathrm{Var}\,(x)$

Let us for simplicity write the Cramer-Rao inequality as, for the case of an unbiased estimator,

$$\mathrm{Var}\,(\hat\theta) \geq \mathrm{Min\ Var}\,(\hat\theta)$$

where

$$\mathrm{Min\ Var}\,(\hat\theta) \equiv \frac{1}{nE\left(\dfrac{\partial \log f}{\partial\theta}\right)^2}$$

Now using this Min Var $(\hat\theta)$ we can define *efficiency* on an absolute rather than a relative basis. We say the efficiency of the estimator $\hat\theta$ is

$$E_f = \frac{\mathrm{Min\ Var}\,(\hat\theta)}{\mathrm{Var}\,(\hat\theta)}$$

For the sample mean from a normal distribution, we have

$$\mathrm{Var}\,(\bar X) = \frac{\sigma^2}{n}$$

$$\mathrm{Min\ Var}\,(\bar X) = \frac{1}{nE\left(\dfrac{\partial \log f}{\partial\theta}\right)^2} = \frac{\sigma^2}{n}$$

Thus,

$$E_f = 1$$

In such a case where the efficiency is unity we say the estimator $\bar X$ is an efficient estimator.

Problems

Let $f(x) = \dfrac{1}{\sqrt{2\pi\sigma^2}}\, e^{-\frac{(x-m)^2}{2\sigma^2}}$

Let m = mean be given and σ^2 be the parameter to be estimated.

1. Show that

$$\frac{\partial \log f}{\partial \sigma^2} = \frac{(x - m)^2}{2\sigma^4} - \frac{1}{2\sigma^2}$$

Hint: Set $\sigma^2 = \theta$ to facilitate differentiation. First find $\log f$.

2. Show that

$$E\left[\frac{(x - m)^2}{2\sigma^4}\right] = \frac{1}{2\sigma^2}$$

3. Show that

$$E\left[\left(\frac{\partial \log f}{\partial \sigma^2}\right)^2\right] = \int \left[\frac{(x - m)^2}{2\sigma^4} - \frac{1}{2\sigma^2}\right]^2 f\,dx = \frac{1}{2\sigma^4}$$

Hint: $\left[\dfrac{(x - m)^2}{2\sigma^4} - \dfrac{1}{2\sigma^2}\right]^2 = \dfrac{1}{4\sigma^4}\left[\dfrac{(x - m)^2}{\sigma^2} - 1\right]^2$

Expand and integrate term by term and note that if μ_r is the rth moment about the mean, then,

$$\mu_1 = 0, \qquad \mu_3 = 0,$$

$$\mu_2 = \sigma^2, \qquad \mu_4 = 3\sigma^4$$

In general, $\mu_{2r-1} = 0$, $\mu_{2r} = 1.3 \ldots (2r - 1)\,\sigma^{2r}$.

4. Let $\hat{\theta}$ be an unbiased estimator of σ^2. Then the Cramer-Rao inequality gives

$$\text{Var}\,(\hat{\theta}) \geq \frac{1}{nE\left(\dfrac{\partial \log f}{\partial \theta}\right)^2}$$

Using the above results, write out the right hand side of this inequality and show the minimum variance.

5. Show that

$$E\left(\frac{n}{n - 1}s^2\right) = \sigma^2$$

Using this show that

$$\text{Var}\left(\frac{n}{n - 1}s^2\right) = \frac{2\sigma^4}{n - 1}$$

Hint: (i) $\text{Var}\left(\dfrac{n}{n - 1}s^2\right) = E\left[\dfrac{n}{n - 1}s^2 - \sigma^2\right]^2$

$$= E\left[\left(\frac{n}{n - 1}\right)^2 s^4 - 2\left(\frac{n}{n - 1}\right)s^2\sigma^2 + \sigma^4\right]$$

$$(ii) \; E(s^4) = \mu_2^2 + \frac{\mu_4 - 3\mu_2^2}{n} - \frac{2\mu_4 - 5\mu_2^2}{n^2} + \frac{\mu_4 - 3\mu_2^2}{n^3}$$

where μ_r is the rth moment about the mean. See hint of problem 3.

6. $\dfrac{n}{n-1} s^2$ is an unbiased estimator of σ^2. You have found the variance in problem 5. What is the efficiency of the estimator $\dfrac{n}{n-1} s^2$?

(iii) A class of efficient estimators

Let us consider the sample mean $\bar{X}$ again as an estimator for μ. We have already seen that $\bar{X}$ is an efficient estimator; i.e., it is a minimum variance estimator. It is also an unbiased minimum variance estimator.

We know from the central limit theorem that $\bar{X}$ is $N(\mu, \sigma^2/n)$. If we shift the origin and consider $\bar{X} - \mu$ then this will be $N(0, \sigma^2/n)$. If we change the scale of distribution by

$$\frac{\bar{X} - \mu}{\dfrac{1}{\sqrt{n}}} = \sqrt{n}(\bar{X} - \mu)$$

then it will be $N(0, \sigma^2)$.

What we just did to the sample mean $\bar{X}$ can be done to other estimators. That is, we can find estimators $\hat{\theta}(x_1, x_2, \ldots, x_n)$ such that

$$\sqrt{n}(\hat{\theta} - \theta)$$

approaches $N(0, \sigma^2)$ as $n \to \infty$.

If we confine our attention to such estimators $\hat{\theta}$, and apply the above transformation, then these estimators will be distributed normally with zero mean but with different variances. Thus, we can compare the magnitude of the various variances and if we have an estimator $\hat{\theta}$ of θ such that $\sqrt{n}(\hat{\theta} - \theta)$ approaches $N(0, \sigma^2)$ and any other estimator $\hat{\theta}'$ such that $\sqrt{n}(\hat{\theta}' - \theta)$ approaches $N(0, \sigma'^2)$, and if $\sigma'^2 \geq \sigma^2$ always, then $\hat{\theta}$ is an efficient estimator.

A question remains: How can efficient estimators be found? It is known that if an efficient estimator exists, it can be found by the method of maximum likelihood. We will discuss this method later. But before that we will discuss another characteristic, the *criterion of sufficiency*.

Problems

Discuss the following statements.

1. An unbiased estimator may not be consistent.

2. A consistent estimator is unbiased.

3. Efficient estimators are consistent estimators.

14.5 Sufficiency

So far we have had unbiasedness, consistency, and efficiency as desirable properties of estimators. We next take up the property of sufficiency which was introduced by R. A. Fisher, who states:

> The essential feature of statistical estimates which satisfy the criterion of sufficiency is that they by themselves convey the whole of the information, which the sample of observations, contains, respecting the value of the parameters of which they are sufficient estimates. This property is manifestly true of a statistic T_1, if for any other estimate T_2 of the same parameter, θ, the simultaneous sampling distribution of T_1 and T_2 for given θ, is such that given T_1, the distribution of T_2 does not involve θ: for if this is so it is obvious that once T_1 is known, a knowledge of T_2, in addition, is wholly irrelevant: and if the property holds for all alternative estimates, the estimate T_1 will contain the whole of the information which the sample supplies.*

For example let us toss a loaded coin n times. Then we have a sequence of independent and identically distributed random variables,

$$X_1, X_2, \ldots , X_n$$

We wish to estimate $\theta = p =$ population proportion. We have

$$P(X_i = 1) = p$$
$$P(X_i = 0) = q = 1 - p$$

Let $T_1 = \Sigma\, X_i$ be the total number of heads in n tosses. We claim that T_1 is a sufficient statistic for the purpose of estimating $\theta = p$. Let t be the number of heads in n throws, and $T_1 = t$.

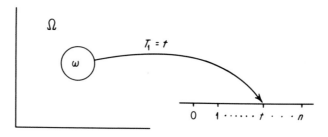

Fig. 14–1

In diagrammatic terms, the original space is an n-dimensional space and the 2^n points show the different possible samples. The statistic T_1 maps this space Ω into a new one-dimensional space which is made up of the points

$$t = 0, 1, 2, \ldots , n$$

* Reprinted from R. A. Fisher: "Two new properties of mathematical likelihood," *Proceedings of the Royal Society*, Series A, Vol. 144, p. 288, 1934. By permission of the author and publishers.

Within Ω we have a subspace ω that consists of points which have exactly t heads among the n outcomes. Each of these points in ω have a probability density of $p^t q^{n-t}$ associated to it. There are $\binom{n}{t}$ such points. We can designate these points in ω by T_2. The question then is, does the knowledge of T_2 along with T_1 give more information about $p = \theta$ than just T_1 alone? For this we find the conditional distribution of T_2 given T_1. Since each point has a probability of $p^t q^{n-t}$ associated to it, and the total probability of the points in ω is

$$\binom{n}{t} p^t q^{n-t}$$

the conditional distribution of the points in ω, when given $T_1 = t$, is

$$f(T_2 \mid T_1) = \frac{p^t q^{n-t}}{\binom{n}{t} p^t q^{n-t}} = \frac{1}{\binom{n}{t}}$$

Thus, when we are given $T_1 = t$, the distribution of T_2 does not involve p. That is, the knowledge of the individual points in ω do not give us any additional information that we do not already have from $T_1 = t$.

From simple common sense, one can heuristically see that when a coin is flipped n times, if we get t heads, regardless of what order we get the heads, we would use t/n as an estimate of $\theta = p$.

The above approach uses conditional probabilities. Furthermore, it is necessary to investigate other estimators T_2 to find out if T_1 is a sufficient estimator. J. Neyman (1934) developed a criterion to avoid this laborious work. Halmos and Savage (AMS, 1949, p. 225) generalized it. It is called the Neyman (or factorability) criterion.

$T = t(x_1, \ldots, x_n)$ is a sufficient statistic for θ, if and only if the probability density function can be factored into

$$f(x_1, \ldots, x_n, \theta) = g_1(T : \theta) g_2(x_1, \ldots, x_n)$$

where $g_1(T : \theta)$ is dependent only on T and θ, and $g_2(x_1, \ldots, x_n)$ is independent of θ.

Applying this to our present illustration, we have

$$f(x_i, \theta) = p^x q^{1-x}, \qquad x_i = 1 \quad \text{or} \quad 0$$

Thus, the joint distribution associated to the points in the n-dimensional space can be shown as

$$f(x_1, \ldots, x_n, \theta) = \prod f(x_i, \theta) = p^{\Sigma x} q^{n - \Sigma x}$$

Let $\Sigma x = t$ to simplify notation, then,

$$f(x_1, \ldots, x_n, p) = p^t q^{n-t} = g_1(T, p) g_2(x_1, \ldots, x_n)$$

where $g_1(T, p) = p^t q^{n-t}$ and $g_2(x_1, \ldots, x_n) = 1$. Thus, $T = \Sigma x = t$ is a sufficient statistic for p.

Example—Normal Distribution. Let us have $X_1, X_2, \ldots, X_n$, each $N(\mu, \sigma^2)$. Assume σ^2 is given and we want to estimate $\theta = \mu$. Query: is

$$\bar{X} = \frac{1}{n} \sum X_i$$

a sufficient statistic for $\theta = \mu$?

We have

$$f(x_i, \mu) = \left(\frac{1}{2\pi\sigma^2}\right)^{1/2} e^{-(x-\mu)^2/2\sigma^2} = \left(\frac{1}{2\pi\sigma^2}\right)^{1/2} \exp\left[-\frac{(x-\mu)^2}{2\sigma^2}\right]$$

Thus,

$$f(x_1, \ldots, x_n, \mu) = \prod f(x_i, \mu) = (2\pi\sigma^2)^{-n/2} \exp\left[-\frac{1}{2\sigma^2} \sum_{i=1}^{n} (x_i - \mu)^2\right]$$

Now,

$$\sum (x_i - \mu)^2 = \sum (x_i - \bar{x})^2 + n(\bar{x} - \mu)^2$$

Thus,

$$\prod f(x_i, \mu) = (2\pi\sigma^2)^{-n/2} \exp\left[-\frac{1}{2\sigma^2} \sum (x_i - \bar{x})^2\right] \exp\left[-\frac{1}{2\sigma^2} n(\bar{x} - \mu)^2\right]$$

$$= c g_2(x_1, \ldots, x_n) g_1(T, \mu)$$

Therefore, $\bar{X}$ is a sufficient statistic for μ.

Problems

1. Show that

$$\sum (x_i - \mu)^2 = \sum (x_i - \bar{x})^2 + n(\bar{x} - \mu)^2$$

2. Given $X_1, X_2, \ldots, X_n$, each independent and having a poisson distribution,

$$f(x_i, \lambda) = \frac{e^{-\lambda} \lambda^{x_i}}{x_i!}$$

Show that $T = \sum_{i=1}^{n} X_i$ is a sufficient statistic for $\theta = \lambda$.

14.6 Method of maximum likelihood (ML)

We have so far discussed properties of a good estimator. In the process we picked out, say, the sample mean or the sample proportion and used them as estimators for the population mean and population proportion. Now we want to discuss some of the mathematical procedures that can be used to obtain estimators. We shall discuss first the method of *maximum likelihood* (ML). Later we shall discuss the method of least squares. There are also the method of moments, and the minimum χ^2 method which we shall not take up.

The reason why we discuss the ML method and show favor to it is because the estimators obtained from this method give us the desirable properties we have been discussing, if the parameters to be estimated do have estimators with these properties. For example, if the parameter has a sufficient estimator, then the ML estimator will be the sufficient estimator. Furthermore, the ML method gives us efficient and consistent estimators, if they exist.

Let us first discuss the idea of the ML method in simple terms.

(i) The likelihood function

Consider a binomial distribution with the density function

$$f(x, p) = p^x q^{1-x}, \qquad x = 0 \quad \text{or} \quad 1$$

As an illustration, let us assume we have an urn that has black and white balls in it where the proportion of black balls is p. Let $x = 1$ when a black ball is drawn, and $x = 0$ when a white ball is drawn. Then,

Fig. 14-2

$$f(x, p) = p^1 q^{1-1} = p$$

shows the probability of drawing a black ball. Let us make two drawings with replacement. We have selected a random sample of size two. This is shown diagrammatically in Figure 14-2. There are 2^2 different samples, when we consider the order. The joint density function associated to these four points (samples of size 2) is

$$f(x_1, x_2, p) = f(x_1, p)f(x_2, p)$$
$$= p^{x_1} q^{1-x_1} p^{x_2} q^{1-x_2} = p^{x_1 + x_2} q^{2 - (x_1 + x_2)}$$

If we take a sample of size n, then the joint density function is,

$$f(x_1, \ldots, x_n, p) = \Pi f(x_i, p)$$
$$= p^{\Sigma x_i} q^{n - \Sigma x_i}$$

Any particular sample $(x_1, x_2, \ldots, x_n)$ gives us the coordinates of a specific point in the n-dimensional sample space. The order of the x's are important, and we shall denote this sample space by Ω. Then to each of the points in Ω we have associated the joint density function we just obtained, i.e.,

$$f(x_1, \ldots, x_n, p) = p^{\Sigma x_i} q^{n - \Sigma x_i}$$

Here we are considering $f(x_1, \ldots, x_n, p)$ to be a function of the x_i with p given.

But we can also think that the sample $(x_1, \ldots, x_n)$ is given and that $f(x_1, \ldots, x_n, p)$ is a function of p. This means we have a family of Ω's, each with a specific p.

Thus the question becomes, from which Ω did the sample we have before us come?

Let us use a crude illustration and explain again. We shall assume we have urns with 100 balls in each that are either black or white. We can have an urn that has no black balls. Let us call this the 0-th urn. An urn with 1 black ball will be called the 1st urn, and so forth for the 2nd, 3rd, up to the 100th urn, which will have 100 black balls and no white balls. Thus, we have 101 urns,

$$p_0 = 0 \quad p_1 = \frac{1}{100} \quad p_2 = \frac{2}{100} \quad \cdots\cdots \quad p_{100} = \frac{100}{100}$$

Let p_i be the proportion of black balls and let $p_i = i/100$ where $i = 0, 1, 2, \ldots, 100$.

Let us take a sample of 25 balls. Thus, we have a 25-dimensional space. The joint density function

$$f(x_1, \ldots, x_{25}, p)$$

associated to the sample space will depend on p. In our simple case, p takes on values $p = i/100$ ($i = 0, 1, 2, \ldots, 100$). Thus, we have 101 spaces which we can denote by

$$\Omega_0, \Omega_1, \ldots, \Omega_{100}$$

each with a specific p.

We have before us a given sample of 25 balls with, say, 8 black balls. The question is: Which of the 101 spaces is most likely to yield the actually observed sample we have before us?

Could it have come from Ω_0? Obviously not, because in Ω_0, there are no black balls. Could it have come from Ω_1, Ω_2, or some other Ω? To answer this question R. A. Fisher proposes the idea of *likelihood*.

The idea is to select the space Ω which will yield the given sample before us more frequently than any other space. The question is, therefore: What is to be used as a criterion to determine which sample space will yield the observed sample more frequently?

Fisher uses the joint density function obtained from the observed sample and looks upon it as a function of p, letting the sample value be fixed. When the joint density function is observed in this manner, he calls it the *likelihood function L*. Thus,

$$L = f(x_1, \ldots, x_n, p) = \Pi f(x_i, p)$$

which is considered a function of p.

The joint density function is a probability associated to each of the points in Ω and as a first approximation can be thought of as showing the probability of a certain point (sample) being selected. In terms of our illustration we have, excluding Ω_0 which has no black balls in it, 100 Ω's from which the observed sample can be selected.

We wish to find the Ω which will yield the observed sample most frequently, relative to the other Ω's.

Thus, the question is, in which one of these 100 Ω's is the $L = \Pi f(x_i, p)$ associated to the observed sample the largest?

Fisher explains this as follows:

> We must return to the actual fact that one value of p, of the frequency of which we know nothing, would yield the observed result three times as frequently as would another value of p. If we need a word to characterise this relative property of different values of p, I suggest that we may speak without confusion of the *likelihood* of one value of p being three times the likelihood of another, bearing always in mind that likelihood is not here used loosely as a synonym of probability, but simply to express the relative frequencies with which such values of the hypothetical quantity p would in fact yield the observed sample.*

This quotation is taken from a context where he discusses other methods of estimation with which he does not agree. And, using his own example he states what is quoted above. His example and the example we use are different, but nevertheless his explanation should be instructive.

(ii) The maximum likelihood estimator

We are now faced with the problem of finding a Ω in which $L = \Pi f(x_i, p)$ is the largest. This is the same thing as finding the p which maximizes L. Then the Ω that is characterized by this p will be the Ω we are looking for and the problem reduces to finding the p that maximizes L.

In our present case we have

$$L = \Pi f(x_i, p) = p^{\Sigma x_i} q^{n - \Sigma x_i}$$

We can apply ordinary calculus procedures to find the p that maximizes L, but it is usually easier to take the logarithm of L and maximize $\log L$ instead of L. This is because L is in the form of a product so that $\log L$ will be in the form of a sum which will make calculations easier. Since a logarithm is a monotone function, the maximum of $\log L$ and the maximum of L will be obtained by the same p.

Furthermore, in our particular example, let $\Sigma x = y$ to simplify. Thus,

$$\log L = \log p^y q^{n-y} = y \log p + (n - y) \log q$$

$$\frac{\partial \log L}{\partial p} = \frac{y}{p} + \frac{n - y}{1 - p}(-1) = 0$$

---

* Reprinted from R. A. Fisher: "On the mathematical foundations of theoretical statistics," *Philosophical Transactions of the Royal Society*, Series A, Vol. 222, p. 326 (1922). By permission of the author and publishers.

Thus,

$$\hat{p} = \frac{y}{n} = \frac{1}{n}\sum x_i$$

In our present case we have 8 black balls in 25 drawings. Thus,

$$\hat{p} = \frac{\sum x_i}{n} = \frac{8}{25} = \frac{32}{100}$$

as we anticipated. In terms of the Ω_i's, the Ω_{32} is the sample space that will yield the observed sample most frequently relative to the other Ω and it is the Ω that is characterized by $\hat{p} = 32/100$. We consider this $\hat{p} = 32/100$ as the estimator of the parameter in the population.

As can be seen we are assuming that the sample is representative of the population. Fisher presents this idea in the following way:

> It should be noted that there is no falsehood in interpreting any set of independent measurements as a random sample from an infinite population: for any such set of numbers are a random sample from the totality of numbers produced by the same matrix of causal conditions: the hypothetical population which we are studying is an aspect of the totality of the effects of these conditions, of whatever nature they may be. The postulate of randomness thus resolves itself into the question, "Of what population is this a random sample?" which must frequently be asked by every practical statistician.*

(iii) *Example*

Let $X_1, \ldots, X_n$ be independent and normally distributed r.v.'s with unknown mean μ and given variance σ^2. Find the ML estimator of μ.

$$f(x_i, \mu) = \frac{1}{\sigma\sqrt{2\pi}}\, e^{-(x_i - \mu)^2/2\sigma^2}$$

$$\log L = \log\left(\frac{1}{2\pi\sigma^2}\right)^{n/2} - \frac{\sum(x_i - \mu)^2}{2\sigma^2}$$

$$\frac{\partial \log L}{\partial \mu} = 0 - \frac{1}{2\sigma^2}\left[2\sum(x_i - \mu)(-1)\right] = 0$$

$$\therefore \quad \sum(x_i - \mu) = 0$$

$$\sum x_i = n\mu$$

$$\therefore \quad \hat{\mu} = \frac{1}{n}\sum x_i$$

Thus the ML estimator of μ is $\bar{X}$.

* Reprinted from R. A. Fisher: op. cit., p. 313. By permission of the author and publishers.

Problems

1. Given a sample of size n of independently and identically distributed normal r.v.'s $X_1, \ldots, X_n$ with given mean μ and unknown variance σ^2, find the ML estimator for the variance.

2. Find the ML estimators for μ and σ^2 simultaneously for the normal case.

3. Let $X_1, \ldots, X_n$ be independent r.v., each being poisson with parameter λ and

$$f(x_i, \lambda) = \frac{\lambda^x e^{-\lambda}}{x!}$$

Find the ML estimator of λ.

4. Let $X_i = \alpha + \beta Z_i + e_i$. Let $E(X_i) = \alpha + \beta Z_i$. Let X_i be normally distributed with mean $E(X_i)$ and variance σ^2. Then,

$$f(x_i) = (2\pi\sigma^2)^{-1/2} \exp \left[-\frac{1}{2\sigma^2} (x_i - \alpha - \beta Z_i)^2 \right]$$

Find the ML estimators for α and β, given a sample $X_1, \ldots, X_n$ (Note that you obtain the *normal equations* of regression analysis.)

14.7 Interval estimation

(i) *The confidence interval*

So far we have been concerned with estimating a parameter, say the mean μ, with a single value, say $\bar{X} = 10$. This is called *estimation by a point*, or simply *point estimation*. We now wish to estimate a parameter, μ, by an interval, say

$$a < \mu < b$$

where a and b are functions of the observations. That is to say, if we select a sample of n observations, and denote this sample as a sample point E in n-dimensional sample space, then $a = a(E)$, $b = b(E)$, and we can write

$$a(E) < \mu < b(E)$$

As an example, let X_1, X_2, X_3, X_4 be a sequence of random variables that are independent and normally distributed with mean μ (unknown) and standard deviation σ. Let the actual observed values be 1, 3, 5, 7. We wish to estimate the population mean using this sample of 4 values. This sample can be looked upon as a sample point in four-dimensional sample space.

We know from the central limit theorem that

$$Z = \frac{\bar{X} - \mu}{\dfrac{\sigma}{\sqrt{n}}} = \frac{\bar{X} - \mu}{\sigma_{\bar{x}}}$$

is asymptotically normal $(0, 1)$. Thus,

$$P\left[-1.96 < \frac{\bar{X} - \mu}{\sigma_{\bar{x}}} < 1.96\right] = 0.95 = \int_{-1.96}^{1.96} \frac{1}{\sqrt{2\pi}} e^{-z^2/2\sigma^2} \, dz = 0.95$$

The above is a legitimate statement because Z is a random variable with a (normal) distribution. Let us rewrite it as

$$P\left[\bar{X} - 1.96 \frac{\sigma}{\sqrt{n}} < \mu < \bar{X} + 1.96 \frac{\sigma}{\sqrt{n}}\right] = 0.95$$

In the last formula, *before* we actually select our sample, we can think that $\bar{X}$ is a random variable although σ and n are given. The value of $\bar{X}$ depends on the sample, i.e., on the sample point E in the sample space. Thus,

$$\bar{X} - 1.96 \frac{\sigma}{\sqrt{n}} = a(E)$$

$$\bar{X} + 1.96 \frac{\sigma}{\sqrt{n}} = b(E)$$

can be thought of as random variables. The meaning of

$$P[a(E) < \mu < b(E)] = 0.95$$

in the above case can be interpreted as follows. From the central limit theorem, we know that $\bar{X}$ is asymptotically normal $N(\mu, \sigma^2/n)$. Diagrammatically we have as shown in Figure 14–3. The r.v. $\bar{X}$ takes on various

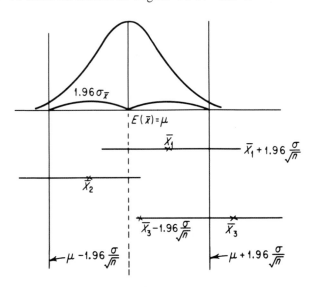

Fig. 14–3

values. Let us express them by $\bar{X}_1$, $\bar{X}_2$, ... Now for example, let $\bar{X}_1$ take on the value as indicated in the graph. Then the interval will be

$$\bar{X}_1 - 1.96 \frac{\sigma}{\sqrt{n}} \quad \text{to} \quad \bar{X}_1 + 1.96 \frac{\sigma}{\sqrt{n}}$$

As the graph shows, this will include μ. Likewise for another value $\bar{X}_2$ we have

$$\bar{X}_2 - 1.96 \frac{\sigma}{\sqrt{n}} \quad \text{to} \quad \bar{X}_2 + 1.96 \frac{\sigma}{\sqrt{n}}$$

which also includes μ.

But $\bar{X}_3$, as shown in our graph, gives us the interval,

$$\bar{X}_3 - 1.96 \frac{\sigma}{\sqrt{n}} \quad \text{to} \quad \bar{X}_3 + 1.96 \frac{\sigma}{\sqrt{n}}$$

which does not include μ. As we can see graphically, the $\bar{X}_3$ falls outside of the two limiting values of $\mu \pm 1.96\sigma_{\bar{x}}$.

The probability that $\bar{X}$ will be in the interval $\mu \pm 1.96\sigma_{\bar{x}}$ is 0.95, i.e., there are 95 chances out of 100 the $\bar{X}$ will be between $\mu - 1.96\sigma_{\bar{x}}$ and $\mu + 1.96\sigma_{\bar{x}}$, given that the μ is in fact the true value of the parameter.

We see from our graph that when we construct our interval,

$$\bar{X} - 1.96 \frac{\sigma}{\sqrt{n}} \quad \text{to} \quad \bar{X} + 1.96 \frac{\sigma}{\sqrt{n}}$$

we can expect that 95 out of 100 such intervals will include μ. Thus,

$$P\left[\bar{X} - 1.96 \frac{\sigma}{\sqrt{n}} < \mu < \bar{X} + 1.96 \frac{\sigma}{\sqrt{n}}\right] = 0.95$$

But once we select a sample and compute $\bar{X}$, for example,

$$\bar{X} = \tfrac{1}{4}(1 + 3 + 5 + 7) = 4$$

then $\bar{X}$ is a fixed constant and is no longer a r.v. Then, for example we have

$$P\left[4 - 1.96 \frac{\sigma}{\sqrt{n}} < \mu < 4 + 1.96 \frac{\sigma}{\sqrt{n}}\right] = 0.95$$

But

$$4 - 1.96 \frac{\sigma}{\sqrt{n}} \quad \text{to} \quad 4 + 1.96 \frac{\sigma}{\sqrt{n}}$$

is a fixed interval so that μ is either in the interval or outside of it and the probability is either 1 or 0.

Let us denote a specific sample that has been observed by E_0. Then,

$$P[a(E_0) < \mu < b(E_0)] = 0.95$$

is not a legitimate probability. J. Neyman has called the interval $[a(E_0), b(E_0)]$ a *confidence interval* and 0.95 is called a *confidence coefficient* to distinguish it from a legitimate probability. Nevertheless, with the above explanation in mind, the 0.95 confidence interval is a meaningful measure of the reliability we place on our interval.

It will be recalled we did not have such a measure when we were talking about point estimation.

It should also be noted that we are assuming that $\theta = \mu$ is the true value of the parameter. Thus, we should write

$$P[a(E_0) < \mu < b(E_0) \mid \mu] = 0.95$$

In general, we can write

$$P[a(E_0) < \theta < b(E_0) \mid \theta] = \alpha$$

where α is the confidence coefficient.

(ii) The best confidence interval

In general, there exist infinitely many confidence intervals. The previous example is shown diagrammatically in Figure 14–4. The $\bar{X}$ was in the interval, for $\alpha = 0.95$,

$$(\mu - 1.96\sigma_{\bar{x}}) \quad \text{to} \quad (\mu + 1.96\sigma_{\bar{x}})$$

and as the diagram shows, we have taken $1.96\sigma_{\bar{x}}$ on both sides of μ which gave us 2.5 per cent on each tail end, thus giving us the 95 per cent confidence coefficient.

Instead of taking $1.96\sigma_{\bar{x}}$ symmetrically on both sides, we can take it a little longer on the left side, say a' and a little shorter on the right side, say b'.

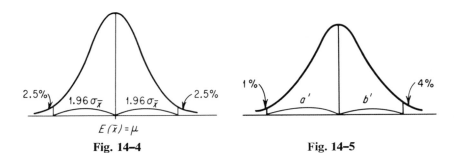

Fig. 14–4   Fig. 14–5

As can be seen by changing the lengths of a' and b' we can find an infinite number of intervals $(\mu - a')$ to $(\mu + b')$ such that the probability of $\bar{X}$ in this interval is 95 per cent. Then, using these intervals a confidence interval of 95 per cent for μ can be constructed. We will have an infinite number of 95 per cent confidence intervals for μ.

The question is, which of these intervals is best?

Several criteria have been suggested, but we shall only mention one. It is that the shortest confidence interval is the most desirable. We merely mention that when we have a symmetrical distribution such as the normal distribution the shortest confidence interval will be obtained when the a and b of above are equal; i.e., $a = b$. But many distributions are not symmetrical and the shortest confidence interval is the exception rather than the rule.

(iii) Other confidence intervals

The theory of confidence intervals we have been discussing is due to J. Neyman. Prior to this approach R. A. Fisher proposed his method which is based on the idea of *fiducial probability* and *fiducial interval*. Neyman's approach was developed from this.

When there is only a single parameter involved both approaches usually give the same results. There are more general approaches based on A. Wald's decision theory and there is still much controversy on these subjects. We shall limit ourselves to the Neyman approach.

It should also be noted that we have discussed the case of a single parameter. When there are two or more parameters to be estimated, we get regions rather than intervals.

Problems

1. Given a r.v. X that is $N(\mu, \sigma = \sqrt{45})$, take a random sample of 5 values, 2, 4, 6, 8, 10. Find the 0.90 confidence interval.

2. Confidence interval for μ of a normal distribution when σ is unknown is obtained from the t-distribution. In most practical cases the σ of the population is not known. The t-distribution gives an exact distribution, avoiding the use of σ. The t-statistic is

$$t = \frac{\bar{X} - \mu}{\sqrt{\dfrac{\sum (X_i - \bar{X})^2}{n(n-1)}}}$$

Noting that $P[-a < t < a] = \alpha$ and using this statistic t, construct a confidence interval with confidence coefficient α.

3. Confidence interval for the variance of a normal distribution is obtained by use of the χ^2 distribution. The χ^2 statistic is

$$\chi^2 = \frac{\sum (X_i - \bar{X})^2}{\sigma^2}$$

Noting that

$$P[a < \chi^2 < b] = \alpha$$

find a confidence interval for σ^2 with confidence coefficient α.

Notes and References

Estimation is usually discussed in two parts, point estimation and interval estimation. See Mood (1950), Chapter 8, "Point Estimation;" and Chapter 11, "Interval Estimation."

For advanced references see Cramer (1946), Chapter 32, "Classification of Estimates;" Chapter 33, "Methods of Estimation;" and Chapter 34, "Confidence Regions." The Cramer-Rao inequality is explained in Chapter 32, the method of maximum likelihood in Chapter 33. Interval estimation is discussed in Chapter 34.

For further discussion of the Cramer-Rao inequality see Lehman (1950), and Chapman and Robbins (1951). Lehman (1950) in Chapter 2 discusses the Cramer-Rao inequality and specifies the regularity conditions which need to be satisfied for the Cramer-Rao inequality to hold. But in certain cases, such as the rectangular distribution, some of the regularity conditions (the condition that we can differentiate the density function under an integral sign) may not hold. Chapman and Robbins (1951) have provided an inequality that is free from these regularity conditions and is at least equal to the Cramer-Rao inequality. Hence, the Cramer-Rao inequality in some cases will not provide the greatest lower bound for the variance of the estimators.

The two papers with which R. A. Fisher presented the maximum likelihood method and explained point estimation are "On the Mathematical Foundations of Theoretical Statistics" (1922), and "Theory of Statistical Estimation" (1925). Both of these papers can be found in Fisher (1950), which is a collection of Fisher's important papers. We have quoted from Fisher's paper "On the Mathematical Foundations" (1922) and also from "Two New Properties of Mathematical Likelihood" (1934). This latter article is also presented in Fisher (1950).

As for interval estimation, as was pointed out in the text, Fisher adopts the fiducial probability approach while J. Neyman uses the confidence interval. We have used the latter. For discussion of the confidence interval approach see Kendall (1948), Chapter 19, "Confidence Interval." For Neyman's paper see "Outline of A Theory of Statistical Estimation" (1937).

For fiducial probability see Kendall (1948), Chapter 20, "Fiducial Inference." Fisher has a number of papers on this subject in the 1930's but his views can also be found in Fisher (1956).

A. Wald has presented a general statistical decision theory and has incorporated estimation theory in this framework. His theory can be found in Wald (1950). But this book is too difficult for an economist who is not professionally trained in mathematical statistics. Fortunately an excellent book is available, Chernoff and Moses (1959). Chapters 7 and 10 are the relevant chapters.

Also see Fraser (1958), Chapter 9 and Rao (1952), Chapter 4. Fraser discusses how the maximum likelihood method is applied to linear models.

For applications of estimation in economics see Valavanis (1959); Klein (1953); Koopmans (1950); and Koopmans (1951). Valavanis (1959) gives a non-technical explanation of the maximum likelihood method. Klein (1953) discusses it by applying it to an econometric model. Koopmans (1950) and Koopmans (1951) are compilations of articles written by members of the Cowles Commission. Several articles in each book discuss various aspects of the maximum likelihood method as related to econometric models.

Bibliography

Chapman, D. G., and Robbins, H., "Minimum Variance Estimation Without Regularity Assumptions," *Annals of Mathematical Statistics*, Vol. 22, pp. 581–586, 1951.

Chernoff, H., and Moses, L. E., *Elementary Decision Theory*. New York: John Wiley & Sons, 1959.

Fisher, R. A., "On the Mathematical Foundations of Theoretical Statistics," *Philosophical Transactions of the Royal Society*, Series A, Vol. 222, 1922.

Fisher, R. A., "Theory of Statistical Estimation," *Proceedings of the Cambridge Philosophical Society*, Vol. 22, 1925.

Fisher, R. A., "Two New Properties of Mathematical Likelihood," *Proceedings of the Royal Society*, Series A, Vol. 144, p. 288, 1934.

Fisher, R. A., *Contributions to Mathematical Statistics*. New York: John Wiley & Sons, 1950.

Halmos, P. R., and Savage, L. J., "Applications of the Radon-Nikodym Theorem to the Theory of Sufficient Statistics," *Annals of Mathematical Statistics*, p. 225, 1949.

Kendall, M. G., *The Advanced Theory of Statistics*. London: Charles Griffen and Company, 2nd ed., 1948.

Klein, L. R., *Econometrics*. Evanston, Illinois: Row, Peterson and Company, 1953.

Lehman, E. L., *Notes on the Theory of Estimation*. Recorded by Colin Blyth. Berkeley, Calif.: Associated Students' Store, University of California, 1950.

Neyman, J., "Outline of a Theory of Statistical Estimation Based on the Classical Theory of Probability," *Philosophical Transactions of the Royal Society*, Series A, Vol. 236, 1937.

Rao, C. R., *Advanced Statistical Methods in Biometric Research*. New York: John Wiley & Sons, 1958.

Valavanis, S., *Econometrics, An Introduction to Maximum Likelihood Methods*. New York: McGraw-Hill Book Co., 1959.

Wald, A., *Statistical Decision Functions*. New York: John Wiley & Sons, 1950.

CHAPTER 15

Testing Hypotheses

15.1 The two-decision problem

The two main aspects of statistics we are discussing are *estimation* and *testing hypotheses*. We will now discuss briefly the latter topic.

Let us develop the problem by using a simple illustration. Consider two urns that have red, green, and black balls in it as shown in Figure 15–1. Let ω_1 and ω_2 indicate the two urns. The ω's are called *states of nature* and indicate in our present problem the distribution of the balls in each urn.

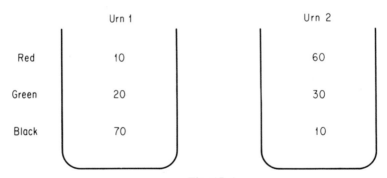

	Urn 1	Urn 2
Red	10	60
Green	20	30
Black	70	10

Fig. 15–1

We perform an experiment of drawing a ball. There are three possible outcomes. Let us assume a black ball has been drawn from one of the urns. From which urn we do not know. But based on the black ball we have drawn, we wish to make a "decision" as to which urn it came from. Or we can say, we wish to decide, on the basis of the observation, which is the true state of nature.

Let us assume we decide that when a black ball is drawn, it came from urn 1, or that the true state of nature is ω_1; when a green ball is drawn it came from ω_2; and when a red ball is drawn, it came from ω_2. Thus, we have set up a "rule" by which we will decide which urn to select when a certain color ball is drawn.

614

Let us further introduce the word *action* and say when ω_1 is selected we have taken action A_1, and when ω_2 is selected, we have taken action A_2. Then the above results may be stated as

outcomes X	action
red	A_2
green	A_2
black	A_1

But now let us perform the same experiment with the following rule.

outcome X	action
r	A_1
b	A_1
g	A_1

That is, we will take action A_1 regardless of what color ball has been drawn. This is the second "rule" that we have adopted.

There are $2^3 = 8$ such rules, and can be shown as in Table 15–1.

Table 15–1

X	d_1	d_2	d_3	d_4	d_5	d_6	d_7	d_8
r	A_1	A_1	A_1	A_2	A_1	A_2	A_2	A_2
g	A_1	A_1	A_2	A_1	A_2	A_1	A_2	A_2
b	A_1	A_2	A_1	A_1	A_2	A_2	A_1	A_2

Based on these rules, either action A_1 or A_2 will be taken when an observation is made. These rules are called *decision rules*.

15.2 Decision rules and sample space

Of the eight decision rules, which one shall we adopt? Before taking up this problem let us formulate it using statistical terms we have studied.

The states of nature ω_1 and ω_2 indicate distributions. In our present case each urn has a tri-nomial distribution. We have shown only two, but we can think that there are many different ω's for the tri-nomial distribution. We shall say we have a *class of possible tri-nomial distributions*. Let us denote this by the general symbol Ω. Thus, for example, the binomial distribution, normal distribution, etc., each form a class. The ω's can be thought of as elements of, or subclasses of Ω. In our example ω_1 is a specific element of the class Ω of tri-nomial distributions.

The three possible outcomes red, green, and black are denoted by X which is a r.v. When a single ball is drawn, we have a sample of size one, and we obtain a one-dimensional *sample space*. There are three *sample points* and the probabilities associated to these points will depend on which ω we

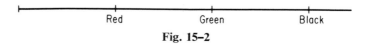

Red   Green   Black

Fig. 15–2

are considering. In our present case we have

$$\omega_1: \quad \{0.10 \quad 0.20 \quad 0.70\} = \{P(r\,|\,\omega_1),\, P(g\,|\,\omega_1),\, P(b\,|\,\omega_1)\}$$
$$\omega_2: \quad \{0.60 \quad 0.30 \quad 0.10\} = \{P(r\,|\,\omega_2),\, P(g\,|\,\omega_2),\, P(b\,|\,\omega_2)\}$$

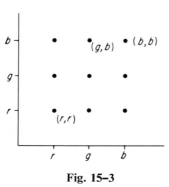

Fig. 15–3

When two balls are drawn (with replacement) we have a two-dimensional sample space, and each sample point is a sample of size 2. The joint distribution function associated with these sample points is given as

$$f(x_1, x_2) = f(x_1)f(x_2)$$

In our present case, for a black and green sample for example

$$f(x_1^b, x_2^g\,|\,\omega_i) = P(b\,|\,\omega_i)\,P(g\,|\,\omega_i), \qquad i = 1, 2$$

And if we have ω_1 and the point (x_1^b, x_2^g), then

$$f(x_1^b, x_2^g\,|\,\omega_1) = 0.70 \times 0.20$$

As is seen, this can be easily extended to an n-dimensional sample space where each sample point is a sample of size n.

In the one-dimensional sample space we had eight decision rules. These decision rules split the sample space up into two parts. One part called the *acceptance region* includes sample points that tell us to take action A_1. The other part includes sample points that tell us to take action A_2. For example, d_2 was

red	A_1
green	A_1
black	A_2

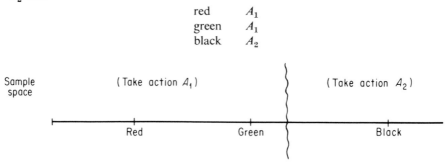

Sample space   (Take action A_1)   (Take action A_2)

Red   Green   Black

Fig. 15–4

Thus we have as shown in Figure 15–4 and likewise for each other decision rule.

When we take a sample of size two, we have a two-dimensional sample space with $3^2 = 9$ sample points. Thus, there are 9 possible outcomes, and hence 2^9 possible decision rules. Let d_i be one of the rules as shown below.

	X	d_i
1.	r, r	A_2
2.	r, g	A_2
3.	r, b	A_2
4.	g, r	A_2
5.	g, g	A_2
6.	g, b	A_1
7.	b, r	A_1
8.	b, g	A_1
9.	b, b	A_1

Fig. 15–5

Then, diagrammatically, we have Figure 15–5.

The sample space is split into two parts, the *acceptance region* which includes samples that tell us (according to d_i) to take action A_1 and a *rejection (critical) region* which has samples telling us to take action A_2.

For the general case, when a sample of size n is selected, we have an n-dimensional sample space. If each r.v. X_i $(i = 1, \dots, n)$ has three possible outcomes, there will be 3^n sample points. Then there will be 2^{3^n} possible decision rules, or different ways of splitting up this sample space.

Each decision rule splits this sample space up into an acceptance region and rejection region (R). When a sample point falls in R, we reject action A_1; i.e., we accept action A_2. Or, in conventional terminology, when the sample point falls in R, we reject the null hypothesis.

The selection of R is thus a problem of selecting a certain group of decision rules from all the possible decision rules. To select something, we need a criterion for selection which will characterize the decision rules. We shall appraise the decision rules and use the appraisals as the criteria for selection. So let us now discuss ways of appraising the decision rules.

15.3 Appraisal of decision rules

We have as follows:

X	ω_1, f	ω_2, g
red	0.10	0.60
green	0.20	0.30
black	0.70	0.10

Table 15–2

X	d_1	d_2	d_3	d_4	d_5	d_6	d_7	d_8
R	A_1	A_1	A_1	A_2	A_1	A_2	A_2	A_2
G	A_1	A_1	A_2	A_1	A_2	A_1	A_2	A_2
B	A_1	A_2	A_1	A_1	A_2	A_2	A_1	A_2

$P(A_1 \mid \omega_1)$	1	0.30	0.80	0.90	0.10	0.20	0.70	0
$P(A_2 \mid \omega_1)$	0	0.70	0.20	0.10	0.90	0.80	0.30	1
$P(A_1 \mid \omega_2)$	1	0.90	0.70	0.40	0.60	0.30	0.10	0
$P(A_2 \mid \omega_2)$	0	0.10	0.30	0.60	0.40	0.70	0.90	1

Consider decision rule d_1, for example, which tells us to take action A_1 regardless of the observation. We can appraise this as follows:

When we use rule d_1, and are given urn one (which we do not know), and draw a ball, we will take action A_1 and claim the true state of nature is ω_1. Thus a correct decision has been made and the probability of making this correct decision is

$$P_{d_1}(A_1 \mid \omega_1) = f(x_1) + f(x_2) + f(x_3) = 0.1 + 0.2 + 0.7 = 1$$

On the other hand, if we should be given urn one (which we do not know) what is the probability that we will take action A_2 and reject A_1? According to rule d_1 action A_1 is taken regardless of the outcome. Thus, the probability that action A_2 is taken is

$$P_{d_1}(A_2 \mid \omega_1) = 0$$

It is quite obvious that

$$P_{d_1}(A_1 \mid \omega_1) + P_{d_1}(A_2 \mid \omega_1) = 1$$

since given ω_1 either action A_1 or A_2 is taken.

Now let us assume that we are given urn two (ω_2) without our knowledge. The probability that we will take action A_1 and make the error of rejecting ω_2 will be

$$P_{d_1}(A_1 \mid \omega_2) = g(x_1) + g(x_2) + g(x_3) = 1$$

On the other hand, the probability of making the correct decision and selecting ω_2 will be

$$P_{d_1}(A_2 \mid \omega_2) = 0$$

since, according to d_1 we always decide on action A_1. Thus we have evaluated d_1, i.e.,

$$P(A_1 \mid \omega_1) = 1$$
$$P(A_2 \mid \omega_1) = 0$$
$$P(A_1 \mid \omega_2) = 1$$
$$P(A_2 \mid \omega_2) = 0$$

The relation between states of nature and actions can be shown schematically as

	ω_1	ω_2
A_1	correct decision $P(A_1 \mid \omega_1)$	incorrect decision $\beta = P(A_1 \mid \omega_2)$
A_2	incorrect decision $\alpha = P(A_2 \mid \omega_1)$	correct decision $P(A_2 \mid \omega_2)$

To take action A_2, given ω_1, is called the *type* I *error*. The probability of making the type I error is shown by

$$\alpha = P(A_2 \mid \omega_1)$$

It is also called the α-error probability, α-risk, and in quality control the producer's risk. To take action A_1, given ω_2, is called the *type* II *error*. The probability of making the type II error is shown by

$$\beta = P(A_1 \mid \omega_2)$$

It is also called the β-error probability, β-risk, and in quality control the consumer's risk.

A simple illustration may be presented.

	ω_1 good student	ω_2 poor student
A_1 pass		$\beta = P(A_1 \mid \omega_2)$
A_2 fail	$\alpha = P(A_2 \mid \omega_1)$	

The type I error is to fail a good student. The type II error is to pass a poor student. Note that depending on how the states of nature and actions are taken, the type I and type II error may be reversed.

	ω_1 poor student	ω_2 good student
(fail) A_1		$\beta = P(A_1 \mid \omega_2)$
(pass) A_2	$\alpha = P(A_2 \mid \omega_1)$	

This shows that passing a poor student is the type I error, and failing a good student is the type II error which is the reverse of what we had above. In applied statistics, the type I error is usually the error that we are more interested in avoiding.

Obviously we would like α and β to be as small as possible. Thus if there are two decision rules d_i and d_j and if

$$\alpha(d_i) < \alpha(d_j)$$
$$\beta(d_i) < \beta(d_j)$$

then the rule d_i which has smaller α and β risks is better than the rule d_j. Let us now evaluate the rest of the decision rules. For example,

$$P_{d_2}(A_1 \mid \omega_1) = f(x_1) + f(x_2) = 0.1 + 0.2 = 0.30$$
$$P_{d_2}(A_2 \mid \omega_1) = f(x_3) = 0.70$$
$$P_{d_2}(A_1 \mid \omega_2) = 0.90$$
$$P_{d_2}(A_2 \mid \omega_2) = 0.10$$

Problem

Evaluate the rest of the rules and check your results with Table 15–2.

15.4 Admissible rules

From the α and β risks in Table 15–2 we have Table 15–3.

Table 15–3

	d_1	d_2	d_3	d_4	d_5	d_6	d_7	d_8
$\alpha = P(A_2 \mid \omega_1)$	0	0.70	0.20	0.10	0.90	0.80	0.30	1
$\beta = P(A_1 \mid \omega_2)$	1	0.90	0.70	0.40	0.60	0.30	0.10	0

Now after characterizing the decision rules we want some kind of a criterion to pick out the most desirable rules. We have already mentioned that we consider the rule with the smaller α and β risks better. Let us formalize this criterion as follows:

Definition. The decision rule d_i is said to be *inadmissible* if there exists another rule d_j such that

$$\alpha_j \leq \alpha_i$$
$$\beta_j \leq \beta_i$$

and one of the $\leq$ is a strict inequality.

Let us apply this criterion to our problems. We see that

$$d_4 \quad \text{is better than} \quad d_2, d_3$$
$$d_7 \quad \text{is better than} \quad d_5, d_6$$

d_1, d_4, d_7, d_8 are rules which are better in either the α or β aspect, and we shall consider these rules as the *class of admissible rules*.

Let us show the decision rules dia-grammatically as in Figure 15–6. Each decision rule can be shown by a point on the (α, β) diagram. Since the smaller α, β are the better the rule, the ideal point would be the origin $(0, 0)$. We can see that the points closer to the origin are better than those further away and the graph shows that the points that corre-spond to d_1, d_4, d_7, d_8 are better than the other points.

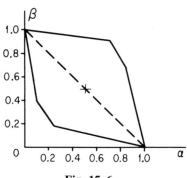

Fig. 15–6

It should also be noted that the points are symmetric about the point $(0.5, 0.5)$. This symmetry arises because one can always make an opposite decision rule. That is, to every admissible rule there is a symmetrical inadmissible rule.

Leaving out the extreme rules, that is, d_1 and d_8, we have d_4 and d_7.

X	d_4	d_7
r	A_2	A_2
g	A_1	A_2
b	A_1	A_1

Each of these decision rules have split the sample space into two regions: *acceptance* and *rejection region*.

In our simple example we had only two admissible rules left. But in the general case it is easy to see that there will be a large number of admissible rules. Thus, the next question that arises is: Which of the admissible rules are more desirable?

Problems

Given the distribution of red, green, and black balls shown below, answer the following.

	ω_1	ω_2
Red	10	60
Green	30	20
Black	60	20

1. Construct a table of decision rules (as in Table 15–2).

2. Evaluate all the decision rules.

3. Find the class of admissible rules.

4. Draw a diagram of the α and β risks.

15.5 The Neyman-Pearson theory

The Neyman-Pearson theory approaches the problem of selecting a decision rule by first selecting a reasonable α risk, or what is called a *significance level*, and then tries to find the smallest β risk.

The graph of the α, β risks was a convex polyhedron. (If we had continuous data it would be a convex region.) The Neyman theory can be shown by first selecting a level of significance α_0, and then finding as we did in the graph the admissible rule with the best β. This is shown in Figure 15–7 by β_0.

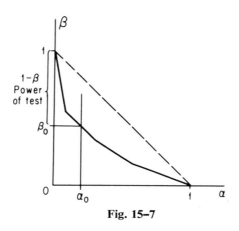

Fig. 15–7

But, if we increase the α_0 we get a smaller β and if we lower the α_0, we get a larger β. The point at which α_0 is to be determined will depend on the nature of the problem and the behavior of the α, β errors. The α risk is usually set at 5, 1, or 0.1 per cent.

(i) The Neyman-Pearson test

Let us now use an illustration and explain the Neyman-Pearson test in more detail. Assume we have a normal distribution with unknown mean and known σ^2. We wish to test the hypothesis that

$$H_0 : \mu = \mu_0$$

In terms of our previous terminology, $\mu = \mu_0$ is the ω_1, and to accept H_0 is to take action A_1.

The *alternative hypothesis* is

$$H_1 : \mu \neq \mu_0$$

and this is where we differ from our previous terminology. That is, $\mu \neq \mu_0$ is not equivalent to ω_2. $\mu \neq \mu_0$ indicates all the other μ's that are not μ_0.

ω_2 indicates only one of these μ's. The present case is not symmetrical as in our previous case.

But, for convenience let us say that the alternative is comparable to ω_2 and to accept H_2, i.e., to reject H_1, is to take action A_2.

Fig. 15–8

Let us take a sample of size 2. Then we have a two-dimensional space with r.v.'s X_1 and X_2. Graphically we have as shown in Figure 15–8. We wish, on the basis of the sample, to determine whether to take action A_1 or A_2. The problem is shown schematically as

	ω_1	ω_2
A_1	$P(A_1 \mid \omega_1)$	$P(A_1 \mid \omega_2) = \beta$
A_2	$P(A_2 \mid \omega_1) = \alpha$	$P(A_2 \mid \omega_2)$

We will set $\alpha = 5$ per cent. The conventional way of solving this problem is to map the sample space into a new space by means of a *sufficient statistic* so that it will be easier to handle. We use the sufficient statistic $\bar{X}$ (the sample mean) which is a new r.v. It is the function defined on the original two-dimensional sample space, which can be considered the domain of the r.v. The new space is the range of the r.v. $\bar{X}$ and is shown in Figure 15–9.

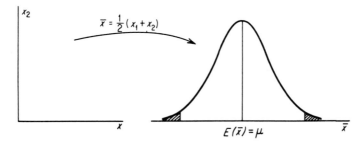

Fig. 15–9

From the central limit theorem, we know the sampling distribution of $\bar{X}$ is normal. Thus the two-dimensional sample space has been reduced to a one-dimensional sample space of $\bar{X}$. If we took a sample of size n, then the n-dimensional sample space will be reduced to a one-dimensional sample space by the r.v. $\bar{X}$. The advantage is, instead of considering an n-dimensional sample space, we need only consider the one-dimensional sample space because $\bar{X}$ is a sufficient statistic. Instead of finding an acceptance region in n-dimensions, we need only to find it in the new one-dimensional sample space. Thus if,

$$\bar{X} > \mu + 1.96 \frac{\sigma}{\sqrt{n}} \quad \text{or} \quad \bar{X} < \mu - 1.96 \frac{\sigma}{\sqrt{n}} \qquad \dots \text{take action } A_2$$

$$\mu - 1.96 \frac{\sigma}{\sqrt{n}} < \bar{X} < \mu + 1.96 \frac{\sigma}{\sqrt{n}} \qquad \dots \text{take action } A_1$$

and we know that

$$P\left[\mu - 1.96 \frac{\sigma}{\sqrt{n}} < \bar{X} < \mu + 1.96 \frac{\sigma}{\sqrt{n}}\right] = 0.95$$

Therefore, the shaded region in the right hand graph is the rejection region R and in-between is the acceptance region.

In terms of the original sample space, R is obtained from the two inequalities,

$$\bar{X} > \mu + 1.96 \frac{\sigma}{\sqrt{n}}$$

$$\bar{X} < \mu - 1.96 \frac{\sigma}{\sqrt{n}}$$

This is,

$$\frac{1}{2}(X_1 + X_2) > \mu + 1.96 \frac{\sigma}{\sqrt{n}}$$

$$\frac{1}{2}(X_1 + X_2) < \mu - 1.96 \frac{\sigma}{\sqrt{n}}$$

In graphical terms we have as shown in Figure 15–10. If we integrate over R given ω_1, we get

$$\alpha = P(A_2 \mid \omega_1) = \int_R f_1(x_1, x_2) \, dx_1 \, dx_2$$

where the subscript 1 of f_1 indicates it is the density function of ω_1.

(ii) The power of a test

Now a question arises: Are there any regions R other than the one we have selected? The answer is yes. Look at the sampling distribution of $\bar{X}$ in Figure 15–9. The shaded area was 5 per cent. But we can change the

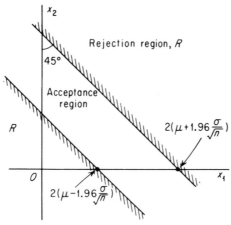

Fig. 15–10

amount of the shaded area on both sides and maintain the same amount of 5 per cent shaded area. Thus, we may have infinitely many rejection regions.

Take as an illustration the case where 5 per cent of the shaded area is all on the right tail of the normal curve. Let this region be R_1. Then the question is: which of the rejection regions R or R_1 is better? Since both have $\alpha = 5$ per cent, we compare the β. This is carried out by use of the idea of the *power of a test*. Let us discuss this idea.

The *power of a test is*

$$1 - \beta = 1 - P(A_1 \mid \omega_2) = 1 - \int_R f_2(x_1, x_2)\, dx_1\, dx_2$$

As can be seen,

$$1 - \beta = 1 - P(A_1 \mid \omega_2) = P(A_2 \mid \omega_2)$$

That is, it is the probability of taking action A_2 given ω_2 which is a correct decision. Thus, the larger the power of a test the better. The power of the test is taken with respect to the alternative hypothesis. In our original problem, the alternative hypothesis was $\mu \neq \mu_0$, which is a composite hypothesis. Hence, to compute the power we need to specify the alternative, and, as different alternatives are specified, we find a sequence of powers.

Let us illustrate by use of an example. Assume a r.v. X which indicates the scores of students in a test. This r.v. X is assumed to be $N(\mu, \sigma = 6)$. That is, we know the standard deviation is $\sigma = 6$ points but we do not know its mean μ. We wish to test whether or not the mean is $\mu = 30$ points. Thus, we set up our hypothesis as

$$H_0: \quad \mu = 30$$
$$H_1: \quad \mu \neq 30$$

To test this hypothesis, we shall take a random sample of size $n = 4$. Thus, we have a sequence of four r.v.'s, X_1, X_2, X_3, X_4. We combine these four r.v.'s and construct a new r.v.,

$$\bar{X} = \tfrac{1}{4}(X_1 + X_2 + X_3 + X_4)$$

which is the sample mean, and we will use this new r.v. $\bar{X}$ for the test. $\bar{X}$ is a function defined on the four-dimensional sample space. What we are doing is mapping the probabilities of a four-dimensional sample space into a one-dimensional sample space by use of the new r.v. $\bar{X}$ which is a sufficient statistic.

Fig. 15–11

From the central limit theorem we know that the new one-dimensional sample space will be $N(\mu, \sigma_{\bar{X}} = 6/2 = 3)$. What we want to do is to use this one-dimensional sample space to test the hypothesis because we can use the normal probability table and calculate probabilities quicker and easier than in the four-dimensional sample space. This new one-dimensional sample space which we call the sampling distribution of the sample mean $\bar{X}$ can be shown as in Figure 15–11.

We are assuming the scores to be from 0 to 100. The sampling distribution of $\bar{X}$ which corresponds to H_0; $\mu = 30$ is shown by ω_1 where the $E(\bar{X}) = 30$. The sampling distribution of $\bar{X}$ which corresponds to H_1; $\mu \neq 30$ is shown by ω_2. There will be many such sampling distributions. We have shown one such distribution where $E(\bar{X}) = 41.88$.

Next, let A_1 be the action of adopting H_0, and A_2 be the action of adopting H_1. Then we can set up our problem schematically.

	ω_1 $\mu = 30$	ω_2 $\mu \neq 30$
A_1	$P(A_1 \mid \omega_1)$	$\beta = P(A_1 \mid \omega_2)$
A_2	$\alpha = P(A_2 \mid \omega_1)$	$P(A_2 \mid \omega_2)$

Let us set the level of significance, that is, the α-risk, at

$$\alpha = P(A_2 \mid \omega_1) = 5 \text{ per cent}$$

In terms of our diagram, we take 2.5 per cent on each tail of ω_1. From the normal probability table we know that the area will be located 1.96 standard deviations away from $E(\bar{X}) = 30$. Since $\sigma_{\bar{x}} = 3$ points, we have

$$1.96 \times 3 = 5.88 \text{ points}$$

Thus, for example, the upper tail of ω_1 will be at $30 + 5.88 = 35.88$ points, and the lower tail will be at $30 - 5.88 = 24.12$ points as shown in the diagram.

This means that if μ was in fact 30 points, then there are 5 chances in 100 that $\bar{X}$ will fall outside of the interval (24.12, 35.88). When $\bar{X}$ falls in this interval, we take action A_1.

Let us now consider the β-risk. For purposes of illustration, set $H_1 : \mu = 41.88$. Then the shaded area in the left-hand tail can be calculated.

$$\frac{E(\bar{X} \mid \omega_2) - \bar{X}}{\sigma_{\bar{x}}} = \frac{41.88 - 35.88}{3} = \frac{6}{3} = 2$$

Thus the shaded area is $2\sigma_{\bar{x}}$ away from $E(\bar{X}) = 41.88$ and the shaded area is 2.28 per cent of the total area. Thus,

$$\beta = P(A_1 \mid \omega_2) = 2.28 \text{ per cent}$$

An alternative way of showing this is

$$\beta = P(A_1 \mid \omega_2) = \int_{24.12}^{35.88} \frac{1}{\sqrt{2\pi}\,\sigma_{\bar{x}}}\, e^{-(\bar{x} - 41.88)^2 / 2\sigma_{\bar{x}}^2}\, d\bar{x} = 0.0228$$

The unshaded area is $1 - \beta$ which is the power of the test for the hypothesis $H_1 : \mu = 41.88$. Let us consider other situations. Let $H_1 : \mu = 35.88$. Then, from the normal probability table

$$\beta = P(A_1 \mid \omega_2) = \int_{24.12}^{35.88} (\sqrt{2\pi}\sigma_{\bar{x}})^{-1} \exp\left[-\frac{(\bar{x} - 35.88)^2}{2\sigma_{\bar{x}}^2} \right] d\bar{x} = 0.50$$

For $H_1 : \mu = 30$ we get

$$\beta = P(A_1 \mid \omega_2) = 1 - P(A_2 \mid \omega_2)$$

$$= \int_{24.12}^{35.88} (\sqrt{2\pi}\sigma_{\bar{x}})^{-1} \exp\left[-\frac{(\bar{x} - 30)^2}{2\sigma_{\bar{x}}^2} \right] d\bar{x} = 0.95$$

Two other cases are

$$H_1 : \mu = 24.12:$$
$$\beta = P(A_1 \mid \omega_2) = 0.50$$
$$H_1 : \mu = 18.12$$
$$\beta = P(A_1 \mid \omega_2) = 0.0228$$

Let us graph these results as in Figure 15–12.

Table 15–4

ω_2	β	$1 - \beta$
41.88	2.28 per cent	97.72
35.88	50.00	50.00
30.00	95.00	5.00
24.12	50.00	50.00
18.12	2.28	97.72

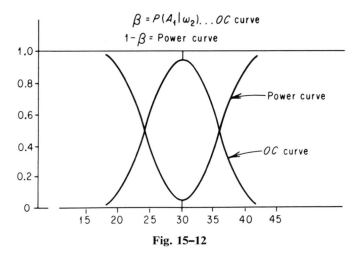

Fig. 15–12

The curve based on the ω_2 values and the β values is called the *operating characteristic curve of the region R* and is usually abbreviated the *OC curve*. The curve based on the ω_2 values and the power of the test $1 - \beta$ is called the *power curve of the region R*.

We have shown the power curve when the rejection region was taken on both tails of the normal curve. Let us now obtain the power function (curve) for the other region R_1 where the 5 per cent region of rejection is all in the right-hand tail of the curve. Graphically we have Figure 15–13. Then computations will give us the following results.

Table 15–5

ω_2	$\beta = P(A_1 \mid \omega_2)$	$1 - \beta$
40.92	2.28	97.72
34.92	50.00	50.00
30.00	95.00	5.00
25.00	100.00	0.00

Let us plot the power curve for the regions R and R_1 as in Figure 15–14.

As the graph shows the power curve for R_1 is above the power curve for

R when $\mu > 30$, and coincides with it when $\mu = 30$, then falls below it when $\mu < 30$. We know that $1 - \beta = P(A_2 \mid \omega_2)$ shows the chances of *NOT* making an error and hence the higher the curve, the less chances of making an error. Therefore when $\mu > 30$, the test which uses region R_1 (one-tail test) is superior to the test that uses region R (two-tail test).

On the other hand, for $\mu < 30$, the test that uses region R is better.

Fig. 15–13

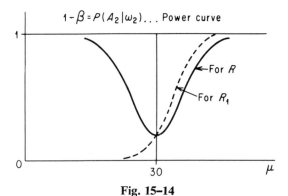

Fig. 15–14

If we could find a test with a rejection region R such that the power curve of this region R is above any other test based on any other region, it would be the uniformly most superior test. Such a test is called the *uniformly most powerful test* and the region is called the *uniformly most powerful region*.

There are important tests that are UMP tests. The one-tail test of means just used as an example is an illustration. But as the one-tail test shows the choice of R depends on the problem we have. Since there are many other tests that are not UMP, other criteria have been proposed such as an *unbiased test* but we shall not discuss these here.

(iii) The fundamental lemma

We have seen that given a significance level α_0, we wish to find a most powerful test. The question we now discuss is: How do we find a most powerful test?

When we have a simple hypothesis and a simple alternative, we can use Neyman's Fundamental Lemma to find a most powerful test. Let us discuss the rationale of this Lemma with our urn illustration.

We had two urns:

	urn 1—$f(x)$	urn 2—$g(x)$
red	10	60
green	20	30
black	70	10

Let us divide $g(x)$ by $f(x)$

$$\text{red:} \quad g(x^r)/f(x^r) = 0.6/0.1 = 6$$
$$\text{green:} \quad g(x^g)/f(x^g) = 0.3/0.2 = 1.5$$
$$\text{black:} \quad g(x^b)/f(x^b) = 0.1/0.7 = 0.14$$

The ratio $g(x^r)/f(x^r) = 6$ tells us that the probability associated to the red ball in urn 2 is 6 times greater than that of urn 1.

If $g(x)/f(x) = 1$, the probabilities associated to x are the same in ω_1 and ω_2.

If $g(x)/f(x) > 1$, then the probability associated to x in ω_1 is smaller than in ω_2.

Now if we were to select a red ball, it is natural for us to think that it came from urn 2 because the probability in urn 2 is 0.6 whereas in urn 1 it is 0.1. This is indicated by the ratio $g(x)/f(x) = 6$. In general, let $g/f > k$. Then, the larger k is, the more probable it is that x came from urn 2, i.e., ω_2.

By adjusting the value of k we are selecting the region R. For example when

$$g(x)/f(x) > k = 0.1$$

all three sample points will satisfy this relation. When $k = 1$, only x^r and x^g satisfy the relation. When $k = 5$, only x^r satisfies the relation. When $k = 7$, no sample point satisfies the relation.

Thus by making k larger, two things are being accomplished. The first is that $f(x)$ must become small relative to $g(x)$ which implies that it is more probable that the x are from ω_2. The second is that the set of sample points (i.e., samples) that satisfy $g/f > k$ becomes smaller.

When two balls are selected, we have a two-dimensional sample space, and each sample point has associated to it the probabilities

$$f(x_1, x_2) = f(x_1)f(x_2)$$

or

$$g(x_1, x_2) = g(x_1)g(x_2)$$

Then the ratio becomes

$$\frac{g(x_1, x_2)}{f(x_1, x_2)} > k$$

and we can apply the same reasoning as for the single ball case. When a sample of size n is selected, we have

$$\frac{g(x_1, \ldots, x_n)}{f(x_1, \ldots, x_n)} > k$$

Each sample of size n is now a sample point in n-dimensional sample space.

Now the fundamental lemma states:

A most powerful test for a given level of significance α (i.e., the probability of type I error) is obtained when one chooses as the rejection region R the set of points in ω_1 that satisfy

$$\frac{g(x_1, \ldots, x_n)}{f(x_1, \ldots, x_n)} > k$$

where k is selected so that

$$\int_R f(x_1, \ldots, x_n)\, dx_1 \ldots dx_n = \alpha$$

The value of k determines the set of sample points R to be selected in ω_1 such that the cumulative probability over these points will be equal to α (say, $\alpha = 0.05$). This means that the probability of selecting a point in R given ω_1 is 0.05. That is, the probability of selecting a sample from R given the state of nature ω_1, is 0.05.

Since the condition $g/f > k$ implies that the points more likely have come from ω_2 than ω_1, the rejection of the null hypothesis ω_1 and acceptance of ω_2 when a point (i.e., sample) in R is selected, is reasonable. Nevertheless, there is always the risk that the point (sample) may have actually come from ω_1.

The α risk (or the probability of the type I error) is the probability of making the error of rejecting the null hypothesis (ω_1) when in fact it is true. For example, $\alpha = 0.05$ means the probability of making the error of rejecting ω_1 when in fact it is true, is 5 chances in 100. Or we may say, there are 5 chances in 100 of selecting a sample that leads to the rejection of the null hypothesis ω_1.

We shall call g/f the *probability ratio* to distinguish it from the likelihood ratio which is discussed later. We assume that these functions f and g are functions of $E = (x_1, \ldots, x_n)$, the sample points. The term likelihood is reserved for the case when we look upon the functions as functions of the parameters.

Problems

1. Recompute the illustration using $\alpha = 10\%$ and do the following.

    (a) Draw a diagram similar to Figure 15–11 and put in new figures, and explain what is being done.

    (b) Calculate several β's as in Table 15–4 and draw the power curve and OC curve.

    (c) Compute the β's for a one-tail test as in Figure 15–13 and Table 15–5 and draw the power curve for this case in the figure you have drawn in (b) above.

    (d) Increase the sample size from 4 to 9 and find the power curve. Explain what you observe.

2. Given the hypothesis

$$H_0 : \mu = \mu_0$$
$$H_1 : \mu \neq \mu_0$$

    and the normal distribution

$$f(x) = \frac{1}{\sqrt{2\pi}\sigma} e^{-(x-\mu)^2/2\sigma^2}$$

    answer the following.

    (a) Take a random sample of size n and find

$$f(x_1, x_2, \ldots, x_n)$$

    (b) Find the probability ratio

$$\frac{g(x_1, \ldots, x_n)}{f(x_1, \ldots, x_n)}$$

    where for $g(x_1, \ldots, x_n)$, assume that $\mu = \mu_1$. Show that this ratio becomes

$$\exp\left[\frac{1}{2\sigma^2}\sum(x_i - \mu_0)^2 - \frac{1}{2\sigma^2}\sum(x_i - \mu_1)^2\right]$$

    Note that this result includes μ_1.

15.6 The minimax rule

We have discussed the Neyman-Pearson approach as a way of selecting the α and β risks and choosing a decision rule. We will discuss another method, the *likelihood ratio test*. But before that let us mention briefly another method, viz., the *minimax rule*.

In our original example we had as admissible rules

$$
\begin{array}{lll}
d_4 & \alpha = 0.10, & \beta = 0.40 \\
d_7 & \alpha = 0.30, & \beta = 0.10
\end{array}
$$

The maximum error of d_4 is $\beta = 0.40$. For d_7 it is $\alpha = 0.30$. The minimax rule says: Pick the decision rule where the maximum of the errors is smaller. Thus, between d_4 and d_7, the smaller maximum error is $\alpha = 0.30$ of d_7 and we pick d_7 as the decision rule.

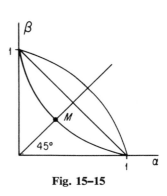

Fig. 15–15

Now, if we had continuous data, the convex region in the α-β graph would be as shown in Figure 15–15. Since the minimax rule wants to minimize the maximum error of a decision rule, the admissible decision rule would be that rule that is characterized by $\alpha = \beta$ or point M on the graph. Any other point on the southwest line of the convex region which shows the admissible rules would give a larger α (if we go down from M) or a larger β (if we go up from M). Thus, the point M provides the minimax rule where $\alpha = \beta$. We can write this as

$$\min \, [\max \, (\alpha, \beta)]$$

We shall discuss the minimax concept later in game theory.

15.7 The likelihood-ratio test

Let us summarize what we have done so far. (1) Given a two-decision problem, we first found all the possible decision rules. (2) Then, the rules were divided into two classes, admissible and inadmissible rules. (3) From the class of admissible rules, the Neyman-Pearson lemma was used to select desirable rules. We also pointed out the minimax criterion for selection.

The Neyman-Pearson criterion of selection was suitable when we had a simple hypothesis and a simple alternative. But most practical problems have a simple hypothesis with composite alternatives. In such cases how do we select desirable rules from the class of admissible rules? For this we have the *likelihood ratio test*.

Let us first present a heuristic explanation. Consider a group of students whose I.Q.'s are distributed normally with unknown mean μ and known standard deviation $\sigma = 10$ points. Assume for brevity that the I.Q.'s are from 60 points to 140 points and are given in integers. Let $\omega(60)$ denote the normal distribution of I.Q.'s with mean $\mu = 60$ and $\sigma = 10$. $\omega(61)$ is the distribution with mean $\mu = 61$ and $\sigma = 10$, and so forth. Thus, we have a class of normal distributions.

$$\Omega: \quad \omega(60), \; \omega(61), \; \ldots \; \omega(100), \; \ldots \; \omega(140)$$

We wish to test whether or not the group of students have an I.Q. of $\mu = 100$. Thus, the hypothesis is

$$H_0: \quad \mu = 100 \quad \ldots \quad \omega(100)$$
$$H_1: \quad \mu \neq 100 \quad \ldots \quad \Omega - \omega(100)$$

As can be seen, the H_0 is a simple hypothesis whereas the alternative hypothesis H_1 is composite.

To test this hypothesis select a random sample of size n ($n = 2$ for simplicity) and assume the result is

$$X_1 = 105, \qquad X_2 = 107$$

Now let us ask the question: From which of the various ω's is it most likely that this sample came? According to the maximum likelihood estimators we studied, we know that the ML estimator for the mean of a normal distribution is

$$\hat{\mu} = \bar{X}$$

Thus the ML estimate based on our sample is

$$\hat{\mu} = \bar{X} = \tfrac{1}{2}(105 + 107) = 106$$

This means that when the sample of $n = 2$, (105, 107) is taken from $\omega(106)$, the likelihood function

$$L(\hat{\Omega}) = \prod_{i=1}^{2} f(x_i) = \left(\frac{1}{\sqrt{2\pi}\sigma}\right)^2 \exp\left(-\frac{1}{2\sigma^2} \sum_{i=1}^{2}(x_i - 106)^2\right)$$

will be at a maximum. This can be easily seen from the fact that $L(\hat{\Omega})$ becomes larger as the absolute value of the exponent becomes smaller. σ^2 is given. Thus, $L(\hat{\Omega})$ will be at a maximum when $\sum (x_i - \mu)^2$ is at a minimum. But this is at a minimum when $\mu = \bar{X}$.

The likelihood function, when we assume the sample came from $\omega(100)$, is

$$L(\hat{\omega}) = \left(\frac{1}{\sqrt{2\pi}\sigma}\right)^2 e^{-(1/2\sigma^2)\Sigma(x_i - 100)^2}$$

As we can see

$$\sum (x_i - 100)^2 = (105 - 100)^2 + (107 - 100)^2 = 84$$

whereas for $L(\hat{\Omega})$,

$$\sum (x_i - \bar{X})^2 = (105 - 106)^2 + (107 - 106)^2 = 2$$

Thus $L(\hat{\omega})$ will be much smaller than $L(\hat{\Omega})$. We can interpret this to mean that the sample, (105, 107), is more likely to come from $L(\hat{\Omega})$ than $L(\hat{\omega})$.

To express this comparison set

$$\lambda = \frac{L(\hat{\omega})}{L(\hat{\Omega})}$$

Then λ will range between $0 \leq \lambda \leq 1$. For example, if we set the hypothesis as

$$H_0: \quad \mu = 106 \quad \ldots \quad \omega(106)$$

$$H_1: \quad \mu \neq 106 \quad \ldots \quad \Omega - \omega(106)$$

then $\lambda = 1$. The common sense of this is that if we first assume that the mean I.Q. is $\mu = 106$, and then select a sample of $n = 2$ which gives us $X_1 = 105$, $X_2 = 107$, we would be reasonably confident that our assumption of $\mu = 106$ is not far off.

On the other hand, if we assumed that $\mu = 70$, and the sample gave us $X_1 = 105$, $X_2 = 107$, then we would not be confident that our assumption of $\mu = 70$ is correct. In this case, $L(\hat{\omega})$ will be very small, and thus,

$$\lambda = \frac{L(\hat{\omega})}{L(\hat{\Omega})}$$

will also be very small. Therefore, λ becomes an index of how sure we can be about our hypothesis.

The point to note is that we have used the ML estimate to find $L(\hat{\Omega})$. If H_0 is also a composite hypothesis, then we would also find the ML estimate for ω and find the likelihood function $L(\hat{\omega})$. Hence we call it a *likelihood ratio*.

Now that we have found λ we need to find a value k such that when $0 \leq \lambda \leq k \leq 1$, we reject the hypothesis, and in so doing the probability of making the type I error is at the desired level, say $\alpha = 5$ per cent. α is the risk of rejecting $H_0(\mu = 100)$ when in fact it is true. In terms of a diagram (Figure 15–16), we have the distribution of I.Q.'s under the hypothesis that

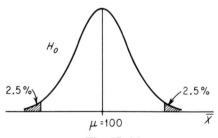

Fig. 15–16

$\mu = 100$. And $\alpha = 5$ per cent means we want the rejection region to be the shaded tail end which has 2.5 per cent of the area in each tail. (Actually, we do not yet know whether or not to take 2.5 per cent on both tails or, say, 2 per cent on one tail and 3 per cent on the other.) For this we have to find the relation between λ and $\bar{X}$ and also the distribution of λ. We have already seen that the likelihood ratio λ is

$$\lambda = \frac{L(\hat{\omega})}{L(\hat{\Omega})} = \exp\left[\frac{1}{2\sigma^2}\Sigma(x_i - \bar{x})^2 - \frac{1}{2\sigma^2}\Sigma(x_i - \mu_0)^2\right]$$

$$= \exp\frac{-n}{2\sigma^2}(\bar{x} - \mu_0)^2$$

Taking the natural log on both sides, we find

$$-2\ln\lambda = \frac{n}{\sigma^2}(\bar{x} - \mu_0)^2 = \frac{(\bar{x} - \mu_0)^2}{\dfrac{\sigma^2}{n}}$$

Let us set $-2\ln\lambda = \chi^2$. Then we have

$$\chi^2 = \frac{(\bar{x} - \mu_0)^2}{\sigma_{\bar{x}}^2}$$

where $\sigma_{\bar{x}}^2 = \sigma^2/n$. This is a Chi-square distribution with one degree of freedom.

What we want is

$$P[\chi^2 > m] = 0.05$$

From the Table of χ^2-distribution we find $m = 3.841$. Thus,

$$P\left[\frac{(\bar{x} - \mu_0)^2}{\sigma_{\bar{x}}^2} > 3.841\right] = 0.05$$

or $$P\left[-1.96 < \frac{\bar{x} - \mu_0}{\sigma_{\bar{x}}} < 1.96\right] = 0.95 \qquad (\sqrt{3.841} = 1.96)$$

or $$P[\mu_0 - 1.96\sigma_{\bar{x}} < \bar{x} < \mu_0 + 1.96\sigma_{\bar{x}}] = 0.95$$

In terms of Figure 15–16, the critical region is found to be the tail ends beyond $\mu_0 \pm 1.96\sigma_{\bar{x}}$. (This shows we should take 2.5 per cent on each tail as we have done.)

Let us summarize our discussion. We first found the maximum likelihood estimates for the H_0 case and H_1 case. Second we constructed the likelihood ratio λ. Third, it was shown that this λ (i.e., $-2\ln\lambda$) had a χ^2 distribution. And from this χ^2 distribution we found that when

$$\chi^2 > 3.841 = m$$

the probability was 5 per cent. This means

$$-2\ln\lambda > m$$

$$\lambda < e^{-m/2} = k$$

Thus, we have found a k such that, given H_0 the critical region is given by $0 < \lambda < k$, which gives $\alpha = 5$ per cent. Fourth, we have seen that this χ^2 relation with $\bar{X}$ can be shown to be the familiar two tail test of sample means.

In our present case, $-2 \ln \lambda$ was an exact χ^2-distribution. But in general, Wilks (1950) has shown that when we have a large sample, $-2 \ln \lambda$ will be approximately distributed as a χ^2-distribution.

Summarizing from a broader point, we first found all possible decision rules. Second, we selected a class of admissible rules. Third, from this class of admissible rules, we selected the desirable rules by use of the likelihood-ratio test.

Problems

1. Show that

$$\frac{1}{2\sigma^2} \sum (x_i - \bar{x})^2 - \frac{1}{2\sigma^2} \sum (x_i - \mu_0)^2 = -\frac{n}{2\sigma^2} (\bar{x} - \mu_0)^2$$

2. Using the references at the end of the chapter, study the application of the likelihood-ratio test to the following cases.

    (a) Tests on the mean of a normal population, with mean and variance unknown.

    (b) Tests on the variance of a normal distribution.

Notes and References

The basic reference for the decision theory approach is Wald (1950) but it is too advanced for non-mathematicians. The Chernoff and Moses (1959) book provides the theory on an elementary level accessible to economists. The three other books that discuss this approach are Savage (1954), Schlaifer (1959), and Raiffa and Schlaifer (1961) that were mentioned in the Notes and References of Chapter 13. Several important topics necessary for further study of this decision theory approach that we have not discussed are the concepts of subjective probabilities, utility, and Bayes strategies. These can be found in the above mentioned references.

What we have done is to use part of this general decision theory approach and re-interpret the classical theory of testing hypothesis which was mainly developed by R. A. Fisher, J. Neyman, and K. Pearson.

A basic reference for the classical approach is Lehmann (1959) but it is too advanced for non-mathematicians. However, there are many elementary references and the following are recommended: Neyman (1950), Chapter 5; Mood (1950), Chapter 12; Fraser (1958), Chapter 10; and Hoel (1954), Chapter 10. Lehmann discusses two concepts, unbiasedness (Chapters 4, 5) and invariance (Chapter 6) for testing hypothesis which we have not discussed. Fraser (1957), Chapter 5, discusses testing hypothesis for non-parametric methods.

A short historical note with a very extensive annotated bibliography on testing hypothesis is in Lehmann (1959), pp. 120–124. Similarly, extensive bibliographies on unbiasedness and invariance are also in Lehmann (1959) after the respective Chapters that discuss these subjects.

Bibliography

Lehmann, E. L., *Testing Statistical Hypotheses.* New York: John Wiley & Sons, Inc., 1959.

Fraser, D. A. S., *Nonparametric Methods in Statistics.* New York: John Wiley & Sons, Inc., 1957.

CHAPTER 16

Regression Analysis

One of the most widely used techniques in economics is regression analysis. Illustrations of its use can be found in time series, consumption functions, demand functions, and various other statistical problems. We shall discuss it theoretically at an elementary level. Computational techniques such as the Doolittle method which can be found in standard statistics text books are not discussed.

16.1 Introduction

Three models of linear regression that are most frequently used in economics are discussed. For purposes of explanation, consider the following model

$$Y = A + BX + \epsilon$$

This is shown in Figure 16–1. $A + BX$ shows the straight line. Y is an individual value of Y. ϵ is the deviation of Y from $A + BX$. Using this model, the following three cases are distinguished.

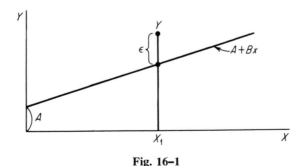

Fig. 16–1

Model 1. Y is a random variable; X is a fixed constant (a mathematical variable); ϵ is a random variable that is $N(O, \sigma^2)$ where σ^2 is unknown; and

A and B are parameters. The difference between Y and X is that Y has a probability distribution, whereas X has not. The statistical problem is to select a sample of values and estimate the parameters A and B.

Model 2. ϵ is a random variable such that $E(\epsilon) = 0$, Var $(\epsilon) = \sigma^2$ where σ^2 is unknown. We do *not* assume ϵ is normally distributed.

Model 3. X and Y have a joint normal distribution. ϵ is also normally distributed with $E(\epsilon) = 0$, Var $(\epsilon) = \sigma^2$.

16.2 Model 1—one independent variable case

(i) *The population*

Assume that we wish to find the relation between the height of fathers (X) and sons (Y). For each given (fixed) height of X, there is associated a sub-population of Y values. This is shown in Table 16–1.

Table 16–1

X	Y (son)		
X_1	Y_{11}	Y_{12}	...
X_2	Y_{21}	Y_{22}	...
$\vdots$	$\vdots$	$\vdots$	
X_k	Y_{k1}	Y_{k2}	...

The whole population is made up of a family of k subpopulations.

Let μ_i be the mean of the i-th subpopulation and assume the following linear hypothesis

$$(1) \qquad \mu_i = A + BX_i$$

That is, the mean μ_i is a linear function of X_i.

Let Y_{ij} be the j-th individual value of the i-th subpopulation. Then,

$$(2) \qquad \epsilon_{ij} = Y_{ij} - \mu_i \qquad \begin{aligned} i &= 1, 2, \dots k \\ j &= 1, 2, \dots . \end{aligned}$$

is the deviation of Y_{ij} from μ_i. From (1) and (2) we find

$$(3) \qquad Y_{ij} = A + BX_i + \epsilon_{ij}$$

The assumption of this model is that ϵ_{ij} are normally distributed with $E(\epsilon) = 0$, Var $(\epsilon) = \sigma^2$. We have not designated the distribution of Y_{ij}, except that it is a random variable. Let us now find the distribution of Y_{ij} with the help of Jacobian transformations, using the assumptions concerning ϵ_{ij}.

First note that

$$E(Y_{ij}) = A + BX_i + E(\epsilon_{ij})$$
$$= A + BX_i = \mu_i$$

Next we find that

$$\text{Var}\,(\epsilon) = E[\epsilon - E(\epsilon)]^2 = E(\epsilon)^2$$

$$= E[Y_{ij} - \mu_i]^2 = \text{Var}\,(Y_{ij})$$

Thus,

$$\text{Var}\,(\epsilon) = \text{Var}\,(Y_{ij}) = \sigma^2$$

This implies that the variances for the subpopulations are all equal. It is usually called the assumption of homoscedasticity.

Since ϵ_{ij} is $N(O, \sigma^2)$, the density function is

$$g(\epsilon) = \frac{1}{\sqrt{2\pi}\sigma}\,e^{-(1/2\sigma^2)\epsilon^2}$$

Using the Jacobian transformation on transformation (2), the probability element of Y_{ij} is

(4) $$f(Y)\,dY = g(\epsilon(Y)) \cdot |J| \cdot dY$$

$$= \frac{1}{\sqrt{2\pi}\sigma}\,e^{-(1/2\sigma^2)(Y - \mu)^2} \cdot |1| \cdot dY$$

$$= \frac{1}{\sqrt{2\pi}\sigma}\,e^{-(1/2\sigma^2)(Y - \mu)^2}\,dY$$

where $|J|$ is

$$|J| = \left|\frac{\partial(\epsilon)}{\partial Y}\right| = \left|\frac{\partial(Y - \mu)}{\partial Y}\right| = 1$$

Thus from (4) we see that Y is normally distributed with mean μ and variance σ^2. (Note that when there is no confusion, the subscripts will be omitted to simplify notation.)

(ii) Estimating A and B

Let us now take a sample of size n. This sample can be expressed in two ways. One is a sample of n values of ϵ i.e., ϵ_1, ϵ_2, ..., ϵ_n. A second way is to express it by showing the sample as $(X_1, Y_1), (X_2, Y_2), ..., (X_n, Y_n)$. In practice, it is the X and Y that are observed. However, since the two are equivalent, they will be used interchangeably in theoretical discussions.

Since ϵ is normally distributed, we will use the method of maximum likelihood to estimate A, B, and σ^2. For this we need the likelihood function for the sample. This is,

$$L = \prod_{i=1}^{n} g(\epsilon) = (2\pi\sigma^2)^{-n/2}\exp\left[-\frac{1}{2\sigma^2}\sum_{i=1}^{n}\epsilon_i^2\right]$$

$$= (2\pi\sigma^2)^{-n/2}\exp\left[-\frac{1}{2\sigma^2}\sum(Y_i - A - BX_i)^2\right]$$

As can be seen, this likelihood function is equivalent to

$$L = \prod_{i=1}^{n} g(\epsilon) = \prod_{i=1}^{n} f(Y)$$

The necessary conditions for L to be a maximum with respect to A, B, and σ^2 are

$$\frac{\partial L}{\partial A} = 0, \qquad \frac{\partial L}{\partial B} = 0, \qquad \frac{\partial L}{\partial \sigma^2} = 0$$

To simplify differentiation, we first find $\log L$ and then differentiate. This is permissible because the logarithmic function is monotonic and hence does not effect the conditions for a maximum. The results of differentiation are

(5) $$n\sigma^2 = \sum_{i=1}^{n} (Y_i - A - BX_i)^2$$

(6) $$\sum (Y_i - A - BX_i) = 0$$

(7) $$\sum X_i(Y_i - A - BX_i) = 0$$

Solving these equations, we find

$$\hat{A} = \bar{Y} - \hat{B}\bar{X}$$

$$\hat{B} = \frac{\sum (Y_i - \bar{Y})(X_i - \bar{X})}{\sum (X_i - \bar{X})^2}$$

$$\hat{\sigma}^2 = \frac{1}{n} \sum (Y_i - \hat{A} - \hat{B}X_i)^2$$

where $\bar{X}$ and $\bar{Y}$ are the sample means, i.e.,

$$\bar{X} = \frac{1}{n} \sum X_i, \qquad \bar{Y} = \frac{1}{n} \sum Y_i$$

Equations (6) and (7) are called the *normal equations*.

Let $\hat{A} = a$, $\hat{B} = b$, then the estimated equation for (1) becomes

(8) $$Y_c = a + bX$$

Note that Y_c is the estimate of μ and is an average.

An individual value Y of the sample can be shown as

$$Y = Y_c + e$$

where e shows the deviation of the individual Y's from the Y_c's.

The normal equations are usually shown as

(9)
$$\sum Y = na + b \sum X$$
$$\sum XY = a \sum X + b \sum X^2$$

(iii) Shifting the origin

We have seen that

$$a = \bar{Y} - b\bar{X}$$

Substituting this into (8), we get

(10) $$Y_c = \bar{Y} + b(X - \bar{X})$$

or

$$Y_c - \bar{Y} = b(X - \bar{X})$$

Let $$y_c = Y_c - \bar{Y}, \qquad x = X - \bar{X}$$

Then

(11) $$y_c = bx$$

As is seen, equation (11) is obtained from equation (8) by shifting the origin to $(\bar{Y}, \bar{X})$ and letting y_c and x be the deviations from the mean.

Problems

1. Work out the details of $\dfrac{\partial L}{\partial A} = 0$, $\dfrac{\partial L}{\partial B} = 0$, and $\dfrac{\partial L}{\partial \sigma^2} = 0$ and find equations (5), (6), and (7).

2. Draw a graph of the linear regression line

$$Y_c = a + bX$$

and show graphically the situations when the origin has been shifted to $(\bar{X}, 0)$, $(0, \bar{Y})$, and $(\bar{X}, \bar{Y})$. Also express the regression lines in terms of the three new origins.

3. Given a consumption function

$$c = \alpha y + \beta + u$$

when c is consumption, y is disposable income, and u is the random element that is $N(O, \sigma^2)$. Take a sample of size n and estimate α and β by the method of maximum likelihood.

16.3 Model 1—two independent variables case

Let us now assume that

(1) $$\mu = A + B_1 X_1 + B_2 X_2$$

where the additional (mathematical) variable X_2 is the mother's height. Then the deviations ϵ are

(2) $$\epsilon = Y - \mu$$

and

(3) $$Y = A + B_1 X_1 + B_2 X_2 + \epsilon$$

The distribution of Y is found in exactly the same manner as in Section 16.2. It is $N(\mu, \sigma^2)$. Note that the Jacobian is $|J| = 1$ for the transformation (2).

To find estimates of A, B_1, B_2, and σ^2 we take a sample of size n and apply the method of maximum likelihood. Let the sample be

$$(Y_1, X_{11}, X_{12}), (Y_2, X_{21}, X_{22}), \ldots, (Y_n, X_{n1}, X_{n2})$$

or $\epsilon_1, \epsilon_2, \ldots, \epsilon_n$.

The likelihood function is

$$
(4) \qquad L = \prod_{i=1}^{n} g(\epsilon) = \prod_{i=1}^{n} f(Y)
$$

$$
= (2\pi\sigma^2)^{-n/2} \exp\left[-\frac{1}{2\sigma^2} \sum (Y - A - B_1X_1 - B_2X_2)^2\right]
$$

To simplify differentiation, take the logarithm of L. Then,

$$
(4') \quad \log L = -\frac{n}{2}\log 2\pi - \frac{n}{2}\log \sigma^2 - \frac{1}{2\sigma^2}\sum(Y - A - B_1X_1 - B_2X_2)^2
$$

Differentiate with respect to A, B_1, B_2, and σ^2. Then, setting the partial derivatives equal to zero we find

$$
(5) \qquad n\sigma^2 = \sum_{i=1}^{n}(Y_i - A - B_1X_{i1} - B_2X_{i2})^2
$$

$$
(6) \qquad \sum(Y_i - A - B_1X_{i1} - B_2X_{i2}) = 0
$$

$$
(7) \qquad \sum X_{i1}(Y_i - A - B_1X_{i1} - B_2X_{i2}) = 0
$$

$$
(8) \qquad \sum X_{i2}(Y - A - B_1X_{i1} - B_2X_{i2}) = 0
$$

Equations (6), (7), and (8) which are the normal equations become

$$
\sum Y = na + b_1 \sum X_1 + b_2 \sum X_2
$$

$$
(9) \qquad \sum X_1 Y = a \sum X_1 + b_1 \sum X_1^2 + b_2 \sum X_1 X_2
$$

$$
\sum X_2 Y = a \sum X_2 + b_1 \sum X_1 X_2 + b_2 \sum X_2^2
$$

The parameters a, b_1, and b_2 are found by solving these equations simultaneously. However, to simplify computations, let us shift the origin to the sample mean $(\bar{Y}, \bar{X}_1, \bar{X}_2)$. Then the first equation of (9) becomes

$$
\sum(Y - \bar{Y}) = na + b_1 \sum(X_1 - \bar{X}_1) + b_2 \sum(X_2 - \bar{X}_2)
$$

However,

$$
\sum(Y - \bar{Y}) = 0, \quad \sum(X_1 - \bar{X}_1) = 0, \quad \text{and} \quad \sum(X_2 - \bar{X}_2) = 0
$$

Thus, $na = 0$, i.e., $a = 0$. This means the linear regression line (surface) goes through $(\bar{Y}, \bar{X}_1, \bar{X}_2)$.

The remaining two normal equations become

(10)
$$\sum (X_1 - \bar{X_1})(Y - \bar{Y}) = b_1 \sum (X_1 - \bar{X_1})^2 + b_2 \sum (X_1 - \bar{X_1})(X_2 - \bar{X_2})$$
$$\sum (X_2 - \bar{X_2})(Y - \bar{Y}) = b_1 \sum (X_1 - \bar{X_1})(X_2 - \bar{X_2}) + b_2 \sum (X_2 - \bar{X_2})^2$$

If we let

$$X_1 - \bar{X_1} = x_1, \qquad X_2 - \bar{X_2} = x_2$$

be the deviations from the sample means, the normal equations become

(11)
$$\sum x_1 y = b_1 \sum x_1^2 + b_2 \sum x_1 x_2$$
$$\sum x_2 y = b_1 \sum x_1 x_2 + b_2 \sum x_2^2$$

From the normal equations, the b_1 and b_2 are found. The a can then be obtained from the first equation of (9). That is,

$$a = \bar{Y} - b_1 \bar{X_1} - b_2 \bar{X_2}$$

As is seen, a does not have any effect on the estimation of the b's. In terms of the one variable model, a is the Y-intercept, and b is the slope of the line. The slope b is not effected by the shift in the origin. Thus to simplify notation for our theoretical discussion we shall assume that $\bar{Y} = \bar{X_1} = \bar{X_2} = 0$ and $a = 0$. Then the model becomes

(12)
$$\mu = B_1 X_1 + B_2 X_2$$

(12')
$$Y = B_1 X_1 + B_2 X_2 + \epsilon$$

and the normal equations become

(13)
$$b_1 \sum X_1^2 + b_2 \sum X_1 X_2 = \sum X_1 Y$$
$$b_1 \sum X_1 X_2 + b_2 \sum X_2^2 = \sum X_2 Y$$

In our subsequent discussion we will use equations (12), (12'), and (13) as our model.

The estimated equations are shown as

(14)
$$Y_c = b_1 X_1 + b_2 X_2$$

(15)
$$Y = b_1 X_1 + b_2 X_2 + e$$

where e shows the deviation $e = Y - Y_c$.

For k variables, the model is

(16)
$$\mu = B_1 X_1 + B_2 X_2 + \ldots + B_k X_k$$

(16')
$$Y = B_1 X_1 + B_2 X_2 + \ldots + B_k X_k + \epsilon$$

and the normal equations are

(17)
$$
\begin{aligned}
b_1 \sum X_1^2 + b_2 \sum X_1 X_2 + \ldots + b_k \sum X_1 X_k &= \sum X_1 Y \\
b_1 \sum X_1 X_2 + b_2 \sum X_2^2 + \ldots + b_k \sum X_2 X_k &= \sum X_2 Y \\
\ldots \qquad\qquad \ldots \qquad\qquad \ldots \\
b_1 \sum X_1 X_k + b_2 \sum X_2 X_k + \ldots + b_k \sum X_k^2 &= \sum X_k Y
\end{aligned}
$$

In matrix notation this is

$$
\begin{bmatrix}
\sum X_1^2 & \sum X_1 X_2 & \cdots & \sum X_1 X_k \\
\sum X_2 X_1 & \sum X_2^2 & \cdots & \sum X_2 X_k \\
\cdots & & & \\
\sum X_k X_1 & \sum X_k X_2 & \cdots & \sum X_k^2
\end{bmatrix}
\begin{bmatrix}
b_1 \\ b_2 \\ \vdots \\ b_k
\end{bmatrix}
=
\begin{bmatrix}
\sum X_1 Y \\ \sum X_2 Y \\ \cdots \\ \sum X_k Y
\end{bmatrix}
$$

If the inverse of the first matrix can be found, the solution for the b's will be

$$
\begin{bmatrix}
b_1 \\ b_2 \\ \cdots \\ b_k
\end{bmatrix}
=
\begin{bmatrix}
\sum X_1^2 & \sum X_1 X_2 & \cdots & \sum X_1 X_k \\
\sum X_2 X_1 & \sum X_2^2 & \cdots & \sum X_2 X_k \\
\cdots & & & \\
\sum X_k X_1 & \sum X_k X_2 & \cdots & \sum X_k^2
\end{bmatrix}^{-1}
\begin{bmatrix}
\sum X_1 Y \\ \sum X_2 Y \\ \cdots \\ \sum X_k Y
\end{bmatrix}
$$

Let us set this as

$$
\begin{bmatrix}
b_1 \\ b_2 \\ \cdots \\ b_k
\end{bmatrix}
=
\begin{bmatrix}
c_{11} & c_{12} & \cdots & c_{1k} \\
c_{21} & c_{22} & \cdots & c_{2k} \\
\cdots & & & \\
c_{k1} & c_{k2} & \cdots & c_{kk}
\end{bmatrix}
\begin{bmatrix}
\sum X_1 Y \\ \sum X_2 Y \\ \cdots \\ \sum X_k Y
\end{bmatrix}
$$

Once the c_{ij} are found which are called (Gauss) multipliers, the b's can be easily computed. For example,

$$
b_i = c_{i1} \sum X_1 Y + c_{i2} \sum X_2 Y + \ldots + c_{ik} \sum X_k Y
$$

The estimated equations are shown as

(18) $Y_c = b_1 X_1 + b_2 X_2 + \ldots + b_k X_k$

(19) $Y = b_1 X_1 + b_2 X_2 + \ldots + b_k X_k + e$

Problems

1. Work out the details of differentiating equation (4') with respect to A, B_1, B_2 and σ^2 and find equations (5), (6), (7), and (8).

2. Using the model expressed by (12'), take a sample of size n and estimate B_1, B_2, and σ^2 by the method of maximum likelihood.

3. $\begin{bmatrix} \sum X_1^2 & \sum X_1 X_2 \\ \sum X_1 X_2 & \sum X_2^2 \end{bmatrix}^{-1} = \begin{bmatrix} c_{11} & c_{12} \\ c_{21} & c_{22} \end{bmatrix}$
   Find the multipliers c_{ij}.

16.4 Model 2

Consider the population model

(1) $$\mu = B_1 X_1 + B_2 X_2$$

(2) $$Y = B_1 X_1 + B_2 X_2 + \epsilon$$

where Y and ϵ are random variables, X_1 and X_2 are constants (mathematical variables). We assume $E(\epsilon) = 0$ and Var $(\epsilon) = \sigma^2$, but the distribution of ϵ is unspecified. Thus, we cannot use the method of maximum likelihood to estimate the parameters B_1 and B_2.

The method of estimation we will use is the method of least squares. The method of least squares says, take a sample of size n and find b_1 and b_2 such that

$$\Sigma (Y - b_1 X_1 - b_2 X_2)^2 = \Sigma e^2$$

is a minimum, where the sum Σ is taken over the sample.

Using the estimates b_1 and b_2 the estimates of (1) and (2) are shown as

(3) $$Y_c = b_1 X_1 + b_2 X_2$$

(4) $$Y = b_1 X_1 + b_2 X_2 + e$$

where e shows the deviation of the individual sample values of Y from Y_c.

The results of this model expressed in more general terms is known as Markoff's theorem and has been investigated by David and Neyman (1938). The proof of the results is very difficult, and we will only outline it. Let us first state the theorem.

For simplicity assume a sample of size $n = 3$. We are given
(a) Three sample observations Y_1, Y_2, and Y_3.
(b) The expectation of each Y_i is a linear function of the parameters B_j $(j = 1, 2)$ that are unknown, and, fixed independent variables X_{ij}. That is,

(5) $$E(Y_i) = B_1 X_{i1} + B_2 X_{i2}$$

(c) Of the three equations

$$E(Y_1) = B_1 X_{11} + B_2 X_{12}$$
$$E(Y_2) = B_1 X_{21} + B_2 X_{22}$$
$$E(Y_3) = B_1 X_{31} + B_2 X_{32}$$

there is at least one set of two equations that gives a solution for B_1 and B_2.

(d) The variance of Y_i satisfies the relation

$$\text{Var } (Y_i) = \sigma_i^2 = \frac{\sigma^2}{P_i} \qquad i = 1, 2, 3.$$

where σ^2 may be unknown but the weights P_i are known.

Then

The best linear unbiased estimate of μ is

(6)
$$Y_c = b_1 X_1 + b_2 X_2$$

where the b's are obtained by minimizing the weighted sum of squares

$$S = \sum_{i=1}^{3} (Y_i - b_1 X_{i1} - b_2 X_{i2})^2 P_i = \min$$

This gives us the normal equations

$$b_1 \sum X_{i1}^2 P_i + b_2 \sum X_{i1} X_{i2} P_i = \sum X_{i1} Y_i P_i$$
$$b_1 \sum X_{i1} X_{i2} P_i + b_2 \sum X_{i2}^2 P_i = \sum X_{i2} Y_i P_i$$

First several related results are derived, viz., that $\hat{B}_i = b_i$ estimated by the least squares is a linear function of the Y's, and that this estimate is the best linear unbiased estimate. For simplicity we shall set $P_i = 1$ for this discussion. Secondly, the statement that equation (6) is the best linear unbiased estimate of Y is discussed.

(i) b_i is a linear function of the Y_i

We have seen that

$$b_1 = c_{11} \sum X_1 Y + c_{12} \sum X_2 Y$$
$$b_2 = c_{21} \sum X_1 Y + c_{22} \sum X_2 Y$$

where the c_{ij} are the multipliers. The sum Σ is taken over the sample, $n = 3$. Then, for example, b_1 becomes

$$b_1 = c_{11} \sum_{i=1}^{3} X_{i1} Y_i + c_{12} \sum_{i=1}^{3} X_{i2} Y_i$$
$$= Y_1 (c_{11} X_{11} + c_{12} X_{12})$$
$$+ Y_2 (c_{11} X_{21} + c_{12} X_{22})$$
$$+ Y_3 (c_{11} X_{31} + c_{12} X_{32})$$

Thus b_1 is a linear function of the Y's. Similarly, b_2 can be shown as a linear function of the Y's.

(ii) b_i is an unbiased estimate of B_i

We know that

$$\begin{bmatrix} \sum X_1^2 & \sum X_1 X_2 \\ \sum X_1 X_2 & \sum X_2^2 \end{bmatrix} \begin{bmatrix} c_{11} & c_{12} \\ c_{21} & c_{22} \end{bmatrix} = \begin{bmatrix} 1 & 0 \\ 0 & 1 \end{bmatrix}$$

This becomes

$$(7) \quad \begin{bmatrix} c_{11} \sum X_1^2 + c_{12} \sum X_1 X_2 & c_{12} \sum X_1^2 + c_{22} \sum X_1 X_2 \\ c_{11} \sum X_1 X_2 + c_{12} \sum X_2^2 & c_{12} \sum X_1 X_2 + c_{22} \sum X_2^2 \end{bmatrix} = \begin{bmatrix} 1 & 0 \\ 0 & 1 \end{bmatrix}$$

Thus for example,

$$c_{11} \sum X_1^2 + c_{21} \sum X_1 X_2 = 1$$

Note that the matrix c is symmetric, i.e., $c_{12} = c_{21}$.

Using the results in (7), we find, for example, by substituting (2) into b_1,

$$b_1 = c_{11} \sum X_1 Y + c_{12} \sum X_2 Y$$

$$= c_{11} \sum X_1 (B_1 X_1 + B_2 X_2 + \epsilon)$$
$$+ c_{12} \sum X_2 (B_1 X_1 + B_2 X_2 + \epsilon)$$

$$= B_1 [c_{11} \sum X_1^2 + c_{12} \sum X_1 X_2]$$
$$+ B_2 [c_{11} \sum X_1 X_2 + c_{12} \sum X_2^2]$$
$$+ c_{11} \sum X_1 \epsilon + c_{12} \sum X_2 \epsilon$$

$$= B_1 + c_{11} \sum X_1 \epsilon + c_{12} \sum X_2 \epsilon$$

The expected value of b_1 is

$$E(b_1) = B_1 + c_{11} \sum X_1 E(\epsilon) + c_{12} \sum X_2 E(\epsilon)$$

$$\therefore \quad E(b_1) = B_1$$

That is, b_1 is an unbiased estimator of B_1. A similar argument applies to b_2.

(iii) b_i is the best estimate of B_i

When b_i has the smallest variance of all the linear estimators of B_i, it is called the best linear estimator. To show that b_i has the smallest (minimum) variance, an arbitrary linear estimator of B_i is constructed, and its variance is computed. Then the two variances are compared, and if we can show that Var (b_i) is smaller, we conclude that b_i has the minimum variance and hence is the best linear estimator.

The sample of size $n = 3$ that has been taken can be shown by

$$(8) \quad \begin{bmatrix} Y_1 \\ Y_2 \\ Y_3 \end{bmatrix} = \begin{bmatrix} X_{11} & X_{12} \\ X_{21} & X_{22} \\ X_{31} & X_{32} \end{bmatrix} \begin{bmatrix} B_1 \\ B_2 \end{bmatrix} + \begin{bmatrix} \epsilon_1 \\ \epsilon_2 \\ \epsilon_3 \end{bmatrix}$$

The B's are estimated by the method of least squares. Then the result is shown by

$$(9) \quad \begin{bmatrix} Y_1 \\ Y_2 \\ Y_3 \end{bmatrix} = \begin{bmatrix} X_{11} & X_{12} \\ X_{21} & X_{22} \\ X_{31} & X_{32} \end{bmatrix} \begin{bmatrix} b_1 \\ b_2 \end{bmatrix} + \begin{bmatrix} e_1 \\ e_2 \\ e_3 \end{bmatrix}$$

where the b's are estimates of the B's. Equation (8) can be shown in matrix form as

(10) $Y = XB + \epsilon$

With this much background, let us now construct the following arbitrary linear functions of Y which are to be estimates of B_1 and B_2.

(11)
$$a_{11} Y_1 + a_{21} Y_2 + a_{31} Y_3 = b_1$$
$$a_{12} Y_1 + a_{22} Y_2 + a_{32} Y_3 = b_2$$

where the a's are constants. In matrix notation this becomes

(12) $AY = b$

If these linear functions of Y are to be unbiased estimators of B, we need, from equation (12),

(13) $E(AY) = B$

Substituting equation (10) into (13), we get for the left-hand side,

$$E(AY) = E[A(XB + \epsilon)] = E(AXB + A\epsilon)$$
$$= E(AXB) + AE(\epsilon) = E(AXB)$$
$$= AXB$$

Thus for (13) to hold, we need

(14) $AX = I$

That is,

$$\begin{bmatrix} a_{11}X_{11} + a_{21}X_{21} + a_{31}X_{31} & a_{11}X_{12} + a_{21}X_{22} + a_{31}X_{32} \\ a_{12}X_{11} + a_{22}X_{21} + a_{32}X_{31} & a_{12}X_{12} + a_{22}X_{22} + a_{32}X_{32} \end{bmatrix} = \begin{bmatrix} 1 & 0 \\ 0 & 1 \end{bmatrix}$$

This shows that the linear functions of Y in (12) will be unbiased estimates of B when given the condition (14).

The estimates of B obtained by the method of least squares were shown by

$$\begin{bmatrix} b_1 \\ b_2 \end{bmatrix} = \begin{bmatrix} \sum X_1^2 & \sum X_1 X_2 \\ \sum X_1 X_2 & \sum X_2^2 \end{bmatrix}^{-1} \begin{bmatrix} \sum X_1 Y \\ \sum X_2 Y \end{bmatrix}$$

or in matrix notation,

(15) $b = (X'X)^{-1}X'Y$

Our problem now is to compare the variance of the b that is estimated by (15) to the variance of b that is estimated by (12). Let us first find the variance of (15). Since we have unbiased estimators, $E(b) = B$. Therefore, the variance of b is defined as

(16) $E[(b - B)(b - B)']$

$$= E\left[\begin{pmatrix} b_1 - B_1 \\ b_2 - B_2 \end{pmatrix} (b_1 - B_1 \quad b_2 - B_2) \right]$$

$$= \begin{bmatrix} E(b_1 - B_1)^2 & E(b_1 - B_1)(b_2 - B_2) \\ E(b_2 - B_2)(b_1 - B_1) & E(b_2 - B_2)^2 \end{bmatrix}$$

$$= \begin{bmatrix} \text{Var}(b_1) & \text{Cov}(b_1, b_2) \\ \text{Cov}(b_1, b_2) & \text{Var}(b_2) \end{bmatrix}$$

This is called the variance-covariance matrix of the estimates b_1 and b_2 and is denoted by $\mathbf{V}$. We are mainly interested in Var (b_1) and Var (b_2).

Also note from (15) that,

$$b = (X'X)^{-1}X'Y = (X'X)^{-1}X'(XB + \epsilon)$$

$$= (X'X)^{-1}X'XB + (X'X)^{-1}X'\epsilon$$

$$= B + (X'X)^{-1}X'\epsilon$$

This leads to

(17) $b - B = (X'X)^{-1}X'\epsilon$

Substituting (17) into the variance-covariance matrix (16), we find

$$E[(X'X)^{-1}X'\epsilon((X'X)^{-1}X'\epsilon)']$$

$$= E[(X'X)^{-1}X'\epsilon\epsilon'X(X'X)^{-1}]$$

$$= (X'X)^{-1}X'X(X'X)^{-1}E(\epsilon\epsilon')$$

$$= (X'X)^{-1}\sigma^2$$

since we assumed Var $(\epsilon) = \sigma^2$ (homoscedasticity). Thus, we conclude that

(18) $\mathbf{V} = (X'X)^{-1}\sigma^2$

Let us now find the variance-covariance matrix for the arbitrary linear estimate of B given by (12). Equation (12) was $b = AY$. To differentiate this arbitrary linear estimate and the estimate obtained by (15), we let A be different from $(X'X)^{-1}X'$. Set

(19) $A = (X'X)^{-1}X' + D$

where D is a matrix of scalars. Then, if this A is to satisfy the condition that the linear estimate AY is to be an unbiased estimate of B, we need the condition (14) to be satisfied, i.e.,

$$AX = [(X'X)^{-1}X' + D]X = I$$

This becomes

$$(X'X)^{-1}X'X + DX = I$$

$$\therefore \quad DX = 0$$

Thus, if we can find a matrix D such that $DX = 0$, AY is an unbiased estimator of B, where A is given by (19).

Using this result, let us find the variance of this linear function $AY = b$. First note that

$$b = AY = ((X'X)^{-1}X' + D)Y$$

$$= [(X'X)^{-1}X' + D](XB + \epsilon)$$

$$= (X'X)^{-1}X'XB + DXB + (X'X)^{-1}X'\epsilon + D\epsilon$$

$$= B + [(X'X)^{-1}X + D]\epsilon$$

Thus, the deviation of b from B becomes

$$b - B = [(X'X)^{-1}X + D]\epsilon$$

From this we find that the variance of b is, noting that $DX = 0$,

$$(20) \quad E[(b - B)(b - B)']$$

$$= E[\{[(X'X)^{-1}X' + D]\epsilon\}\{[(X'X)^{-1}X' + D]\epsilon\}']$$

$$= E[((X'X)^{-1}X' + D)\epsilon\epsilon'(X(X'X)^{-1} + D')]$$

$$= \sigma^2[(X'X)^{-1}X'X(X'X)^{-1} + DX(X'X)^{-1} + (X'X)^{-1}X'D' + DD']$$

$$= \sigma^2[(X'X)^{-1} + DD']$$

Thus the variance-covariance matrix for the b obtained from (12) becomes

$$(21) \qquad \mathbf{V} = \sigma^2[(X'X)^{-1} + DD']$$

$$= \sigma^2 \begin{bmatrix} c_{11} + \sum d_{i1}^2 & c_{12} + \sum d_{i1} d_{i2} \\ c_{21} + \sum d_{i1} d_{i2} & c_{22} + \sum d_{i2}^2 \end{bmatrix}$$

where

$$DD' = \begin{bmatrix} d_{11} & d_{21} & d_{31} \\ d_{12} & d_{22} & d_{32} \end{bmatrix} \begin{bmatrix} d_{11} & d_{12} \\ d_{21} & d_{22} \\ d_{31} & d_{32} \end{bmatrix}$$

$$= \begin{bmatrix} \sum d_{i1}^2 & \sum d_{i1} d_{i2} \\ \sum d_{i1} d_{i2} & \sum d_{i2}^2 \end{bmatrix}$$

$$(X'X)^{-1} = \begin{bmatrix} c_{11} & c_{12} \\ c_{21} & c_{22} \end{bmatrix}$$

From (18) we know that the variance-covariance matrix for the b's estimated by the method of least squares is

$$(22) \qquad \mathbf{V} = \sigma^2(X'X)^{-1} = \begin{bmatrix} c_{11}\sigma^2 & c_{12}\sigma^2 \\ c_{21}\sigma^2 & c_{22}\sigma^2 \end{bmatrix}$$

and $c_{11}\sigma^2$, $c_{22}\sigma^2$ are the variances of b_1 and b_2. Then the variance of b_1 and b_2 of (11) will be

$$\text{Var}(b_1) = \sigma^2(c_{11} + \textstyle\sum d_{i1}^2) \geq c_{11}\sigma^2$$
$$\text{Var}(b_2) = \sigma^2(c_{22} + \textstyle\sum d_{i2}^2) \geq c_{22}\sigma^2$$

When $\Sigma d_{i1}^2 > 0$, $\Sigma d_{i2}^2 > 0$ these variances are greater than the variances of the b_1 and b_2 obtained from the method of least squares.

When $\Sigma d_{i1}^2 = 0$, $\Sigma d_{i2}^2 = 0$ the linear estimate becomes the same as the least squares linear estimate.

Thus, the conclusion is the linear estimates of B obtained from the least squares method is the best estimate, i.e., it has minimum variance, when compared to estimates obtained from arbitrary linear functions of Y, as given by (12).

16.5 Model 2—continued

(i) Weights $P_i \neq 1$ case

The second problem to be considered is that the best linear unbiased estimate of μ, that is,

$$(1) \qquad \mu = B_1 X_1 + B_2 X_2$$

is Y_c, that is,

$$(2) \qquad Y_c = b_1 X_1 + b_2 X_2$$

where b_1 and b_2 are obtained by the method of weighted least squares. That is,

$$(3) \qquad \sum_{i=1}^{3} (Y_i - b_i X_{i1} - b_2 X_{i2})^2 P_i = \sum e_i^2 P_i = \text{min.}$$

Let us include the weights P_i in this discussion. The normal equations become

$$(4) \qquad \begin{aligned} b_1 \sum X_{i1}^2 P_i + b_2 \sum X_{i1} X_{i2} P_i &= \sum X_{i1} Y_i P_i \\ b_2 \sum X_{i1} X_{i2} P_i + b_2 \sum X_{i2}^2 P_i &= \sum X_{i2} Y_i P_i \end{aligned}$$

In matrix notation this is

$$(5) \qquad X'PXb = X'PY$$

where

$$P = \begin{bmatrix} P_1 & & \\ & P_2 & \\ & & P_3 \end{bmatrix}$$

If $|X'PX| \neq 0$, then b is

(6) $b = (X'PX)^{-1}X'PY$

We wish to show that when the b's of equation (2) are estimated as in (6), the estimate Y_c will have minimum variance and will also be unbiased.

The non-rigorous proof that is presented is constructed as follows. A linear function

(7) $\hat{Y}_i = \lambda_{i1}Y_1 + \lambda_{i2}Y_2 + \lambda_{i3}Y_3$

is constructed. In matrix notation this is shown as

(7')
$$\begin{bmatrix} \hat{Y}_1 \\ \hat{Y}_2 \\ \hat{Y}_3 \end{bmatrix} = \begin{bmatrix} \lambda_{11} & \lambda_{12} & \lambda_{13} \\ \lambda_{21} & \lambda_{22} & \lambda_{23} \\ \lambda_{31} & \lambda_{32} & \lambda_{33} \end{bmatrix} \begin{bmatrix} Y_1 \\ Y_2 \\ Y_3 \end{bmatrix}$$

This linear function of $\hat{Y}_i$ is to be an unbiased and minimum variance estimator of $E(Y_i) = \mu_i$. The λ's that satisfy these two conditions are found. Then it is shown that when using these λ's, this linear function is identical (2). Thus (2) is an unbiased minimum variance estimator of $E(Y_i) = \mu_i$.

Step 1

From equation (7) or (7'), a single equation is selected and the subscript i is dropped to simplify notation. Then (7) becomes

(7'') $\hat{Y} = \lambda_1 Y_1 + \lambda_2 Y_2 + \lambda_3 Y_3$

In matrix notation this is,

(7''')
$$\hat{Y} = \begin{bmatrix} \lambda_1 & \lambda_2 & \lambda_3 \end{bmatrix} \begin{bmatrix} Y_1 \\ Y_2 \\ Y_3 \end{bmatrix} = \lambda'Y$$

The necessary conditions for this linear function (7'') to be an unbiased estimate is obtained by setting

$$E(\hat{Y}) = \sum_{i=1}^{3} \lambda_i E(Y_i)$$
$$= \sum \lambda_i(B_1 X_{i1} + B_2 X_{i2})$$
$$= B_1 X_1 + B_2 X_2$$

and finding the conditions as

(8)
$$X_1 = \sum \lambda_i X_{i1} = \lambda_1 X_{11} + \lambda_2 X_{21} + \lambda_3 X_{31}$$
$$X_2 = \sum \lambda_i X_{i2} = \lambda_1 X_{12} + \lambda_2 X_{22} + \lambda_3 X_{32}$$

In matrix notation this is

(8')
$$
\begin{bmatrix} X_1 \\ X_2 \end{bmatrix} = \begin{bmatrix} X_{11} & X_{21} & X_{31} \\ X_{12} & X_{22} & X_{32} \end{bmatrix} \begin{bmatrix} \lambda_1 \\ \lambda_2 \\ \lambda_3 \end{bmatrix} = X'\lambda
$$

If we can find λ_i that satisfy (8), equation (7'') will be an unbiased estimator of (1).

Step 2

Let us next find the conditions for $\hat{Y}$ of equation (7'') to have minimum variance. The variance of (7'') is

(9)
$$
\text{Var}\,(\hat{Y}) = \text{Var}\,(\textstyle\sum \lambda_i Y_i) = \sum \sigma^2 \frac{\lambda_i^2}{P_i} = \min.
$$

Note that $\text{Var}\,(Y_i) = \sigma^2/P_i$ from the assumptions and that P_i are known positive constants but σ^2 may be unknown. Thus the problem is to find the λ_i that give us a minimum $\text{Var}\,(\hat{Y})$ and at the same time satisfy (8) which were the necessary conditions for unbiasedness. Using the Lagrange Multiplier Method, we construct the function V as follows.

$$
V = \sum_{i=1}^{3} \frac{\lambda_i^2}{P_i} - 2\alpha_1 \sum_{i=1}^{3} \lambda_i X_{i1} - 2\alpha_2 \sum_{i=1}^{3} \lambda_i X_{i2}
$$

where α_1 and α_2 are the Lagrange multipliers. Note that σ^2 is omitted because it is a constant and has no effect. Differentiate V with respect to λ_i and set the result equal to zero. Then,

$$
\frac{\partial V}{\partial \lambda_1} = 0: \quad \lambda_1 = \alpha_1 X_{11} P_1 + \alpha_2 X_{12} P_1
$$

$$
\frac{\partial V}{\partial \lambda_2} = 0: \quad \lambda_2 = \alpha_1 X_{21} P_2 + \alpha_2 X_{22} P_2
$$

$$
\frac{\partial V}{\partial \lambda_3} = 0: \quad \lambda_3 = \alpha_1 X_{31} P_3 + \alpha_2 X_{32} P_3
$$

In matrix notation this is

$$
\begin{bmatrix} \lambda_1 \\ \lambda_2 \\ \lambda_3 \end{bmatrix} = \begin{bmatrix} P_1 & & \\ & P_2 & \\ & & P_3 \end{bmatrix} \begin{bmatrix} X_{11} & X_{12} \\ X_{21} & X_{22} \\ X_{31} & X_{32} \end{bmatrix} \begin{bmatrix} \alpha_1 \\ \alpha_2 \end{bmatrix}
$$

or

(10)
$$
\lambda = PX\alpha
$$

To solve for the five unknowns λ_1, λ_2, λ_3, α_1, α_2, the three equations of (10) and the two constraints which are the two equations (8) are combined and solved simultaneously. This is performed in Step 3.

Step 3

(11)
$$\begin{bmatrix} X_1 \\ X_2 \end{bmatrix} = X'PX\alpha$$

From (11) we can solve for the Lagrange multipliers α. They become

(12)
$$\alpha = (X'PX)^{-1}\begin{bmatrix} X_1 \\ X_2 \end{bmatrix}$$

Using (12) and (10) we can now find λ which is what we are really after.

(13)
$$\lambda = PX\alpha = PX(X'PX)^{-1}\begin{bmatrix} X_1 \\ X_2 \end{bmatrix}$$

The λ has been found and note that it is expressed in terms of X's and P. It is the λ that satisfies the conditions that (7") will be an unbiased and minimum variance estimator of $E(Y)$.

Our next step is to substitute (13) into (7") and show that this becomes equal to (2).

Step 4

Substituting (13) into (7") we find

(14)
$$\hat{Y} = \lambda'Y = [X_1\ X_2](X'PX)^{-1}X'PY$$

Substituting (6) into (14), we find

$$\hat{Y} = \lambda'Y = [X_1\ X_2]b$$
$$= b_1X_1 + b_2X_2$$

We have shown that equation (2) which is the equation where the coefficients b are obtained by the method of weighted least squares, and, equation (7") which is the linear unbiased minimum variance equation, are equal. Thus we conclude that equation (2) is an unbiased minimum variance estimator of $E(Y_i)$. That is, the estimator obtained by the method of weighted least squares is an unbiased minimum variance estimator of $E(Y_i)$.

The result may be stated in an alternative way as follows. Let

(15)
$$B_1X_1 + B_2X_2$$

be a linear function of the B's. Then the best linear unbiased estimate of (15) is

(16)
$$b_1X_1 + b_2X_2$$

where the individual b_i's are the best linear unbiased estimates of individual B_i's which are obtained by

(17)
$$b = (X'PX)^{-1}X'PY$$

(ii) *Weights $P_i = 1$ case*

When $P_i = 1$, the matrix P becomes

$$P = \begin{bmatrix} P_1 & & \\ & P_2 & \\ & & P_3 \end{bmatrix} = \begin{bmatrix} 1 & & \\ & 1 & \\ & & 1 \end{bmatrix} = I$$

The results for the $P_i = 1$ case are obtained by replacing P_i and P by 1 and I in the previous Section (i). The results of the $P_i \neq 1$ case and $P_i = 1$ case are the same, except that equation (17) becomes

(18) $$b = (X'X)^{-1}X'Y$$

Problem

1. Work out the $P_i = 1$ case in detail.

16.6 Estimate of the variances

(i) *The estimate of the variance of Y_c*

Equation (5) in Section 16.2 gives an estimate of the variance as

(1) $$\hat{\sigma}^2 = \frac{1}{n}\sum (Y_i - \hat{A} - \hat{B}X_i)^2 = \frac{1}{n}\sum (Y_i - Y_c)^2$$

for the one variable case. For two variables, equation (5) of Section 16.3 gives

(2) $$\hat{\sigma}^2 = \frac{1}{n}\sum (Y_i - \hat{A} - \hat{B}_1 X_{i1} - \hat{B}_2 X_{i2})^2$$

$$= \frac{1}{n}\sum (Y_i - Y_c)^2$$

Equations (1) and (2) are expressed in matrix notation as

$$\frac{(Y - Y_c)'(Y - Y_c)}{n}$$

where Y and Y_c indicate vectors. For example, if the sample size is $n = 3$, we have

$$[(Y_1 - Y_{c1})(Y_2 - Y_{c2})(Y_3 - Y_{c3})]\begin{bmatrix} Y_1 - Y_{c1} \\ Y_2 - Y_{c2} \\ Y_3 - Y_{c3} \end{bmatrix}$$

$$= \sum_{i=1}^{3} (Y_i - Y_{ci})^2$$

Thus, (1) and (2) may be expressed in matrix notation as

(3) $$\hat{\sigma}^2 = \frac{1}{n}(Y - Y_c)'(Y - Y_c)$$

It turns out that (3) is a biased estimator of the population variance. An unbiased estimator is

(4) $$\hat{\sigma}^2 = \frac{1}{n-r}(Y - Y_c)'(Y - Y_c)$$

where $n - r$ is the number of degrees of freedom. Assuming that the origin has been shifted to the mean, the parameter that corresponds to $\hat{A} = a$ in the linear regression model is zero. Thus r is the number of b's in

$$\hat{Y} = Xb$$

In our present example, $r = 2$. For our subsequent discussion we shall only consider the unbiased estimator given by (4).

The numerator of (4) can be expressed as

$$(Y - Xb)'(Y - Xb) = (Y' - b'X')(Y - Xb)$$
$$= Y'Y - b'X'Y - Y'Xb + b'X'Xb$$

But

$$b'X'Xb = b'X'X(X'X)^{-1}X'Y = b'X'Y$$

Then the numerator becomes

$$(Y - Xb)'(Y - Xb) = Y'Y - Y'Xb$$

Substituting this into (4), the estimated variance becomes

$$\hat{\sigma}^2 = \frac{1}{n-r}(Y'Y - Y'Xb)$$

We also state that this is the unbiased estimate of the variance of Y_c for the second model that was based on Markoff's theorem.

(ii) *Estimate of the variance of* b_i

We have seen that the variance-covariance matrix of b_i was

$$V = \sigma^2(X'X)^{-1} = \begin{bmatrix} c_{11}\sigma^2 & c_{12}\sigma^2 \\ c_{21}\sigma^2 & c_{22}\sigma^2 \end{bmatrix}$$

and

$$\text{Var}(b_1) = c_{11}\sigma^2, \qquad \text{Var}(b_2) = c_{22}\sigma^2$$

where c_{ij} are the Gauss multipliers. Thus, an estimate of Var (b_i) is obtained by using the estimate $\hat{\sigma}^2$;

$$\hat{\sigma}^2_{b_i} = c_{ii}\hat{\sigma}^2$$

(iii) *Confidence interval for B_i*

We now state without proof that b_i is distributed normally with mean $E(b_i) = B$ and variance Var $(b_i) = c_{ii}\sigma^2$. Thus the distribution of the standardized variable

$$\frac{b_i - B_i}{\sigma\sqrt{c_{ii}}}$$

is normally distributed with mean zero and variance unity.

However, σ which is the population parameter is unknown and we have to use an estimator. We have found the estimator $\hat{\sigma}^2$ with $n - r$ degrees of freedom. Thus, we state without proof that

$$\frac{b_i - B_i}{\hat{\sigma}\sqrt{c_{ii}}}$$

has a t-distribution with $n - r$ (in our present example $n - 2$) degrees of freedom. If the null hypothesis is $B_i = 0$, we have

$$t = \frac{b_i}{\hat{\sigma}\sqrt{c_{ii}}}$$

The confidence interval for B_i is

$$b_i - t_{\alpha/2}\sqrt{c_{ii}\hat{\sigma}^2} \leqq B_i \leqq b_i + t_{\alpha/2}\sqrt{c_{ii}\hat{\sigma}^2}$$

where α is the level of significance. We have a $(1 - \alpha)$ confidence interval.

(iv) *Computation formulas*

In the previous sections, various results were expressed in terms of matrices. In this section the results will be expressed in terms of determinants to show the computational procedures. The two main problems are to find an expression for the b's and hence the regression line, and, the estimated variance.

(a) Computation formula for the b's

The b's were obtained from the normal equations

(1)
$$b_1 \sum X_{i1}^2 + b_2 \sum X_{i1}X_{i2} = \sum X_{i1}Y_i$$
$$b_1 \sum X_{i1}X_{i2} + b_2 \sum X_{i2}^2 = \sum X_{i2}Y_i$$

Using Cramer's rule the b's are found as

$$b_1 = \frac{\begin{vmatrix} \sum X_{i1}Y_i & \sum X_{i1}X_{i2} \\ \sum X_{i2}Y_i & \sum X_{i2}^2 \end{vmatrix}}{\begin{vmatrix} \sum X_{i1}^2 & \sum X_{i1}X_{i2} \\ \sum X_{i1}X_{i2} & \sum X_{i2}^2 \end{vmatrix}}$$

$$b_2 = \frac{\begin{vmatrix} \sum X_{i1}^2 & \sum X_{i1}Y_i \\ \sum X_{i1}X_{i2} & \sum X_{i2}Y_i \end{vmatrix}}{\begin{vmatrix} \sum X_{i1}^2 & \sum X_{i1}X_{i2} \\ \sum X_{i1}X_{i2} & \sum X_{i2}^2 \end{vmatrix}}$$

provided the determinant in the denominator which we shall denote by Δ is not zero.

Using these computation formulas for the b's, the estimated regression line becomes

(2)
$$\hat{Y} = b_1 X_{i1} + b_2 X_{i2}$$

$$= \frac{1}{\Delta}\left\{ X_{i1} \begin{vmatrix} \sum X_{i1}Y_i & \sum X_{i1}X_{i2} \\ \sum X_{i2}Y_i & \sum X_{i2}^2 \end{vmatrix} \right.$$

$$\left. + X_{i2} \begin{vmatrix} \sum X_{i1}^2 & \sum X_{i1}Y_i \\ \sum X_{i1}X_{i2} & \sum X_{i2}Y_i \end{vmatrix} \right\}$$

The part in the braces can be rearranged into determinant form as follows.

$$X_{i1}\begin{vmatrix} \sum X_{i1}Y_i & \sum X_{i1}X_{i2} \\ \sum X_{i2}Y_i & \sum X_{i2}^2 \end{vmatrix} + X_{i2}\begin{vmatrix} \sum X_{i1}^2 & \sum X_{i1}Y_i \\ \sum X_{i1}X_{i2} & \sum X_{i2}Y_i \end{vmatrix}$$

$$= \left\{ 0 \begin{vmatrix} \sum X_{i1}^2 & \sum X_{i1}X_{i2} \\ \sum X_{i1}X_{i2} & \sum X_{i2}^2 \end{vmatrix} + X_{i1}\begin{vmatrix} \sum X_{i1}Y_i & \sum X_{i1}X_{i2} \\ \sum X_{i2}Y_i & \sum X_{i2}^2 \end{vmatrix} \right.$$

$$\left. - X_{i2}\begin{vmatrix} \sum X_{i1}Y_i & \sum X_{i1}^2 \\ \sum X_{i2}Y_i & \sum X_{i1}X_{i2} \end{vmatrix} \right\}$$

$$= -\begin{vmatrix} 0 & X_{i1} & X_{i2} \\ \sum X_{i1}Y_i & \sum X_{i1}^2 & \sum X_{i1}X_{i2} \\ \sum X_{i2}Y_i & \sum X_{i1}X_{i2} & \sum X_{i2}^2 \end{vmatrix} = -\Delta_1$$

Substituting this result into (2), we find,

(3) $$\hat{Y} = -\frac{\Delta_1}{\Delta}$$

This result is for the case where we have two b's. But it can be easily general-ized for a regression line of any number of b's.

(b) The variance σ^2
   The estimate of the variance σ^2 was given as

$$\hat{\sigma}^2 = \frac{1}{n-r} \{(Y - Xb)'(Y - Xb)\}$$

$$= \frac{1}{n-2} \{Y'Y - Y'Xb\}$$

The $Y'Y$ is

$$Y'Y = [Y_1 \quad Y_2 \quad Y_3] \begin{bmatrix} Y_1 \\ Y_2 \\ Y_3 \end{bmatrix} = \sum_{i=1}^{3} Y_i^2$$

The $Y'X$ is

$$Y'X = [Y_1 \quad Y_2 \quad Y_3] \begin{bmatrix} X_{11} & X_{12} \\ X_{21} & X_{22} \\ X_{31} & X_{32} \end{bmatrix} = [\sum X_{i1}Y_i \quad \sum X_{i2}Y_i]$$

Then the $Y'Xb$ is

$$Y'Xb = [\sum X_{i1}Y_i \quad \sum X_{i2}Y_i] \begin{bmatrix} b_1 \\ b_2 \end{bmatrix}$$

$$= b_1 \sum X_{i1}Y_i + b_2 \sum X_{i2}Y_i$$

Thus, $\hat{\sigma}^2$ becomes

$$\hat{\sigma}^2 = \frac{1}{n-2} \left\{ \sum_{i=1}^{3} Y_i^2 - b_1 \sum_{i=1}^{3} X_{i1}Y_i - b_2 \sum_{i=1}^{3} X_{i2}Y_i \right\}$$

Since the b's have been calculated by the formulas in (i) above, the $\hat{\sigma}^2$ can easily be obtained.

16.7 Bivariate normal distribution

We now take up the third approach, based on a multivariate normal distribution. We shall start with an explanation of the bivariate normal distribution.

(i) Bivariate normal distribution

To give a simple illustration, let us construct a hypothetical table of values as follows:

Height of father (inches) X_2

Height of son (inches) X_1	60	61	62	63	64	65	66	67	68	69
60	6	3	1							
61	13	7	5	3	1					
62	14	15	9	6	7	3				
63	12	10	14	9	10	10	5	4	3	1
64	8	8	10	10	13	14	10	8	6	4
65	4	5	8	12	15	17	15	13	11	9
66	1	3	4	11	12	18	15	1	12	10
67		1	2	7	9	14	17	15	15	12
68			1	4	5	8	10	18	19	10
69				1	1	6	7	14	20	21

For example, in the $X_1 = 64$, $X_2 = 63$ cell we find 10 which means there are 10 pairs of father and son where the father is 63 inches and the son is 64 inches. The characteristic of the table is that, when fathers are short they tend to have short sons and when they are tall they tend to have tall sons. This is shown by the concentration of frequencies along the diagonal running from the upper left-hand corner to the lower right-hand corner.

Looking at a specific column, say $X_2 = 63$, we see at first the frequencies are few and then reach a maximum around 64 tapering off again. This holds true for the other columns and also for the rows. The above is only a sample of the infinite possible values. We assume that in the population each of the columns and rows will have a normal distribution. That is, X_1 and X_2 respectively have normal distributions.

But X_1 and X_2 are generally not independent of each other, and their joint distribution can be looked upon as an extension of the *univariate normal distribution*. This *bivariate normal distribution* has a density function as follows:

$$(1) \qquad f(x_1, x_2) = \frac{1}{2\pi\sigma_1\sigma_2\sqrt{1-\rho^2}} \exp\left[-\frac{1}{2(1-\rho^2)}\left\{\left(\frac{x_1-\mu_1}{\sigma_1}\right)^2 - 2\rho\frac{x_1-\mu_1}{\sigma_1}\frac{x_2-\mu_2}{\sigma_2} + \left(\frac{x_2-\mu_2}{\sigma_2}\right)^2\right\}\right]$$

where

$$E(X_1) = \mu_1, \qquad E(X_2) = \mu_2$$
$$\text{Var}(X_1) = \sigma_1^2, \qquad \text{Var}(X_2) = \sigma_2^2$$

The ρ is the *correlation coefficient* and is defined as

$$\rho = \rho(X_1, X_2) = \frac{\text{Cov}(X_1, X_2)}{\sigma_1\sigma_2}$$

where covariance is defined as

$$\text{Cov}\,(X_1, X_2) = E[(X_1 - \mu_1)(X_2 - \mu_2)]$$

ρ will be discussed later.

(ii) *Conditional distributions*

From our table we can select a value $X_2 = 63$ inches and find the distribution of X_1. This is shown as $f(x_1 \mid x_2)$ which is the conditional distribution of X_1 given X_2. $f(x_1 \mid x_2)$ is given as

$$(2) \qquad\qquad f(x_1 \mid x_2) = \frac{f(x_1, x_2)}{f_2(x_2)}$$

where $f_2(x_2)$ is called the marginal distribution. In terms of the bivariate normal distribution we are discussing, $f_2(x_2)$ is

$$(3) \qquad f_2(x_2) = \int_{-\infty}^{\infty} f(x_1, x_2)\,dx_1 = \frac{1}{\sqrt{2\pi}\sigma_2} \exp\left[-\frac{1}{2}\left(\frac{x_2 - \mu_2}{\sigma_2}\right)^2 \right]$$

This result is given without derivation. We know $f(x_1, x_2)$. Thus, we can find $f(x_1 \mid x_2)$. It turns out to be

$$(4) \qquad f(x_1 \mid x_2) = \frac{1}{\sqrt{2\pi}\,\sigma_1 \sqrt{1 - \rho^2}}$$

$$\times \exp\left[-\frac{1}{2\sigma_1^2(1 - \rho^2)}\left[x_1 - u_1 - \frac{\rho\sigma_1}{\sigma_2}(x_2 - u_2)\right]^2 \right]$$

This shows that $f(x_1 \mid x_2)$ is a normal density function with

$$(5) \qquad\qquad \text{mean:}\quad \mu_1 + \frac{\rho\sigma_1}{\sigma_2}(X_2 - \mu_2)$$

$$(6) \qquad\qquad \text{variance:}\quad \sigma_1^2(1 - \rho^2)$$

The $f(x_1 \mid x_2)$ is shown graphically in Figure 16–2. The conditional mean

$$(7) \qquad\qquad E(X_1 \mid X_2) = \mu_1 + \frac{\rho\sigma_1}{\sigma_2}(X_2 - \mu_2)$$

is given to us by a *linear equation*. Thus, we may draw a straight line as we did in our graph to show the various values of $E(X_1)$, given values of X_2. Let us denote $E(X_1 \mid X_2) = \mu_{12}$. The subscript 12 will mean X_1 is dependent on X_2. We can do the same for $E(X_2 \mid X_1)$.

In passing, it should be noticed that, when $X_2 = \mu_2$, then

$$E(X_1 \mid X_2 = \mu_2) = \mu_1 + 0 = \mu_1$$

Thus when $X_2 = \mu_2$, then $\mu_{12} = \mu_1$; i.e., the straight line passes through the point (μ_1, μ_2).

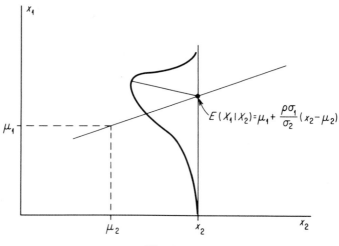

Fig. 16–2

(iii) Regression

The *regression function* of X_1 (son's height) on X_2 (father's height) is defined as

(8) $$E(X_1 \mid X_2 = x_2) = \int_{-\infty}^{+\infty} x_1 f(x_1 \mid x_2)\, dx_1$$

In terms of our illustration, we wish to find a functional relationship between the mean value of the son's height and a given (fixed) father's height.

Since we have a bivariate normal distribution the conditional distribution $f(x_1 \mid x_2)$ is also normal with mean $= \mu_1 + (\rho \sigma_1 / \sigma_2)(X_2 - \mu_2)$ and variance $= \sigma_1^2(1 - \rho^2)$. Thus, equation (8) becomes

(9) $$E(X_1 \mid X_2 = x_2) = \mu_1 + \frac{\rho \sigma_1}{\sigma_2}(X_2 - \mu_2)$$

or

$$\mu_{12} = \mu_1 + \frac{\rho \sigma_1}{\sigma_2}(X_2 - \mu_2)$$

As is seen μ_2, μ_1, ρ, σ_2, σ_1 are all constants and we have a *linear relationship* between μ_{12} and X_2. This is shown graphically in Figure 16–3.

The straight line showing the regression function is called the *regression curve*. In our case we have a linear regression curve of X_1 on X_2. In general, when we have

$$E(X_1 \mid X_2) = \alpha + \beta X_2$$

we have a linear regression function of X_1 on X_2. α and β are called *regression coefficients*.

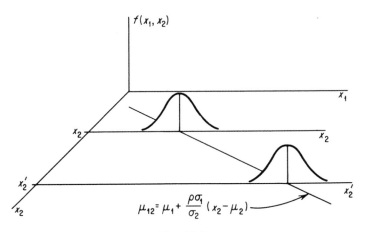

$$\mu_{12} = \mu_1 + \frac{\rho\sigma_1}{\sigma_2}(x_2 - \mu_2)$$

Fig. 16–3

(iv) Estimators of σ_1, σ_2, μ_1, μ_2 and ρ

Let us take a sample of size n from this bivariate population and apply the *maximum likelihood method*. The likelihood function will be

$$L = \prod_{i=1}^{n} f(x_{1i}, x_{2i}) = (2\pi\sigma_1\sigma_2\sqrt{1 - \rho^2})^{-n} \exp\left[-\frac{1}{2(1 - \rho^2)} \Sigma \left\{\left(\frac{x_{1i} - \mu_1}{\sigma_1}\right)^2\right.\right.$$

$$\left.\left. - 2\rho\left(\frac{x_{1i} - \mu_1}{\sigma_1}\right)\left(\frac{x_{2i} - \mu_2}{\sigma_2}\right) + \left(\frac{x_{2i} - \mu_2}{\sigma_2}\right)^2\right\}\right]$$

Taking the log and differentiating with respect to μ_1, μ_2, σ_1, σ_2, and ρ and setting the results equal to zero, we find their maximum likelihood estimators. Anticipating results, we will set

$$s_1^2 = \frac{1}{n}\Sigma(X_1 - \bar{X}_1)^2$$

$$s_2^2 = \frac{1}{n}\Sigma(X_2 - \bar{X}_2)^2$$

$$r = \frac{\Sigma(X_1 - \bar{X}_1)(X_2 - \bar{X}_2)}{\sqrt{\Sigma(X_1 - \bar{X}_1)^2 \Sigma(X_2 - \bar{X}_2)^2}} = \frac{\Sigma(X_1 - \bar{X}_1)(X_2 - \bar{X}_2)}{ns_1 s_2}$$

Then it turns out that

$$\hat{\mu}_1 = \bar{X}_1, \qquad \hat{\mu}_2 = \bar{X}_2$$

$$\hat{\sigma}_1 = s_1, \qquad \hat{\sigma}_2 = s_2, \qquad \hat{\rho} = r$$

Thus, the regression function

$$\mu_{12} = \mu_1 + \frac{\rho \sigma_1}{\sigma_2}(X_2 - \mu_2)$$

is estimated by

$$X_{12} = \bar{X}_1 + \frac{r s_1}{s_2}(X_2 - \bar{X}_2)$$

Let us set

$$a_1 = \bar{X}_1, \qquad b_{12} = \frac{r s_1}{s_2}$$

Then,

$$X_{12} = a_1 + b_{12}(X_2 - \bar{X}_2)$$

For the reverse case we have

$$X_{21} = \bar{X}_2 + \frac{r s_2}{s_1}(X_1 - \bar{X}_1)$$

$$= a_2 + b_{21}(X_1 - \bar{X}_1)$$

We note that

$$b_{12}b_{21} = \frac{r s_1}{s_2} \cdot \frac{r s_2}{s_1} = r^2$$

and

$$r = \sqrt{b_{12}b_{21}}$$

That is, r is the geometric average of the regression coefficients. This shows that r treats X_1 and X_2 simultaneously. The b's treat them one at a time. For example, b_{21} is the case where X_1 takes on fixed values and X_2 varies.

To summarize, we have

$$\mu_{12} = \mu_1 + \frac{\rho \sigma_1}{\sigma_2}(X_2 - \mu_2)$$

$$\mu_{21} = \mu_2 + \frac{\rho \sigma_2}{\sigma_1}(X_1 - \mu_1)$$

and, as estimates

$$X_{12} = \bar{X}_1 + \frac{r s_1}{s_2}(X_2 - \bar{X}_2)$$

$$X_{21} = \bar{X}_2 + \frac{r s_2}{s_1}(X_1 - \bar{X}_1)$$

and

$$b_{12} = \frac{r s_1}{s_2}, \qquad b_{21} = \frac{r s_2}{s_1}$$

Problems

1. Show that $\hat{\mu}_1 = \bar{X}_1$, $\hat{\mu}_2 = \bar{X}_2$

2. Show that $\dfrac{\partial \ln L}{\partial \sigma_1} = 0$ will become

$$\frac{\sum (X_{1i} - \mu_1)^2}{\sigma_1^2} = \frac{\rho \sum (X_{1i} - \mu_1)(X_{2i} - \mu_2)}{\sigma_1 \sigma_2} + n(1 - \rho^2)$$

Also find $\dfrac{\partial \ln L}{\partial \sigma_2} = 0$

3. From $r = \dfrac{\sum (X_1 - \bar{X}_1)(X_2 - \bar{X}_2)}{ns_1 s_2}$

we have

$$\sum (X_1 - \bar{X}_1)(X_2 - \bar{X}_2) = rns_1 s_2$$

Using this result, show that from the result in Problem 2 above, we have

$$\frac{s_1^2}{\sigma_1^2} = \rho r \frac{s_1 s_2}{\sigma_1 \sigma_2} + (1 - \rho^2)$$

from $\dfrac{\partial \ln L}{\partial \sigma_1} = 0$. Also find the result for $\dfrac{\partial \ln L}{\partial \sigma_2} = 0$.

4. Using the two results in Problem 3, show that

$$\frac{s_1}{\sigma_1} = \frac{s_2}{\sigma_2} = \sqrt{\frac{1 - \rho^2}{1 - \rho r}}$$

5. $\dfrac{\partial \ln L}{\partial \rho} = 0$ becomes

$$n\rho(1 - \rho^2) + (1 + \rho^2) \sum \left(\frac{X_{1i} - \mu_1}{\sigma_1} \right) \left(\frac{X_{2i} - \mu_2}{\sigma_2} \right)$$

$$= \rho \sum \left[\left(\frac{X_{1i} - \mu_1}{\sigma_1} \right)^2 + \left(\frac{X_{2i} - \mu_2}{\sigma_2} \right)^2 \right]$$

Using the results $\hat{\mu}_1 = \bar{X}_1$, $\hat{\mu}_2 = \bar{X}_2$, $\dfrac{s_1}{\sigma_1} = \dfrac{s_2}{\sigma_2} = \sqrt{\dfrac{1 - \rho^2}{1 - \rho r}}$, show that this

equation reduces to

$$\rho = r$$

That is, the maximum likelihood estimator of ρ is $\hat{\rho} = r$.

6. Using this result $\hat{\rho} = r$, and $s_1/\sigma_1 = \sqrt{(1 - \rho^2)/(1 - \rho r)}$, show that $\sigma_1 = s_1$. That is, the maximum likelihood estimator of σ_1 is $\hat{\sigma}_1 = s_1$. Likewise for $\hat{\sigma}_2 = s_2$.

16.8 Matrix notation

(i) Multivariate normal distribution

As is seen, the notation has become quite clumsy, even for the bivariate case. To facilitate computations, matrix notation can be used. Let

$$\sigma_1^2 = E(X_1 - \bar{X}_1)^2 = \sigma_{11}$$
$$\sigma_2^2 = E(X_2 - \bar{X}_2)^2 = \sigma_{22}$$
$$\sigma_{12} = \sigma_{21} = E(X_1 - \bar{X}_1)(X_2 - \bar{X}_2) = \text{Cov}\,(X_1, X_2)$$

Then,

$$\rho = \rho_{12} = \rho_{21} = \frac{\text{Cov}\,(X_1, X_2)}{\sigma_1\sigma_2} = \frac{\sigma_{12}}{\sqrt{\sigma_{11}\sigma_{22}}}$$

$$\sigma_{12} = \rho_{12}\sqrt{\sigma_{11}\sigma_{22}} = \rho_{12}\sigma_1\sigma_2$$

We define the *variance-covariance matrix* $\mathbf{V}$ as

$$\mathbf{V} = \begin{bmatrix} \sigma_{11} & \sigma_{12} \\ \sigma_{21} & \sigma_{22} \end{bmatrix} = \begin{bmatrix} E(X_1 - \bar{X}_1)^2 & E(X_1 - \bar{X}_1)(X_2 - \bar{X}_2) \\ E(X_2 - \bar{X}_2)(X_1 - \bar{X}_1) & E(X_2 - \bar{X}_2)^2 \end{bmatrix}$$

We may think of this as the variance of the bivariate distribution. The value of the determinant of $\mathbf{V}$ is

$$|\mathbf{V}| = \sigma_{11}\sigma_{22} - \sigma_{12}^2 = \sigma_{11}\sigma_{22} - \rho^2\sigma_{11}\sigma_{22} = \sigma_{11}\sigma_{22}(1 - \rho^2)$$

Let us find the inverse of $\mathbf{V}$.

$$\mathbf{V}^{-1} = \begin{bmatrix} \dfrac{\mathbf{V}_{ji}}{|\mathbf{V}|} \end{bmatrix} = \frac{1}{|\mathbf{V}|} \begin{bmatrix} \mathbf{V}_{22} & -\mathbf{V}_{21} \\ -\mathbf{V}_{12} & \mathbf{V}_{11} \end{bmatrix} = \frac{1}{\sigma_{11}\sigma_{22}(1 - \rho^2)} \begin{bmatrix} \sigma_{22} & -\sigma_{21} \\ -\sigma_{12} & \sigma_{11} \end{bmatrix}$$

$$= \frac{1}{(1 - \rho^2)} \begin{bmatrix} \dfrac{1}{\sigma_{11}} & -\dfrac{\rho}{\sqrt{\sigma_{11}\sigma_{22}}} \\ -\dfrac{\rho}{\sqrt{\sigma_{11}\sigma_{22}}} & \dfrac{1}{\sigma_{22}} \end{bmatrix} = \frac{1}{(1 - \rho^2)} \begin{bmatrix} \dfrac{1}{\sigma_1^2} & \dfrac{-\rho}{\sigma_1\sigma_2} \\ \dfrac{-\rho}{\sigma_1\sigma_2} & \dfrac{1}{\sigma_2^2} \end{bmatrix}$$

Noting that the elements of $\mathbf{V}^{-1}$ are the coefficients in the quadratic exponent of the bivariate normal distribution, we can write the exponent as

$$[X_1 - \mu_1,\ X_2 - \mu_2] \cdot \begin{bmatrix} \dfrac{1}{\sigma_1^2(1 - \rho^2)} & \dfrac{-\rho}{\sigma_1\sigma_2(1 - \rho^2)} \\ \dfrac{-\rho}{\sigma_1\sigma_2(1 - \rho^2)} & \dfrac{1}{\sigma_2^2(1 - \rho^2)} \end{bmatrix} \cdot \begin{bmatrix} X_1 - \mu_1 \\ X_2 - \mu_2 \end{bmatrix}$$

$$= \frac{1}{1 - \rho^2} \left[\frac{(X_1 - \mu_1)^2}{\sigma_1^2} - 2\frac{\rho}{\sigma_1\sigma_2}(X_1 - \mu_1)(X_2 - \mu_2) + \frac{(X_2 - \mu_2)^2}{\sigma_2^2} \right]$$

Set,

$$X = \begin{bmatrix} X_1 \\ X_2 \end{bmatrix} = \begin{bmatrix} \text{father's height} \\ \text{son's height} \end{bmatrix}$$

and call this a *random vector*. Then we may write

$$E(X) = \mu = \begin{bmatrix} E(X_1) \\ E(X_2) \end{bmatrix} = \begin{bmatrix} \mu_1 \\ \mu_2 \end{bmatrix}$$

Then, the exponent becomes

$$(X - \mu)'V^{-1}(X - \mu)$$

and the bivariate normal distribution is

$$(2\pi)^{-p/2} \, |V|^{-1/2} \exp\left[-\tfrac{1}{2}(X - \mu)'V^{-1}(X - \mu)\right]$$

where $p = 2$.

For a trivariate normal distribution we have, say,

$$X = \begin{bmatrix} X_1 \\ X_2 \\ X_3 \end{bmatrix} = \begin{bmatrix} \text{son's height} \\ \text{father's height} \\ \text{mother's height} \end{bmatrix}$$

$$E(X) = \mu = \begin{bmatrix} \mu_1 \\ \mu_2 \\ \mu_3 \end{bmatrix}$$

and

$$V = \begin{bmatrix} \sigma_{11} & \sigma_{12} & \sigma_{13} \\ \sigma_{21} & \sigma_{22} & \sigma_{23} \\ \sigma_{31} & \sigma_{32} & \sigma_{33} \end{bmatrix}$$

where

$$\sigma_{ij} = \sqrt{\sigma_{ii}\sigma_{jj}} \, \rho_{ij}$$

And so the tri-normal distribution becomes

$$(2\pi)^{-p/2} \, |V|^{-1/2} \exp\left[-\tfrac{1}{2}(X - \mu)'V^{-1}(X - \mu)\right]$$

where $p = 3$. This can be generalized to the *n*-normal distribution.

(*ii*) *Conditional distribution for tri-normal case*

Let us partition the random vector as follows.

$$X = \begin{bmatrix} X_1 \\ X_2 \\ X_3 \end{bmatrix} = \begin{bmatrix} \text{son's height} \\ \text{father's height} \\ \text{mother's height} \end{bmatrix} = \begin{bmatrix} X^{(1)} \\ X^{(2)} \end{bmatrix}$$

where

$$X^{(1)} = [X_1] \qquad X^{(2)} = \begin{bmatrix} X_2 \\ X_3 \end{bmatrix}$$

will be called *subvectors*. Note we use superscripts with brackets. Let

$$E(X) = \mu = \begin{bmatrix} \mu^{(1)} \\ \mu^{(2)} \end{bmatrix}$$

Also partition the **V** as

$$\mathbf{V} = \begin{bmatrix} \mathbf{V}_{11} & \mathbf{V}_{12} \\ \mathbf{V}_{21} & \mathbf{V}_{22} \end{bmatrix}$$

where

$$\mathbf{V}_{11} = E(X^{(1)} - \mu^{(1)})'(X^{(1)} - \mu^{(1)})$$
$$\mathbf{V}_{22} = E(X^{(2)} - \mu^{(2)})'(X^{(2)} - \mu^{(2)})$$
$$\mathbf{V}_{12} = E(X^{(1)} - \mu^{(1)})'(X^{(2)} - \mu^{(2)})$$

We are interested in the conditional distribution of X_1, given X_2 and X_3. That is, we want to find $E(X^{(1)} \mid X^{(2)})$. It can be shown that the conditional distribution of X_1 given X_2, X_3 will be a normal distribution with mean and covariance as follows

$$E(X^{(1)} \mid X^{(2)}) = \mu_1 + \mathbf{V}_{12}\mathbf{V}_{22}^{-1}(X^{(2)} - \mu^{(2)})$$
$$\text{Covariance} = \mathbf{V}_{11} - \mathbf{V}_{12}\mathbf{V}_{22}^{-1}\mathbf{V}_{21}$$

The first equation is the *regression function* we are interested in. We have used three variables X_1, X_2, X_3 to explain it, but it can be generalized. Let us work it out fully for the two and three variable case and show how it relates to the non-matrix presentation.

Case 1—X_1, X_2. Here $X^{(1)} = X_1$, $X^{(2)} = X_2$. Then,

$$E(X_1 \mid X_2) = \mu_1 + \mathbf{V}_{12}\mathbf{V}_{22}^{-1}(X_2 - \mu_2)$$

$$\mathbf{V} = \begin{bmatrix} \sigma_{11} & \sigma_{12} \\ \sigma_{21} & \sigma_{22} \end{bmatrix}$$

$$\mathbf{V}_{12} = \sigma_{12} = E(X_1 - \mu_1)(X_2 - \mu_2)$$
$$= \rho\sqrt{\sigma_{11}\sigma_{22}} = \rho\sigma_1\sigma_2$$
$$\mathbf{V}_{22} = \sigma_{22} = E(X_2 - \mu_2)^2 = \sigma_2^2$$

Thus,

$$E(X_1 \mid X_2) = \mu_1 + \rho\sigma_1\sigma_2 \frac{1}{\sigma_2^2}(X_2 - \mu_2)$$

$$\mu_{12} = \mu_1 + \rho\frac{\sigma_1}{\sigma_2}(X_2 - \mu_2)$$

This is the same result as in our non-matrix case, and we set $\beta_{12} = \rho(\sigma_1/\sigma_2)$.

The covariance matrix for the conditional distribution which we shall denote by $\mathbf{V}_{11.2}$ is

$$\mathbf{V}_{11.2} = \mathbf{V}_{11} - \mathbf{V}_{12}\mathbf{V}_{22}^{-1}\mathbf{V}_{21}$$

$$= \sigma_{11} - \sigma_{12}\frac{1}{\sigma_{22}}\sigma_{21}$$

$$= \sigma_1^2 - \rho\sigma_1\sigma_2 \cdot \frac{1}{\sigma_2^2}\rho\sigma_2\sigma_1$$

$$= \sigma_1^2 - \rho^2\sigma_1^2 = \sigma^2(1 - \rho^2)$$

We know that $\sigma^2(1 - \rho^2)$ is the covariance of the bivariate normal distribution from our previous discussion.

Case 2—X_1, X_2, X_3. Let us try it with $X^{(1)} = X_1$, $X^{(2)} = [X_2, X_3]$. Then,

$$E(X_1 \mid X_2, X_3) = \mu_1 + V_{12}V_{22}^{-1}(X^{(2)} - \mu^{(2)})$$

The covariance matrix is

$$V = \begin{bmatrix} \sigma_{11} & \sigma_{12} & \sigma_{13} \\ \sigma_{21} & \sigma_{22} & \sigma_{23} \\ \sigma_{31} & \sigma_{32} & \sigma_{33} \end{bmatrix}$$

and

$$V_{12} = \begin{bmatrix} \sigma_{12} & \sigma_{13} \end{bmatrix}$$

$$V_{22} = \begin{bmatrix} \sigma_{22} & \sigma_{23} \\ \sigma_{32} & \sigma_{33} \end{bmatrix}$$

$$V_{22}^{-1} = \frac{1}{|V_{22}|} \begin{bmatrix} \sigma_{33} & -\sigma_{32} \\ -\sigma_{23} & \sigma_{22} \end{bmatrix}$$

Thus,

$$V_{12}V_{22}^{-1} = \frac{1}{|V_{22}|} \begin{bmatrix} \sigma_{12} & \sigma_{13} \end{bmatrix} \begin{bmatrix} \sigma_{33} & -\sigma_{32} \\ -\sigma_{23} & \sigma_{22} \end{bmatrix}$$

$$= \frac{1}{|V_{22}|} \begin{bmatrix} \sigma_{12}\sigma_{33} - \sigma_{13}\sigma_{23} & \sigma_{13}\sigma_{22} - \sigma_{12}\sigma_{32} \end{bmatrix}$$

Thus,

$$E(X_1 \mid X_2, X_3) = \mu_1 + \frac{1}{|V_{22}|} \begin{bmatrix} \sigma_{12}\sigma_{33} - \sigma_{13}\sigma_{33} & \sigma_{13}\sigma_{22} - \sigma_{12}\sigma_{32} \end{bmatrix} \cdot \begin{bmatrix} X_2 - \mu_2 \\ X_3 - \mu_3 \end{bmatrix}$$

$$= \mu_1 + \beta_{12}(X_2 - \mu_2) + \beta_{13}(X_3 - \mu_3)$$

where

$$\beta_{12} = \frac{1}{|V_{22}|} (\sigma_{12}\sigma_{33} - \sigma_{13}\sigma_{23})$$

$$\beta_{13} = \frac{1}{|V_{22}|} (\sigma_{13}\sigma_{22} - \sigma_{12}\sigma_{32})$$

The covariance matrix for the conditional distribution is

$$V_{11.2} = V_{11} - V_{12}V_{22}^{-1}V_{21}$$

$$= \begin{bmatrix} \sigma_{11} \end{bmatrix} - \begin{bmatrix} \sigma_{12} & \sigma_{13} \end{bmatrix} \frac{1}{|V_{22}|} \begin{bmatrix} \sigma_{33} & -\sigma_{32} \\ -\sigma_{23} & \sigma_{22} \end{bmatrix} \begin{bmatrix} \sigma_{21} \\ \sigma_{31} \end{bmatrix}$$

$$= \sigma_{11} - |V_{22}|^{-1} [\sigma_{12}^2\sigma_{33} - 2\sigma_{12}\sigma_{13}\sigma_{23} + \sigma_{13}^2\sigma_{22}]$$

(iii) Estimation of β_2, β_3

We now wish to estimate the parameters of the distribution and also the β's of the regression function. For this we take a sample of size n. Each element in the sample will be made up of a son, father, and mother. Let the observations be x_1, x_2, ..., x_n where each x is a vector of order three. They are sometimes called *observation vectors*. The likelihood function can be shown as

$$L = (2\pi)^{-np/2}|\mathbf{V}|^{-n/2} \exp\left[-\frac{1}{2}\sum_{\alpha=1}^{n}(x_\alpha - \mu)'\mathbf{V}^{-1}(x_\alpha - \mu)\right]$$

L is a function of μ and $\mathbf{V}$.

When we apply the method of maximum likelihood, we find the following results.*

$$\hat{\mu} = \begin{bmatrix} \hat{\mu}_1 \\ \hat{\mu}_2 \\ \hat{\mu}_3 \end{bmatrix} = \begin{bmatrix} \bar{X}_1 \\ \bar{X}_2 \\ \bar{X}_3 \end{bmatrix}$$

That is, the maximum likelihood estimators of μ_i are the sample means $\bar{X}_i$.

The maximum likelihood estimator of the covariance matrix $\mathbf{V}$ is

$$\hat{\mathbf{V}} = \frac{1}{n}\sum_\alpha (X_\alpha - \bar{X})'(X_\alpha - \bar{X}) = \frac{1}{n}\left[\sum_\alpha X_\alpha'X_\alpha - n\bar{X}'\bar{X}\right]$$

where

$$\sum_{\alpha=1}^{n} X_\alpha'X_\alpha = \begin{bmatrix} \sum X_{1\alpha}X_{1\alpha} & \sum X_{1\alpha}X_{2\alpha} & \sum X_{1\alpha}X_{3\alpha} \\ \sum X_{2\alpha}X_{1\alpha} & \sum X_{2\alpha}X_{2\alpha} & \sum X_{2\alpha}X_{3\alpha} \\ \sum X_{3\alpha}X_{1\alpha} & \sum X_{3\alpha}X_{2\alpha} & \sum X_{3\alpha}X_{3\alpha} \end{bmatrix}$$

$$n\bar{X}'\bar{X} = n\begin{bmatrix} \bar{X}_1\bar{X}_1 & \bar{X}_1\bar{X}_2 & \bar{X}_1\bar{X}_3 \\ \bar{X}_2\bar{X}_1 & \bar{X}_2\bar{X}_2 & \bar{X}_2\bar{X}_3 \\ \bar{X}_3\bar{X}_1 & \bar{X}_3\bar{X}_2 & \bar{X}_3\bar{X}_3 \end{bmatrix}$$

Thus,

$$\hat{\mathbf{V}} = \begin{bmatrix} \frac{1}{n}\sum X_{1\alpha}^2 - \bar{X}_1^2 & \frac{1}{n}\sum X_{1\alpha}X_{2\alpha} - \bar{X}_1\bar{X}_2 & \frac{1}{n}\sum X_{1\alpha}X_{3\alpha} - \bar{X}_1\bar{X}_3 \\ \frac{1}{n}\sum X_{2\alpha}X_{1\alpha} - \bar{X}_2\bar{X}_1 & \frac{1}{n}\sum X_{2\alpha}^2 - \bar{X}_2^2 & \frac{1}{n}\sum X_{2\alpha}X_{3\alpha} - \bar{X}_2\bar{X}_3 \\ \frac{1}{n}\sum X_{3\alpha}X_{1\alpha} - \bar{X}_3\bar{X}_1 & \frac{1}{n}\sum X_{3\alpha}X_{2\alpha} - \bar{X}_3\bar{X}_2 & \frac{1}{n}\sum X_{3\alpha}^2 - \bar{X}_3^2 \end{bmatrix}$$

$$= \begin{bmatrix} \hat{\sigma}_{11} & \hat{\sigma}_{12} & \hat{\sigma}_{13} \\ \hat{\sigma}_{21} & \hat{\sigma}_{22} & \hat{\sigma}_{23} \\ \hat{\sigma}_{31} & \hat{\sigma}_{32} & \hat{\sigma}_{33} \end{bmatrix} \equiv \begin{bmatrix} s_{11} & s_{12} & s_{13} \\ s_{21} & s_{22} & s_{23} \\ s_{31} & s_{32} & s_{33} \end{bmatrix}$$

We have seen that

$$E(X^{(1)} \mid X^{(2)}) = \mu^{(1)} + \mathbf{V}_{12}\mathbf{V}_{22}^{-1}(X^{(2)} - \mu^{(2)})$$

* For proof, see Anderson (1958), p. 48.

where

$$V_{12}V_{22}^{-1} = \left[\frac{\sigma_{12}\sigma_{33} - \sigma_{13}\sigma_{23}}{|V_{22}|} \quad \frac{\sigma_{13}\sigma_{22} - \sigma_{12}\sigma_{32}}{|V_{22}|} \right]$$

$$= [\beta_2 \quad \beta_3]$$

Since we have estimated V, we can find the estimators of β_2 and β_3. That is, for example,

$$\hat{\beta}_2 = \frac{\hat{\sigma}_{12}\hat{\sigma}_{33} - \hat{\sigma}_{13}\hat{\sigma}_{23}}{|\hat{V}_{22}|}$$

where all the elements are obtained from the sample elements.

Problems

1. Given a random vector

$$X = \begin{bmatrix} X^{(1)} \\ X^{(2)} \end{bmatrix} = \begin{bmatrix} X_1 \\ X_2 \\ X_3 \\ X_4 \end{bmatrix}, \quad X^{(1)} = X_1$$

where X is normally distributed, answer the following.
   (a) Write out this four-dimensional normal distribution using matrix notation.
   (b) Write out the mean and variance of the conditional distribution of $X^{(1)}$ on $X^{(2)}$.
   (c) $E(X^{(1)} \mid X^{(2)})$ is the regression function. Find the β coefficients.
   (d) Take a sample of size n. Write out the estimate of the covariance matrix V.

2. Show that
   (a) $\sum (X - \bar{X})^2 = \sum X^2 - n\bar{X}^2$
       $\sum (X_1 - \bar{X}_1)(X_2 - \bar{X}_2) = \sum X_1 X_2 - n\bar{X}_1\bar{X}_2$
   (b) Let $\sum (X_1 - \bar{X}_1)^2 = \sum x_1^2$
       $\sum (X_1 - \bar{X}_1)(X_2 - \bar{X}_2) = \sum x_1 x_2$

   Show that

$$V = \frac{1}{n} \begin{bmatrix} \sum x_1^2 & \sum x_1 x_2 & \sum x_1 x_3 \\ \sum x_2 x_1 & \sum x_2^2 & \sum x_2 x_3 \\ \sum x_3 x_1 & \sum x_3 x_2 & \sum x_3^2 \end{bmatrix}$$

   Note that these are the coefficients of the normal equation multiplied by $1/n$.

16.9 Moment notation

(i) Definitions

A useful form of notation used frequently in regression problems by economists is the moment notation. The r-th moment of a random variable X about the mean was defined as

$$E\{(x - \mu)^r\}$$

where μ is $\mu = E(X)$.

Corresponding to this population concept, let us define the r-th sample moment about the sample mean as

$$M_r = \frac{1}{n} \sum_{i=1}^{n} (x_i - \bar{x})^r$$

Since we are usually concerned with first and second moments, we shall alter the above notation in the following manner. Consider the estimated linear regression line

$$Y_c = a + bX$$

Then we define the moments as follows, assuming a sample of size n.

$$M_{xx} = \frac{1}{n} \sum (x - \bar{x})^2$$

$$M_{xy} = \frac{1}{n} \sum (x - \bar{x})(y - \bar{y})$$

M_{xx} may be considered as the sample variance and M_{xy} as the sample covariance. The first moment is

$$M_x = \frac{1}{n} \sum (x - \bar{x}) = 0$$

That is, the first sample moment is zero when taken around the mean. However, there are occasions when we need the first moment around the origin, i.e.,

$$1/n \sum x = \bar{x}$$

To show this in moment notation so that uniformity in notation may be obtained, we shall write

$$\bar{M}_x = \frac{1}{n} \sum x = \bar{x}$$

using the overbar to indicate that it is taken around the origin. Then,

$$\bar{M}_{qx} = \frac{1}{n} \sum qx = q \frac{1}{n} \sum x = q\bar{M}_x$$

where q is a constant. We also find that

$$M_{qxy} = \frac{1}{n}\sum (qx - q\bar{x})(y - \bar{y})$$

$$= \frac{1}{n}\sum (x - \bar{x})(qy - q\bar{y}) = qM_{xy}$$

The parameters a and b of the regression line are, from the method of least squares,

$$b = \frac{\sum (X - \bar{X})(Y - \bar{Y})}{\sum (X - \bar{X})^2}$$

$$a = \frac{1}{n}\sum Y - b\frac{1}{n}\sum X$$

Thus in moment notation this becomes

$$b = \frac{M_{xy}}{M_{xx}}$$

$$a = \bar{M}_y - \frac{M_{xy}}{M_{xx}}\bar{M}_x = \frac{M_{xx}\bar{M}_y - M_{xy}\bar{M}_x}{M_{xx}}$$

(ii) *Notation for Multiple Linear Regression Case*

Consider

(1) $$Y_c = a + b_1 X_1 + b_2 X_2$$

We know that we can shift the origin to the sample mean and rewrite (1) as

(2) $$Y_c - \bar{Y}_c = b_1(X_1 - \bar{X}_1) + b_2(X_2 - \bar{X}_2)$$

$$a = \bar{Y}_c - b_1\bar{X}_1 - b_2\bar{X}_2$$

Using lower case letters for deviations from the mean, (2) becomes

(3) $$y = b_1 x_1 + b_2 x_2$$

The normal equations for (3) were

(4) $$\sum x_1 y = b_1 \sum x_1^2 + b_2 \sum x_1 x_2$$
$$\sum x_2 y = b_2 \sum x_1 x_2 + b_2 \sum x_2^2$$

In matrix notation this is

$$\begin{bmatrix} \sum x_1^2 & \sum x_1 x_2 \\ \sum x_1 x_2 & \sum x_2^2 \end{bmatrix} \begin{bmatrix} b_1 \\ b_2 \end{bmatrix} = \begin{bmatrix} \sum x_1 y \\ \sum x_2 y \end{bmatrix}$$

Using the moment notation this becomes

$$\begin{bmatrix} M_{x_1x_1} & M_{x_1x_2} \\ M_{x_1x_2} & M_{x_2x_2} \end{bmatrix} \begin{bmatrix} b_1 \\ b_2 \end{bmatrix} = \begin{bmatrix} M_{x_1y} \\ M_{x_2y} \end{bmatrix}$$

Note that both sides have been multiplied by $1/n$.

Using Cramer's rule, b_1 becomes

$$b_1 = \frac{\begin{vmatrix} M_{x_1y} & M_{x_1x_2} \\ M_{x_2y} & M_{x_2x_2} \end{vmatrix}}{\begin{vmatrix} M_{x_1x_1} & M_{x_1x_2} \\ M_{x_1x_2} & M_{x_2x_2} \end{vmatrix}}$$

Let us develop additional moment notation to simplify the expression for b_1. Define

$$M_{(x_1x_2)(x_1x_2)} = \begin{bmatrix} M_{x_1x_1} & M_{x_1x_2} \\ M_{x_2x_1} & M_{x_2x_2} \end{bmatrix}$$

where the subscript of $M_{(x_1x_2)(x_1x_2)}$ indicates the rows and columns of the moment matrix respectively. For example,

$$M_{(x_1x_2)(y)} = \begin{bmatrix} M_{x_1y} \\ M_{x_2y} \end{bmatrix}$$

$$M_{(x_1)(x_1y)} = \begin{bmatrix} M_{x_1x_1} & M_{x_1y} \end{bmatrix}$$

$$M_{(x_1x_2)(y_1y_2)} = \begin{bmatrix} M_{x_1y_1} & M_{x_1y_2} \\ M_{x_2y_1} & M_{x_2y_2} \end{bmatrix}$$

This can be generalized to k variables.

Using this notation, b_1 becomes

$$b_1 = \frac{M_{(x_1x_2)(yx_2)}}{M_{(x_1x_2)(x_1x_2)}}$$

The case for more than two variables is obtained in a similar manner.

(iii) *Other properties of the moment notation*

(a) $\overline{M}_{(a+y)} = \dfrac{1}{n}\sum (a + y) = a + \overline{M}_y$

(b) $\overline{M}_{(x+y)} = \dfrac{1}{n}\sum (x + y) = \overline{M}_x + \overline{M}_y$

(c) $M_{(x+y)y} = M_{xy+yy} = M_{xy} + M_{yy}$

(d) $M_{(x+y)(x+y)} = M_{xx+2xy+yy} = M_{xx} + 2M_{xy} + M_{yy}$

(iv) *Example*

Consider a consumption function

$$c = \alpha + \beta y + \epsilon$$

where c is consumption, y is income, and ϵ is a random shock variable that is $N(0, \sigma^2)$. Take a sample of size n and estimate α and β by the method of least squares. We know that

$$\hat{\beta} = b = \frac{M_{cy}}{M_{yy}}$$

$$\hat{\alpha} = a = \frac{M_{yy}\overline{M}_c - M_{cy}\overline{M}_y}{M_{yy}}$$

$\hat{\beta} = b$ is the estimate of the marginal propensity to consume. This becomes

$$\hat{\beta} = b = \frac{M_{cy}}{M_{yy}} = \frac{M_{(\alpha+\beta y+\epsilon)y}}{M_{yy}}$$

$$= \frac{M_{\alpha y} + M_{\beta yy} + M_{\epsilon y}}{M_{yy}}$$

$$= \beta + \frac{M_{\epsilon y}}{M_{yy}}$$

Note that $M_{\alpha y} = 0$. The random shock variable ϵ covers factors such as income distribution that affect consumption c. The ϵ and y are not completely independent, and thus we may assume $M_{\epsilon y} \neq 0$, as $n \to \infty$. Thus,

$$E(b) = \beta + E\left(\frac{M_{\epsilon y}}{M_{yy}}\right)$$

That is, b is a biased estimate of β.

(v) *Matrix Notation*

The moment matrix $M_{(x_1 x_2)(x_1 x_2)}$ for example, may be expressed in matrix notation as M_{XX} where $X = (x_1 x_2)$. Thus, if we have a regression line with six independent variables,

$$Y = b_1 X_1 + b_2 X_2 + b_3 X_3 + b_4 X_4 + b_5 X_5 + b_6 X_6$$

the b_3 will be

$$b_3 = \frac{M_{XY}}{M_{XX}}$$

where

$$X = (x_1 \ x_2 \ x_3 \ x_4 \ x_5 \ x_6)$$
$$Y = (x_1 \ x_2 \ y \ x_4 \ x_5 \ x_6)$$

By defining the X and Y to suit the circumstances, various variations of the basic definition may be obtained that will simplify notation considerably.

Problems

1. Write out the following moment matrices.

   M_{XY} where:

   (a) $X = (x_1 \, x_2)$, $Y = (y_1 \, y_2 \, y_3)$

   (b) $X = (x_1 \, x_2 \, x_3)$, $Y = (y_1)$

2. Work out the properties of section (*iii*) above.

3. Given the linear regression equation

$$Y = b_1 X_1 + b_2 X_2 + b_3 X_3$$

   express the b_3 in moment notation.

4. Given the following data:

y	c
$100	$ 90
200	160
300	210
400	240

   where y is income and c is consumption, estimate the α and β of

$$c = \alpha + \beta y$$

   by finding M_{cy}, M_{yy}, $\overline{M}_c$, $\overline{M}_y$ and calculating

$$\beta = \frac{M_{cy}}{M_{yy}}, \qquad \alpha = \frac{M_{yy}\overline{M}_c - M_{cy}\overline{M}_y}{M_{yy}}$$

Notes and References

Regression analysis is a broad topic and the discussion in this chapter has been confined to linear regression which is the main technique used by economists. References that do not require calculus and also explain computing techniques are Snedecor (1956), Chapters 6, 14, and 15; and Ezekiel and Fox (1959). Both books provide many illustrations and also cover curvilinear regression.

Intermediate references that require calculus are Mood (1950), Chapter 13; Wilks (1950), Chapter 8; Fraser (1958), Chapter 12; and Hoel (1954), Chapter 7.

Advanced references are Anderson and Bancroft (1952); Plackett (1960); Graybill (1961); Cramer (1946); and Anderson (1958). Anderson and Bancroft (1952) provide extensive discussion on computational techniques and shows various illustrations of applications. Graybill (1961) discusses linear regression and is very comprehensive. Anderson (1958) is an excellent book on multivariate analysis but is mathematically advanced. See his book for proofs that we have left out concerning multivariate analysis.

For further discussion of the Markoff theorem, see David (1951), Chapters 13 and 14; and Anderson and Bancroft (1952), Chapter 14.

In Section 16.1 and 16.2, the models were single equations. But in econometric models systems of equations are frequently used. The Jacobian transformations are then applied to these systems of equations. Members of the Cowles Commission have developed this simultaneous equation estimation technique and one of the books they have published is Koopmans (1953). See Chapter 6 for a discussion of this technique and Chapters 4 and 5 for illustrations. Valavanis (1959); Klein (1953); and Koopmans (1950) also discuss this technique. A symposium on simultaneous equation estimation may be found in Econometrica, October, 1960.

For a thorough discussion of the matrix notation see Anderson (1958), Chapters 2, 3, 4, and 8. Also see Graybill (1961), Chapter 3.

Examples of moment notation in economics may be found in Valavanis (1959); and Koopmans (1953). See the well known article by T. Haavelmo, "Methods of Measuring the Marginal Propensity to Consume," in Koopmans (1953) as an illustration of the use of moment notation. This article may also be found in the Journal of the American Statistical Association, March, 1947, pp. 105–122. Also see Chapter 6 of Koopmans (1953) for illustrations. Klein (1954) also gives extensive discussion on moment notation and computational techniques in Chapter 5. His notation is slightly different from ours in that he has, for example, $M_{xx} = \sum (x - \bar{x})^2$, that is, he does not divide by $1/n$.

Bibliography

Anderson, T. W., *An Introduction to Multivariate Analysis*. New York: John Wiley and Sons, Inc., 1958.

Anderson, R. L., and Bancroft, T. A. *Statistical Theory in Research*. New York: McGraw-Hill Book Co., Inc., 1952.

David, F. N., *Probability Theory for Statistical Methods*. Cambridge: Cambridge University Press, 1949.

Ezekiel, M., and Fox, K. A. *Methods of Correlation and Regression Analysis*. New York: John Wiley and Sons, Inc., 3rd ed., 1959.

Graybill, F. A., *An Introduction to Linear Statistical Models, Vol. I*. New York: McGraw-Hill Book Co., Inc., 1961.

Plackett, R. L., *Principles of Regression Analysis*. New York: Oxford University Press, 1960.

Snedecor, G. W., *Statistical Methods*. Ames, Iowa: Iowa State College Press, 5th ed., 1956.

"A Symposium on Simultaneous Equation Estimation," *Econometrica*, (Oct., 1960).

Christ, C. F., "Simultaneous Equation Estimation: Any Verdict Yet?," pp. 835–845.

Hildreth, C., "Simultaneous Equations, Any Verdict Yet?", pp. 846–854.

Liu, T., "Underidentification, Structural Estimation, and Forecasting," pp. 855–865.

Klein, L. R., "Single Equation vs. Equation System Methods of Estimation in Econometrics," pp. 866–871.

17.1 Introduction

The correlation coefficient is a measure that shows the degree of relationship between the random variables in a bivariate or multivariate distribution. Different correlation coefficients are defined according to the way the variables are related to each other. For example, let X_1 (son's height), X_2 (father's height), and X_3 (mother's height) make up a trivariate normal distribution. Then the relation between X_i and X_j is written ρ_{ij} and is called the total *correlation coefficient*. When there are only two variables, i.e., when we have a bivariate distribution, it is called the *simple correlation coefficient*.

The ρ_{12} which shows the relation between X_1 (son's height) and X_2 (father's height) may be affected by X_3 (mother's height). When it is desirable to find the degree of relationship between X_1 and X_2 excluding X_3, this is accomplished by holding X_3 fixed and finding the correlation between X_1 and X_2. This is written as $\rho_{12.3}$ and is called the *partial correlation coefficient* between X_1 and X_2. If we have four variables, X_1, X_2, X_3, and X_4, the partial correlation coefficient is written $\rho_{12.34}$ where X_3 and X_4 are held constant.

The relation between X_1 and (X_2, X_3) is written $\rho_{1.23}$ and is called the *multiple correlation coefficient* of X_1 on X_2 and X_3.

We shall now present a brief survey of simple, partial, and multiple correlation coefficients.

17.2 Simple correlation coefficient

(i) *Definition of ρ*

In Chapter 16 the correlation coefficient was defined as

(1)
$$\rho = \frac{E(X - \mu_x)(Y - \mu_y)}{\sqrt{E(X - \mu_x)^2 E(Y - \mu_y)^2}}$$

where $E(X - \mu_x)(Y - \mu_y)$ was called the covariance of X and Y, and ρ was one of the parameters in the bivariate normal distribution. The maximum likelihood estimator of ρ was

(2) $$\hat{\rho} = r = \frac{\sum (X - \bar{X})(Y - \bar{Y})}{\sqrt{\sum (X - \bar{X})^2 \sum (Y - \bar{Y})^2}}$$

where the sum is taken over the sample. In statistics this formula is usually presented for calculation purposes as

(3) $$r = \frac{n \sum XY - \sum X \sum Y}{\sqrt{n \sum X^2 - (\sum X)^2} \sqrt{n \sum Y^2 - (\sum Y)^2}}$$

which avoids calculating the deviations $X - \bar{X} = x$ and $Y - \bar{Y} = y$.

Let us next derive the r from the regression function which will give us more insight into the nature of r.

(ii) *Derivation of r*

Consider the regression function

(4) $$Y_c = \bar{Y} + b(X - \bar{X})$$

How useful is this regression line for estimating purposes, or to put it another way, what part of the covariation between X and Y can be explained by the regression line? Equation (4) is shown in Figure 17–1.

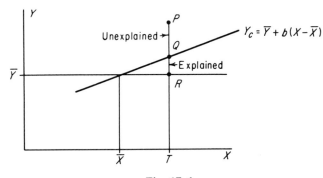

Fig. 17–1

First note from the graph that

$$PR = QR + PQ$$

which in terms of variables is

(5) $$(Y - \bar{Y}) = (Y_c - \bar{Y}) + (Y - Y_c)$$
$$\text{total} \qquad \text{explained} \quad \text{unexplained}$$

$PR = (Y - \bar{Y})$ is called the total deviation; $QR = (Y_c - \bar{Y})$ is called the explained deviation; and $PQ = (Y - Y_c)$ is called the unexplained deviation.

When no regression line is fitted, a representative value of the Y's will be $\bar{Y}$. Thus, when a value of Y is to be estimated for a given X and the estimated value of Y is represented by $\bar{Y}$, there is a deviation of $Y - \bar{Y}$ between the actual Y and the $\bar{Y}$. Hence, $Y - \bar{Y}$ is called the total deviation which indicates the deviation when no regression line is fitted.

When a regression line is fitted, a representative value of Y for a given X is Y_c. The Y_c is usually a better estimate of the actual Y than $\bar{Y}$. Nevertheless, the estimation is not perfect and there is usually a deviation $Y - Y_c$ between the actual Y and the Y_c. This may be considered as the amount of error remaining after a regression line has been fitted.

As is seen from Figure 17–1, if the observed Y value was on the regression line, the deviation is $Y - Y_c = 0$, and Y_c estimates Y perfectly.

The deviation $Y_c - \bar{Y}$ may thus be thought of as the amount of improvement brought about by the regression line.

Let us square both sides of (5) and sum over all the points in the sample. Then (see problem 1)

$$(6) \qquad \sum (Y - \bar{Y})^2 = \sum (Y_c - \bar{Y})^2 + \sum (Y - Y_c)^2$$

This allows us to consider the deviations for all of the sample points, not only for one point as was the situation in equation (5). The sum of the squared deviations $\sum (Y - \bar{Y})^2$ has been split up into two parts. Following our line of reasoning above, $\sum (Y - \bar{Y})^2$ can be thought of as the total amount of error when no regression line is fitted.

$\sum (Y - Y_c)^2$ can be thought of as the amount of error remaining after a regression line is fitted.

$\sum (Y_c - \bar{Y})^2$ can be thought of as the amount of improvement due to the regression line.

Thus, the ratio

$$(7) \qquad \frac{\sum (Y_c - \bar{Y})^2}{\sum (Y - \bar{Y})^2}$$

is a quantitative measure of the improvement or amount explained by the regression line. For example, if the ratio is 0.95, this may be interpreted as saying that 95 per cent of the relationship between X (say, height) and Y (say, weight) has been explained by the regression line and

$$\frac{\sum (Y - Y_c)^2}{\sum (Y - \bar{Y})^2} = 0.05$$

is unexplained.

From equation (4) we find

$$Y_c - \bar{Y} = b(X - \bar{X})$$

Squaring both sides, this becomes

$$(Y_c - \bar{Y})^2 = b^2(X - \bar{X})^2$$

Substituting this into (7) we get

$$\frac{\sum (Y_c - \bar{Y})^2}{\sum (Y - \bar{Y})^2} = \frac{b^2 \sum (X - \bar{X})^2}{\sum (Y - \bar{Y})^2}$$

However, we know that

$$b = \frac{\sum (X - \bar{X})(Y - \bar{Y})}{\sum (X - \bar{X})^2}$$

Substituting this into the above formula, we get,

$$\frac{\sum (Y_c - \bar{Y})^2}{\sum (Y - \bar{Y})^2} = \frac{\sum (X - \bar{X})^2}{\sum (Y - \bar{Y})^2} \cdot \left(\frac{\sum (X - \bar{X})(Y - \bar{Y})}{\sum (X - \bar{X})^2} \right)^2$$

$$= \left\{ \frac{\sum (X - \bar{X})(Y - \bar{Y})}{\sqrt{\sum (X - \bar{X})^2 \sum (Y - \bar{Y})^2}} \right\}^2 = r^2$$

Thus,

(8) $$r^2 = \frac{\sum (Y_c - \bar{Y})^2}{\sum (Y - \bar{Y})^2}$$

r^2 is called the *coefficient of determination* and shows the amount of deviation that has been explained. r is called the *correlation coefficient*.

When the sample points fall on the regression line, then $Y = Y_c$, and hence (6) becomes

$$\sum (Y - \bar{Y})^2 = \sum (Y_c - \bar{Y})^2$$

Thus, from (8)

$$r^2 = 1$$

When the sample points are such that $Y_c = \bar{Y}$, then $\sum (Y_c - \bar{Y})^2 = 0$. Thus, from (8), $r^2 = 0$.

This shows that

$$0 \leq r^2 \leq 1$$

and hence

$$-1 \leq r \leq 1$$

The definition of ρ given by equation (1) may also be interpreted as follows. Equation (1) is rewritten as

$$\rho = \frac{\text{Cov}(X, Y)}{\sigma_x \sigma_y}$$

Then ρ is a measure of the covariation of X and Y. By dividing by σ_x and σ_y, ρ has become an index without any unit attached to it. For example, if X is height, then the unit of X is, say, inches. If Y is weight, then the unit is pounds. σ_x has the unit inches and σ_y the unit pound. Thus ρ is the covariance between X and Y expressed as a number and also standardized.

This interpretation does not give the impression that X is the cause of Y or vice versa but gives the impression of treating X and Y on an equal basis.

(iii) *Comments on regression and correlation*

Correlation applies to a bivariate (multivariate) distribution. Regression analysis had two situations. The first case was where the independent variable was a mathematical variable without a probability distribution. An example of this is where various fixed amounts of diets are given to hogs to see the affect on weights. The mathematical variable X is the fixed amounts of feed and the dependent random variable Y is the weight.

The second case is where all variables are random variables, i.e., where we have a bivariate (multivariate) distribution. An example is the relation between the height of father and son. Recall that we found the conditional distribution of the son's height for a given father's height.

Correlation analysis assumes a bivariate (multivariate) distribution, and pairs of X and Y are selected at random as a sample. If one of the variables is selected first, and then the other variable is selected at random, there may be a bias in the computed r. Thus the second case mentioned above, although it is a multivariate distribution, is not the correct way of selecting a sample for purposes of correlation analysis. Nevertheless, in practice, this procedure of selecting X and Y together is sometimes neglected.

Covariation and causality. In regression analysis, we generally have a fair idea of the order of X and Y. For example, when considering the relation between yield and fertilizer, we assume that the amount of fertilizer affects the yields. Thus, we would let fertilizer be the independent variable and yield the dependent variable.

When we cannot determine the order of X and Y, it is appropriate to use correlation analysis. For example, heavy smoking and indigestion, which may both be due to emotional disturbances, may be correlated. The stature or I.Q. between brothers and sisters, which may be due to hereditary factors, are other examples.

Measure of linearity. The simple correlation coefficient is also called the linear correlation coefficient. When the relation between X and Y is said to be linear, it means that the relation can be shown as a straight line on the graph.

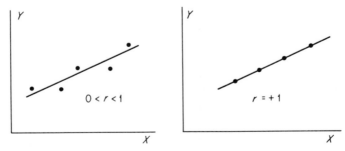

We know that as $r \to \pm 1$, the points approach a straight line, and when $r = \pm 1$, they fall on a straight line. When $r = 0$, we have the other extreme. Thus, r can be regarded as a measure of the degree of linearity between X and Y.

Independence implies $r = 0$. If we know that X and Y are independent, then $r = 0$. For example, we may throw two dice X and Y and record the numbers that appear. It may happen that there is $r = 0.5$, say. But we see intuitively that die X has no influence on die Y. Therefore, $r = 0.5$ is non-sense. From our original formula we have

$$\rho = \frac{E(X - \bar{X})(Y - \bar{Y})}{\sqrt{E(X - \bar{X})^2 E(Y - \bar{Y})^2}}$$

When X and Y are independent, then

$$E(X - \bar{X})(Y - \bar{Y}) = E(X - \bar{X})E(Y - \bar{Y}) = 0$$

Thus, independence implies $\rho = 0$.

$r = 0$ does not necessarily imply independence. For example, the correlation coefficient of the scores X and Y between two strong baseball teams playing a series of games against each other may be zero, i.e., $r = 0$, although the scores of each team are clearly dependent on the other team.

Correlation analysis is a stochastic process. Regression and correlation are stochastic processes. That is, a regression line

$$Y_c = a + bX$$

is estimating the expected Y value by X with a certain degree of probability.

When r becomes equal to ± 1, the situation degenerates to a case where there is a complete functional dependence between X and Y. When $-1 < r < 1$ we are, in a sense, denying this functional relationship between X and Y, and when $r = 0$, we are saying there is no functional relationship between X and Y and neither variable can be used to estimate the other.

Causation and correlation. It is necessary to consider the sampling distribution of the r to decide whether or not we should accept the hypothesis that the variables in the population are related. But, aside from this technical aspect of a relation between two variables, it is necessary for a social scientist to consider whether or not correlation indicates a cause and effect relationship.

It is possible to correlate the temperature of the sidewalks of New York City with the birth rate of some country, and it is possible that a high positive correlation may be found showing that when the sidewalk's temperature is high, the birth rate is high, and when the temperature is low the birth rate is low.

There is no meaning to such a correlation. There is no causal relationship between the two phenomena.

This example illustrates that you can correlate anything, and there are chances you may obtain a high correlation which may have no significant meaning at all. A high correlation simply tells us that the data we have collected is *consistent* with the hypothesis we set up. That is, it supports our hypothesis. We may have the following situations that brought about a high correlation.

1. X is the cause of Y,
2. Y is the cause of X,
3. there is a third factor Z that affects X and Y such that they show a close relation,
4. the correlation of X and Y may be due to chance.

Only by more thorough investigation which may be economic, sociological, etc. can we come to some conclusion as to whether or not X is the cause of Y.

Problem

1. Prove

$$\sum (Y - \bar{Y})^2 = \sum (Y_c - \bar{Y})^2 + \sum (Y - Y_c)^2$$

Note that

$$Y - \bar{Y} = (Y_c - \bar{Y}) + (Y - Y_c)$$

$$b = \frac{\sum (X - \bar{X})(Y - \bar{Y})}{\sum (X - \bar{X})^2}$$

$$Y_c = \bar{Y} + b(X - \bar{X})$$

17.3 Partial correlation coefficients

(i) Multiple regression plane

Consider a tri-variate normal distribution with random variables X_1 (son's height), X_2 (father's height) and X_3 (mother's height). From the conditional distribution of X_1 given X_2, X_3, we found the conditional mean $E(X_1 \mid X_2, X_3) = \mu_{1.23}$ as

$$\mu_{1.23} = \mu^{(1)} + \mathbf{V}_{12}\mathbf{V}_{22}^{-1}(X^{(2)} - \mu^{(2)})$$

or

$$\mu_{1.23} = \mu_1 + \beta_2(X_2 - \mu_2) + \beta_3(X_3 - \mu_3)$$

If we let

$$\alpha = \mu_1 - \beta_2\mu_2 - \beta_3\mu_3$$

then

$$\mu_{1.23} = \alpha + \beta_2 X_2 + \beta_3 X_3$$

We also saw that the sample estimate of this regression function was

$$X_{1.23} = a + b_2 X_2 + b_3 X_3$$
$$X_{1.23} = \bar{X}_1 + b_2(X_2 - \bar{X}_2) + b_3(X_3 - \bar{X}_3)$$

Geometrically, we have a regression plane. The deviation $(X_1 - \bar{X}_1)$ is the total deviation of the sample points from $\bar{X}_1$ before the regression plane is fitted. $(X_{1.23} - \bar{X}_1)$ is the amount of deviation that has been explained, or the amount of improvement due to the regression plane. $(X_1 - X_{1.23})$ is the remaining unexplained deviation.

The estimated regression line was obtained from the sample by the method of maximum likelihood. But when we have a normal distribution we can also use the method of least squares and obtain the same results. From the least squares point of view, we wish to fit the regression plane, i.e., find the b's, so that the unexplained deviation will be at a minimum. That is,

$$\sum (X_1 - X_{1.23})^2 = \sum e^2 = \text{Minimum}$$

The necessary conditions for a minimum are that the partial derivatives with respect to the b's are set equal to zero. We have

$$f = \sum (X_1 - X_{1.23})^2$$
$$= \sum [X_1 - \bar{X}_1 - b_2(X_2 - \bar{X}_2) - b_3(X_3 - \bar{X}_3)]^2$$
$$= \sum [x_1 - b_2 x_2 - b_3 x_3]^2$$

Thus, from $\partial f / \partial b_2 = 0$ and $\partial f / \partial b_3 = 0$ we find

$$b_2 \sum x_2^2 + b_3 \sum x_2 x_3 = \sum x_1 x_2$$
$$b_2 \sum x_3 x_2 + b_3 \sum x_3^2 = \sum x_1 x_3$$

In matrix notation the b's become

$$\begin{bmatrix} b_2 \\ b_3 \end{bmatrix} = \begin{bmatrix} \sum x_2^2 & \sum x_2 x_3 \\ \sum x_2 x_3 & \sum x_3^2 \end{bmatrix}^{-1} \begin{bmatrix} \sum x_1 x_2 \\ \sum x_1 x_3 \end{bmatrix}$$

According to our previous matrix notation, the b's were $\hat{\mathbf{V}}_{12} \hat{\mathbf{V}}_{22}^{-1}$ where

$$\hat{\mathbf{V}} = \begin{bmatrix} \hat{\mathbf{V}}_{11} & \hat{\mathbf{V}}_{12} \\ \hat{\mathbf{V}}_{21} & \hat{\mathbf{V}}_{22} \end{bmatrix} = \begin{bmatrix} \hat{\sigma}_{11} & \hat{\sigma}_{12} & \hat{\sigma}_{13} \\ \hat{\sigma}_{21} & \hat{\sigma}_{22} & \hat{\sigma}_{23} \\ \hat{\sigma}_{31} & \hat{\sigma}_{23} & \hat{\sigma}_{33} \end{bmatrix}$$

where

$$\hat{\sigma}_{ij} = \frac{1}{n} \sum (X_i - \bar{X}_i)(X_j - \bar{X}_j) = \frac{1}{n} \sum x_i x_j$$

A check will show that this result obtained via the maximum likelihood method and the result we just obtained via the method of least squares are the same.

Using these results we can now define the partial and multiple correlation coefficient.

(ii) Partial correlation coefficient

The partial correlation coefficient is defined as

$$\rho_{12.3} = \frac{E(X_1 - \mu_{1.3})(X_2 - \mu_{2.3})}{\sqrt{E(X_1 - \mu_{1.3})^2}\sqrt{E(X_2 - \mu_{2.3})^2}}$$

where
$$\mu_{1.3} = \mu_1 + \beta_3(X_3 - \mu_3)$$
$$\mu_{2.3} = \mu_2 + \beta_3(X_3 - \mu_3)$$

It can be shown that this is equal to

$$\rho_{12.3} = \frac{\rho_{12} - \rho_{13}\rho_{23}}{\sqrt{1 - \rho_{23}^2}\sqrt{1 - \rho_{13}^2}}$$

It can also be shown that the maximum likelihood estimator will become

$$r_{12.3} = \frac{r_{12} - r_{13}\,r_{23}}{\sqrt{1 - r_{23}^2}\sqrt{1 - r_{13}^2}}$$

If we have four variables, X_1, X_2, X_3, X_4, then

$$r_{12.34} = \frac{r_{12.3} - r_{24.3}r_{14.3}}{\sqrt{(1 - r_{24.3}^2)}\sqrt{(1 - r_{14.3}^2)}}$$

$$= \frac{r_{12.4} - r_{23.4}r_{13.4}}{\sqrt{(1 - r_{23.4}^2)}\sqrt{(1 - r_{13.4}^2)}}$$

This pattern repeats itself for other cases. As can be seen, $r_{12.34}$ can be obtained by first finding r_{ij}, then $r_{ij.p}$.

Various computational schemes can be found in standard text books.

17.4 Multiple correlation coefficient

(i) Definition

The multiple correlation coefficient between X_1 and (X_2, X_3) is defined as

(1)
$$\rho_{1.23} = \frac{E(X_1 - \mu_1)(X_{1.23} - \mu_{1.23})}{\sqrt{E(X_1 - \mu_1)^2}\sqrt{E(X_{1.23} - \mu_{1.23})^2}}$$

It can also be shown as

(2)
$$\rho_{1.23} = \frac{V_{12}V_{22}^{-1}V_{21}}{\sqrt{\sigma_{11}}\sqrt{V_{12}V_{22}^{-1}V_{21}}}$$

$$= \sqrt{\frac{V_{12}V_{22}^{-1}V_{21}}{\sigma_{11}}}$$

where

$$V = \begin{bmatrix} V_{11} & V_{12} \\ V_{21} & V_{22} \end{bmatrix} = \begin{bmatrix} \sigma_{11} & \sigma_{12} & \sigma_{13} \\ \sigma_{21} & \sigma_{22} & \sigma_{23} \\ \sigma_{31} & \sigma_{32} & \sigma_{33} \end{bmatrix}$$

We know that

$$V_{12}V_{22}^{-1} = [\beta_2 \quad \beta_3]$$

Thus,

$$\rho_{1.23}^2 = \frac{\beta_2\sigma_{21} + \beta_3\sigma_{31}}{\sigma_{11}}$$

The estimator for this will be

(3)
$$\hat{\rho}_{1.23}^2 = R_{1.23}^2 = \frac{\hat{\beta}_2\hat{\sigma}_{21} + \hat{\beta}_3\hat{\sigma}_{31}}{\hat{\sigma}_{11}}$$
$$= \frac{b_2 \sum x_1x_2 + b_3 \sum x_1x_3}{\sum x_1^2}$$

$R_{1.23}^2$ is called the coefficient of multiple determination. $R_{1.23}$ is the multiple correlation coefficient.

(ii) *Alternative definition* ·

Let us approach this last formula in an alternative way. The multiple correlation coefficient shows the improvement due to the regression function. This can be shown as

(4)
$$R_{1.23}^2 = \frac{\sum (X_{1.23} - \bar{X}_1)^2}{\sum (X_1 - \bar{X}_1)^2}$$

where $(X_{1.23} - \bar{X}_1)$ is the explained deviation and $(X_1 - \bar{X}_1)$ is the total deviation.

We also have the relationship

$$\sum (X_1 - \bar{X}_1)^2 = \sum (X_{1.23} - \bar{X}_1)^2 + \sum (X_1 - X_{1.23})^2$$

Thus, we have

(5)
$$\sum (X_{1.23} - \bar{X}_1)^2 = \sum (X_1 - \bar{X}_1)^2 - \sum (X_1 - X_{1.23})^2$$
$$= \sum x_1^2 - \sum [X_1 - \bar{X}_1 - b_2x_2 - b_3x_3]^2$$
$$= b_2 \sum x_1x_2 + b_3 \sum x_1x_3$$

Note that, for example,

$$b_2 \sum x_2(x_1 - b_2x_2 - b_3x_3) = 0$$

from the necessary conditions of setting partial derivatives zero. Thus,

(6)
$$R_{1.23}^2 = \frac{\sum (X_{1.23} - \bar{X}_1)^2}{\sum (X_1 - \bar{X}_1)^2} = \frac{b_2 \sum x_1x_2 + b_3 \sum x_1x_3}{\sum x_1^2}$$

Also note that

$$R_{1.23} = \frac{\sum (X_1 - \bar{X}_1)^2 - \sum (X_1 - X_{1.23})^2}{\sum (X_1 - \bar{X}_1)^2}$$

$$= 1 - \frac{\sum (X_1 - X_{1.23})^2}{\sum (X_1 - \bar{X}_1)^2} = 1 - \frac{s_{1.23}^2}{s_1^2}$$

Problems

1. Given X_1, X_2, X_3, X_4 which are normally distributed, express $\rho_{1.234}^2$ using formula (17.4.2). Show what V_{12}, V_{22}^{-1} and V_{21} are.

2. Express $\hat{\rho}_{1.234}^2$ in terms of equation (17.4.3).

3. Prove that (17.4.5) holds. Note that

$$\sum x_2(x_1 - b_2 x_2 - b_3 x_3) = 0$$

Notes and References

For the theoretical aspects of correlation analysis, see Anderson (1958), Chapter 4 (He also has extensive references on p. 96 which should be consulted for further study); Cramer (1946), pp. 277–279, 305–308, 394–401, 410–415; Kendall (1952). All three references are on an advanced level. Hoel (1954), Chapter 7; and Kenney and Keeping (1951), Chapter 11 are on an elementary level.

Four non-mathematical references are Snedecor (1956), Chapter 7, 13, and 14; Fisher (1954), Chapter 6; Ezekiel and Fox (1959); and Ferber (1949), Chapter 11, 12, and 13.

Ezekiel, M., and Fox, K. A., *Methods of Correlation and Regression Analysis*, 3rd ed. New York: John Wiley & Sons, Inc., 1959.

Ferber, R., *Statistical Techniques in Market Research*. New York: McGraw-Hill Book Co., Inc., 1949.

Fisher, R. A., *Statistical Methods for Research Workers*, 12th ed. New York: Hafner Publishing Co., 1954.

Kendall, M. G., *The Advanced Theory of Statistics*, 5th ed., Vol. I. London: Charles Griffen and Co. Lim., 1952.

Kenney, J. F. and Keeping, E. S., *Mathematics of Statistics*, 2nd ed., Part Two. New York: D. Van Nostrand Co., Inc., 1951.

CHAPTER 18

Game Theory

The theory of games, or game theory, was developed by a mathematician John von Neumann in his papers published in 1928 and 1937. However, it was not until von Neumann and Morgenstern published their book *The Theory of Games and Economic Behavior* in 1944 that the theory attracted the attention of social scientists as a method for dealing with problems of conflict of interest.

Along with linear programming, game theory has many applications in economic problems such as oligopoly and in business problems such as business games. In statistics, the decision theory approach which we discussed may be interpreted as a game where the two players are the states of nature and the statistician.

In this chapter a few basic ideas of game theory are discussed. Notes and references are provided for further study at the end of the chapter.

18.1 Introduction

Let us assume that player P_1 is to select a number from the set $\{1, 2\} = \{\alpha_1, \alpha_2\}$. Player P_2 is to select a number from the set $\{1, 2\} = \{\beta_1, \beta_2\}$. Under certain predetermined rules, either P_1 or P_2 may win. Let the rules be

P_2

		$\beta_1 = 1$	$\beta_2 = 2$
P_1	$\alpha_1 = 1$	$a_{11} = \$1$	$a_{12} = -4$
	$\alpha_2 = 2$	$a_{21} = \$3$	$a_{22} = 4$

This is to be interpreted as follows: If P_1 selects $\alpha_2 = 2$, and P_2 selects $\beta_2 = 2$, then P_1 will receive from P_2 \$4 as shown by the \$4 in the cell. If P_1 selects $\alpha = 1$ and P_2 selects $\beta_2 = 2$, then P_1 will receive from P_2 \$(-4); i.e., P_1 will pay P_2 \$4. This *game* we have has a predetermined set of rules and a situation

691

of conflict between two players. We shall use the word game in this sense.

When P_1 selects $\alpha_2 = 2$ and P_2 selects $\beta_2 = 2$, and \$4 is paid to P_1, the rules of the game have been realized. This realization of the rules is called a *play*.

We note that in playing this game, both P_1 and P_2 must employ skill and intelligence and play the game. Such a game is called *games of strategy*. Bridge, chess, and similar games are games of strategy.

In contrast, roulette or dice depend on chance; skill and intelligence have no role. Such games are called *games of chance*.

When there are two players P_1 and P_2 playing a game, it is called a *2-person game*. P_1 may be a single person or a group of people. For example, labor and management may play a game where each side is composed of a team of people. We still have a 2-person game. If we have 5 people playing poker we have a 5-person game.

At the end of each play in our illustration, a certain payment is made which may be money or something else. For example, when P_1 selects $\alpha_2 = 2$ and P_2 selects $\beta_2 = 2$, then P_1 receives from P_2 \$4. But, on the other hand, P_2 has lost \$4. Let the payments to P_1 be a_{ij} and those to P_2 be b_{ij}. Then in the present case,

$$a_{22} + b_{22} = \$4 + (-4) = 0$$

If P_1 selects $\alpha_1 = 1$ and P_2 selects $\beta_2 = 2$, then,

$$a_{12} + b_{12} = \$(-4) + (4) = 0$$

No matter what the play is, we always have

$$a_{ij} + b_{ij} = 0$$

i.e., $a_{ij} = -b_{ij}$. In such a case the play is called *zero-sum*, and when all possible plays are zero-sum we have a *zero-sum game*. Take a game of poker of say 4 players. After a play, some will win what others have lost. Then,

$$\sum_i^4 \sum_j^4 (a_{ij} + b_{ij}) = 0$$

Poker and other similar games are examples of zero-sum games. No wealth is created in the process. There has just been a transfer of payments and what some players have gained others have lost.

Since $a_{ij} = -b_{ij}$, it is only necessary to consider a_{ij} in our subsequent analysis.

18.2 Rectangular game

When P_1 and P_2 are to play the game we have set up, they select a number from the set $\{1, 2\}$, and with that one selection, the play is realized. There is only one selection P_1 and P_2 make. This selection is called a *move*. Tick-tack-toe can have a maximum of 9 moves before the play is realized. But it is possible that a play of tick-tack-toe may not need the total of 9 moves to be completed. Theoretically, the game can be completed in 5 moves. A play of chess involves a great many moves and the number of moves necessary to complete a play of chess will depend on the players.

When a play of a game needs only a finite number of moves we have a *finite game*. Those that require an infinite number of moves are called *infinite games*.

For the present we shall consider the 2-person zero-sum game where P_1 and P_2 each have only one move. We shall call such a game a *rectangular game*. Furthermore, we shall assume that both P_1 and P_2 play in total ignorance of the way his opponent plays.

Let us now generalize the schema we have presented above for P_1 and P_2. Instead of $\{\alpha_1, \alpha_2\}$ from which P_1 selected a move, let the set be $\{\alpha_1, ..., \alpha_m\}$, and for P_2 let it be $\{\beta_1, ..., \beta_n\}$. Then our schema becomes

$$P_2$$

	β_1	β_2	$\cdots$	β_j	$\cdots$	β_n
α_1						
α_2						
$\vdots$						
α_i				a_{ij}		
$\vdots$						
α_m						

P_1 (labels the rows)

P_1 selects a single α_i from $\{\alpha_1, ..., \alpha_m\}$. This α_i is called a *pure strategy*. $A = \{\alpha_1, ..., \alpha_m\}$ is called a space of pure strategies for P_1, and, similarly, we have β_j as a pure strategy and $B = \{\beta_1, ..., \beta_n\}$ as a space of pure strategies for P_2.

The schema we have has $m \times n$ cells, and each cell contains a payment to P_1 from P_2. This $m \times n$ matrix of payments is called a *pay-off matrix*. We shall denote the payment in the (i, j) cell by a_{ij} which will be a real valued function. Thus,

$$P_1 \quad \text{receives } a_{ij} \quad \text{from} \quad P_2$$

$$P_2 \quad \text{receives } -a_{ij} \quad \text{from} \quad P_1$$

and we have a zero-sum game.

18.3 Rectangular game with saddle points

Returning to our simple illustration, let us ask which number (i.e., strategy) should P_1 select. From our payoff matrix we can easily see that P_1 should select $\alpha_2 = 2$. In that case he will either get \$3 or \$4.

On the other hand P_2 would not select $\beta_2 = 2$ because it is not hard for him to see that P_1 would select $\alpha_2 = 2$. Thus, P_2 will select $\beta_1 = 1$. The payoff will be $a_{21} = $ \$3 as we see in the payoff matrix. So the *strategy* will be

$$\text{for } P_1: \quad \text{play} \quad \alpha_2 = 2$$

$$\text{for } P_2: \quad \text{play} \quad \beta_1 = 1$$

The payoff $a_{21} = $ \$3 is called the *value of the game*. Note two things about this value. First, it is the minimum of the row in which it appears. Second, it is the maximum of the column in which it appears. There is no inducement for P_1 and P_2 to change their strategies. This pair of pure strategies (α_2, β_1) is called *a pair of equilibrium strategies*. They are also called *optimal strategies*.

The 2×2 matrix game is simple and we have no trouble spotting the optimal strategies. Let us try a 3×3 matrix game and investigate the reasoning behind the optimal strategy. Consider the following pay-off matrix

		β_1	P_2 β_2	β_3
	α_1	\$4	3	-2
P_1	α_2	3	4	10
	α_3	7	6	8

Which strategy should P_1 adopt? Let us assume P_1 is a pessimistic player. Then he notices that if he selects α_3 he will get at least $a_{32} = $ \$6. He cannot get lower than that. Let us call this the *security level* of player P_1 when he selects the pure strategy α_3. If he selects α_2, he can get as high as \$10 $= a_{23}$; but, on the other hand there is a possibility he might get only \$3 $= a_{21}$; i.e., his security level is \$3. And when he selects α_1, he can get a high of \$4 but there is also the possibility he may incur a loss of \$2; i.e., his security level is $-$\$2. Thus, if he selects α_3, he has put a floor under himself and he is assured of at least $a_{32} = $ \$6. This is the minimum of the row α_3. Let us write

$$\min_{j} a_{ij}, \qquad j = 1, 2, 3, \ i = 1, 2, 3.$$

and for

$$i = 1, \ \min_{j} a_{1j} = \$-2, \qquad j = 1, 2, 3$$

$$i = 2, \ \min_{j} a_{2j} = \$3, \qquad j = 1, 2, 3$$

$$i = 3, \ \min_{j} a_{3j} = \$6, \qquad j = 1, 2, 3$$

The reason he picked α_3 was because the \$6 was the largest (maximum) security level P_1 could assure himself among the three strategies α_1, α_2, and α_3. This is expressed as

$$\max_{i} \ \min_{j} \ a_{ij}$$

and in our present case it is

$$\max_{i} \ \min_{j} \ a_{ij} = \$6$$

So far this was for P_1. What is the line of reasoning for P_2? For P_2 we have to note that we are dealing with losses, i.e., he has to pay P_1. Thus, the smaller the loss (the amount he has to pay P_1) the greater the gain for P_2 and the greater the loss the smaller the gain.

With this in mind let us look at β_1. Then P_2 can assure himself of a minimum gain of $a_{31} = -\$7$; i.e., the greatest loss will be \$7. For β_2, P_2 can assure himself of a minimum gain of $a_{32} = -\$6$. For β_3, P_2 can assure himself of a minimum gain of $a_{23} = -\$10$ and we can write

$$\min_{i} \ (-a_{ij})$$

and for

$$j = 1, \qquad \min_{i} \ (-a_{i1}) = -\$7$$

$$j = 2, \qquad \min_{i} \ (-a_{i2}) = -\$6$$

$$j = 3, \qquad \min_{i} \ (-a_{i3}) = -\$10$$

Of these minimum gains, which is the largest? Which is the maximum gain? That is, which is the smallest loss?

$$-\$6 > -7 > -10$$

i.e., $-\$6$ is the maximum minimum gain. We can write this

$$\max_{j} \ \min_{i} \ (-a_{ij}) = -\$6$$

Let us now interpret this as follows: P_2 had minimum gains of

$$-6 > -7 > -10$$

In terms of maximum losses, this will be

$$6 < 7 < 10$$

Then, P_2 would like to minimize the maximum loss. That is \$6. We can write

$$\min_{j} \ \max_{i} \ (a_{ij}) = \$6$$

Mathematically we have

$$\min_{j} \; (-a_{ij}) = -\max \; (a_{ij})$$

and

$$\max_{j} \min_{i} \; (-a_{ij}) = \max_{j} \left[-\max_{i} \; (a_{ij}) \right] = -\min_{j} \max_{i} \; (a_{ij}) = -\$6$$

Thus, we have

for P_1:   in terms of gain $\max\limits_{i} \min\limits_{j} a_{ij} = \$6$

for P_2:   in terms of loss $\min\limits_{j} \max\limits_{i} a_{ij} = \$6$

That is, the maximum minimum gain of P_1 is equal to the minimum maximum loss of P_2. The common value $v = \$6$ is the value of the game.

P_1 is sure of getting at least \$6, and P_2 is sure of not losing more than \$6, or, to put it another way, P_2 is sure of not letting P_1 get more than \$6. This $v = \$6$ has the two characteristics of being the minimum of the row in which it appears and the maximum of the column in which it appears, simultaneously.

When such a value exists in a payoff matrix, we call it a *saddle point* and the two strategies that are adopted to bring it about will be denoted by

$$(\alpha_{i0}, \beta_{j0})$$

and are called the *equilibrium strategies* or *optimal strategies*.

18.4 Mixed strategies

So far we were able to find an optimal (equilibrium pair) strategy for the games we considered because it had a saddle point. That is, there was a value in the payoff matrix that was at the same time the maximum of the column and the minimum of the row. But what if there is no saddle point? For example, consider the following pay-off matrix

$$P_2$$

		β_1	β_2
P_1	α_1	1	5
	α_2	6	4

P_1 will $\max\limits_{i} \min\limits_{j} a_{ij}$. That is, he first minimizes with respect to j, letting $j = 1, 2$ for each i. Then, for

$$i = 1: \quad \min_{j} a_{1j} = a_{11} = \$1 \quad\quad j = 1, 2$$

$$i = 2: \quad \min_{j} a_{2j} = a_{22} = \$4 \quad\quad j = 1, 2$$

Thus, the max min a_{ij} will be $a_{22} = \$4$ and the strategy for P_1 will be to play α_2.

On the other hand, P_2 will min max a_{ij}. That is, he first maximizes with respect to i letting $i = 1, 2$ for each j. Then, for

$$j = 1, \qquad \max_i a_{i1} = a_{21} = \$6$$

$$j = 2, \qquad \max_i a_{i2} = a_{12} = \$5$$

Thus,

$$\min_j \max_i a_{ij} = a_{12} = \$5$$

and the strategy for P_2 will be to play β_2.

When P_1 plays α_2 and P_2 plays β_2, P_1 will be getting what he expects, i.e., $a_{22} = \$4$. But P_2 will be paying $a_{22} = -\$4$ instead of the $a_{12} = -\$5$ which he anticipated from his strategy. The play is favorable to P_2.

The first play was in total ignorance. Each player did not know what move the other player would make. But now let us assume that the game is played repeatedly. If P_1 notices that P_2 choses β_2, then he will choose α_1 instead of α_2 so that he will get $a_{12} = \$5$ instead of $a_{22} = \$4$.

But, if P_2 detects that P_1 has switched to α_1, P_2 will also switch to β_1 so that the payoff to P_2 will be $a_{11} = \$1$ instead of $a_{12} = \$5$.

Then P_1 might switch back to α_2 again hoping for a payoff of $a_{21} = \$6$.

The point is, the game in the above sense is *indeterminate*. Each player will be switching from one strategy to another, trying to outguess the other.

The question then arises: Is there some pattern of behavior (that is, switching back and forth) that P_1 and P_2 should adopt that will be along their original intentions of maximizing the minimum gain? (Or minimizing the maximum loss?)

Let us try a strategy where P_1 will adopt α_1 two times and α_2 three times in that order. If the game is repeatedly played, then P_2 will soon recognize this pattern and he would play β_1 twice and β_2 three times to match P_1. P_1 would also detect what is happening and so, clearly, such a pattern involving regularity cannot be adopted.

This leads us to try to mix up the strategies. P_1 can do this by using some kind of chance mechanism. Assume he has an urn with 20 red beads and 30 black beads in it. He will draw a bead at random. When he has drawn a red bead he will play $\alpha_1 = 1$: when it is a black bead he will play $\alpha_2 = 2$. Then, when the game is repeatedly played, he will play $\alpha_1 = 1$ two-fifths of the time. But now the order of playing α_1 and α_2 will be mixed up so that P_2 cannot specifically anticipate P_1's next play.

But P_2 can detect over the long run that P_1 is playing α_1 and α_2 with a ratio of $2:3$. Let us assume that P_2 plays β_1 and β_2 with a ratio of $1:4$. Then, we can show this situation as

$$P_2$$

		$y_1 = \frac{1}{5}$ β_1	$y_2 = \frac{4}{5}$ β_2
P_1	$x_1 = \frac{2}{5}\alpha_1$	$a_{11} = \$1$	$a_{12} = \$5$
	$x_2 = \frac{3}{5}\alpha_2$	$a_{21} = \$6$	$a_{22} = \$4$

Now the *probability* of P_1 playing α_1 is, as we see, $x_1 = 2/5$. That is, if the game is played 50 times, P_1 will select α_1 approximately 20 times. Let us say, for the sake of simplicity, that it is 20 times.

Now, of these 20 times, how many times will P_1 be in cell $(1, 1)$ and how many times will he be in cell $(1, 2)$? This will depend on how P_2 selects β_1 and β_2. We see that $y_1 = 1/5$ and $y_2 = 4/5$. Then, of these 20 times P_1 selects α_1, we can expect P_1 to be in cell $(1, 1)$, $1/5$ of the time and in cell $(1, 2)$, $4/5$ of the time. Thus, P_1 will be in cell $(1, 1)$

$$(50 \times \tfrac{2}{5}) \times \tfrac{1}{5} = 4 = 50x_1y_1$$

i.e., 4 times out of 50 plays. He will be in cell $(1, 2)$

$$(50 \times \tfrac{2}{5}) \times \tfrac{4}{5} = 16 = 50x_1y_2$$

For cell $(2, 1)$ it is

$$(50 \times \tfrac{3}{5}) \times \tfrac{1}{5} = 50x_2y_1 = 6$$

For cell $(2, 2)$ it is

$$(50 \times \tfrac{3}{5}) \times \tfrac{4}{5} = 50x_2y_2 = 24$$

Thus, for cell (i, j) it is

$$50x_iy_j$$

and, obviously

$$\sum_i \sum_j 50x_iy_j = 50$$

If the game is played n times, we have

$$\sum \sum nx_iy_j = n$$

Since we know the payoffs of this game, we can see that if the game is played in the above fashion, P_1 would expect to get in n plays

$$E' = \$1(nx_1y_1) + \$5(nx_1y_2) + \$6(nx_2y_1) + \$4(nx_2y_2)$$

Thus, the average payoff per game P_1 can expect will be

$$E = \frac{E'}{n} = \$1x_1y_1 + \$5x_1y_2 + \$6x_2y_1 + \$4x_2y_2$$

$$= \sum \sum a_{ij}x_iy_j$$

This function E is called the *expected payoff*, and is denoted by $E(a_{ij})$. If we have an $m \times n$ payoff matrix, then,

$$\sum_{i}^{n} x_i = 1 \quad \text{and} \quad \sum_{j}^{n} y_j = 1$$

$$x_i \geq 0 \qquad\qquad y_j \geq 0$$

$$E(a_{ij}) = \sum_{i}^{m} \sum_{j}^{n} a_{ij} x_i y_j$$

The expected payoff for our present game is

$$E(a_{ij}) = \sum \sum a_{ij} x_i y_j = \$4.32$$

So far so good. But note that we just arbitrarily picked $x_1 = 2/5$, $x_2 = 3/5$ for P_1 and $y_1 = 1/5$, $y_2 = 4/5$ for P_2. The question thus arises: Is this \$4.32 the best situation that P_1 and P_2 can expect? By best situation we mean a situation where the game we are playing will result along the principles of maximizing the minimum gain. Let us investigate this problem.

Let us set

$$X = \{x_1, x_2\}, \qquad Y = \{y_1, y_2\}$$

X and Y are vectors of probabilities. Let us also set

$$A = \{\alpha_1, \alpha_2\}, \qquad B = \{\beta_1, \beta_2\}$$

A and B are vector spaces of pure strategies. Then we can denote a *mixed strategy* due to the use of a probability distribution X by

$$XA^T = \begin{bmatrix} x_1 & x_2 \end{bmatrix} \begin{bmatrix} \alpha_1 \\ \alpha_2 \end{bmatrix} = \begin{bmatrix} x_1 \alpha_1 & x_2 \alpha_2 \end{bmatrix}$$

Similarly for P_2, the mixed strategy will be

$$YB^T = \begin{bmatrix} y_1 & y_2 \end{bmatrix} \begin{bmatrix} \beta_1 \\ \beta_2 \end{bmatrix} = \begin{bmatrix} y_1 \beta_1 & y_2 \beta_2 \end{bmatrix}$$

The X is a specific probability distribution taken from a set of such distributions. Let us denote the set by S_m. Then, $X \in S_m$. Likewise for Y; i.e., $Y \in S_n$.

Using this X and Y notation let us write

$$E(a_{ij}) = E(XY) = \sum \sum a_{ij} x_i y_j$$

Then, our problem is to find a pair (X^*, Y^*) such that the mixed strategy $X^* A^T$ guarantees that P_1 will get at least v while the mixed strategy $Y^* B^T$ will pay at most v.

Using our example we have

$$E(XY) = \sum\sum a_{ij}x_iy_j$$
$$= x_1y_1 + 6(1 - x_1)y_1 + 5x_1(1 - y_1) + 4(1 - x_1)(1 - y_1)$$
$$= x_1 + 2y_1 - 6x_1y_1 + 4$$
$$= -6(x_1 - \tfrac{2}{6})(y_1 - \tfrac{1}{6}) + \tfrac{26}{6}$$

In our example we had $x_1 = 2/5$, $y_1 = 1/5$ and the expected payoff was $E(XY) = \$4.32$. But, as the above equation shows, if P_1 were to let $x_1 = 2/6$ instead of any other x value,

$$E(XY) = 0 + 26/6 = \$4.33$$

He can assure himself of this much. By taking some other value for x it is possible that he may get a larger expected payoff. At the same time there is also the possibility that he may get a smaller expected payoff. It can be shown that this is the highest security level P_1 can expect. Thus, if P_1 sets $x_1 = 2/6$, he eliminates the possibility of getting less than $\$4.33$. It turns out that this $\$4.33$ will be the maximum minimum gain for P_1.

From P_2's standpoint, we can say that if P_2 sets $y_1 = 1/6$, he can be sure that P_1 will get $\$4.33$. For any other value of y_1 it is possible that he may give P_1 less than $\$4.33$ but at the same time there is also the possibility that he may have to pay P_1 more than $\$4.33$. By setting $y_1 = 1/6$, P_2 eliminates the possibility of losing more than $\$4.33$ but at the same time he eliminates the possibility of paying less than $\$4.33$. It turns out that this $\$4.33$ will be the minimum maximum loss for P_2.

Thus, we have found for our simple example a pair of mixed strategies (X^*A^T, Y^*B^T) and a value v such that the mixed strategies are in equilibrium and yield a maxi-min and mini-max strategy for P_1 and P_2. The value of the game is $v = \$4.33$.

Using our new notation we have

$$E(X^*Y^*) = \sum\sum a_{ij}x_{i0}y_{j0} = v$$

$E(XY^*)$ is the expected payoff given Y^*. Thus,

$$E(XY^*) \leq E(X^*Y^*)$$

i.e., P_1 can select any X from S_m and choose a mixed strategy XA^T. But the expected payoff from this mixed strategy will be smaller than the expected payoff $E(X^*Y^*)$ due to the equilibrium pair.

Similarly,

$$E(X^*Y^*) \leq E(X^*Y)$$

i.e., the amount P_2 has to pay P_1, $E(X^*Y)$, using some Y from S_n, is larger than $E(X^*Y^*)$. Thus,

$$E(XY^*) \leq E(X^*Y^*) \leq E(X^*Y)$$

Let us now state the main theorem of a two-person zero-sum game. Proof of the theorem is beyond the scope of this book and thus will not be given.

Every rectangular game has a value v.

There exists a pair of mixed strategies that are due to (X^*Y^*) that are in equilibrium in the sense that

$$E(XY^*) \leq E(X^*Y^*) \leq E(X^*Y)$$

The value of the game is

$$E(X^*Y^*) = \sum \sum a_{ij}x_{i0}y_{j0}$$

and

$$\max_{X \in S_m} \min_{Y \in S_n} E(XY) = \min_{Y \in S_n} \max_{X \in S_m} E(XY)$$

Problems

Find the equilibrium pair (X, Y) for the following problems. Also find the value of the game.

1.

2	3
4	5

2.

3	5
6	4

Notes and References

J. von Neumann's original article of 1928 (in German) is written for mathematicians. But the book by von Neumann and Morgenstern (1944, 1947, 1953) is written for social scientists as well as mathematicians. It is a difficult book.

Aside from the von Neumann and Morgenstern book, the following four books are recommended: Luce and Raiffa (1957); McKinsey (1952); Karlin (1959); and Gale (1960). Luce and Raiffa (1957) discuss game theory with a minimum of mathematics and explain its various implications. There is also an extensive bibliography at the end of the book. McKinsey (1952) gives a concise mathematical presentation of game theory. He has a proof of the mini-max theorem in Chapter 2. Karlin (1959) Vol. I, Chapters 1, 2, and 4 has an excellent discussion of game theory, but uses topological concepts in some places. These are explained in his appendix. His Notes and References to Chapters 1, 2, and 4 are recommended for those interested in further study.

Dorfman, Samuelson, and Solow (1958), Chapters 15 and 16 discuss the interrelations between linear programming and game theory. This interrelation is also discussed in Luce and Raiffa (1957), Appendix 5; and Gale (1960), Chapter 7.

The interrelation between game theory and statistical decision theory is discussed in Luce and Raiffa (1957), Chapter 13; Chernoff and Moses (1959), Appendix F_1; Raiffa and Schlaifer (1961), Chapter 1; and Blackwell and Girshick (1954).

Advanced mathematical references may be found in the *Annals of Mathematics Studies*, Numbers 24, 28, 38, 39, which are published by Princeton University Press.

Some examples of applications of game theory to various branches of social science are as follows. For economics, see Shubik (1959). For political behavior, see Shubik (1954). For business, see the survey article by Cohen and Rhenman in Management Science (1961).

An extensive bibliography on gaming and allied topics has been compiled by Shubik and may be found in the Journal of the American Statistical Association, December, 1960, pp. 736–756. This bibliography also contains references on *simulation*. A symposium on simulation may be found in the American Economic Review, December, 1960, pp. 893–932.

Bibliography

Blackwell, D., and Girshick, M. A., *Theory of Games and Statistical Decisions*. New York: John Wiley & Sons, Inc., 1954.

Cohen, K. J., and Rhenman, E., "The Role of Management Games in Education and Research," *Management Science* (Jan., 1961), pp. 131–166.

Karlin, S., *Mathematical Methods and Theory in Games, Programming, and Economics, Vol. I*. Reading, Mass.: Addison-Wesley Publishing Co., 1959.

Luce, R. D., and Raiffa, H., *Games and Decisions*. New York: John Wiley & Sons, Inc., 1957.

McKinsey, J. C. C., *Introduction to the Theory of Games*. New York: McGraw-Hill Book Co., Inc., 1952.

Shubik, M., (ed.) *Readings in Game Theory and Political Behavior*. New York: Doubleday and Co., Inc., 1954.

Shubik, M., *Strategy and Market Structure*. New York: John Wiley & Sons, Inc., 1959.

Shubik, M., "Games Decisions and Industrial Organization," *Management Science* (July, 1960), pp. 455–474.

Shubik, M., "Bibliography on Simulation, Gaming, Artificial Intelligence, and Allied Topics," *Journal of American Statistical Association* (Dec., 1960), pp. 736–756.

Von Neumann, J. and Morgenstern, O., *Theory of Games and Economics Behavior*. Princeton, N. J.: Princeton University Press, 1st ed., 1944, 2nd ed., 1947, 3rd ed., 1953.

NAME INDEX

A

Aitken, A. C., 430
Albrecht, W. A., Jr., 70
Aleksandrov, A. D., 170
Allen, R. G. D., 69, 108, 230, 276
Anderson, R. L., 679
Anderson, T. W., 679
Andronow, A. A., 556
Apostal, T. M., 69
Arrow, K. J., 510, 556, 557
Ayres, F., Jr., 108, 510

B

Bancroft, T. A., 679
Bartle, R. G., 69
Baumol, W. J., 315
Bellman, R., 296, 430, 556
Bers, L., 510
Birkhoff, G., 430, 510
Blackwell, D., 702
Block, H. D., 556
Botts, T. A., 70
Brand, L., 70
Breuer, J., 36
Buck, R. C., 70
Bushaw, D. W., 557

C

Chaikin, C. E., 556
Chapman, D. G., 613
Charnes, A., 557

Chernoff, H., 613
Chipman, J. S., 557
Christ, C. F., 679
Churchill, R. V., 296
Clower, R. W., 557
Cohen, K. J., 230, 702
Collar, A. R., 430
Cooper, W. W., 557
Courant, R., 70
Cramer, H., 276, 590
Cyert, R. M., 230

D

David, F. N., 679
Davis, H. T., 230
Debreu, G., 36, 510, 511, 556
Dennis, J. B., 557
Domar, E. D., 276
Dorfman, R., 557
Duncan, W. J., 430

E

Ezekiel, M., 679, 690

F

Feller, W., 590
Ferber, R., 690
Ferrar, W. C., 430, 557
Finkbeiner, D. T., 557
Fisher, R. A., 613, 690
Fox, K. A., 679, 690

705

SUBJECT INDEX

A

Action, 615
Adding-up theorem, 168, 226
Adjugate of a determinant, 392
Admissible rules, 620
Argument, 110
Arithmetic continuum, 32, 35

B

Basis, 421
β-risk, 619
Bilinear form, 405
Binomial probability distribution, 575
Bivariate normal distribution, 661
Boundary points, 44
Bounds of subsets, 26
  greatest lower bound, 26
  least upper bound, 26
  lower bound, 26
  upper bound, 26
Brouwer Fixed-point theorem, 509

C

Calculus, fundamental theorem of, 239
Cartesian product, 11
Cauchy sequence, 55
Central limit theorem, 578
Chain rule, 85, 119
Characteristic equation, 432
  characteristic function, 433
  characteristic matrix, determinant, 432

Characteristic equation (*Cont.*)
  characteristic roots, 433
  characteristic vector, 435
  difference equation, 323
  differential equation, 310
  expansion of, 517
  square matrix, 432
Closed subset, 44
Cobb-Douglas production function, 160
Coefficient of determination, 683
Cofactor of a determinant, 381
Complement of a set, 5
Complete space, 51
Complex numbers, 288
Compound interest formula, 265
Concave curves, 174
Conditional distribution, 663
Conditional probabilities, 563
Confidence coefficient, 610
Confidence interval, 607
Consistency, 593
Consistent estimator, 593
Constant outlay curves, 106
Continuity, 63
Convergence of a sequence, 50
Convex cone, 550
Convex hull, 549
Convex linear combinations, 547
Convexity of curves, 173
Convex polyhedron, 551
Convex sets, 546
Correlation coefficient, 680
  multiple correlation coefficient, 688
  partial correlation coefficient, 686
  simple correlation coefficient, 680

712 SUBJECT INDEX